D1097059

HEBDEN :

CHEMISTRY 12

A WORKBOOK FOR STUDENTS

by

James A. Hebden, Ph. D.

Hebden :

Chemistry 12

A Workbook for Students

Seventeenth Printing – December 2007

Hebden Home Publishing
Kamloops, B.C.
CANADA

Distributor: Western Campus Resources Inc.
485 Mountain Highway
North Vancouver, BC V7J 2L3
Telephone: (604)-988-1055 ; toll free: 1-800-995-5283
Fax: (604)-988-3309 ; toll free fax: 1-877-977-4539
e-mail: info@textbookscanada.ca

ISBN 978-0-9682069-0-4

Printed in Canada by Hignell Book Printers

PREFACE

This book covers the British Columbia Chemistry 12 curriculum as revised in 1996. The material included was initially based on the student workbook I wrote in 1989 for the B.C. Ministry of Education's Small Schools Project for Chemistry 12, but has subsequently been modified extensively. Some material from my book Chemistry: Theory and Problems, Book Two (McGraw–Hill Ryerson, 1980) has also been included, with permission.

The exercises in this book are representative of the types of questions found on past Government Exams, including many problems having a “scholarship level” of difficulty. It is hoped that this book will be of use to both teachers and students alike. When students miss a class, having to learn the material on their own is often a frustrating experience for both students and teacher. It is my hope that the notes, explanations and exercises in this book will make it easier to “catch up” (or to work ahead).

DISCLAIMER

The chemical laboratory has hazards, both expected and unexpected. This Workbook does not outline procedures for any chemical experiments. It is beyond the scope of this Workbook to identify specific laboratory hazards or provide protocols to avoid them. The information in this Workbook relating to the safe handling of chemicals, chemical solutions, chemistry equipment and safety equipment is intended to provide a general guide and background that fosters sound safety practices in the laboratory and is not a substitute for proper and specific classroom instruction in chemistry safety procedures. In every case, students must be properly supervised, trained in laboratory procedures and made aware of specific hazards in about-to-be-performed laboratory experiments.

ACKNOWLEDGEMENTS

This book would not have been possible without the unflagging support and advice of my wife, Frances. From the initial concept to the editing of the final product, she has helped bring this book into being.

The experienced advice, mentoring and friendship of Gordon Gore is greatly appreciated and acknowledged. His encouragement and humour was of enormous help in all stages of the preparation of this book. He truly defines the word “educator”.

The twenty cartoons in this book are the creation of the highly talented Ehren Stillman (“ZimBoBwe”), of Mission, B.C. It gives me great pleasure to help display his talent; the cartoons have enriched this book immeasurably.

The legions of students who gave me feedback and suggestions on earlier versions of this book are gratefully acknowledged. Not many books have 1000 editors. Special thanks are extended to Jason Elliott for his exceptional editing suggestions.

COVER PHOTOGRAPH

Some of the main themes of Chemistry 12 are highlighted in the cover photograph. The rapid reaction of nitric acid with copper metal filings produces an equilibrium between red–brown nitrogen dioxide gas and colourless dinitrogen tetroxide gas. In the background, one volumetric flask contains highly soluble green nickel(II) nitrate and the other a strong oxidizing agent, purple potassium permanganate. The reaction of silver nitrate with a mild reducing agent produced a silver mirror inside the flask at the left.

The design of the cover by Loren Hebden is gratefully acknowledged.

PERMISSIONS

The use of materials originally produced for the B.C. Ministry of Education's "Chemistry 12 Course Binder" has been reproduced and adapted with the permission of British Columbia Ministry of Education, Skills and Training.

The information used in the data tables has been reprinted with permission from the "HandBook of Chemistry and Physics", 73rd edition, 1992. Copyright CRC Press, Boca Raton, Florida © 1992

Permission to use some of the material in "Chemistry: Theory and Problems, Book 2", has been granted by McGraw–Hill Ryerson Limited.

The permission of the British Columbia Ministry of Education, Skills and Training to use the layout of the Tables contained in the "Examinations and Assessment Branch Chemistry Data Booklet" is gratefully acknowledged.

TABLE OF CONTENTS

UNIT IV : ACIDS, BASES AND SALTS

UNIT V : ELECTROCHEMISTRY

Answers

INTRODUCTION TO CHEMISTRY 12

Why should you study Chemistry 12 and what are you going to get out of this course? This is a fair question because the course is going to require a substantial amount of your time and effort.

Recall what you studied in Chem 11: how to handle numbers in Chemistry, the physical properties of materials, naming compounds, the mole, balancing chemical equations, types of chemical reactions, heat effects, stoichiometry, the composition of the atom, the periodic table, chemical bonding, solution chemistry, molar concentration, and organic chemistry. It was quite a jumbled mess. Well, that is the nature of a general course which attempts to "survey" many important components of chemistry in one year: you have to jump all over the place. Just when you found something that started to really fascinate you (or that you could finally understand), you jumped to another topic.

Don't despair, because this year you will find that Chemistry 12 has a much more even "flow" of ideas. You will use a great deal of the material you learned in Chemistry 11 as a starting point for your studies this year. Initially you will look at what goes on "inside" a chemical reaction and how to control the rate of a reaction. Then, with a knowledge that you can control a reaction's rate, you will see that many reactions can occur either forward or in reverse ("equilibrium reactions"). You will see how to control the rates of forward versus backward reactions, based on your ability to control reaction rates learned in the first section. Armed with these abilities, you will examine the process of dissolving substances in a solvent, and see how your understanding of equilibrium brings about an understanding of the solubilities of substances. Next, you will examine acids and bases and see how equilibrium processes apply to acid–base chemistry. Finally, you will look at electrochemistry, which is also firmly rooted in equilibrium processes. In a sense, this year you must not lose your equilibrium. In many instances you will be shown how the chemical principles you are learning can be used to understand the natural processes which are going on around you. By the end of the course, you should be able to explain many of the chemical processes which go on in our world.

In order to be successful in Chemistry 12, you should be prepared for the following.

a) The course is government examinable, which means that 40% of your mark will be based on ONE EXAM at the end of the course.

b) Chemistry 12 expects you to have a much deeper understanding of the material than you might have been able to get away with in Chemistry 11. There is much less in Chemistry 12 which is straight memorization; you are expected to think deeply about many topics. Rather than simply memorizing notes, you will be dealing with questions which ask you to APPLY your knowledge to new situations.

c) Chemistry 12 has a substantial emphasis on applying mathematics to problem situations. If you love math you are going to LOVE this course (but if you never did like math then ......). It will be virtually impossible to simply memorize all the types of problems you could be asked. Instead, you will be shown how to analyze problems and modify procedures according to the information given.

Chemistry 12 often serves as a prerequisite to further studies in the sciences at the college or university level. Chemistry is not an easy subject to master, but your studies should repay your efforts handsomely. Many other fields besides Chemistry require a sound chemistry background, including engineering, medicine, animal health technology, art restoration, forensics, biology, environmental studies, and so on. I hope you find your work this year to be personally rewarding; Chemistry is a fascinating subject.

A Special Note on Significant Digits

All the exercises are accompanied by fully–worked–out answers in the Answers Section. Whenever an exercise involves a calculation, the final answer is given to the correct number of significant digits. However, intermediate results are often given to more than the number of digits justified by the starting data, so as to minimize round–off errors. It is expected that whenever you perform a calculation, you will always keep the ongoing results stored in your calculator. Do not simply copy down an intermediate result, clear your calculator, re–enter the intermediate result and continue with the calculation; such a way of using your calculator will frequently lead to serious round–off errors. ***One of the skills which will be tested on your final government exam will be your ability to work accurately to the correct number of significant digits.***

UNIT I : REACTION KINETICS

I.1. INTRODUCTION

Recall that EXOTHERMIC reactions give off heat.

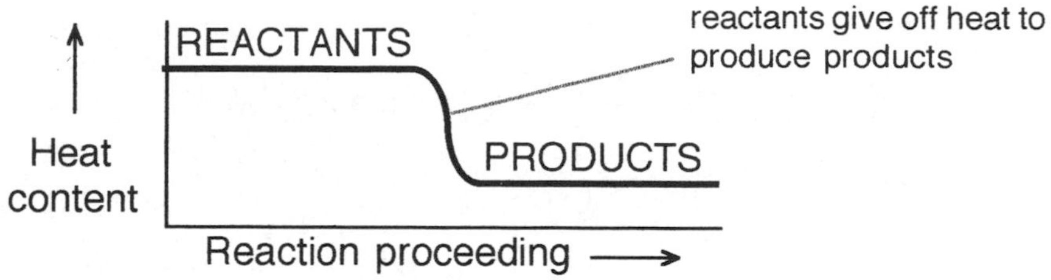

You might expect that such a reaction would proceed spontaneously, like a ball rolling downhill. However, the reaction

$$2\,N_2(g) + 5\,O_2(g) + 2\,H_2O(l) \longrightarrow 4\,HNO_3(l) + 121\text{ kJ}$$

is exothermic, giving off 121 kJ. If this reaction went on its own, as expected, then the air (N_2 and O_2) and water of the world would combine to form nitric acid, thus destroying the world and all life! Since swimming in a lake is not generally considered an act of suicide, some type of "wall" must prevent the oxygen, nitrogen and water from forming nitric acid, as shown below.

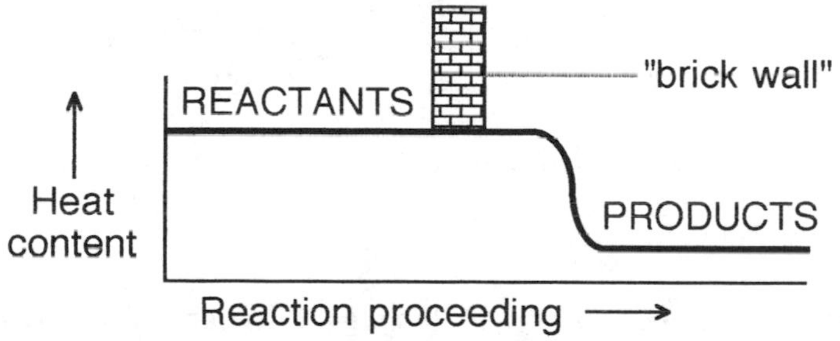

Since the reaction does not appear to go at all or at least seems to have a VERY SLOW rate, there must be a problem. In an effort to find a clue to this mysterious "wall", the following sections will define what is meant by a "reaction rate", find ways to measure the rate of a reaction, and then look at some of the factors which can affect the reaction rate.

REACTION KINETICS is the study of the rates of reactions and the factors which affect the rates.

Definition: REACTION RATE $= \dfrac{\text{amount of product formed}}{\text{time interval}}$

or $= \dfrac{\text{amount of reactant used}}{\text{time interval}}$

or $= \dfrac{\Delta\text{amount}}{\Delta t}$, where "Δ" means "the change in"; "t" stands for "time"

EXAMPLE: If 16 g of HCl are used up after 12 min in a certain reaction, then the average reaction rate is:

$$\text{Rate of using HCl} = \frac{16\ \text{g}}{12\ \text{min}} = \mathbf{1.3\ g/min}\ .$$

If a reaction between $CaCO_3$ and HCl produces 245 mL of $CO_2(g)$ in 17 s, the average reaction rate is:

$$\text{Rate of producing } CO_2 = \frac{245\ \text{mL}}{17\ \text{s}} = \mathbf{14\ mL/s}\ .$$

EXERCISES:

1. A 5.0 g sample of magnesium reacts completely with a hydrochloric acid solution after 150 s. Express the average rate of consumption of magnesium, in units of g/min.

2. How long will it take to completely react 45.0 g of $CaCO_3(s)$ with dilute HCl(aq) if the reaction proceeds at an average rate of 2.35 g $CaCO_3(s)$/min under a given set of conditions?

3. The electrolysis of water produces oxygen gas at the rate of 32.5 mL/min in a certain experiment. What volume of oxygen gas can be produced in 7.50 min?

4. Which of the following are acceptable units for expressing reaction rate?

   (a) moles/second
   (b) minutes/metre
   (c) (moles/litre)/second
   (d) grams/litre
   (e) millilitres/hour
   (f) grams/minute

5. Hydrogen and oxygen gas react in a fuel cell to produce water according to the equation:

   $$2\,H_2(g) + O_2(g) \longrightarrow 2\,H_2O(l)\ .$$

   If the rate of water ***production*** is 1.34 mol/min, what is the rate of oxygen gas ***consumption*** expressed in mol/min?

I.2. METHODS OF MEASURING REACTION RATES

If an Alka Seltzer™ tablet is "plopped" into a beaker of water, you will see bubbles of $CO_2(g)$ forming. The reaction producing the gas is:

$$NaHCO_3(s) + H^+(aq) \longrightarrow CO_2(g) + Na^+(aq) + H_2O(l)\ .$$

The $H^+(aq)$ is produced by the contents of the tablet; $NaHCO_3$ ("baking soda") is another of the tablet's ingredients.

***EXERCISE*:**

6. The following data was obtained for the above reaction (mass includes beaker and contents).

Time (s)	Mass (g)
0	150.00
10	149.94
20	149.88
30	149.82

Plot the above data on the graph below.

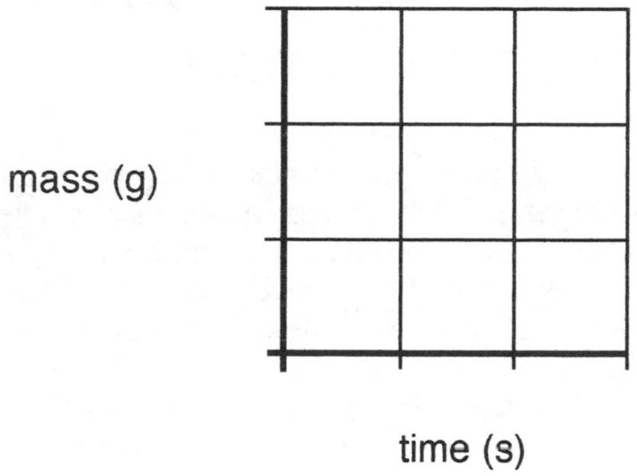

Now answer the following questions.

(a) Why is the mass decreasing?
(b) What is the slope of the line in the above graph, using: slope = RISE / RUN ?
(c) What are the units of: (i) the RISE? (ii) the RUN? (iii) the slope?
(d) What units would you expect to use for the rate of this reaction?
(e) What relationship exists between the slope of the graph and the rate of the reaction? State the value found for the experimentally–determined reaction rate.

In order to illustrate the methods used to determine the rate of a reaction, consider a specific reaction: the reaction of copper metal with nitric acid.

$$\underset{\text{red–brown}}{Cu(s)} + \underset{\text{colourless}}{4\,HNO_3(aq)} \longrightarrow \underset{\text{blue}}{Cu(NO_3)_2(aq)} + 2\,H_2O(l) + \underset{\text{brown}}{2\,NO_2(g)} + \text{heat}$$

The rate of the above reaction can be found by measuring any one of at least four different properties.

a) Colour change

The $Cu(NO_3)_2(aq)$ has a characteristic blue colour. The intensity of the blue colour can be measured with a spectrophotometer.

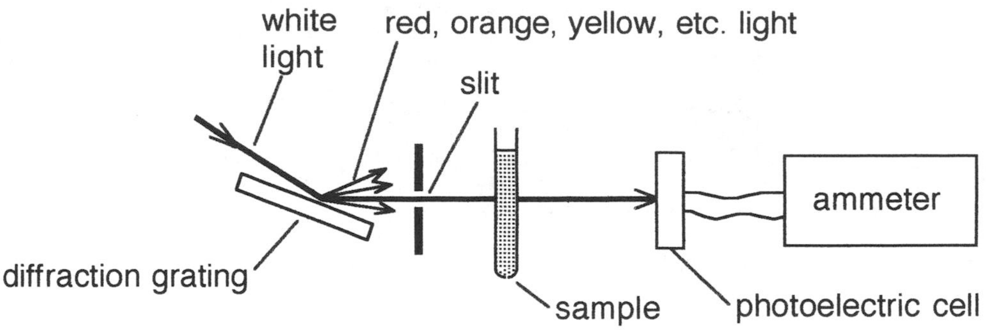

DIAGRAM OF A SIMPLE SPECTROPHOTOMETER

The diffraction grating acts like a prism and splits up the incoming light into the colours of the rainbow. When the diffraction grating is tilted the incoming light is reflected at a particular angle, allowing a specific colour, for example green, to pass through the slit. The amount of light which is absorbed by the sample is directly proportional to the concentration of the light–absorbing chemical. Changes in the amount of light hitting the photocell allow measurement of changes in the concentration of **dissolved** chemicals. (The beam of light must not be blocked by undissolved solids.) In the above reaction, the blue colour of the $Cu(NO_3)_2(aq)$ would be appropriate to measure. As the reaction proceeds, the intensity of the blue colour will increase. Plotting a graph of colour intensity versus time allows the slope of the graph to be found. But recall from exercise 6 that the RATE of the reaction is equal to the SLOPE of graph.

$$\text{Rate} = \frac{\Delta\text{colour intensity}}{\Delta\text{time}}$$

b) Temperature change

Since the reaction is producing heat, the slope of a temperature versus time graph allows you to find the rate of the reaction.

$$\text{Rate} = \frac{\Delta\text{temperature}}{\Delta\text{time}}$$

c) Pressure change

Since the reaction is producing a gas, NO_2, the reaction can be carried out in a sealed vessel attached to a gas pressure gauge. By plotting a graph of pressure versus time you can again find the slope of the graph, that is, the rate of the reaction.

$$\text{Rate} = \frac{\Delta\text{pressure}}{\Delta\text{time}}$$

d) Mass change

Since copper metal is the only solid present in the reaction, the rate at which the copper is used up can be measured as follows. Set up several identical acid solutions and pieces of copper. The mass of the copper must be known. Put the first piece of copper in the first container of acid and let the reaction proceed for 30 s, say. Then, quickly stop the reaction by pouring the acid–copper mixture into water and washing the remaining acid off the copper. Dry and weigh the amount of copper metal left. Repeat the reaction with the second piece of copper and second container of acid, but let the reaction proceed for 60 s, say, before stopping the reaction and weighing the copper. Repeat for several other time intervals. Using the known starting masses and the masses remaining after reacting, the mass which actually reacts is found for each trial. By plotting a graph of the mass of copper which reacts versus time, the slope of the graph and therefore the rate of the reaction is found.

$$\text{Rate} = \frac{\Delta\text{mass}}{\Delta\text{time}}$$

EXERCISES:

7. When measuring the rate at which the mass of copper metal decreases during a reaction with nitric acid, why can't you just put the reaction vessel on a digital balance and record the decrease in mass as the copper is used up?

8. (a) Solutions of $Cu^{2+}(aq)$ are blue, while solutions of $Ag^{+}(aq)$ are colourless. Use only this information to describe how you would measure the rate of the reaction:

$$2\ Ag^{+}(aq) + Cu(s) \longrightarrow 2\ Ag(s) + Cu^{2+}(aq) + 35\ kJ.$$

   (b) Suggest two more methods that could be used to determine the rate of the reaction in part (a). For each method, state the property that you are monitoring.

9. (a) You are to measure the rate of the reaction: $H_2(g) + Cl_2(g) \longrightarrow 2\ HCl(g)$. Why is gas pressure **NOT** a good property to monitor in order to determine the reaction rate?

   (b) Calculate the reaction rate, in mol HCl/s, if 1.2 g of HCl(g) are produced in 2.0 min.

   (c) If the rate of consumption of hydrogen gas under certain conditions is 0.200 L/min, what is the rate of production of HCl(g)?

I.3. FACTORS AFFECTING REACTION RATES

Experiments show the following relationships.

a) When two Alka Seltzer™ tablets are simultaneously "plopped" into equal volumes of hot and cold water, *THE REACTION PROCEEDS FASTER AT HIGHER TEMPERATURES.*

b) When strips of copper metal are simultaneously placed into equal volumes of concentrated nitric acid (15.4 M) and diluted nitric acid (6.0 M), *THE REACTION IS FASTER IN THE MORE CONCENTRATED SOLUTION.*

The results of such experimental work probably are exactly what you would have expected. This section will look at these and other factors which can have an effect on the rate of a reaction and come up with statements such as:

"When the ..... increases, then the rate ....".

No attempt will be made in this section to explain ***why*** these factors have an effect on the rate; explaining why an effect occurs will be left until a later section.

The factors which affect the rate of a reaction are as follows.

a) TEMPERATURE

When temperature ***increases***, the time required for the reaction ***decreases***. But, a ***decrease*** in the time for the reaction is caused by an ***increase*** in the **RATE**, so that when the TEMPERATURE ***increases***, the RATE ***increases***.

b) CONCENTRATION

As reactant concentration ***increases***, the time required for the reaction ***decreases***. Hence, when REACTANT CONCENTRATION ***increases*** the RATE ***increases***.

c) PRESSURE

When the pressure of a gaseous reactant ***increases***, more of the reactant is compressed into a given volume (that is, the reactant concentration ***increases***). Hence, when the REACTANT PRESSURE ***increases***, the RATE ***increases***.

Note: Pressure is just another way to define a concentration.

Important:	The volume of a system is inversely proportional to the pressure applied to the system. In other words, ***when the pressure on a system is increased, the volume of the system decreases, and vice versa.***

d) THE NATURE OF THE REACTANTS

Some reactions are naturally slow because the bonds involved are very strong and unreactive, or the electrons involved are tightly held. Other reactions are naturally fast because the reaction involves breaking weak bonds or removing loosely–held electrons. Chemists have no control over these ***fundamental*** differences in the rates of reactions.

Definition: The **NATURE OF THE REACTANT** is the term used to describe the chemical properties of a substance.

We say that it is simply the "**NATURE OF THE REACTANTS**" to react quickly or slowly. For example, the chemical properties of granite and nitroglycerine dictate that the "weathering" of a granite boulder by the action of sunshine and rain is naturally very slow, whereas the explosion of nitroglycerine is very fast. You can slow down or speed up the weathering of granite and the explosion of nitroglycerine TO A SMALL DEGREE, but you cannot change the fact that the weathering will ALWAYS be much slower than the explosion.

Important: The NATURE OF THE REACTANTS does ***not*** refer to the phase (solid, liquid, gas) of the reactants, but rather to the chemical properties of the specific molecules involved.

With respect to "the nature of the reactants", the bonding may involve more than just how strong the bonds are; the NUMBER OF BONDS being broken and made may need to be considered. For example, the following reaction is RELATIVELY SLOW because many chemical bonds have to be broken and then reformed.

$$5\,C_2O_4^{2-} + 2\,MnO_4^- + 16\,H^+ \longrightarrow 10\,CO_2 + 2\,Mn^{2+} + 8\,H_2O$$

ACTUAL SHAPES OF THE SPECIES

On the other hand, the following reaction is FAST because ***no*** bonds are broken or formed; only a single electron is transferred.

$$Fe^{2+} + Ce^{4+} \longrightarrow Fe^{3+} + Ce^{3+}$$

EXERCISES:

10. Rank the following three reactions in terms of their expected reaction rates (fastest to slowest) at room temperature.

    (a) 2 H–O–O–H ⟶ 2 H–O–H + O=O

    (b) 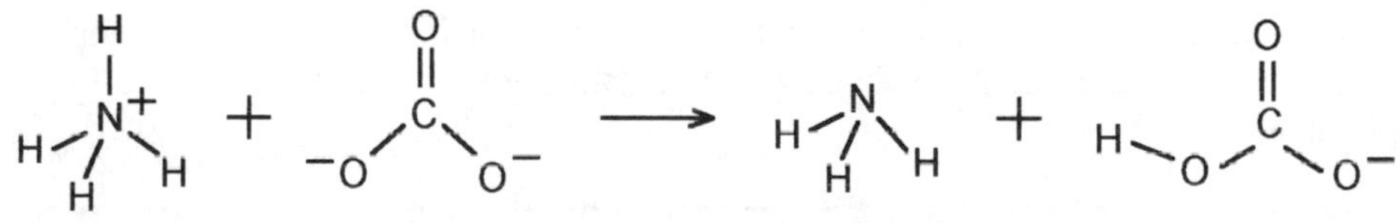

    (c) $2\,CH_3–CH_2–CH_2–CH_2–CH_2–CH_2–CH_2–CH_3 + 25\,O{=}O \longrightarrow 16\,O{=}C{=}O + 18\,H–O–H$
    [Note that this is the combustion of octane ("gasoline")]

11. Experimentally, it is found that at room temperature the reaction between Li(s) and water is much slower than the reaction between K(s) and water. Which of the previous four factors affecting reaction rates would best explain this observation?

e) THE ABILITY OF REACTANTS TO MEET: SURFACE AREA AND PHASE CONSIDERATIONS

If you want to start a campfire, you start with small wood shavings rather than with a huge log. The shavings allow you to start a fire quicker because

THE GREATER THE SURFACE AREA AVAILABLE FOR REACTION, THE GREATER THE RATE OF REACTION.

In a sense, surface area effects are related to concentration effects. That is, if in a given volume you have more surface area exposed, then there is a greater concentration of sites at which a reaction can take place. However, surface area ***is*** a distinct effect, separate from concentration, even though surface area and concentration can be thought of in a similar manner.

Before going any further, let us consider the effect of PHASE on the SURFACE AREA.

Definition: A **HOMOGENEOUS REACTION** is a reaction in which all the reactants are in the same phase.

Some examples of HOMOGENEOUS REACTIONS are reactions between:

- two gases,
- two substances which are both dissolved in water, and
- two liquids which completely dissolve in each other (are "miscible").

Definition: A **HETEROGENEOUS REACTION** is a reaction in which the reactants are present in different phases.

Some examples of HETEROGENEOUS REACTIONS are reactions between:

- a solid and a liquid,
- a liquid and a gas,
- a solid and a gas, and
- two liquids which DO NOT dissolve in each other (are "immiscible").

Surface area is one of the factors which affect the rate of a reaction because surface area controls ***the ability of the reactants to meet.*** The greater the surface area, the greater the ability of the reactants to meet, and the greater the rate of the reaction.

Another important consideration is the **PHASE** in which a reaction occurs. Reactions occurring in the solid phase are slow because the reactants cannot move freely. Reactions between gaseous species and reactions between species in the liquid phase are much faster due to the speed of the gaseous particles or the close proximity of the liquid particles. Aqueous ions have the fastest reaction rates because of their close proximity to each other in solution, their ability to move through the solvent, and their strong positive–negative attractions. In summary, the following trend in reaction rates is found.

FASTEST ⟶ SLOWEST
AQUEOUS IONS > (GASES or LIQUIDS) > SOLIDS

EXERCISES:

12. Will surface area have an effect on a reaction between two gases? Why? How can this conclusion be generalized to the importance of surface area in homogeneous versus heterogeneous reactions?

13. In each of the following pairs of reactions, which would have the faster reaction rate?

    (a) $H_2(g) + I_2(g) \longrightarrow 2\,HI(g)$ **or** $Ag^+(aq) + I^-(aq) \longrightarrow AgI(s)$
    (b) $Fe(s) + 2\,H_2O(l) \longrightarrow Fe(OH)_2(s) + H_2(g)$ **or** $CH_3COOH(aq) + H_2O(l) \longrightarrow CH_3COO^-(aq) + H_3O^+(aq)$
    (c) $Cu(s) + S(s) \longrightarrow CuS(s)$ **or** $CaO(s) + H_2O(l) \longrightarrow Ca(OH)_2(s)$
    (d) $C(s, \text{powder}) + O_2(g) \longrightarrow CO_2(g)$ **or** $C(s, \text{chunk}) + O_2(g) \longrightarrow CO_2(g)$
    (e) $H^+(aq) + OH^-(aq) \longrightarrow H_2O(l)$ **or** $2\,H_2O_2(aq) + 2\,H^+(aq) \longrightarrow 2\,H_3O^+(aq) + O_2(g)$

14. Which of the reactions in the previous exercise are HOMOGENEOUS reactions?

f) CATALYSTS AND INHIBITORS

A **CATALYST** is a chemical which can be added to a reaction to INCREASE the rate of the reaction. After the reaction is complete, there will be as much of the catalyst present as was originally put into the reaction.

An **INHIBITOR** is a chemical which REDUCES a reaction rate by combining with a catalyst or one of the reactants in such a way as to prevent the reaction from occurring. Examples of inhibitors are poisons and antibiotics.

EXERCISES:

15. Which of the above six factors (temperature, concentration, etc.) are important in HOMOGENEOUS reactions? Which are important in HETEROGENEOUS reactions?

16. State 5 ways of increasing the rate of the reaction: $2\,Al(s) + 3\,F_2(g) \longrightarrow 2\,AlF_3(s)$.
Assume the reaction is occurring in a closed container whose volume can be changed.

17. (a) What will happen to the concentration of the reactants as a reaction proceeds?
(b) What will happen to the rate of a reaction as the reaction proceeds?
(c) Which of the following graphs would best represent
i) the ***product concentration*** versus time of a reaction? Explain your selection.
ii) the ***reactant concentration*** versus time of a reaction? Explain your selection.

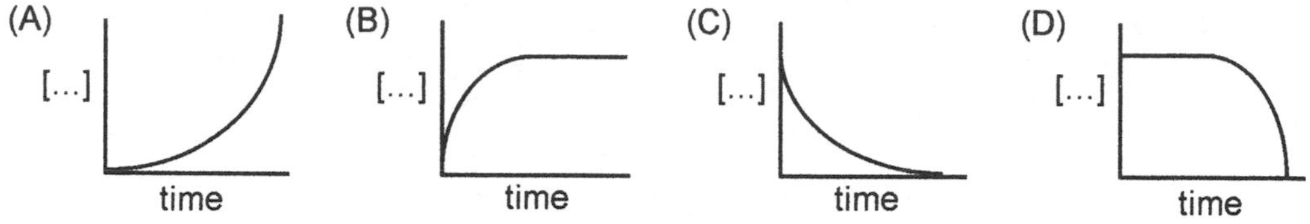

(d) Which of the following graphs would best represent
i) the ***RATE*** at which **reactants** are used versus time of a reaction? Explain.
ii) the ***RATE*** at which **products** are produced versus time of a reaction? Explain.

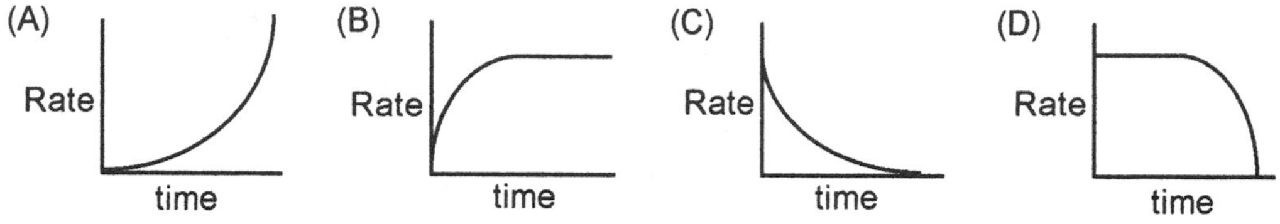

Many everyday situations require the control of reaction rates. Some examples are given below.

a) Body chemistry requires an exact temperature to ensure that the reactions of life occur at an appropriate rate.

b) Fuels burn quickly in air and may explode in pure oxygen. As the oxygen concentration is lowered, the rate of burning drops to zero, which is why "smothering" a fire is effective.

c) Enzymes are catalysts which regulate our body chemistry.

d) Many industrial chemical reactions require precise control of the factors affecting the rate. For example, the production of compounds called "azo dyes" (used to dye wool and cotton) requires the use of low temperatures at one point so as to prevent unstable reactants from decomposing before they have a chance to react.

e) The metal in car bodies will quickly rust unless paint or other protection is used to prevent oxygen from reacting with the iron in the car.

f) The cooking of food requires an increase in temperature. Many of the desirable reactions in the cooking process will not occur except at high temperatures.

g) To preserve food, its temperature can be lowered in order to slow down the reactions which allow bacteria to grow.

I.4. EXPERIMENTAL MEASUREMENT OF REACTION RATES

If the concentration of a reactant is plotted versus time, the following typical behaviour is observed.

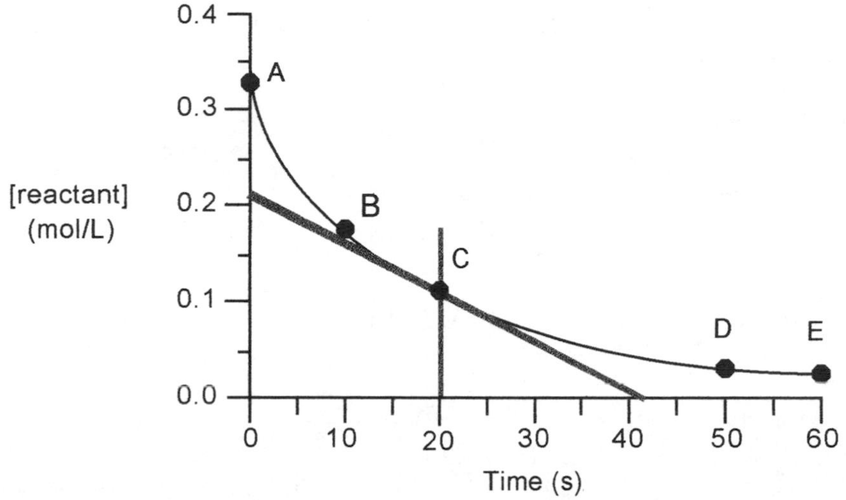

Initially, there is a relatively high [reactant], so that the reactant is used up at a fast rate (in the first 10 s there is a large drop from A to B). Later, when most of the reactant is used up, the low [reactant] causes a slow reaction rate (in the 10 s interval from 50 – 60 s there is only a small drop in [reactant] from D to E).

The exact rate at a given time, for example at 20 s (above), is given by the slope of the line tangent to the curve at that time (see above graph).

EXERCISES:

18. What is the reaction rate at 20 s, according to the above graph?

19. The following data were collected for the reaction $Zn(s) + 2\ HCl(aq) \longrightarrow H_2(g) + ZnCl_2(aq)$ in which zinc metal was reacted with 0.200 M HCl(aq).

Time (s)	Mass Zn (g)
0	31.0
60	24.6
120	20.2
180	17.4

(a) Calculate the average reaction rate, in g/s, from time 0 to 60 s.
(b) Calculate the average reaction rate, in g/s, from time 120 to 180 s.
(c) Explain why the average rate in part (b) is less than that in (a).

I.5. REACTION RATES AND COLLISION THEORY

The **COLLISION THEORY** (or **Kinetic Molecular Theory**) states that molecules act as small, hard spheres which bounce off each other and transfer energy among themselves during their collisions.

Before two molecules can react, they must collide with each other. "Action at a distance" does not exist; that is, there can be no reaction without a collision.

Consider the reaction: $H_2 + I_2 \longrightarrow 2\,HI$.

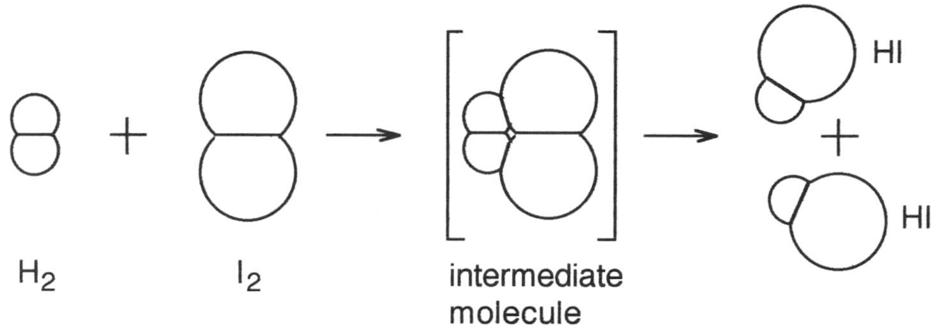

Collision theory provides us with a deeper understanding of what actually causes reaction rates to change when the conditions of the reaction are altered.

a) ***The Effect of Concentration*** – if the $[H_2]$ or $[I_2]$ increases then more collisions are possible between molecules. Therefore, the rate of the reaction increases; that is, the number of collisions per second increases.

b) ***The Effect of Temperature*** – if the temperature increases then the KINETIC ENERGY (KE) of the molecules increases and the speed at which they are moving increases. Because the molecules are moving faster they collide more often ***and*** with more energy, and therefore the reaction rate increases. [NOTE: This is only PART of the reason why rate increases when the temperature increases, as will be seen in Section 7.]

EXERCISES:

20. How can collision theory explain the effect of surface area on reaction rate?

21. The following reaction is taking place at a very slow rate in a closed container at room temperature.

$$S(s) + O_2(g) \longrightarrow SO_2(g)$$

State the effect of the following procedures on the rate of this reaction and explain the effect in terms of collision theory.

(a) The temperature is decreased.
(b) More $O_2(g)$ is added to the same volume.
(c) Some $SO_2(g)$ is removed.
(d) The sulphur is ground up into a powder.
(e) The volume of the container is increased.

22. Explain in terms of collision theory why kindling is used to start a fire, rather than a large block of wood.

I.6. ENTHALPY CHANGES IN CHEMICAL REACTIONS

a) Bond Energies

Consider the reaction shown on the diagram below.

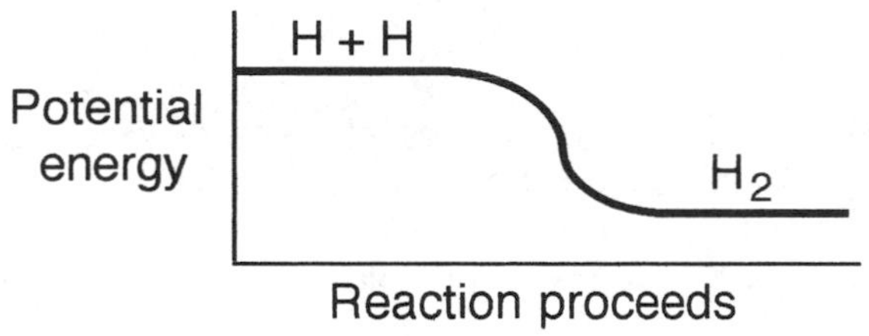

As the atoms combine to form a bond, they give off energy and go to a lower, more stable level of energy. This is more clearly seen by looking at the reaction in reverse. In order to break a chemical bond, energy must be added to the molecule so that the resulting separated atoms contain more energy than before.

The negatively–charged electrons hold the positively–charged nuclei together, forming a chemical bond. Simultaneously, the electrons repel each other and the nuclei repel each other, so that the position of the atoms involved in a chemical bond is a compromise between the attractive forces and repulsive forces existing within a molecule.

The potential energy is the energy possessed by a system as a result of the position of all the particles in the system. More specifically:

> **POTENTIAL ENERGY** is the energy existing as a result of an object's position in space, as well as the sum of all the attractive and repulsive forces existing among the particles which make up the object. As a result, the potential energy (PE) of a chemical system is directly related to the energy of the electrons in the chemical bonds, as well as the number and type of atoms in the molecules.

In contrast:

> **KINETIC ENERGY** is the energy which a system possesses because of movement within the system. This energy may exist as a result of moving the entire system or moving the molecules in the system (or individual atoms within the molecules).

Definition: **BOND ENERGY** is the amount of energy required to break a bond between two atoms.

To break a bond, an amount of energy equal to the bond energy must be added to the bond:

$$Cl_2(g) + 243\ kJ \longrightarrow 2\ Cl(g).$$

Conversely, if two atoms form a bond, an amount of energy equal to the bond energy is released by the atoms:

$$2\ Cl(g) \longrightarrow Cl_2(g) + 243\ kJ.$$

EXERCISE:

23. When breaking the Br–Br bond in Br_2, what happens to the potential energy of the molecule?

b) Reaction Heats

When a chemical reaction occurs, new molecules are formed as chemical bonds are broken and made, phases may change, work may be done on the system or by the system, and heat may be transferred into or out of the system. Accounting for each of these energy changes on an individual basis is complicated and beyond the level of Chemistry 12. Since many chemical reactions are carried out in open flasks or beakers, a special energy term (ENTHALPY) is defined to incorporate all the energies which exist in an open system at constant atmospheric pressure.

Definitions: **ENTHALPY = H** = the total kinetic and potential energy which exists in a system when at constant pressure.

ΔH = $H_{PROD} - H_{REACT}$ = the change in enthalpy during the course of a reaction

where: H_{REACT} = the ***combined*** enthalpies of ***all*** the reactants
H_{PROD} = the ***combined*** enthalpies of ***all*** the products

The relationship between ΔH, H_{PROD} and H_{REACT} is shown on the diagram below.

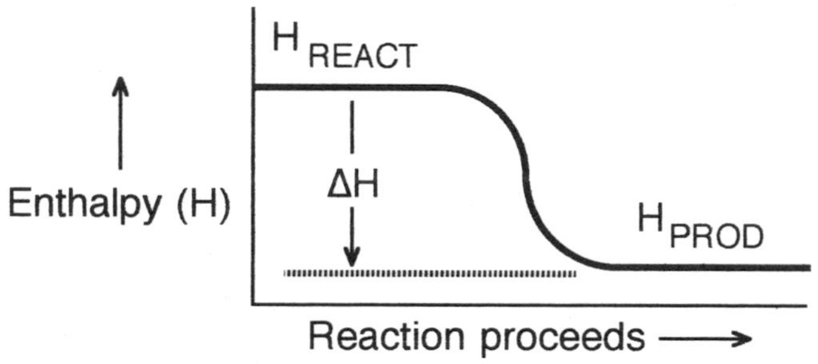

SPECIAL NOTE: In general, the individual values for H_{REACT} and H_{PROD} are never found and are not needed. Only ΔH, the ***difference*** between the values of H_{PROD} and H_{REACT}, is important.

c) The Sign of ΔH:

i) If a reaction is **ENDOTHERMIC** then products have MORE energy than reactants.

Substituting $H_{PROD} > H_{REACT}$ into $\Delta H = H_{PROD} - H_{REACT}$ gives **ΔH > 0.**

EXAMPLE: Two alternate ways to show an ENDOTHERMIC reaction are

$$2\,N_2 + O_2 + 164\text{ kJ} \longrightarrow 2\,N_2O$$

or: $$2\,N_2 + O_2 \longrightarrow 2\,N_2O\ ;\ \Delta H = +164\text{ kJ}$$

Examine the energy diagram below. Note that the arrow associated with ΔH always points **from** the energy level of the reactants **to** the energy level of the products. In this case, the arrow points "up" and the reactants GAIN energy to become products. Heat "**EN**ters" the system in an **EN**dothermic reaction.

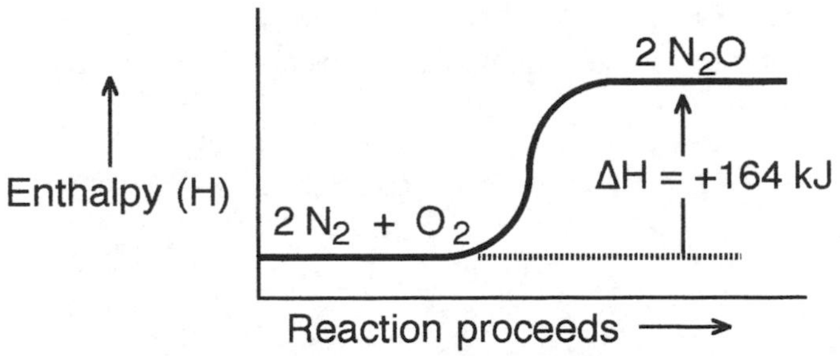

The 164 kJ of heat which is absorbed by the N_2 and O_2 (the "SYSTEM") comes from the surroundings (such as the container, surrounding air, etc.), as indicated by the diagram below.

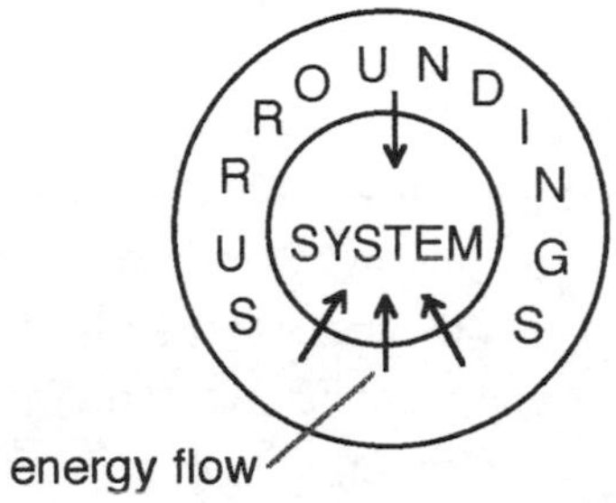

The loss of energy from the surroundings to the system (N_2 and O_2) causes the surroundings to feel cooler.

ii) If a reaction is EXOTHERMIC then products have LESS energy than reactants.

Substituting $H_{PROD} < H_{REACT}$ into $\Delta H = H_{PROD} - H_{REACT}$ gives $\mathbf{\Delta H < 0}$.

EXAMPLE: Two alternate ways to show an EXOTHERMIC reaction are

$H_2 + Cl_2 \longrightarrow 2\,HCl + 184$ kJ

or: $H_2 + Cl_2 \longrightarrow 2\,HCl$; $\Delta H = -184$ kJ

This situation is shown on the energy diagram below. Again, the arrow associated with ΔH points **from** the energy level of the reactants **to** the energy level of the products. In this case, the arrow points "down" and the reactants LOSE energy to become products. Heat "**EX**its" the system in an **EX**othermic reaction.

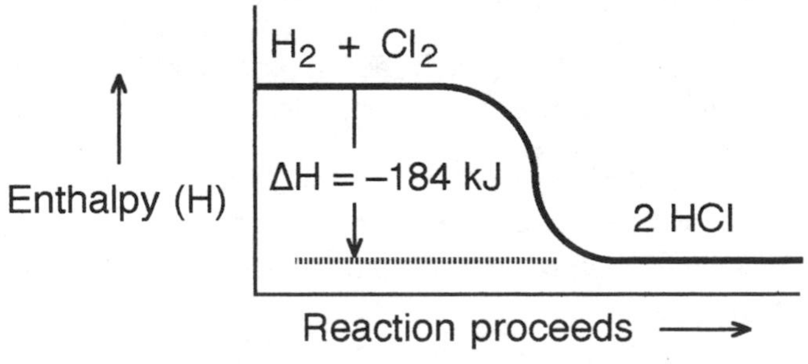

The 184 kJ of heat which is given off by the H_2 and Cl_2 (the "SYSTEM") will be absorbed by the surroundings, as indicated by the diagram below.

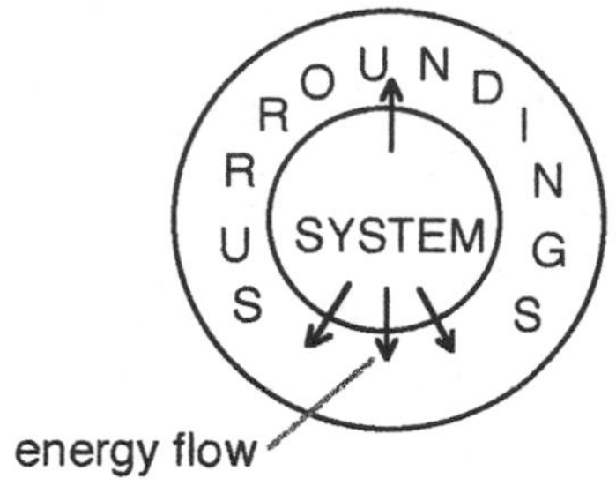

The loss of energy from the H_2 and Cl_2 to the surroundings causes the surroundings to feel warmer.

MEMORY AID: The two possible signs for a number are + and – .
(Notice that it sounds backwards to say – and +.)
In English we read from left to right, so let us put the "+" on the left side of a reaction arrow and the "–" on the right .

This gives us $+ \longrightarrow -$ which is interpreted as :

if the heat term is on the left side , then $\Delta H = +$
if the heat term is on the right side , then $\Delta H = -$

EXERCISES:

24. $\Delta H = -25$ kJ for the reaction: $A \longrightarrow B$. Re–write this equation to show the 25 kJ properly on the reactant or product side. Draw a graph of "enthalpy" versus "reaction proceeds", showing the relative enthalpies of the reactant and product, and the enthalpy change. Will the surroundings feel warmer or cooler as the reaction occurs?

25. If a reaction absorbs 40 kJ of heat, what is ΔH for the reaction?

26. What is ΔH for the reaction $A + 30\text{ kJ} \longrightarrow B$? Which have more energy, reactants or products? Draw a graph of "enthalpy" versus "reaction proceeds", showing the relative enthalpies of the reactant and product, and the enthalpy change. Will the surroundings feel warmer or cooler as the reaction occurs?

27. Draw a graph of "enthalpy" versus "reaction proceeds" for a reaction in which $R \longrightarrow P + 10\text{ kJ}$. Will the surroundings feel warmer or cooler as the reaction occurs?

28. When one mole of HCl reacts with one mole of NaOH to produce one mole of NaCl and one mole of H_2O, 59 kJ of heat is absorbed by the surroundings. Draw a graph of "enthalpy" versus "reaction proceeds", showing the relative enthalpies of the reactant and product, and the enthalpy change.

I.7. KINETIC ENERGY DISTRIBUTIONS

Consider the reaction: $C_2H_5OH \longrightarrow C_2H_4 + H_2O$. At room temperature the reaction rate does not occur at a detectable rate. At 200°C the rate is very slow – some molecules do react BUT only a very small amount. At 400°C the reaction is relatively rapid.

Molecules at room temperature and pressure undergo about 10^{10} collisions/second, so the lack of reactivity at room temperature is ***not*** due to a lack of collisions. Since high temperatures favour fast reaction rates, the energy contained in a molecule must determine whether or not a molecule will react. However, at a given temperature some molecules ***do*** react and some ***do not***, so that there MUST be a CONTINUOUS DISTRIBUTION of energies among the molecules, as shown below.

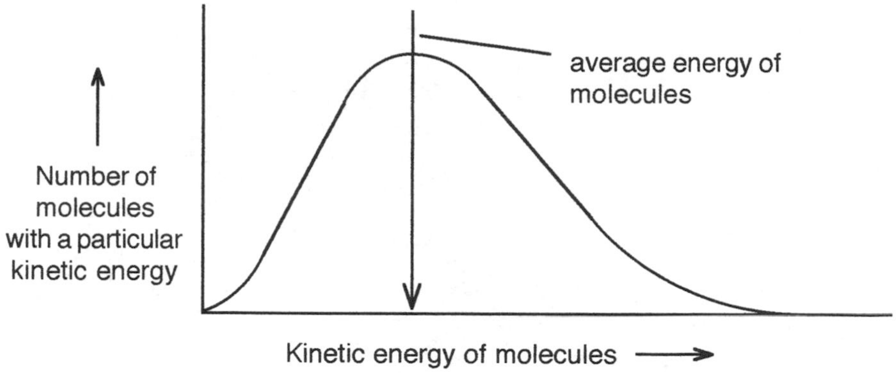

Note that some molecules have a very low kinetic energy and some have a very high kinetic energy.

As the temperature of the system is increased, the average energy of the system is increased.

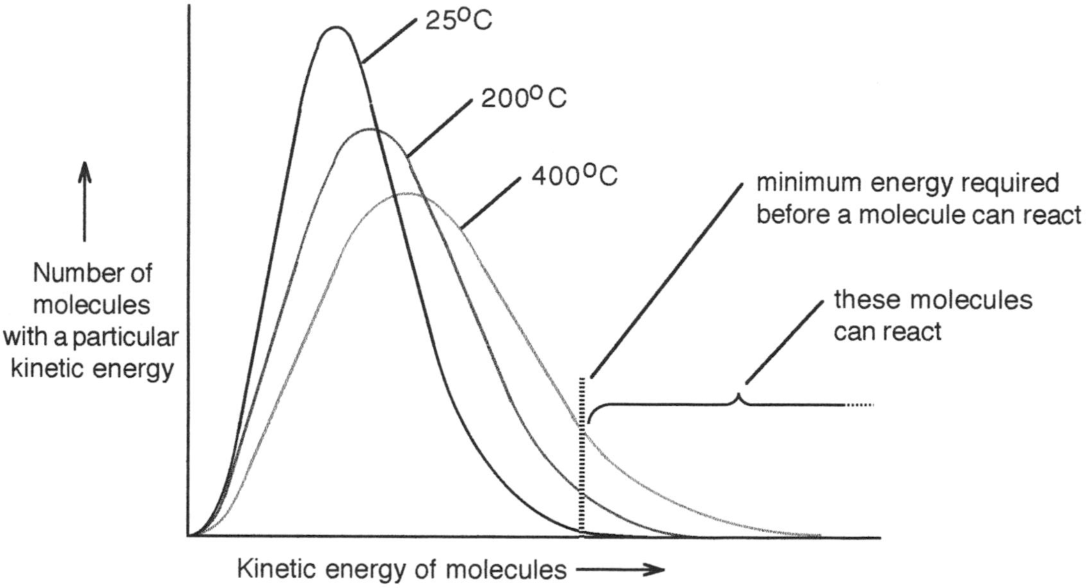

NOTE: 1. The reaction rate is small at room temperature since only a few molecules have sufficient energy to react at a given instant. As the average energy of the molecules increases at higher temperatures, more and more molecules possess the required minimum energy to react, and hence the rate increases.

2. As the temperature increases the molecules undergo more collisions, but the increase in collisions is relatively small. (It can be shown that when going from 100°C to 110°C, the 10°C temperature increase only results in about a 1% increase in the number of collisions!)

Therefore:

THE INCREASED REACTION RATE DUE TO AN INCREASE IN TEMPERATURE IS **PRIMARILY DUE** TO THE INCREASED NUMBER OF MOLECULES WITH SUFFICIENT ENERGY TO REACT, AND NOT TO THE INCREASED NUMBER OF COLLISIONS.

Chemists have a **"rule–of–thumb"** which states that

for a SLOW reaction, a 10°C temperature increase DOUBLES the rate.

The reason for this rule–of–thumb is that at the far right of the KE curves below, the area under curve "B" is about double the area under curve "A" (see below). Since there are twice as many molecules of B which have sufficient energy to react, the rate is doubled. ***Note***: the curves in the graph below have been deliberately distorted to help illustrate the "doubling of area" effect.

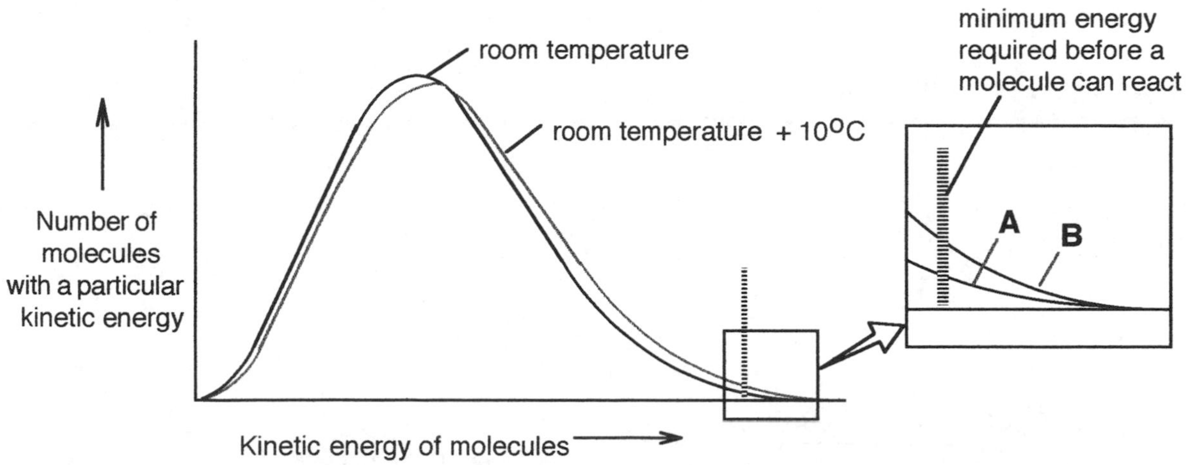

A final comment: The KE curves represent the number of particles with a given KE at a given temperature. The curves would look the same for a collection of reacting particles or non–reacting particles. The curves do not automatically predict whether a particle can react; such predictions can only be made if it is known from other sources how much energy a particle requires to react. The distribution tells us only that a few particles in the collection have low energy, most have an intermediate energy, and a few have very high energy.

EXERCISES:

29. The reaction $C_2H_4(g) + Br_2(g) \longrightarrow C_2H_4Br_2(g)$ proceeds very fast at room temperature.

(a) Which of the following KE diagrams would best explain the rate of this reaction? ("ME" is the minimum KE required before a molecule can react.)

(i)

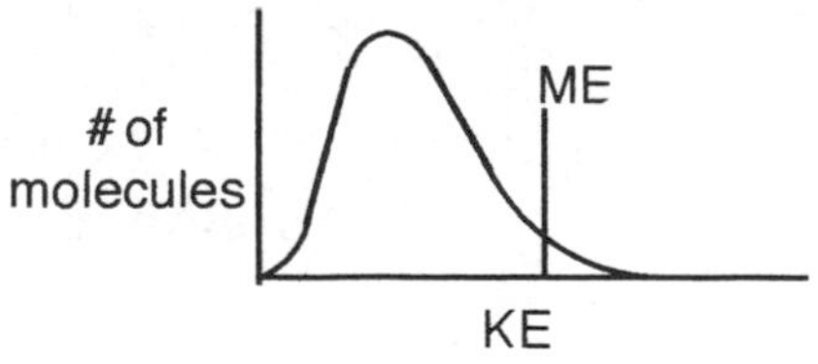

(ii)

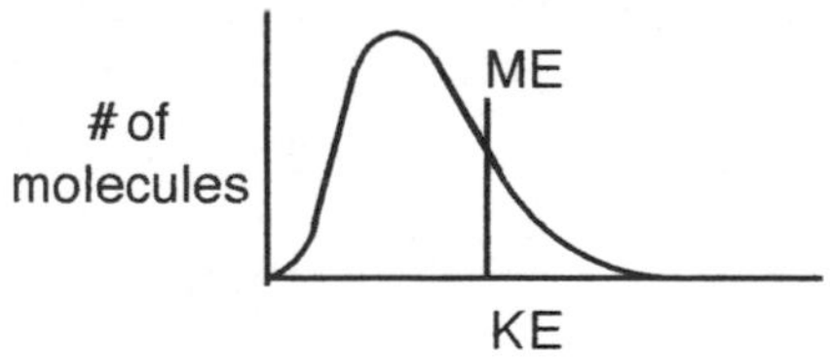

(iii)

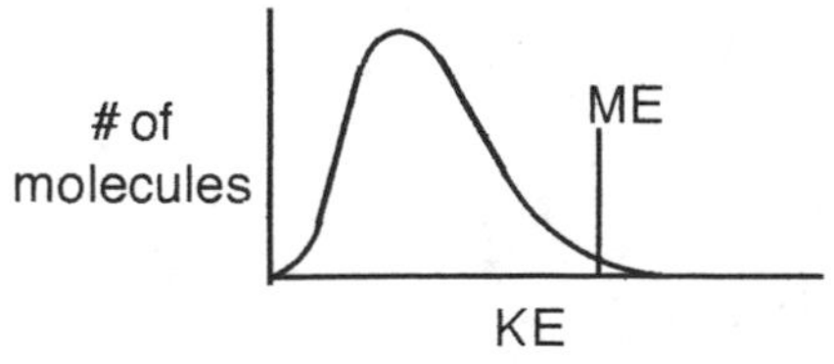

(b) If the temperature were increased by 10°C, would the reaction rate double? Explain.

30. What happens to the shape of the KE distribution curve if the:

(a) reactant is used up at a constant temperature?

(b) temperature is decreased?

(c) reactant surface area is increased?

(d) concentration of reactants is increased?

31. The initial rate of consumption of A in the reaction $A \longrightarrow B$ is very slow: 1.0×10^{-7} mol/s at 20°C. Estimate the rate of the reaction at 40°C.

32. If the rate of a slow reaction is 2.0×10^{-4} mol/s at 10°C, estimate the rate at 40°C.

I.8. ACTIVATION ENERGIES

The existence of a minimum energy requirement before a molecule can react means the molecule has an energy "barrier" to overcome. Specifically:

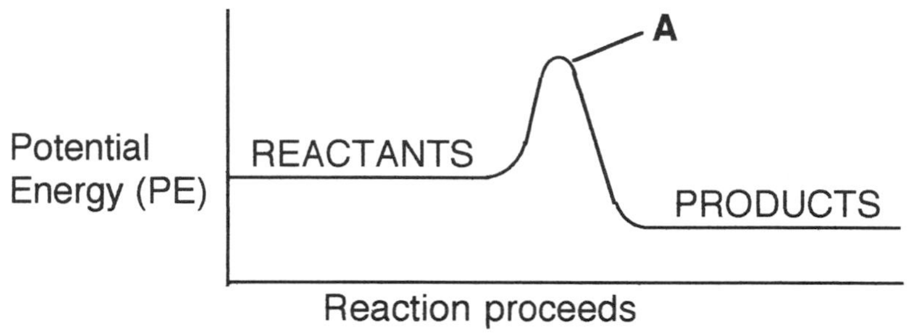

At the peak of the hill (point A) the actual reaction occurs. If the reactants do not possess enough energy to react, they can only climb part way up the hill and don't react. Molecules with insufficient energy just bounce off each other without reacting.

As the molecules approach each other, the outer electrons on one molecule start to repel the electrons on the other, thus slowing down the molecules and converting their KE into PE. In other words, the electrons in the molecule absorb the KE lost and increase their PE. If the molecules can gain sufficient PE (by converting the KE gained into PE, and adding this extra PE to the PE they already possess), bonds can be broken and made and an **ACTIVATED COMPLEX** is formed. After the reaction, the newly–formed product molecules repel each other (their outer electrons repel) and as the molecules start to move away from each other they lose their excess PE by converting it into KE (the molecules pick up speed – "hot" molecules have a high KE).

Overall, then:

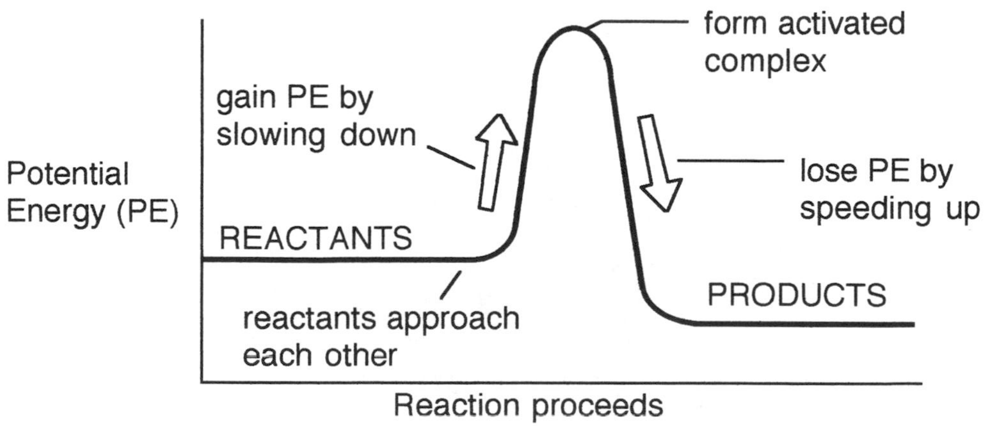

NOTE: The existence of the barrier is due to the mutual repulsion of the outer electrons as the reactants approach each other, as well as the energy required to cause bond breaking to begin. When the number of electrons present at the "reaction site" is increased, the repulsion between the approaching molecules is also increased. A higher energy hill results from the greater PE required to overcome this increased repulsion. In addition, the PE requirements are greater when the bond strengths involved are increased.

Definitions: The **ACTIVATED COMPLEX** is the arrangement of atoms which occurs when the reactants ARE IN THE PROCESS OF REARRANGING to form products. (In other words, it is an intermediate molecule.)

ACTIVATION ENERGY = E_a = the minimum potential energy required to change the reactants into the activated complex.

When two molecules approach each other they will start to convert their KE into PE and "climb the energy hill"; that is, they will "spend" their KE in order to "buy" PE. There are three possible cases to consider with regard to how much KE a pair of approaching molecules may possess.

Case 1: The KE is less than that needed to "buy" an amount of PE equal to the activation energy.

Here, the molecules will not be able to "spend" enough KE to get to the top of the PE hill. Hence, the approaching molecules will come to a halt before a reaction can occur, then move back away from each other (rebound). This is called an **INEFFECTIVE COLLISION.**

Case 2: The total KE is equal to the "minimum energy required for a reaction to occur" (see Section I.7).

Here, the molecules "spend" just enough KE to "buy" the required activation energy. The approaching molecules will have come to standstill, but a reaction will now be possible (although a reaction is not guaranteed; the molecules may simply separate without reacting).

Case 3: The total KE is more than the "minimum energy required for a reaction to occur".

Here, the molecules will be able to "spend" enough KE to be able to "buy" the required activation energy and still have some leftover KE. The reacting molecules will then be locked together while they are moving as a unit through space.

A collision between two particles is *EFFECTIVE* if the collision results in a reaction.

The graphs below will be used to help explain why a reaction proceeds at a fast or a slow rate.

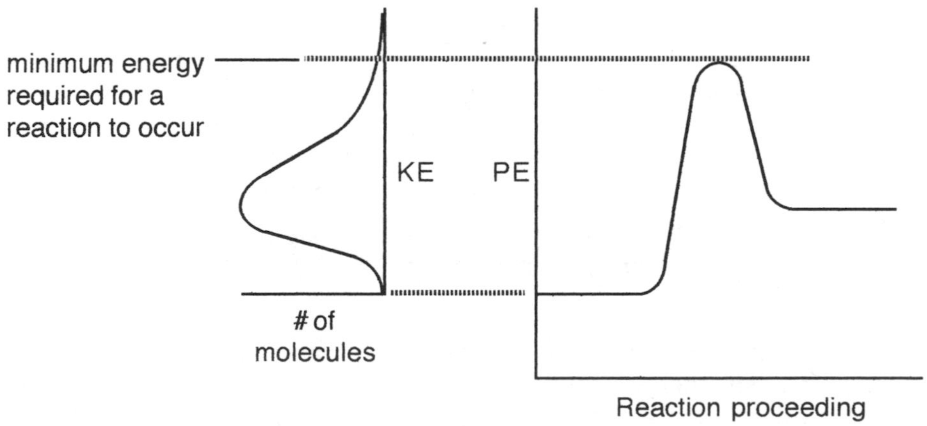

The graph on the left is a KE distribution curve (Section I.7) tilted on its side, so that the KE is now the vertical axis. The graph on the right is a normal PE diagram. The KE diagram shows how many molecules have a

SPECIFIC AMOUNT OF KINETIC ENERGY AVAILABLE. Because the PE hill is so high, there are very few molecules which have a KE greater than or equal to the "minimum energy required for a reaction to occur". As a result, very few molecules will be able to react in a given time interval and the REACTION RATE WILL BE VERY SMALL. If the energy hill were substantially lower, then in a given time interval many more molecules would have the KE required to react and the REACTION RATE WOULD BE LARGE.

Examine the following diagram.

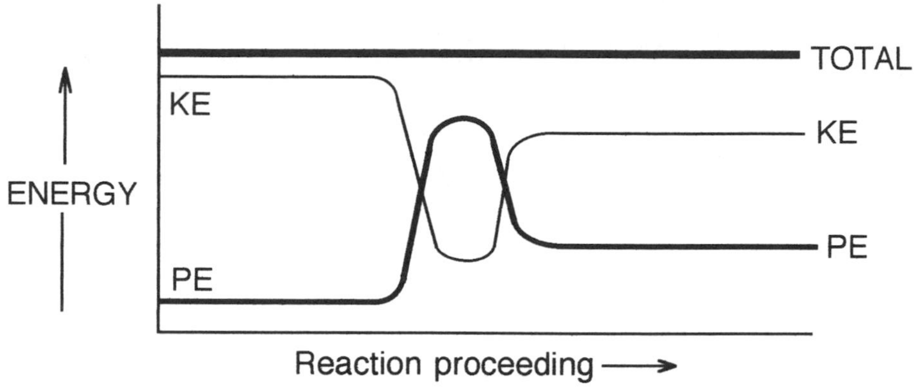

At the start of the reaction, most of the energy is stored as KE. As the molecules approach each other, the PE increases and the KE (as velocity) decreases. After the reaction, the molecules separate and pick up speed as the PE decreases. The total energy of the system never changes: PE + KE = constant.

When two species collide there are two requirements which must be met before a successful reaction can occur. The molecules must possess:

i) ***Sufficient KE*** – If insufficient KE is converted to PE then insufficient PE will be gained.

ii) ***Correct alignment*** – If the reactants are not correctly aligned, the reaction needs more energy to be completed.

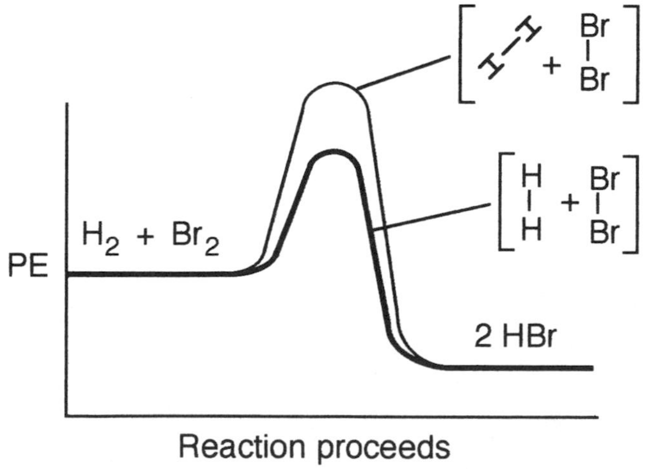

As can be seen in the diagram above, if the reactants are ***not*** correctly aligned (not parallel to each other in this case) the activation energy required is increased. Therefore, experimental values given for the activation energy refer to the activation energy required when there is PERFECT ALIGNMENT of reactants. If the alignment is very poor (for example, one reactant is at right angles to its preferred orientation) the activation energy may be impossibly high.

EXERCISES:

33. Why don't the oceans convert to nitric acid? (Recall that this was the problem posed at the start of this entire section.)

34. (a) Draw a PE diagram for a fast exothermic reaction.
    (b) Draw a PE diagram for a slow exothermic reaction.
    (c) Draw a PE diagram for a fast endothermic reaction.
    (d) Draw a PE diagram for a slow endothermic reaction.
    (e) How is the size of the "energy hill" related to the number of molecules which have sufficient KE to pass over the top of the hill?

35. If two reactant molecules collide with sufficient KE, are they guaranteed to have an ***effective*** collision?

36. (a) As two reactant particles approach each other, what happens to
    (i) their KE? Why? (ii) their PE? Why?
    (b) The total energy of a system is given by: E_{TOTAL} = PE + KE. How does the value of E_{TOTAL} before a collision compare to the value of E_{TOTAL} after a collision?

37. The following is a PE diagram for a collision between molecules A_2 and B_2. The molecules collide with favourable geometry.

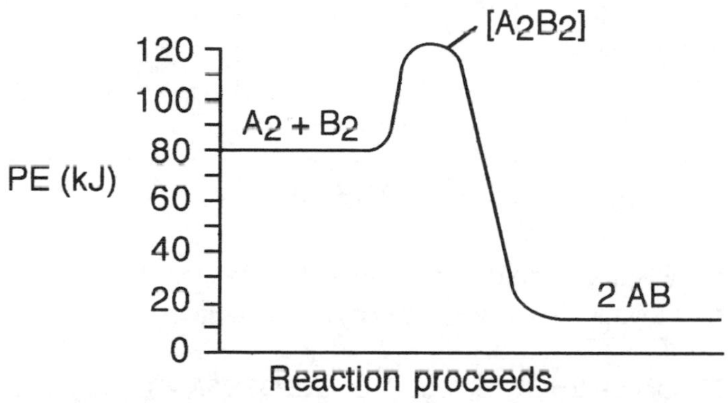

    (a) If A_2 and B_2 had collided with less favourable geometry how would the activation energy compare to that shown above?
    (b) Why does PE decrease when going from the activated complex to the products, AB?
    (c) Is the overall reaction exothermic or endothermic?
    (d) Write a balanced equation for the reaction, including the value for the enthalpy.
    (e) What is the value of the activation energy in the above reaction?

38. The bond energies of F_2 and of I_2 are almost identical. Would you expect the activation energy for

$$H_2 + F_2 \longrightarrow 2\,HF$$

to be equal to, greater than, or less than the activation energy for

$$H_2 + I_2 \longrightarrow 2\,HI\ ?$$

[Hint: why does an activation energy exist in the first place?]

39. Carbon exists in two forms, or ALLOTROPES, called graphite and diamond. The enthalpy for the reaction converting graphite to diamond is only 2 kJ, yet one can't simply heat black, opaque and inexpensive graphite and turn it into transparent and precious diamond. Suggest a reason why the reaction is so difficult to carry out.

40. After a reaction, the product molecules have less kinetic energy than the original reactant molecules. Is the reaction endothermic or exothermic? Explain your answer.

The concept which will now be introduced has a major impact on the rest of Chemistry 12.

If you look at any of the preceding PE diagrams showing an energy hill you should be able to see that there is no apparent reason why molecules can't go over the hill from left to right ***as well as from right to left.*** In other words, reactants can form products and products can re–form reactants.

$$\text{REACTANTS} \rightleftharpoons \text{PRODUCTS}$$

The possibility of going forward and backward now requires us to modify our PE diagrams so as to specify the amount of energy required to convert ***either*** the reactants ***or*** the products into an activated complex.

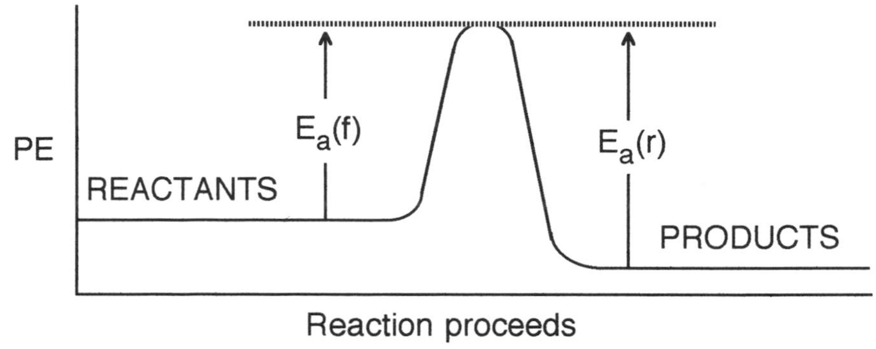

where: $E_a(\mathbf{f})$ = the activation energy for the ***forward*** reaction
$E_a(\mathbf{r})$ = the activation energy for the ***reverse*** reaction

IMPORTANT: THE ACTIVATION ENERGY IS ALWAYS ***ENDOTHERMIC***; THAT IS, ENERGY MUST BE ***ADDED*** TO GET TO THE TOP OF THE ENERGY HILL.

Now to determine the relationship between $E_a(f)$ and $E_a(r)$.

(a) **ENDOTHERMIC REACTIONS**

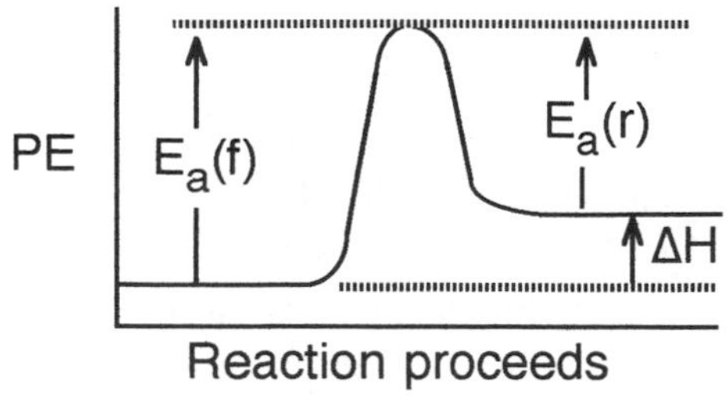

You can see from the above diagram that: $E_a(f) = E_a(r) + \Delta H$ (note that $\Delta H > 0$)

(b) **EXOTHERMIC REACTIONS**

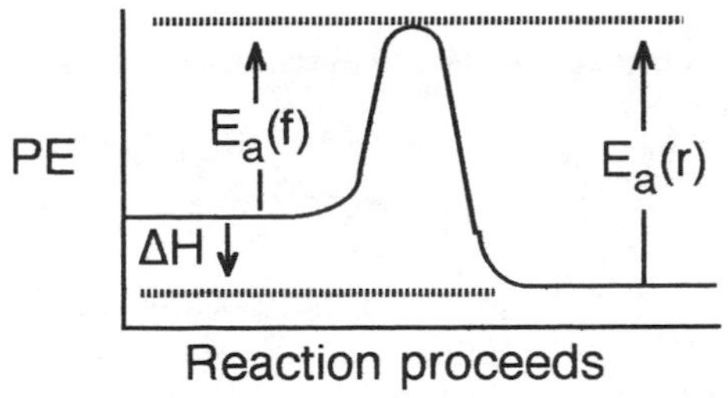

At first glance, it seems that: $E_a(f) + \Delta H = E_a(r)$. However, that can't be correct because if $E_a(f) = 20$ kJ and $\Delta H = -10$ kJ (the reaction is EXOTHERMIC) then: $E_a(r) = 20 + (-10) = 10$ kJ. That is, $E_a(f) > E_a(r)$. But the above diagram for an exothermic reaction shows that $E_a(f) < E_a(r)$. Using the idea that ΔH, $E_a(f)$ and $E_a(r)$ represent energy differences or "energy gaps", the diagram

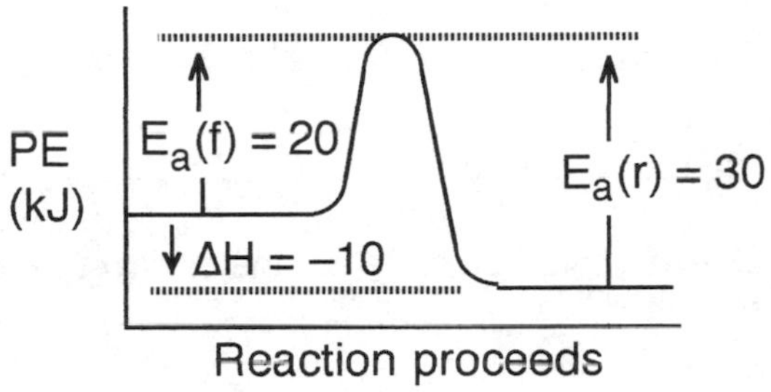

shows that $E_a(f) - \Delta H = E_a(r)$ or, after rearranging:

$E_a(f) = E_a(r) + \Delta H$ (note that $\Delta H < 0$)

which is identical to the expression found for ENDOTHERMIC reactions.

> **SUGGESTION:** If you don't like having to "memorize another equation", a quick sketch of a PE diagram with labelled energy differences will help you calculate a missing value for ΔH, $E_a(f)$ or $E_a(r)$.
>
> A trick to help draw PE diagrams is to start from the "peak" and draw in the E_a values. If ΔH is positive, the products are higher than the reactants – the ΔH arrow points "up" (positive direction). If ΔH is negative, the products are lower than the reactants – the ΔH arrow points "down" (negative direction).

EXERCISES:

41. If $\Delta H = -15$ kJ and $E_a(f) = 40$ kJ, what is the value of $E_a(r)$?

42. A reaction has $E_a(f) = 55$ kJ and $E_a(r) = 30$ kJ. Is the reaction exothermic or endothermic?

43. Draw and label a PE diagram for the reaction: $2\ NOBr(g) \longrightarrow 2\ NO(g) + Br_2(g) + 50$ kJ , in which $E_a(f) = 30$ kJ. Indicate on your diagram the point at which the activated complex exists.

44. Draw and label a PE diagram to show the enthalpy change and activation energies for a reaction in which: $R + 25\ kJ \longrightarrow P$ and $E_a(r) = 10$ kJ.

45. Draw and label a PE diagram showing the enthalpy change and activation energies for a reaction in which $E_a(f) = 20$ kJ and $E_a(r) = 45$ kJ.

I.9. REACTION MECHANISMS

Definition: A **REACTION MECHANISM** is the ***actual sequence of steps*** which make up an overall reaction.

> ***Analogy***: A garment can be made using cloth, needle, thread, scissors and a pattern. Is it reasonable to expect that the garment can be made by simply throwing the cloth, etc. into a bag, shaking the contents, and pulling out a finished garment? Obviously, the process must be carried out in steps.

Assuming that a collision between two particles (a "two particle collision") is certain to occur, it can be shown that the probability of three particles simultaneously arriving at the same place at the same time (a "three particle collision") is 1000 times less likely, and a "four particle collision" is almost impossible. A little thought should convince you that in the reaction

$$5\,C_2O_4^{2-} + 2\,MnO_4^- + 16\,H^+ \longrightarrow 10\,CO_2 + 2\,Mn^{2+} + 8\,H_2O$$

the probability of **23** reactant particles coming together all at once is zero.

Therefore, complex reactions ***cannot*** go in a single step; there ***must*** be more than one step involved in getting from reactants to products.

Let us now examine the experimentally–determined mechanism for the reaction:

$$4\,HBr + O_2 \longrightarrow 2\,H_2O + 2\,Br_2\,.$$

Note: Prediction of reaction mechanisms will ***never*** be required. Years of precise work and complex analysis may be required to determine a mechanism. You may be asked questions about a given reaction mechanism but you will not be asked to dream up a reaction mechanism on your own.

STEP 1: $HBr + O_2 \longrightarrow HOOBr$ (experimentally found to be slow)

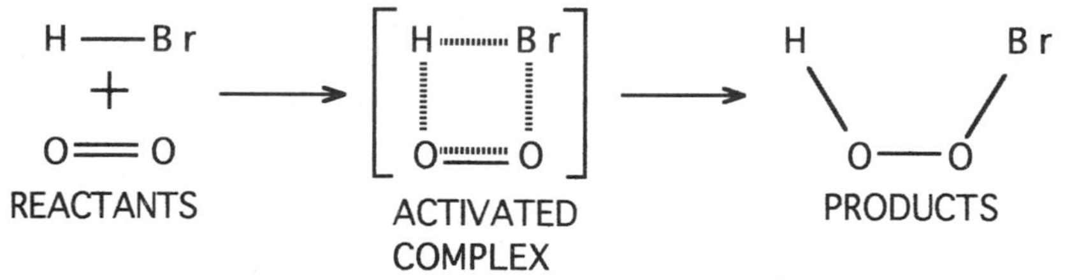

(NOTE: Dots mean the bonds are in the process of forming or breaking; going from "bond" to "no bond" and vice versa. Look at the bond between the H and Br, above. In the reactants there is a "bond". In the activated complex the bond is in the process of breaking. In the products the bond does not exist.)

STEP 2: HOOBr + HBr ⟶ 2 HOBr (experimentally found to be very fast)

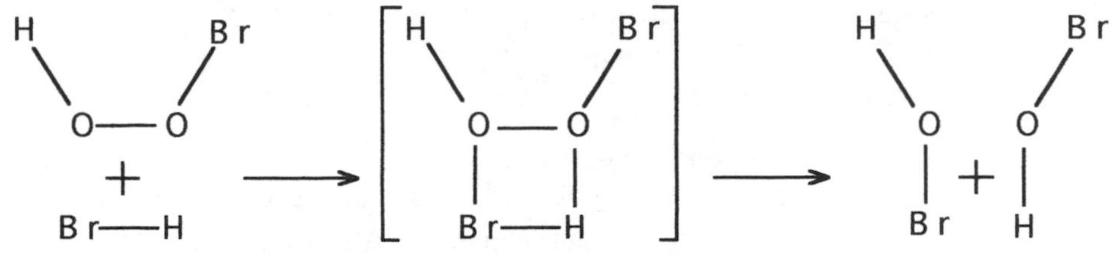

STEP 3: HOBr + HBr ⟶ $H_2O + Br_2$ (experimentally found to be very fast)

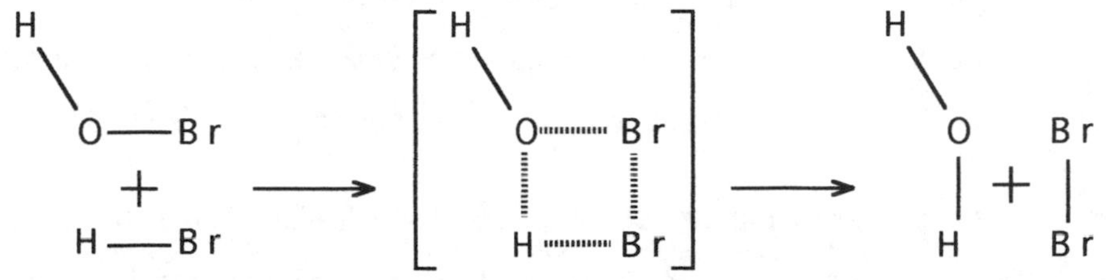

Definition: An **ELEMENTARY PROCESS** is an individual step in a reaction mechanism.

Therefore, the above reaction mechanism is made up of three elementary processes.

NOTES:

a) The ***slowest step*** in a reaction is called the **RATE–DETERMINING STEP,** or "BOTTLE–NECK STEP". (Step 1 is the rate–determining step in the above reaction.)

b) If the reaction is instantly "frozen", very little HOOBr or HOBr will be present – they can't build up in concentration since they are made very slowly and react very fast.

c) The OVERALL RATE is unaffected by adding HOOBr or HOBr since they are not used in the rate–determining step (and are quickly eliminated from the reaction).

d) To determine the OVERALL reaction from the reaction mechanism, simply add up all the steps in the reaction equations (and cancel any species which occur on both sides of the final equation).

HBr + O_2 ⟶ ~~HOOBr~~
HBr + ~~HOOBr~~ ⟶ ~~2 HOBr~~
2 HBr + ~~2 HOBr~~ ⟶ 2 H_2O + 2 Br_2

---

4 HBr + O_2 ⟶ 2 H_2O + 2 Br_2

e) The HOOBr and HOBr are called "reaction intermediates" or simply "intermediates." They can exist indefinitely on their own, but happen to react quickly in the above reaction mechanism.

f) The formula of an activated complex is found by simply adding up all the atoms involved in the two reacting molecules. For example, in Step 2 (above) the activated complex is $H_2O_2Br_2$ (the order of the atoms is not important).

***EXERCISES*:**

46. A reaction is thought to proceed according to the following mechanism.

$$2\,NO + H_2 \longrightarrow N_2 + H_2O_2 \quad \text{(slow)}$$
$$H_2O_2 + H_2 \longrightarrow 2\,H_2O \quad \text{(fast)}$$

   a) What is the overall reaction equation?
   b) What is true about the $[H_2O_2]$ at any time during the reaction?
   c) Which of the steps in the mechanism is the rate–determining step?
   d) What would happen to the overall rate if some extra NO was injected into the reaction mixture?
   e) If it were somehow possible to speed up the second step in the mechanism, what effect would this have on the overall rate of the reaction?
   f) What is the formula of the activated complex in the 1st step of the reaction? In the second step?
   g) How many elementary processes are involved in the reaction?

47. What is the difference between an activated complex and a reaction intermediate?

48. The reaction $A \longrightarrow C$ is known to have the mechanism: $A \longrightarrow B$ (fast)
$B \longrightarrow C$ (slow)

   What would you expect to be true about the concentration of B as the reaction proceeds?

49. You have been told that phosphorous can be prepared by means of the reaction

$$2\,Ca_3(PO_4)_2 + 6\,SiO_2 + 10\,C \longrightarrow P_4 + 6\,CaSiO_3 + 10\,CO\,.$$

   Why can you be certain that the reaction equation shown does not represent a reaction mechanism?

50. A two step mechanism is proposed for a reaction: $ClO^- + ClO^- \longrightarrow ClO_2^- + Cl^-$
$ClO_2^- + ClO^- \longrightarrow ClO_3^- + Cl^-$

   (a) What is the overall reaction which occurs?
   (b) Is ClO_2^- a reaction intermediate or an activated complex?
   (c) What is the chemical formula for the activated complex in the second step?

51. The decomposition of acetone, $(CH_3)_2CO$, proceeds according to

$$2\,(CH_3)_2CO \longrightarrow C_2H_4 + 2\,CO + 2\,CH_4\,.$$

   If the decomposition is a two–step reaction, and the second step is

$$2\,CH_2CO \longrightarrow C_2H_4 + 2\,CO\,,$$

   (a) what is the first step?
   (b) what is the formula for the activated complex in the first step? The second step?

52. A chemist suggested that the reaction: $2\,NO + O_2 \longrightarrow 2\,NO_2$ has a three–step mechanism. If the proposed first and third steps are: $2\,NO \longrightarrow N_2O_2$ (first)
$N_2O_4 \longrightarrow 2\,NO_2$ (third),

   (a) what is the second step in the proposed reaction?
   (b) what is the formula of the activated complex in the second step?

53. The reaction between gaseous hydrogen and chlorine proceeds as follows.

$$Cl_2 + \text{light} \longrightarrow 2\,Cl \quad \ldots.\,(1)$$
$$Cl + H_2 \longrightarrow HCl + H \quad \ldots.\,(2)$$
$$H + Cl_2 \longrightarrow HCl + Cl \quad \ldots.\,(3)$$

   (a) Suggest what step might occur after step 3? [Hint: Steps 2 and 3 show what happens when an ***individual*** pair of Cl and H_2 react; not all the Cl's and H_2's react at once.]
   (b) What function is served by the light?
   (c) Suggest why this reaction is called a "chain reaction".

I.10. ENERGY DIAGRAM OF A REACTION MECHANISM

Recall the reaction mechanism:

$HBr + O_2 \longrightarrow HOOBr$ (slow)
$HBr + HOOBr \longrightarrow 2\,HOBr$ (fast)
$2\,HBr + 2\,HOBr \longrightarrow 2\,H_2O + 2\,Br_2$ (fast).

Each step involves an individual activated complex and activation energy. Since there are three steps, there are three "humps" in the PE diagram. The overall PE diagram for the reaction

$$4\,HBr + O_2 \longrightarrow 2\,H_2O + 2\,Br_2$$

has been experimentally determined to have the following form.

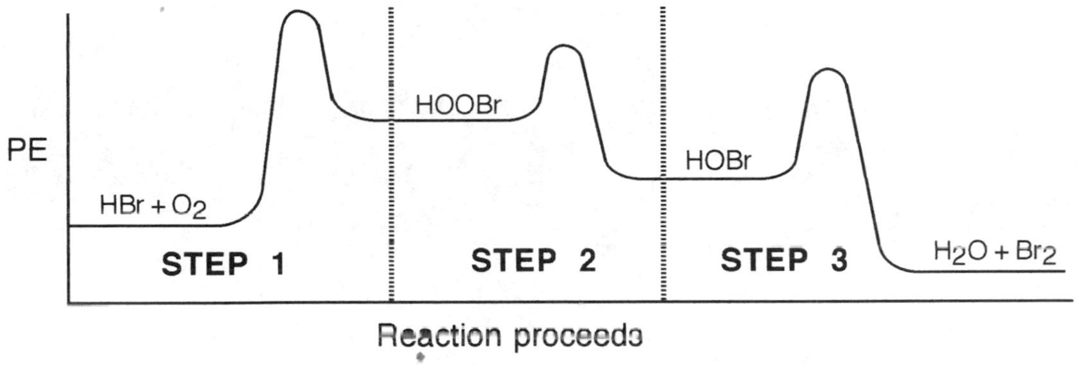

The activation energy, E_a, for a particular step in a reaction can be defined as

$$E_a = PE(\text{activated complex}) - PE(\text{reactants for the step})\ .$$

For step 2 of the reaction $4\,HBr + O_2 \longrightarrow 2\,H_2O + 2\,Br_2$, the activation energy is the PE difference between the activated complex for the 2nd step and the reactants involved in the 2nd step.

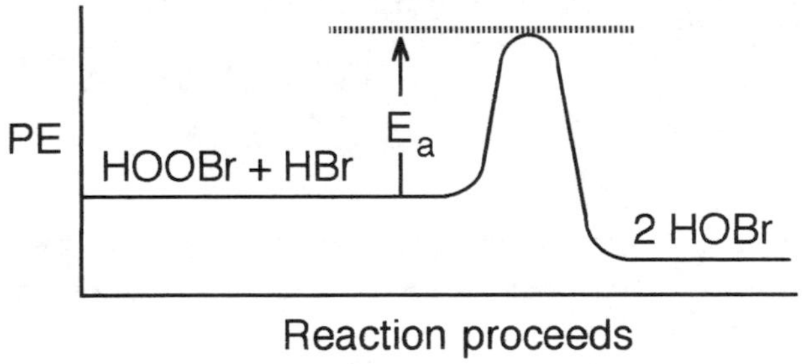

It is ***NOT*** correct to show the activation energy for step 2 as the difference between the PE possessed by the original reactants and the PE possessed by the 2nd activated complex, as shown below.

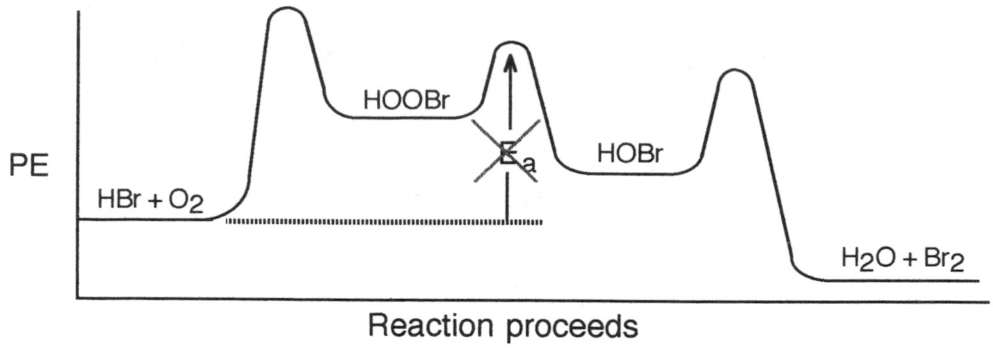

EXERCISES:

54. Which of the steps in the reaction $4\ HBr + O_2 \longrightarrow 2\ H_2O + 2\ Br_2$ has the greatest activation energy? Which has the least?

55. In the following PE diagram:

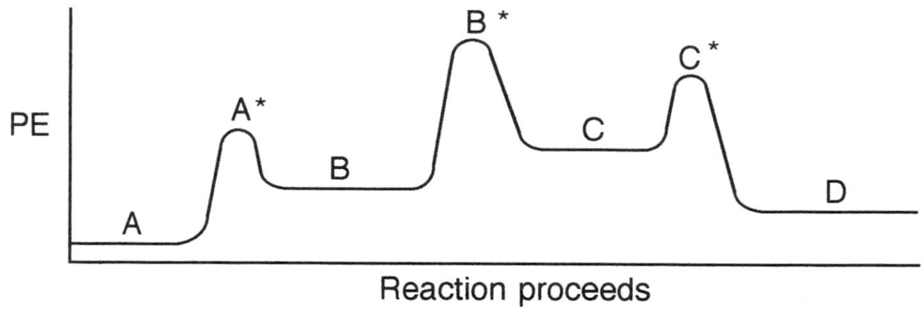

(a) How many steps does this reaction have?
(b) Is the second step ($B \longrightarrow C$) exothermic or endothermic?
(c) Is the overall reaction exothermic or endothermic?

I.11. THE EFFECT OF CATALYSTS ON THE ACTIVATION ENERGY

You know that a catalyst can speed up a reaction. The problem is: how does this increase in rate occur? The research that has been done on catalysts gives us the answer. Rather than simply saying "a catalyst is a substance which speeds up a reaction", the following definition is now favoured.

Definition: A **CATALYST** is a substance which provides an overall reaction with an alternative mechanism having a lower activation energy.

As shown in the diagram below, the energy difference between the reactants and products, ΔH, is not changed but the height of the energy hump is lowered.

EXAMPLE:

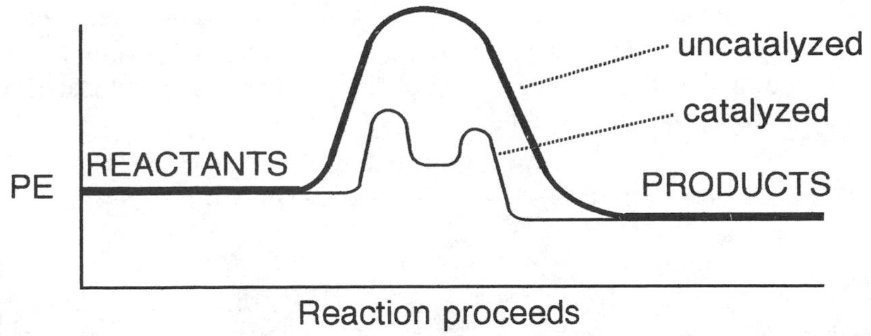

If the activation energy is lowered by adding a catalyst, more reactant molecules will possess the minimum KE required to form the activated complex. Therefore, in a given time interval more molecules can react; that is, the ***forward reaction rate increases***. However, by lowering the height of the "energy hump" not only is the forward activation energy lowered, but the reverse activation energy is also lowered. Therefore, more product molecules possess the kinetic energy required to form the activated complex, more PRODUCT molecules react in a given time, and the ***reverse reaction rate increases.***

It can be shown that **if the forward reaction rate doubles, the reverse reaction rate also doubles.**

NOTE:

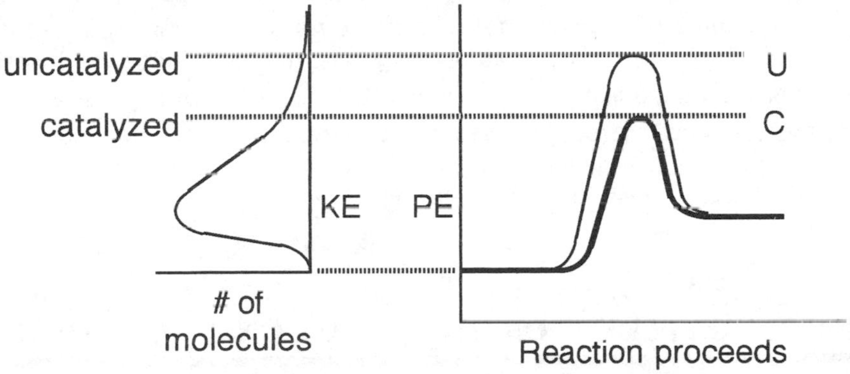

As was seen in Section I.8, those particles which have a critical amount of KE will be able to convert the KE into PE and obtain the critical amount of PE required to reach the peak of the energy hill.

Those particles which go by the uncatalyzed reaction route require more PE (labelled U, above) than those particles which go by the catalyzed route (labelled C, above). The lower PE required in the catalyzed reaction translates as a lower KE requirement for the catalyzed reaction. Since more particles have this lower KE requirement, the reaction rate is faster for the catalyzed reaction. It must be kept in mind that the uncatalyzed pathway is still available, but very few reactants will go over the higher "hump", relative to the numbers that go over the lower, catalyzed hump.

EXAMPLE: The uncatalyzed reaction between H_2 and O_2 to form water is quite complex, having numerous steps in the mechanism. In addition, the reaction requires a substantial activation energy in order to proceed. If a platinum catalyst is used, the reaction proceeds quickly and easily at room temperature in a two–step mechanism.

$$2\,H_2(g) + O_2(g) \xrightarrow{\text{Pt catalyst}} 2\,H_2O(g)$$

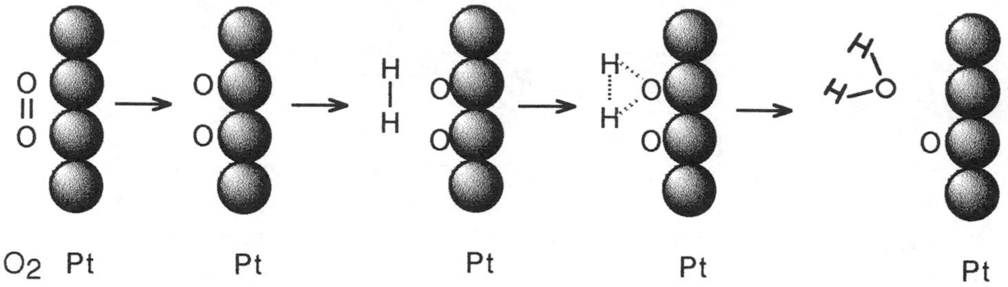

O_2 molecule sticks on the Pt, which supplies enough energy to break the O_2 bond

H_2 attacks the O atoms

The energy given off by the formation of H_2O is absorbed by the Pt

The high energy atoms of platinum metal "loan" some of their energy in order to break the bonds in O_2. The highly reactive individual oxygen atoms form bonds with hydrogen to make water. The overall reaction is highly exothermic (242 kJ/mol H_2O) and the energy given off is received by the platinum, thereby repaying the energy "loaned" by the platinum. As a result, the platinum gets very hot. This additional heat makes it even easier for the platinum to catalyze subsequent reactions between hydrogen and oxygen.

I.12. THE EFFECT OF A CATALYST ON THE REACTION MECHANISM

Let us examine the reaction: $OCl^- + I^- \longrightarrow OI^- + Cl^-$. The uncatalyzed reaction has a very high activation energy because it demands that two negatively charged species approach each other and react. This requires a substantial energy input. Therefore, the uncatalyzed reaction shown in the diagram below is very unlikely to occur.

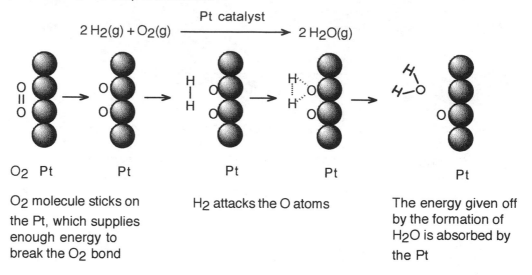

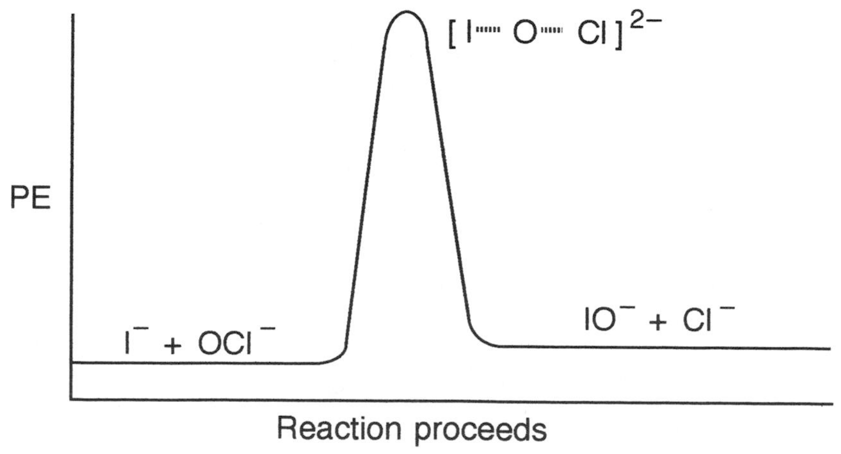

On the other hand, water acting as a catalyst for this reaction *provides an alternate mechanism with a lower overall activation energy.*

STEP 1: $ClO^- + H_2O \longrightarrow$ $\left[\begin{array}{c} O-H \\ H \\ Cl-O \end{array} \right]^-$ $\longrightarrow ClOH + OH^-$

STEP 2: $I^- + ClOH \longrightarrow$ $\left[\begin{array}{c} I \quad H \\ O \\ Cl \end{array} \right]^-$ $\longrightarrow IOH + Cl^-$

STEP 3: $IOH + OH^- \longrightarrow$ $\left[\begin{array}{c} I-O \\ H \\ O-H \end{array} \right]^-$ $\longrightarrow IO^- + H_2O$

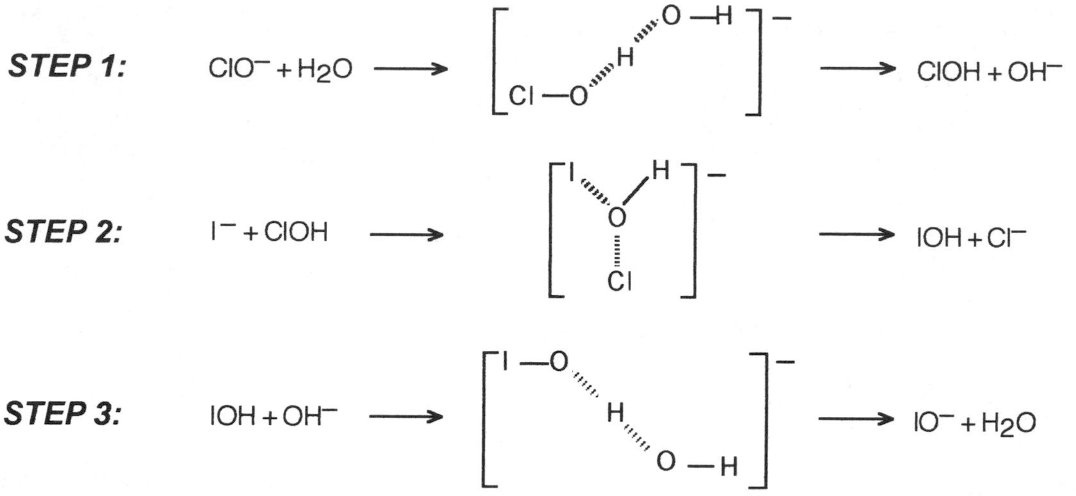

OVERALL: $OCl^- + I^- \longrightarrow OI^- + Cl^-.$

The PE diagram below represents the situation which exists when a catalyst is added.

Reaction proceeds

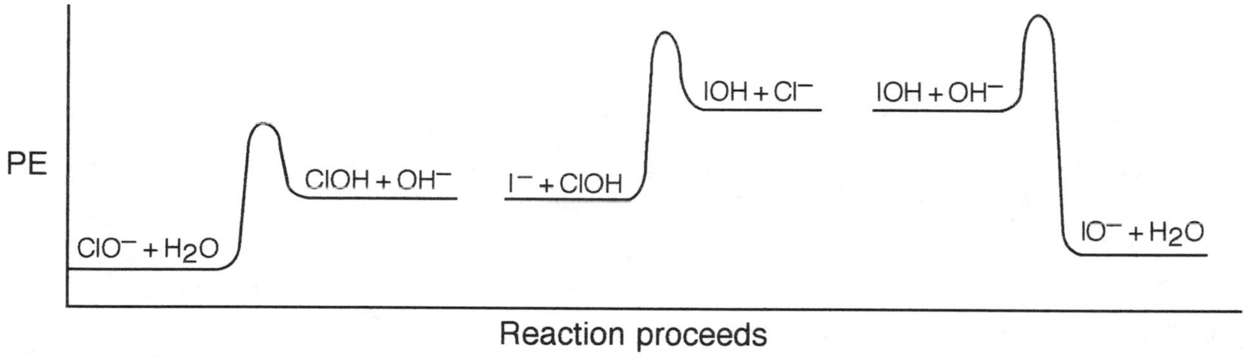

NOTES:

a)   The essential nature of a catalyst is shown in the above mechanism. A catalyst is NOT a substance which "takes no part in a reaction" (as you may have heard previously); rather, *the catalyst is an active participant which is REGENERATED in a later step of the reaction mechanism.* At the end there is as much of the catalyst (H_2O) as there was at the beginning. The catalyst will be used up in some specific step (not necessarily the first) and regenerated at some later step (not necessarily the last).

b)   It should be noted that ΔH for the overall reaction is the same for both the catalyzed and uncatalyzed reaction. The initial and final PE remain the same; only the intermediate reaction details differ.

c)   Both intermediate species and catalysts cancel out when the individual steps in a mechanism are added to get the overall reaction. For example, look carefully at the 3 steps in the above mechanism. **Intermediate species ($ClOH$, IOH and OH^-) do not appear in the overall reaction because they are first produced and then used up as reactants in subsequent steps. On the other hand, the catalyst (H_2O) is initially used up as a reactant and then subsequently produced again.**

EXERCISES:

56. In the following reaction mechanisms identify
    (i) the catalyst (ii) the reaction intermediate(s) (iii) the overall reaction

(a) $CH_2=CH_2 + H^+ \longrightarrow CH_3-CH_2^+$
$CH_3-CH_2^+ + H_2O \longrightarrow CH_3-CH_2-OH + H^+$

(b) $A + B \longrightarrow C$
$C + D \longrightarrow E + F$
$E + B \longrightarrow D + F$

(c) $NH_2NO_2 + CH_3COO^- \longrightarrow CH_3COOH + NHNO_2^-$
$NHNO_2^- \longrightarrow N_2O + OH^-$
$OH^- + CH_3COOH \longrightarrow H_2O + CH_3COO^-$

(d) $Pt + C_2H_2 \longrightarrow PtC_2H_2$
$PtC_2H_2 + H_2 \longrightarrow PtC_2H_4$
$PtC_2H_4 + H_2 \longrightarrow Pt + C_2H_6$

(e) $A \longrightarrow 2B$
$B + C \longrightarrow D + E$
$D + F \longrightarrow C + G$
$B + G \longrightarrow H$

57. "All catalyzed reaction mechanisms have more than one step." Why must this statement be true?

58. Suppose a catalyzed reaction is occurring in a reaction container. If the catalyst is removed, will the reaction stop completely? Explain your answer.

59. Can a catalyst cause an exothermic reaction to become endothermic, or vice versa? Explain.

60. Consider the following reaction mechanism:
$X + Y \longrightarrow Z$ (very fast)
$Z + Y \longrightarrow P$ (very fast)
$P + Y \longrightarrow Q$ (slow)

    Suppose there was a catalyst that worked on step 1, and another catalyst that worked on step 3. Which catalyst would be **ineffective** in increasing the rate of the overall reaction?

61. If you have a slow reaction and add a substance that provides an alternate reaction mechanism having a higher activation energy, what will happen to the reaction rate? Why does this occur?

I.13. SOME USES OF CATALYSTS

Modern chemistry and chemical technology rely extensively on the use of catalysts, but biological systems mastered the use of catalysts long before chemists learned to recognize that catalysts existed. This section will briefly examine some important catalysts and their uses.

(a) Most biological reactions are initiated or aided by catalysts called ENZYMES. Enzymes are protein molecules, each of which depends on its composition and shape to catalyze a specific reaction of a specific molecule. The particular molecule upon which an enzyme acts is called its "substrate". Frequently, a particular reaction may involve several enzymes working together, and even simple cells contain thousands of different enzymes.

    For example the enzyme "maltase" breaks down the sugar "maltose" into the simpler sugar "glucose", but has no effect on other sugars.

$$\underset{\text{maltose}}{C_{12}H_{22}O_{11}} + H_2O \xrightarrow{\text{maltase}} \underset{\text{glucose}}{2\,C_6H_{12}O_6}$$

(b) The industrial process for making H_2SO_4 involves several steps. First, sulphur is burned to make SO_2.

$$S(s) + O_2(g) \longrightarrow SO_2(g)$$

Next, the SO_2 is passed over a catalyst consisting of finely divided particles of platinum (Pt) or vanadium pentoxide (V_2O_5) to form SO_3.

$$2\,SO_2(g) + O_2(g) \xrightarrow{V_2O_5 \text{ catalyst}} 2\,SO_3(g)$$

The resulting SO_3 is then added to water to make sulphuric acid:

$$SO_3(g) + H_2O(l) \longrightarrow H_2SO_4(l).$$

(c) A series of upper atmosphere reactions produces a more or less constant ozone concentration. Initially, ultraviolet (UV) light breaks apart oxygen molecules to form highly reactive oxygen atoms:

$$O_2 + h\nu \longrightarrow 2\,O \qquad \text{(where } h\nu \text{ represents UV light energy)}. \qquad \ldots(1)$$

The oxygen atoms then combine with oxygen molecules to form ozone:

$$O + O_2 \longrightarrow O_3. \qquad \ldots(2)$$

The ozone molecules absorb ultraviolet light, reforming atomic oxygen and an oxygen molecule:

$$O_3 + h\nu \longrightarrow O + O_2. \qquad \ldots(3)$$

In addition, some of the atomic oxygen combines with ozone molecules to reform oxygen molecules:

$$O_3 + O \longrightarrow 2\,O_2. \qquad \ldots(4)$$

(d) Automobile engines operate at sufficiently high temperatures to allow nitrogen and oxygen from the air to combine and form nitric oxide, NO:

$$N_2 + O_2 \longrightarrow 2\,NO.$$

The NO coming out of the exhaust then reacts with more oxygen to form NO_2, a harmful pollutant:

$$2\,NO + O_2 \longrightarrow 2\,NO_2.$$

Carbon monoxide, CO, and unburned hydrocarbons are also emitted from the exhaust.

Many modern automobiles have a catalytic converter which treats the exhaust fumes so as to lessen the amount of harmful pollutants. Most of these catalytic converters have two reaction chambers.

- The first chamber contains particles of finely divided metals, such as platinum, palladium and rhodium, which convert the CO and unburned hydrocarbons to CO_2 and H_2O.
- The second chamber contains a transition metal or transition metal oxide which converts the NO back to N_2 and O_2.

(e) One of the most commonly used catalysts in chemistry is $H^+(aq)$, found in solutions of acids.

EXERCISES:

62. Chlorine atoms are present in the upper atmosphere as a result of emissions from volcanoes and man–made pollutants. The reaction between chlorine atoms and ozone is thought to proceed by a 2–step mechanism:

$$O_3 + Cl \longrightarrow ClO + O_2$$
$$O + ClO \longrightarrow O_2 + Cl.$$

(a) What is the overall reaction?
(b) Identify any reaction intermediates or catalysts present.
(c) Suggest a reason why chlorine atoms in the upper atmosphere are a threat to the environment.
(d) Why does the presence of chlorine atoms in the upper atmosphere allow more UV light to reach the earth's surface? [Hint: look at reaction (3) on the previous page.]

63. The catalyzed reaction between CH_3OH (an alcohol) and CH_3COOH (an organic acid) to make CH_3COOCH_3 (an ester) proceeds as follows.

$$CH_3OH + H^+ \longrightarrow CH_3OH_2^+$$
$$CH_3OH_2^+ \longrightarrow CH_3^+ + H_2O$$
$$CH_3^+ + CH_3COOH \longrightarrow CH_3COOHCH_3^+$$
$$CH_3COOHCH_3^+ \longrightarrow CH_3COOCH_3 + H^+$$

(a) What is the overall reaction?
(b) Why is the reaction said to be "acid catalyzed"?
(c) If the H^+ used in the first step was radioactive, would the CH_3COOCH_3 produced in the 4th step contain a radioactive hydrogen atom? Why?

UNIT II : EQUILIBRIUM

II.1. THE CONCEPT OF DYNAMIC EQUILIBRIUM

If you glance at a book on organic chemistry, you might find the following strange situation.

> Starting with $CH_3{-}CH(OH){-}CH_3$, H_2SO_4 is added as a catalyst to make $CH_3{-}CH{=}CH_2$. Then, starting with $CH_3{-}CH{=}CH_2$, H_2SO_4 is added as a catalyst to make $CH_3{-}CH(OH){-}CH_3$.

According to these recipes, you can start with a reactant and make a product, or take the product and turn it back into the original reactant using the same reaction. Very strange indeed . . . this must be Chemistry!

Consider the following. The ancient Greeks used to chew on willow bark to help relieve headaches; the active ingredient in the willow bark is called salicylic acid. Since salicylic acid irritates stomach linings, chemists react it with a form of acetic acid to make acetylsalicylic acid, better known as ASA or "aspirin". On the other hand, if aspirin is left unused for several years it will develop a vinegar smell which indicates that the ASA has decomposed to form acetic acid. Such old aspirin will irritate the stomach lining due to the presence of salicylic acid . . . the reaction has now gone full circle.

salicylic acid + acetic acid $\longrightarrow$ ASA , followed by
ASA $\longrightarrow$ salicylic acid + acetic acid .

It should not be surprising that a reaction can go backward and forward; in the previous unit you saw that reversible reactions should exist and have separate activation energies for the forward and reverse reactions.

Definition: A reversible reaction is said to be at **EQUILIBRIUM** when the rate of the forward reaction is equal to the rate of the reverse reaction.

Another point must be considered. If a reaction forms products, but the products are able to escape from the reaction vessel, then the products will not be available for the reverse reaction. Therefore, in order for an equilibrium to have a chance to exist, the reaction must take place in a **CLOSED SYSTEM.**

Definition: A **CLOSED SYSTEM** is a system which nothing can enter or leave.

EXERCISES:

1. Strictly speaking, NO system can be completely closed – for example, hot liquid in the best thermos eventually cools down – but for most purposes a system can effectively be "closed". How would you create a system which is more or less closed with respect to:

   (a) heat loss? (b) light? (c) loss of mass?

2. Read the following observations and then answer the questions.
   - Two sealed glass tubes containing a mixture of a red–brown gas, $NO_2(g)$, and a colourless gas, $N_2O_4(g)$, are observed. The colour is an identical medium red–brown in each tube and there is no visible change in the colour of the contents as time passes.
   - One tube is placed in a beaker of boiling water for a minute. The contents of the tube become much darker red–brown in colour. Upon first placing the tube in the hot water, the colour gets continually darker, but after a few seconds the colour stops changing.

- The second tube is placed in a beaker containing dry ice at –78°C. The colour quickly disappears and the contents of the tube remain colourless.
- The hot and cold tubes are taken out of their beakers, placed side by side and allowed to come to room temperature. The tubes have an identical medium red-brown colour when they both are at room temperature.

a) The gases are involved in the reversible reaction: $N_2O_4(g) \rightleftharpoons 2\,NO_2(g)$.
What evidence exists that the forward and reverse rates are equal at room temperature?

b) Can temperature changes affect an equilibrium reaction? How do you know this?

c) What evidence shows that the forward and reverse reaction rates are equal at 100°C? If the temperature were raised above 100°C, what would you expect to happen to the colour?

d) The balanced equation in part (a) should also include "energy". Consider what happened to the colour when a tube was heated. Is the reaction exothermic or endothermic, as written? Explain.

e) What gas was predominantly present at low temperatures? What gas was predominantly present at high temperatures? How would you describe the chemical composition in a tube when it was at room temperature?

f) If one tube were filled with pure $NO_2(g)$ and another tube with pure $N_2O_4(g)$, what might be true of the colours you would expect to see in the tubes after they sit for a minute at the same temperature? What evidence do you have that your prediction should occur?

The following conclusions can be drawn from Exercise 2.

i. Temperature affects the equilibrium.

ii. A new equilibrium is attained at a new temperature.

iii. Since both the hot and cold tubes become the same colour at room temperature, **THE SAME EQUILIBRIUM WILL EXIST REGARDLESS OF WHETHER THE REACTION STARTED WITH AN EXCESS OF REACTANTS OR AN EXCESS OF PRODUCTS.**

iv. When a system is at equilibrium, no **MACROSCOPIC** changes occur.

(***MACROSCOPIC*** = visible, or large scale; as opposed to "microscopic" changes which occur on the atomic or molecular level.)

Definition: **DYNAMIC EQUILIBRIUM** is an equilibrium situation in which microscopic changes occur, but macroscopic changes do not.

(For purposes of comparison, an object in "***STATIC EQUILIBRIUM***", which is the opposite of dynamic equilibrium, ***will not move at all*** unless it is pushed in some manner. For example, a long block of wood balanced on one end is in static equilibrium; the equilibrium is destroyed if the block is pushed over.)

To summarize: **When dynamic equilibrium exists all the observable properties are constant, but at the molecular level there is a constant back–and–forth reaction between reactants and products which is in perfect balance.**

From now on, all references to "equilibrium" will refer to a state of ***dynamic equilibrium.***

EXERCISES:

3. Water is boiling in a kettle at 100°C. Is the system at equilibrium? Explain.

4. Some liquid water is present inside a sealed flask at room temperature. Is water evaporating inside the flask? Is the system at equilibrium? Why?

5. A chemist wished to prepare pure phosgene, $COCl_2(g)$, by reacting carbon monoxide, $CO(g)$, and chlorine gas, $Cl_2(g)$, according to the reaction

$$CO(g) + Cl_2(g) \rightleftharpoons COCl_2(g) .$$

   Why will this reaction NOT produce pure $COCl_2(g)$? If the chemist could somehow obtain a sample of pure $COCl_2(g)$, will it remain pure? Why?

II.2. THE CHARACTERISTICS OF EQUILIBRIUM

Let us see how equilibrium depends on reaction rates.

Since the reactions being examined are REVERSIBLE, there are a FORWARD RATE and a REVERSE RATE for the reaction:

$$\text{REACTANTS} \rightleftharpoons \text{PRODUCTS} .$$

The rate of a reaction increases when the [REACTANT] increases, so that rate must be proportional to [REACTANT].

Define: $RATE_{forward} = k_{forward} \cdot [\text{REACTANTS}]$ (for the forward reaction)

and: $RATE_{reverse} = k_{reverse} \cdot [\text{PRODUCTS}]$ (for the reverse reaction)

where $k_{forward}$ and $k_{reverse}$ are rate constants which describe whether the rate is normally fast or slow. **Note:** You ***don't*** need to worry about how to use $k_{forward}$ and $k_{reverse}$ in this course. The following two problems use values for $k_{forward}$ and $k_{reverse}$ so as to allow certain conclusions to be drawn; the use of $k_{forward}$ and $k_{reverse}$ will not occur again.

EXERCISES:

6. Assume that the simple reaction $A \rightleftharpoons B$ initially has:

$$[A] = 1.200\ M ,\ [B] = 0.000\ M ,\ k_{forward} = 0.50 ,\ k_{reverse} = 0.10 .$$

The following results are produced.

Time (min)	$RATE_{forward}$	$RATE_{reverse}$	[A]	[B]
0	0.600	0.000	1.200	0.000
1	0.300	0.060	0.600	0.600
2	0.180	0.084	0.360	0.840
3	0.132	0.094	0.264	0.936
4	0.113	0.097	0.226	0.974
5	0.105	0.099	0.210	0.990
6	0.102	0.100	0.204	0.996
7	0.101	0.100	0.202	0.998
8	0.100	0.100	0.201	0.999
9	0.100	0.100	0.200	1.000
10	0.100	0.100	0.200	1.000

a) Plot the values of [A]–versus–time and [B]–versus–time on the same graph.

b) When does it appear that equilibrium finally occurs? How did you recognize that equilibrium was attained? What else occurs at equilibrium?

c) Is there a time when [REACTANT] = [PRODUCT]? Is [REACTANT] = [PRODUCT] at equilibrium?

d) When is the forward rate greatest? What happens to the rate as the [A] decreases?

e) What is the numerical value of the ratio $\frac{[\text{PRODUCT}]}{[\text{REACTANT}]}$ at equilibrium?

7. Now let's see what happens if the previous equilibrium is upset by ADDING an extra 0.6 M of B at the 11–th minute, so as to increase [B] from 1.0 M up to 1.6 M.

Time (min)	$RATE_{forward}$	$RATE_{reverse}$	[A]	[B]
11	0.100	0.160	0.200	1.600
12	0.130	0.154	0.260	1.540
13	0.142	0.152	0.284	1.516
14	0.147	0.151	0.294	1.506
15	0.149	0.150	0.297	1.503
16	0.150	0.150	0.299	1.501
17	0.150	0.150	0.300	1.500
18	0.150	0.150	0.300	1.500

a) Extend the graph you plotted in Exercise 6, part (a), to include the above data.

b) When is equilibrium re–established?

c) What is the numerical value of the ratio $\frac{[\text{PRODUCT}]}{[\text{REACTANT}]}$ at equilibrium?

d) When equilibrium IS re–established, what has changed from the previous equilibrium? What remains unchanged?

To summarize, at equilibrium:

a. Rate of consumption of reactants = Rate of production of reactants.
b. [REACTANTS] differs from [PRODUCTS], in general.
c. [REACTANTS] is now constant in time and [PRODUCTS] is constant in time.
d. The forward and reverse rates do not change as time passes.
e. A system which is not at equilibrium will tend to move toward a position of equilibrium.

[Point (e) can be deduced by looking at the data in the above table. The reaction simply proceeded to go toward equilibrium. There was a large forward rate, initially, and zero reverse rate. Eventually the forward rate decreased and the reverse rate increased until they became equal. At this time, reactants were turning into products as fast as products were turning into reactants, so that there was no observable change after that: equilibrium had occurred.]

The above summary needs to be elaborated upon.

Analogy: Pretend your left and right pockets contain different amounts of loose change. Imagine you take a quarter from your left pocket and put it into your right one, and then take a quarter out of the right pocket and put it into the left one. Repeat the process several times. After several "back–and–forth" passes, an observer knows that the amount of change in each pocket remains unchanged, but does not know how much money you have in each pocket.

The following diagram represents the relative amounts of H_2 , Br_2 and HBr which might exist at some temperature for the equilibrium

$$H_2 + Br_2 \rightleftharpoons 2\,HBr\,.$$

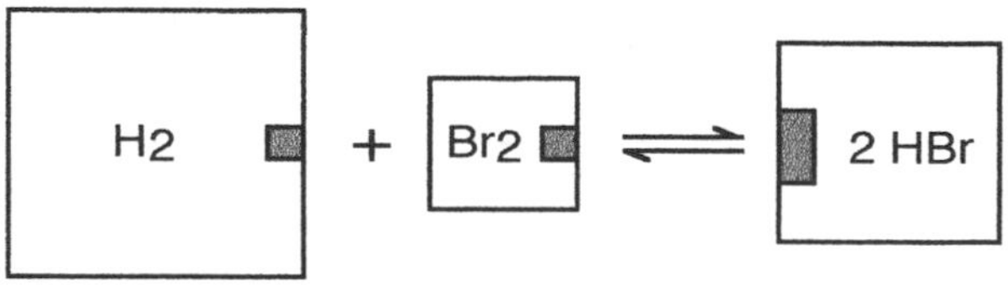

The shaded boxes represent the moles of H_2, Br_2 and HBr which **react** every second. The larger unshaded boxes represent the moles of H_2, Br_2 and HBr **present** at equilibrium. As can be seen, the **NUMBERS OF MOLES OF EACH GAS PRESENT** do not seem to be related to each other in any particular manner. In fact, the only way to find the moles of each gas present is to make an experimental measurement. Exercise 7 gave us a hint that the experimentally–determined ratio of products to reactants does not change when a system is at equilibrium, and this constancy of the [Product]/[Reactant] ratio will be confirmed later in this unit. On the other hand, the number of moles of each gas which reacts each second must be in a 1:1:2 ratio because the balanced reaction equation shows a 1 H_2 : 1 Br_2 : 2 HBr ratio.

In other words, at equilibrium 1 H_2 and 1 Br_2 react to produce 2 HBr for every 2 HBr which decompose back to 1 H_2 and 1 Br_2. The amount of reactants and the amount of products they form (and vice versa) must be in a specific ratio, but the "stockpiles" of each reactant and product present are constant amounts which cannot be predicted without performing an experiment.

IMPORTANT: If the equilibrium $H_2 + Br_2 \rightleftharpoons 2\,HBr$ exists, it is true that Forward rate = Reverse rate but this equality of rates is interpreted as follows:

Rate at which H_2 and Br_2 is reacted = Rate at which H_2 and Br_2 is produced
Rate at which HBr is reacted = Rate at which HBr is produced .

EXERCISES:

8. In the reaction $3\,C_2H_2(g) \rightleftharpoons C_6H_6(g)$, will the ratio of $[C_2H_2(g)]$ to $[C_6H_6(g)]$ at equilibrium be 3:1?
9. What things must be true at equilibrium?
10. Ozone (O_3) and oxygen (O_2) molecules can exist in equilibrium: $2\,O_3(g) \rightleftharpoons 3\,O_2(g)$. If 2 mol of O_3 react for every 2 mol of O_2 reacting in a container, does equilibrium exist in the container? Why?
11. The following equilibrium occurs : $2\,NOCl(g) \rightleftharpoons 2\,NO(g) + Cl_2(g)$. A gaseous mixture of NOCl, NO and Cl_2 is put in a container. After a few minutes it is found that two moles of NOCl react for every three moles of products which react. Is the mixture at equilibrium? Why?

12. Assume you have the reaction $X(g) \rightleftharpoons Y(g)$, and that you start with pure X and allow the reaction to come to equilibrium. Plot a graph of rate versus time which shows how the forward and reverse reaction rates change from the time the reaction starts until equilibrium is attained.

13. In the equilibrium $2\,NH_3(g) \rightleftharpoons N_2(g) + 3\,H_2(g)$, why does the $[N_2]$ remain unchanged even though the forward reaction continues to occur?

II.3. PREDICTING WHETHER A REACTION IS SPONTANEOUS OR NOT

Definition: A **SPONTANEOUS** change is a change which occurs by itself, without outside assistance.

This section examines the conditions that allow or forbid the spontaneous occurrence of a chemical reaction.

When the energy barrier is low enough, a reaction is expected to move spontaneously to the side of the reaction having the minimum energy. That is, EXOTHERMIC reactions should be spontaneous, as shown in the following diagram.

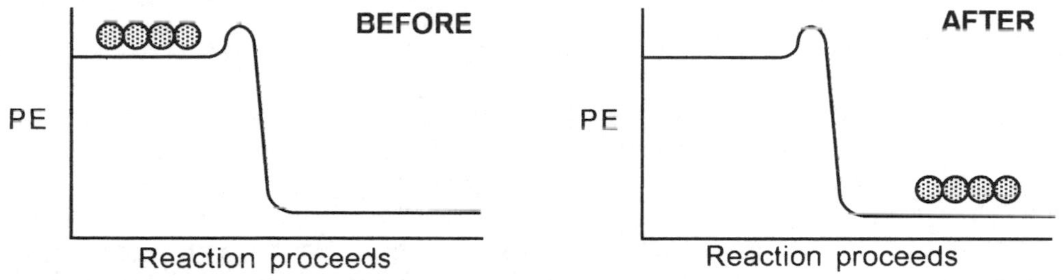

There are countless examples which show that this expectation often materializes: touch a match to paper and the paper burns, ignite an explosive and an explosion occurs, etc.

On the other hand, ENDOTHERMIC reactions require the input of energy and hence such reactions are not expected to occur spontaneously if sufficient heat is not available. For example, iron will not melt at room temperature.

Summarizing: In any reaction, the molecules on the "downhill" side of the energy hill will REMAIN there (unless extra energy is supplied to them), and any molecules on the uphill side of the energy hill will tend to roll down the hill (provided sufficient activation energy is available).

The side of the reaction having ***minimum energy*** (that is, ***minimum enthalpy***) is said to be **"favoured"** because molecules will tend to go to or remain at minimum energy. Although the above summary is true, there is an additional factor which has to be considered. This additional factor is shown to exist by two experimentally observed facts.

Fact 1: Some endothermic reactions DO occur spontaneously. "Chemical cold packs" are used in First Aid work. Upon mixing the necessary chemicals in a plastic pouch the mixture spontaneously absorbs heat from its surroundings and causes the surroundings to cool down.

Fact 2: Exothermic reactions DO NOT NECESSARILY go to completion (the reverse reaction may proceed to some extent and allow equilibrium to occur).

The name of this additional factor is **RANDOMNESS.** Let's see why randomness is important.

The following two systems are HIGHLY ORGANIZED.

(a) a box full of dice all arranged the same way:

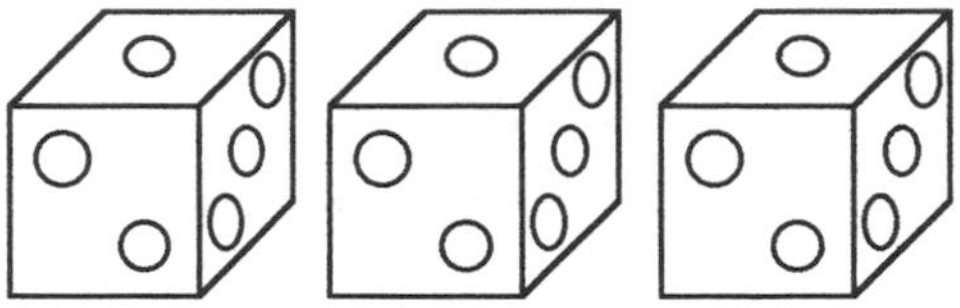

(b) a single crystal of NaCl:

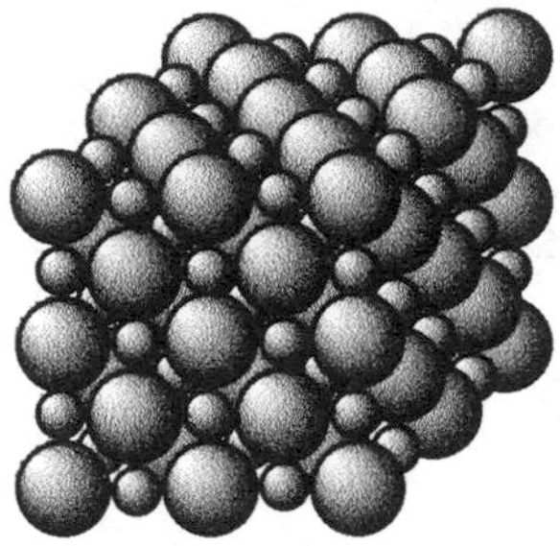

When you shake the dice, their arrangement becomes ***random***; that is, they lose all their ***orderliness.*** Similarly, when the crystal of NaCl is put in water it dissolves spontaneously and the Na^+ and Cl^- ions become randomly scattered throughout the solution. This may seem a little silly to ask, but ***why do the dice and salt crystal become random***?

The answer lies in considering the **PROBABILITIES** underlying the events.

a) ***The dice***: When the dice are thrown there are only a few ways to get an ***ordered*** result (eg. all 6's, all 3's, etc.) whereas there is a large number of ways to get a ***random*** result. Therefore, when the dice are thrown there is a very large PROBABILITY of getting a random result.

NOTE: Each separate outcome of a throw has the same probability as any other outcome. However, only a few outcomes are "special" enough to attract attention and cause them to be labelled as "ordered", whereas most of the outcomes are not special enough to attract attention and so are labelled as "random".

b) ***The crystal***: Consider the crystal after a few of its ions have gone into solution.

(i) If some energy is added to an ion on the outer surface of the crystal, there is a high probability that the ion will go into the solution (see (i) on diagram below). The most likely way for the ion to move is ***out*** of the crystal.

(ii) If some energy is added to an ion in the solution there is a very low probability that the ion will travel in such a way as to hit the crystal (see (ii) on diagram). Only one general direction of travel, indicated by the dotted line, will carry the ion to the crystal.

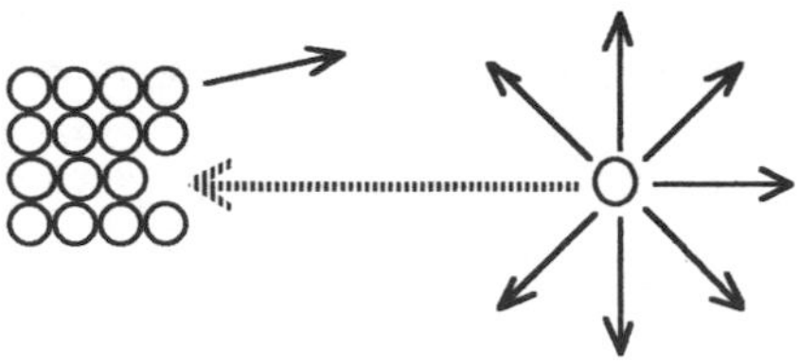

(i) (ii)

As a result of (i) and (ii), the crystal of NaCl dissolves: randomness favours the dissolving process. Note that the crystal does not "want to dissolve". Rather, dissolving is simply the most probable process to occur and therefore is **favoured.**

CONCLUSION: Highly RANDOM states are favoured to occur over highly ORDERED states because there are ***more*** random states possible.

Definition: **ENTROPY** = the amount of randomness in a system.

In general: Entropy tends to a maximum value.

To put this another way, "things tend to become jumbled as time passes." For example: you clean up your bedroom, and a few days later . . . . a mess again.

Fair enough, things do become disorganized, but how can disorganization or randomness be considered a driving force in a chemical reaction? Consider the following reaction:

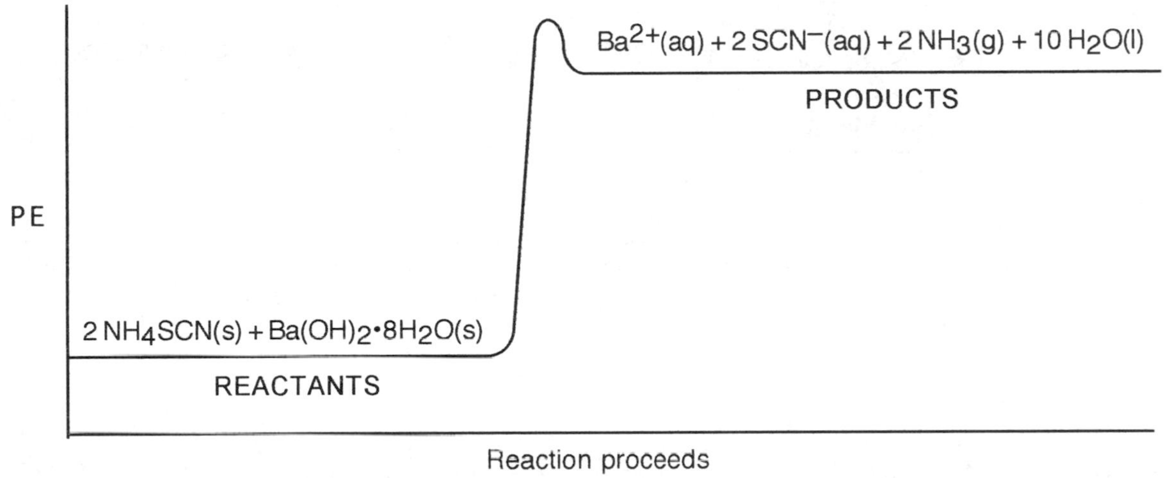

(a) The reactants are highly ordered crystals, and the products are highly random (many molecules form; some gaseous and some in solution). The forward reaction is said to be FAVOURED or "DRIVEN" by the entropy of the system. The greater the difference in the amount of randomness of products versus reactants, the greater the "entropy drive" of the system.

(b) Since the reaction is ENDOTHERMIC, the reactants must absorb energy to form products (which are ***very*** random). Because the products are very random, any reactants which go to the product side are unable to properly arrange themselves to get back to the reactant side. Hence, there is a steady one-way movement of molecules from the reactant side. The reaction therefore SPONTANEOUSLY occurs and the reactants steadily absorb great amounts of energy from their surroundings, causing them to get VERY COLD (–55°C is possible).

CONCLUSION: Two "drives" or "tendencies" exist in any reaction:

a) the tendency for a reaction to go to the side with the **MAXIMUM RANDOMNESS (MAXIMUM ENTROPY).**

b) the tendency for a reaction to go to the side with the **MINIMUM ENERGY (MINIMUM ENTHALPY).**

A tendency or drive is said to "favour" a particular side of a reaction equation if the reaction attempts to go to that side of the equation as a result of the tendency.

Before proceeding further, a procedure will be established to decide which side of a reaction equation is favoured by the tendency to "minimum enthalpy" and which side of an equation is favoured by the tendency to "maximum entropy".

A. The tendency to minimum enthalpy

The tendency to go to the side with minimum enthalpy is a tendency to go to (and remain on) the "downhill" side in a reaction. In an EXOTHERMIC reaction the product side is favoured (see below, left) and in an ENDOTHERMIC reaction the reactant side is favoured (see below, right).

EXOTHERMIC

$A \longrightarrow B + \text{heat}$

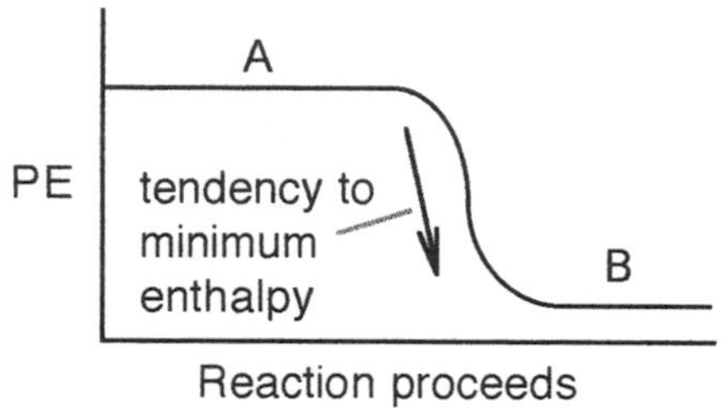

ENDOTHERMIC

$C + \text{heat} \longrightarrow D$

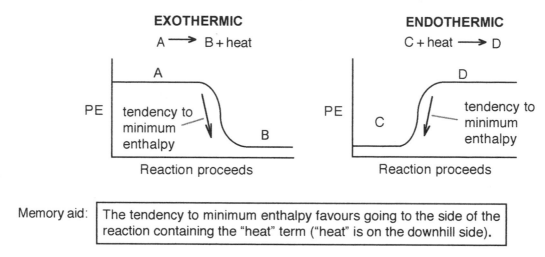

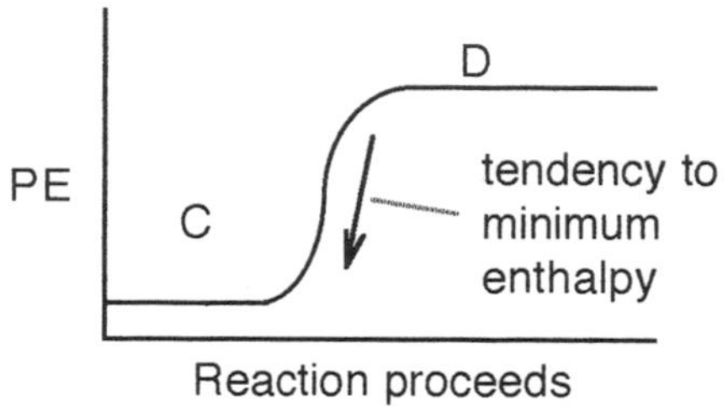

Memory aid:

The tendency to minimum enthalpy favours going to the side of the reaction containing the "heat" term ("heat" is on the downhill side).

B. The tendency to maximum entropy

Several questions must be answered to decide which side is favoured by the tendency to maximum entropy.

1. What is the most random phase present?

- Solids are very orderly, and crystals have **zero** randomness.
- Pure liquids are **much more random** than solids.
- Solutions are **more random** than pure liquids because a mixture (such as a solution) is more scrambled than a liquid consisting of only one type of molecule.
- Gases are **much more random** than pure liquids or solutions (and solids).

Overall, the randomness of phases (from most random to most ordered) is:

gases >> solutions > liquids >> solids

Note: Since a single chunk of wood is much more ordered than a pile of sawdust made from the same log, then ***if there is only a single phase in the entire reaction the side of the reaction having the most molecules is the most random side.***

2. What if more than one phase is present in the reaction equation?

- the side having the most random phase is the side with "maximum randomness".

EXAMPLE: $CaC_2(s) + 2\,H_2O(l) \rightleftharpoons C_2H_2(g) + Ca(OH)_2(aq)$

The most random phase present is a gas and therefore the product side is most random.

- if both sides contain particles having equally random phases then the side having the greater number of particles of the most random phase will have the "maximum randomness".

EXAMPLE: $A(g) + B(s) \rightleftharpoons 2\,C(g) + D(s)$

Both sides contain a gas (most random phase) but products are more random since there are two gas molecules on the product side and only one molecule of gas on the reactant side.

Note: Once you have identified the most random phase present, there is no need to consider any other phase.

CONCLUSION: **The side of a reaction equation favoured by the tendency to maximum randomness (maximum entropy) is the side containing THE MOST PARTICLES OF THE MOST RANDOM PHASE.**

Now examine the two examples below to see how the tendencies to minimum enthalpy and maximum entropy combine to determine the OVERALL tendency for a reaction to occur.

EXAMPLES:

a) Consider the reaction $C_2H_2(g) + 2\,Cl_2(g) \longrightarrow C_2H_2Cl_4(l) + 386\ kJ$.

The tendency to go to the side with **maximum entropy favours the formation of REACTANTS** ("gas" is the most random phase present, and the only gas molecules are on the reactant side).

The tendency to go to the side with **minimum enthalpy favours the formation of PRODUCTS** (heat is on the product side).

Overall then, the two tendencies oppose each other and the reaction forms an **EQUILIBRIUM.**

b) Consider the reaction $CH_4(g) + O_2(g) \longrightarrow CO_2(g) + 2\,H_2O(g) + 394\ KJ$.

The tendency to go to the side with **maximum entropy favours the formation of PRODUCTS** ("gas" is the most random phase present and there are more gas molecules on the product side).

The tendency to go to the side with **minimum enthalpy favours the formation of PRODUCTS** (heat is on the products side).

Overall then, the two tendencies both favour the formation of products and the reaction **WILL GO 100%.**

c) Consider the reaction $4\ Au(s) + 3\ O_2(g) + 162\ kJ \longrightarrow 2\ Au_2O_3(s)$.

The tendency to go to the side with **maximum entropy favours the formation of REACTANTS** ("gas" is the most random phase present and the only gas molecules are on the reactant side).

The tendency to go to the side with **minimum enthalpy favours the formation of REACTANTS** (heat is on the reactant side).

Overall then, the two tendencies both favour the formation of reactants and the reaction **GOES 0%** (that is, **will not occur**).
[This conclusion is supported by the fact that gold remains unreacted by years of exposure to air.]

EXERCISES:

14. In each of the following pairs of substances, select the one which has greater entropy.
    a) $H_2O(l)$ or $H_2O(g)$
    b) $Cl_2(g)$ or $2\ Cl^-(aq)$
    c) $NH_3(l)$ or $NH_3(aq)$
    d) $CH_3COOH(aq)$ or $CH_3COO^-(aq) + H^+(aq)$

15. In each of the following, decide
    i) which side is favoured by the tendency to minimum enthalpy; that is, which side of the reaction has the lower energy.
    ii) which side is favoured by the tendency to maximum entropy; that is, which side of the reaction has the more random species.
    iii) whether the reaction will be
       - a spontaneous reaction which goes to completion ("GOES 100%"), or
       - a non–spontaneous reaction in which NO products are formed ("WON'T OCCUR"), or
       - a spontaneous equilibrium reaction in which the tendency to minimum enthalpy will be balanced by an opposing tendency to maximum entropy ("EQUILIBRIUM").

Note: in parts (a) to (d) all the species are GASES

a)
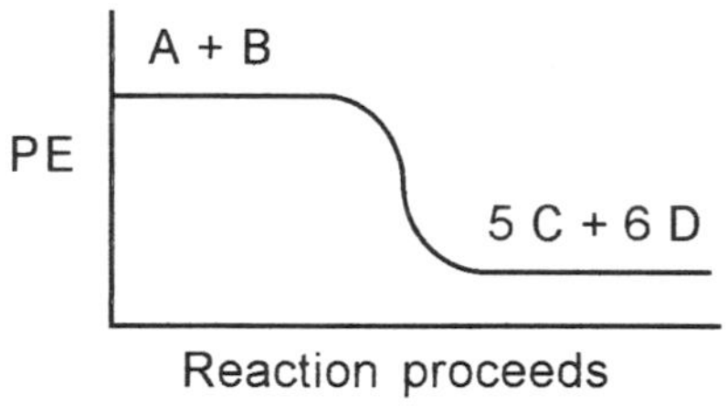

b)
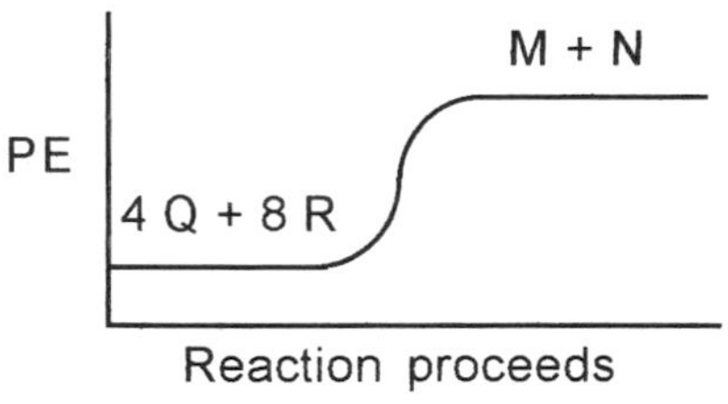

c)
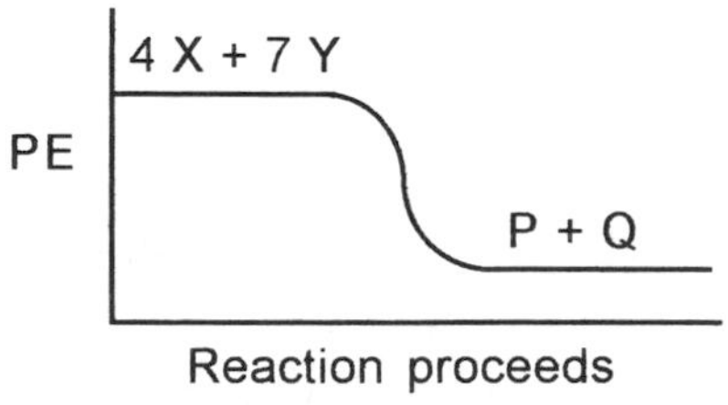

d)
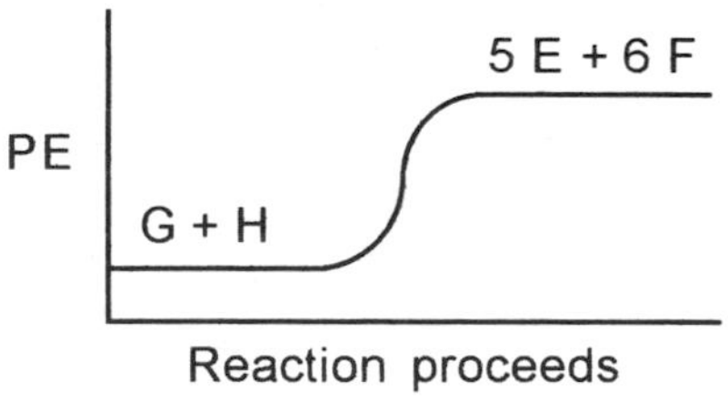

e) $H_2SO_4(l) + H_2O(l) \longrightarrow H_2SO_4(aq) + 150\ kJ$
f) $C_2H_6(g) \longrightarrow C_2H_2(g) + 2\ H_2(g)$; $\Delta H = 311\ kJ$
g) $C_2H_2(g) + Ca(OH)_2(aq) \longrightarrow CaC_2(s) + 2\ H_2O(l)$; $\Delta H = 183\ kJ$
h) $2\ C(s) + O_2(g) \longrightarrow 2\ CO(g)$; $\Delta H = -221\ kJ$

16. What tendencies to minimum enthalpy and maximum entropy must exist in the following situations?

a) Liquid nitroglycerine explodes, forming an expanding cloud of gases.
b) Solid AgBr is almost insoluble in water; that is, very little $Ag^+(aq)$ and $Br^-(aq)$ are formed when AgBr(s) is mixed with water.
c) Water and alcohol mix completely in any proportions; that is, they are "miscible".
d) The reaction: $3\ N_2(g) + Pb(s) \longrightarrow Pb(N_3)_2(s)$ does not occur.
e) When $N_2O_4(g)$ is put in a container, some of it decomposes into $2\ NO_2(g)$.
f) Smoke, carbon dioxide and water vapour will not react to make wood and oxygen.

II.4. LE CHATELIER'S PRINCIPLE

Experimental work shows that the following equilibrium can exist:

$$Fe^{3+} + SCN^- \rightleftharpoons FeSCN^{2+}.$$

When the $[Fe^{3+}]$ or $[SCN^-]$ is increased, the amount of $FeSCN^{2+}$ increases. When the $[Fe^{3+}]$ is reduced by precipitating out the Fe^{3+}, the amount of $FeSCN^{2+}$ decreases. All of these observations can be summarized by

> **Le Chatelier's Principle:** If a closed system at equilibrium is subjected to a change, processes will occur that ***tend*** to counteract that change.

To paraphrase this: **"WHATEVER WE DO, NATURE TRIES TO UNDO".**

(Note that this latter statement is a convenient way to ***think*** of Le Chatelier's Principle, but it is NOT Le Chatelier's Principle.)

Le Chatelier's Principle will prove to be a very powerful tool for dealing with equilibrium from now to the end of this course. It will give us the ability to QUICKLY and EASILY predict the effect that any change of conditions will have on an equilibrium.

The result of changing the temperature, concentration and pressure conditions of the equilibrium

$$2\,NO(g) + Cl_2(g) \rightleftharpoons 2\,NOCl(g) + 76\ kJ$$

is predicted by applying Le Chatelier's Principle.

1. The Effect of Temperature Changes

If the temperature of the equilibrium system is decreased, Le Chatelier's Principle tells us that

when the amount of heat energy is decreased, the reaction "shifts" so as to produce more heat.

That is: $$2\,NO(g) + Cl_2(g) \rightleftharpoons 2\,NOCl(g) + \mathbf{76\ kJ}.$$

Since the heat term is on the product side, the reaction shifts to the product side to produce more heat. That is, removing heat from the reaction causes the equilibrium to shift to the side of the equation which contains heat.

The effect of a temperature change can also be described in terms of reaction rates. If the temperature is decreased (and ***maintained*** at the lower temperature) then the reverse reaction rate decreases, since heat is a necessary "reactant" in the reverse reaction:

$$2\,NO(g) + Cl_2(g) \rightleftharpoons 2\,NOCl(g) + \mathbf{76\ kJ}.$$

The reaction "SHIFTS" to the product side; that is, more reactants become products.

(If the new temperature is NOT MAINTAINED, so that the reaction mixture is simply cooled for a short time on a "once–only" basis, the reaction is unchanged once it comes back to the previous temperature.)

Graphically, the shifting of the reaction to the product side as a result of a temperature decrease is shown below.

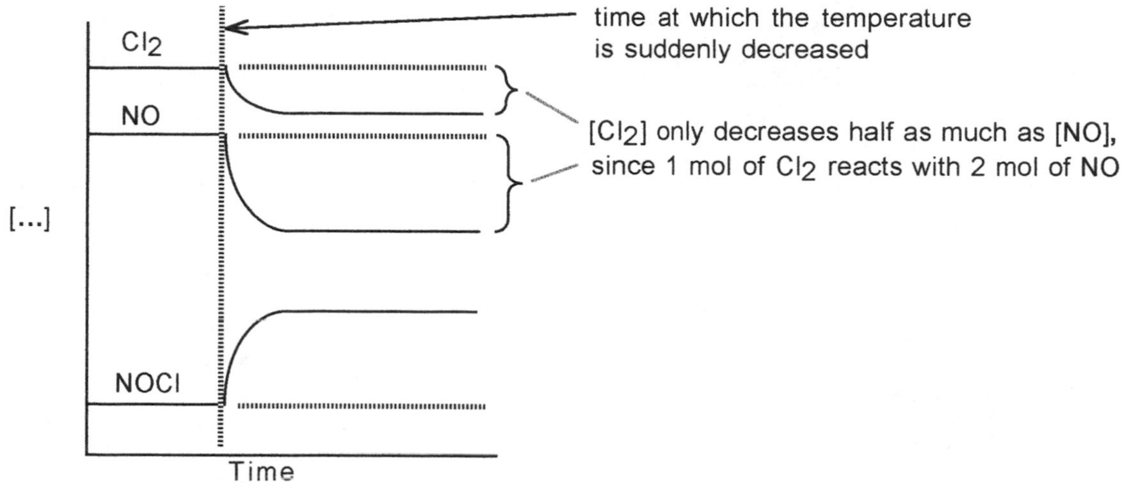

2. The Effect of Concentration Changes

If the concentration of Cl_2 increases, Le Chatelier's Principle tells us that

> **when the $[Cl_2]$ increases, the reaction shifts so as to partly decrease the amount of added Cl_2.**

That is: $2\,NO(g) + \mathbf{Cl_2(g)} \rightleftharpoons 2\,NOCl(g) + 76\text{ kJ}$.

Since the Cl_2 is on the reactant side, the reaction shifts to the product side to use up the added Cl_2. That is, if Cl_2 is added to the reaction the equilibrium shifts to the side which does not have Cl_2.

Again, the concentration change can be interpreted in terms of reaction rates. If the $[Cl_2]$ increases, the rate of the forward reaction increases (reaction rate increases when concentration increases):

$$2\,NO(g) + \mathbf{Cl_2(g)} \rightleftharpoons 2\,NOCl(g) + 76\text{ kJ}.$$

The reaction has "shifted" to the product side.

Graphically, the shifting of the reaction to the product side due to an increase in $[Cl_2]$ is shown below.

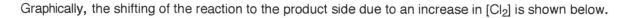

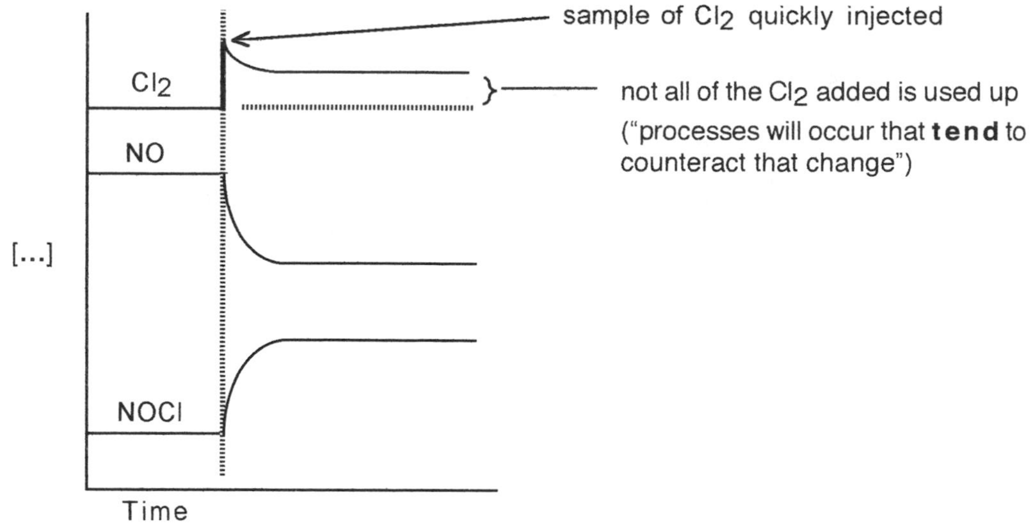

3. The Effect of Pressure Changes

A **decrease** in volume **increases** the pressure and simultaneously ***increases*** the concentration of **ALL gaseous species present.** According to Le Chatelier's Principle, the reaction shifts in response to the change so as to tend to **lower** the overall pressure. Since 2 mol of products – 2 NOCl(g) – are produced for every 3 mol of reactants used up – 2 NO(g) and 1 Cl_2(g) – then a shift to the product side results in fewer moles of gas present and the pressure decreases:

$$2\,NO(g) + Cl_2(g) \rightleftharpoons 2\,NOCl(g) + 76\text{ kJ}.$$

The following method helps to predict the correct shift.

- Count up the number of GASEOUS molecules on both sides of the reaction equation.
- Label the side of the reaction with the most gas molecules (the "higher number of molecules") as "HIGH", and label the other side (the "lower number of molecules") as "LOW".
- Since the pressure is INCREASED, the equilibrium shifts to the LOW pressure side. Draw an arrow from the "HIGH" side to the "LOW" side to show the "shift":

$$\begin{array}{ccc} 2\,NO(g) + Cl_2(g) & \rightleftharpoons & 2\,NOCl(g) + 76\text{ kJ}. \\ \text{HIGH} & \longrightarrow & \text{LOW} \end{array}$$

Therefore, **if the pressure is increased the reaction will shift to the side having the least number of gaseous molecules.**

Graphically, the shifting of the reaction to the product side due to an increase in overall pressure is shown as follows.

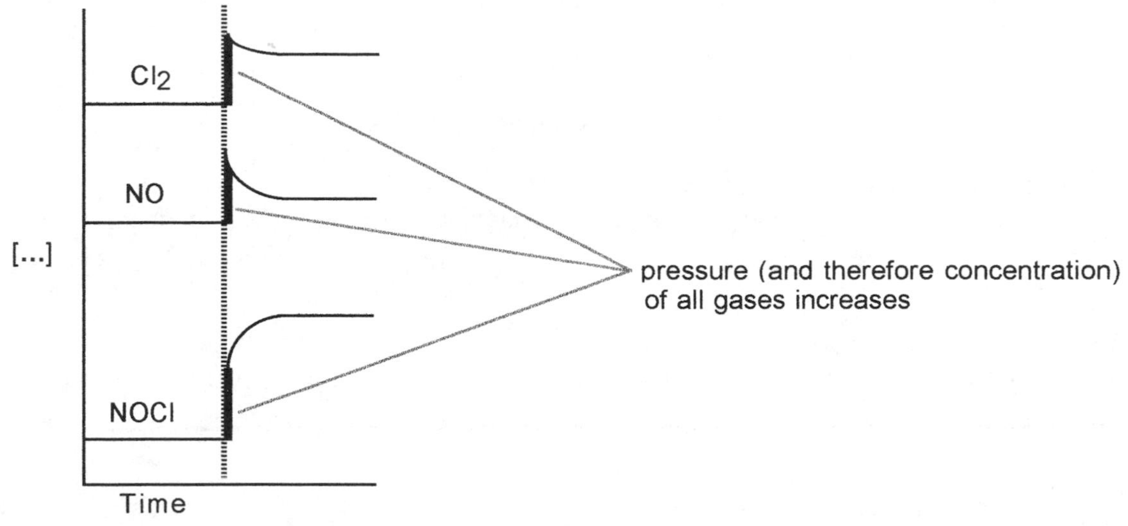

4. The Effect of Adding a Catalyst

A catalyst accelerates the reaction rate and helps a system reach equilibrium more quickly. If a reaction is already at equilibrium, the forward and reverse reaction rates must be equal. According to section I.11 in unit I, **adding a catalyst speeds up the forward and reverse rates by an equal amount, so that a reaction at equilibrium remains at equilibrium.**

Let us summarize the types of changes which can be made to an equilibrium and the effects seen on the graphs. You might find it useful to look back at the graphs as you read the following.

a) **CHANGING THE TEMPERATURE:** the concentrations shown start to SLOWLY change to a new value. There is NO SUDDEN CHANGE in the graph.

b) **CHANGING THE CONCENTRATION OF A SPECIES:** the concentration of the species being added SUDDENLY jumps up or down.

c) **CHANGING THE PRESSURE:** the concentrations of ALL SPECIES simultaneously jump up or down.

A NOTE ON HOW TO SOLVE THE FOLLOWING EXERCISES

Be careful to separate two things in your mind:
- what you do to the equilibrium, and
- what the equilibrium does in response to your changes.

In deciding how an equilibrium responds, ask yourself these questions:

What is being done to the system?
The opposite of the change imposed on the system will be what the system does.

or

What is the system doing?
The opposite of what the system does is the change imposed on the system.

EXERCISES:

Use Le Chatelier's Principle to describe the effect of the following changes on the position of the equilibrium.

17. The equilibrium is: $N_2O_3(g) \rightleftharpoons NO(g) + NO_2(g)$.
    a) increase the [NO]
    b) increase the $[N_2O_3]$
    c) increase the pressure by decreasing the volume
    d) add a catalyst

18. The equilibrium is: $2\,H_2(g) + 2\,NO(g) \rightleftharpoons N_2(g) + 2\,H_2O(g)$.
    a) decrease the $[N_2]$
    b) decrease the [NO]
    c) decrease the pressure by increasing the volume

19. The equilibrium is: $2\,CO(g) + O_2(g) \rightleftharpoons 2\,CO_2(g) + 566\text{ kJ}$.
    a) increase the temperature
    b) increase the $[O_2]$
    c) introduce a catalyst

20. The equilibrium is: $I_2(g) + Cl_2(g) \rightleftharpoons 2\,ICl(g)$; $\Delta H = 35.0\text{ kJ}$.
    a) decrease the temperature
    b) decrease the $[Cl_2]$
    c) increase the pressure by decreasing the volume

For each of Exercises 21 – 23, describe the effect on the concentration of the bold substance by the following changes. Write **INC** for increase, **DEC** for decrease or **NC** for no change.

21. The equilibrium is: $N_2(g) + \mathbf{3\,H_2(g)} \rightleftharpoons 2\,NH_3(g)$; $\Delta H = -92\text{ kJ}$.
    a) increase the $[N_2]$
    b) increase the temperature
    c) increase the volume
    d) add a catalyst

22. The equilibrium is: $2\,HF(g) \rightleftharpoons \mathbf{F_2(g)} + H_2(g)$; $\Delta H = 536\text{ kJ}$.
    a) decrease the temperature
    b) decrease the $[H_2]$
    c) decrease the volume

23. The equilibrium is: $SnO_2(s) + 2\,CO(g) \rightleftharpoons Sn(s) + \mathbf{2\,CO_2(g)}$; $\Delta H = 13\text{ kJ}$.
    a) increase the temperature
    b) add a catalyst
    c) increase the [CO]

Show the following situations graphically.

NOTE: In Exercises 24–26 the relative positioning of the molecules is not relevant; simply place them on the graph so the reactants are separated from the products. The only thing required here is to show what an individual substance's concentration does after the conditions change.

24. The equilibrium is: $H_2(g) + I_2(g) \rightleftharpoons 2\,HI(g) + 52\,kJ$.
    a) increase the temperature
    b) inject some $H_2(g)$
    c) decrease the volume
    d) add a catalyst

25. The equilibrium is: $2\,SO_2(g) + O_2(g) \rightleftharpoons 2\,SO_3(g)$; $\Delta H = -197$ kJ.
    a) inject some $SO_2(g)$
    b) increase the volume
    c) decrease the temperature
    d) increase the $[SO_3]$

26. The equilibrium is: $CO(g) + H_2O(g) \rightleftharpoons CO_2(g) + H_2(g)$; $\Delta H = -41$ kJ.
    a) inject some $CO_2(g)$
    b) remove some of the $H_2O(g)$ with a very rapidly acting drying agent
    c) increase the temperature
    d) decrease the pressure by increasing the volume

Interpret the following graphs in terms of the changes which must have been imposed on the equilibrium.

27. The equilibrium is: $PCl_5(g) + 92.5\,kJ \rightleftharpoons PCl_3(g) + Cl_2(g)$.

a)

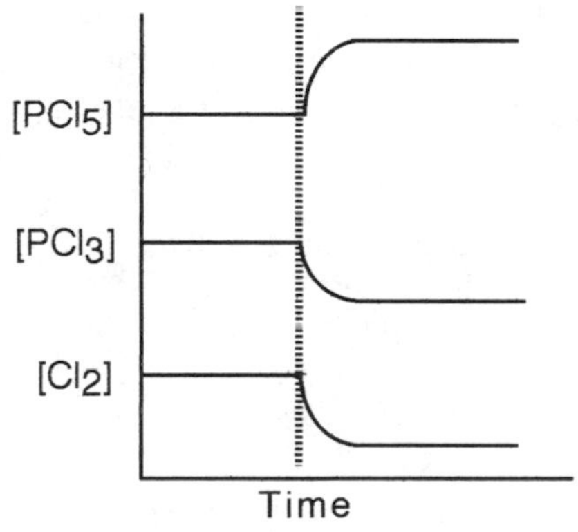

b)

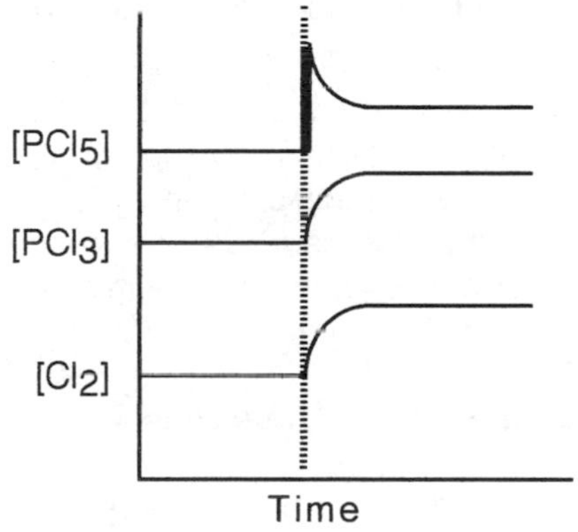

28. The equilibrium is: $H_2O(g) + Cl_2O(g) \rightleftharpoons 2\,HOCl(g) + 70\,kJ$.

a)

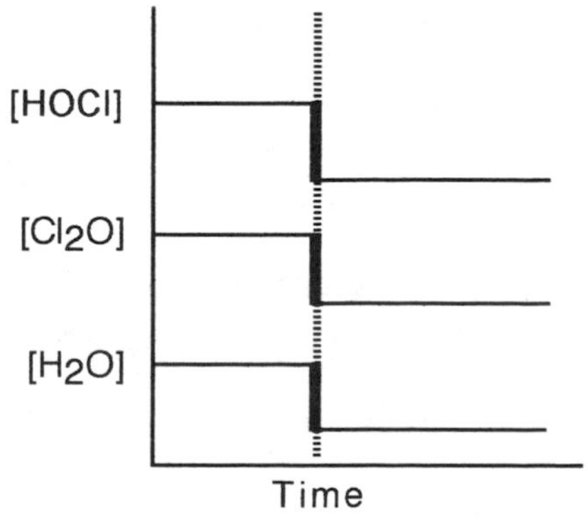

b)

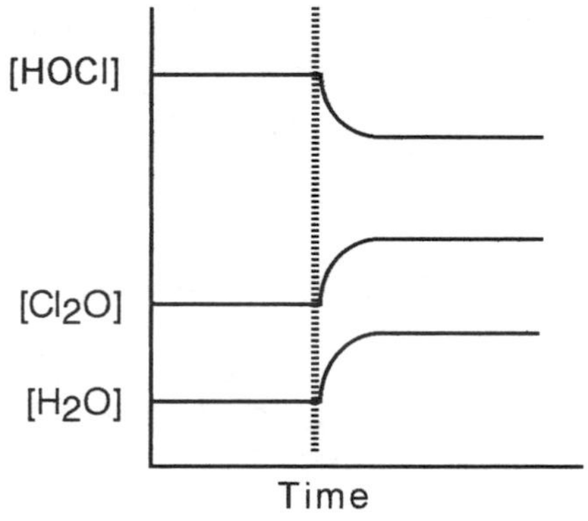

II.5. INDUSTRIAL APPLICATIONS OF EQUILIBRIUM PRINCIPLES

Equilibrium reactions are widely used in the manufacturing of chemicals. By changing the pressure, concentration or temperature, a given reaction can be shifted so as to produce more of a wanted product or less of an undesired reactant. Consider the following two examples.

A. The Haber Process for Making Ammonia

In the years prior to the first World War, the German chemist Fritz Haber was faced with a problem. If war were to break out, Germany would be unable to obtain nitrates from Chile. Blockades of shipping lanes would mean that the nitrates, which were used to make explosives, would not be available and Germany would find itself in a dangerous situation. Haber set out to find a way to obtain nitrates from another source. He knew that ammonia, NH_3, could be quickly and easily converted to nitrates, but how could he make ammonia on a large scale? Haber eventually discovered a way to make ammonia using the following reaction:

$$N_2(g) + 3\,H_2(g) \rightleftharpoons 2\,NH_3(g) + 92\text{ kJ}\,.$$

Let's see if you can determine how Haber solved his problem.

***EXERCISE*:**

29. (a) In order to get the highest yield of $NH_3(g)$, should you use high or low pressure?
    (b) In order to get the highest yield of $NH_3(g)$, should you use high or low temperature?
    (c) In order to have the fastest reaction rate, should you use high or low temperature?
    (d) Look at your answers to parts (b) and (c). What problem now exists? Suggest a suitable way to resolve this problem.
    (e) What else can be done to speed up the reaction rate? (Industry uses iron oxide for this purpose, in the form of ground up, rusted automobile bodies.)

B. Making Cement from Limestone

Limestone, $CaCO_3$, can be used to produce "quicklime", CaO, according to the reaction:

$$CaCO_3(s) + 175\text{ kJ} \rightleftharpoons CaO(s) + CO_2(g)\,.$$

The quicklime can then be added to a mixture of sand, clay, iron oxide and gypsum ($CaSO_4$) to make Portland cement powder. Let's see what conditions favour the production of CaO in the above equilibrium.

***EXERCISE*:**

30. (a) Should high or low temperatures be used to get the greatest yield of CaO?
    (b) Should high or low pressures be used to get the highest yield of CaO? How would you accomplish this in actual practice?
    (c) Should high or low temperatures be used to obtain the fastest reaction rate? Is there a conflict between the answers for parts (a) and (c)?

II.6. THE EQUILIBRIUM EXPRESSION AND THE EQUILIBRIUM CONSTANT

Take a moment and look again at the table in Exercise 6 in section II.2. The [A] and [B] eventually became constant, with more B than A; in fact there was five times as much B as A. Now look at the table in Exercise 7. When equilibrium is re–established there is again five times as much B as A. One could get suspicious that the ratio of [B] to [A] is a constant!

Consider the **EQUILIBRIUM EQUATION:** $A + B \rightleftharpoons C + D$.

Experimentally, it is found that: $$K_{eq} = \frac{[C] \times [D]}{[A] \times [B]} = \text{a constant}$$

This expression is called the **EQUILIBRIUM EXPRESSION*** and the **numerical value** of K_{eq} is called the **EQUILIBRIUM CONSTANT.**

EXAMPLES:

a) If the equilibrium equation is $H_2O(g) + CO(g) \rightleftharpoons H_2(g) + CO_2(g)$

then the equilibrium expression will be $$K_{eq} = \frac{[H_2(g)]\,[CO_2(g)]}{[H_2O(g)]\,[CO(g)]}.$$

b) If the equilibrium equation is $PCl_5(g) \rightleftharpoons PCl_3(g) + Cl_2(g)$

then the equilibrium expression will be $$K_{eq} = \frac{[PCl_3(g)]\,[Cl_2(g)]}{[PCl_5(g)]}.$$

c) If the equilibrium equation is $H_2(g) + F_2(g) \rightleftharpoons HF(g) + HF(g)$

then the equilibrium expression will be $$K_{eq} = \frac{[HF(g)]\,[HF(g)]}{[H_2(g)]\,[F_2(g)]} = \frac{[HF(g)]^2}{[H_2(g)]\,[F_2(g)]}.$$

But the equilibrium equation can also be written as: $H_2(g) + F_2(g) \rightleftharpoons 2\,HF(g)$.

AHA! The coefficient "2" in the equilibrium equation appears as the power "2" in the equilibrium expression.

---

* Chemistry texts seem to be equally divided between calling this expression the "equilibrium expression", the "equilibrium law", the "equilibrium constant" and the "equilibrium constant expression".

Let us generalize this "coefficient–becomes–a–power" idea. If the equilibrium equation is

$$a\,A + b\,B + c\,C + \ldots \rightleftharpoons p\,P + q\,Q + r\,R + \ldots$$

where: a, b, c, p, q, r are coefficients and A, B, C, P, Q, R are chemical species, then the equilibrium expression will be

$$K_{eq} = \frac{[P]^p[Q]^q[R]^r \ldots}{[A]^a[B]^b[C]^c \ldots}.$$

In order to make it easier to remember which concentrations are in the numerator of the fraction, a shorthand equation is often used:

$$\boxed{K_{eq} = \frac{[\text{PRODUCTS}]}{[\text{REACTANTS}]}}.$$

but you must remember how to write out the actual expression in terms of individual concentrations and their powers.

There is one other important thing to know about how to write out equilibrium expressions. Consider the equilibrium equation.

$$CaF_2(s) \rightleftharpoons Ca^{2+}(aq) + 2\,F^-(aq)$$

You might expect to write the equilibrium expression as

$$K_{eq} = \frac{[Ca^{2+}(aq)]\,[F^-(aq)]^2}{[CaF_2(s)]}.$$

However, $CaF_2(s)$ has a constant density of 3.18×10^3 g/L, which can be converted to a molar concentration as follows:

$$[CaF_2(s)] = \frac{3.18 \times 10^3\ \text{g}}{\text{L}} \times \frac{1\ \text{mol}}{78.1\ \text{g}} = \mathbf{40.7\ M}.$$

Further, the measured value of the ratio $\dfrac{[Ca^{2+}(aq)]\,[F^-(aq)]^2}{[CaF_2(s)]}$ is 8.4×10^{-13}.

Substituting: $$K_{eq} = 8.4 \times 10^{-13} = \frac{[Ca^{2+}(aq)]\,[F^-(aq)]^2}{40.7}.$$

Since it is silly to have two constant numbers floating around in the same equation, collecting the constant terms gives

$$[Ca^{2+}(aq)][F^-(aq)]^2 = 3.4 \times 10^{-11}.$$

The expression then becomes

$$K_{eq}(\text{new}) = 3.4 \times 10^{-11} = [Ca^{2+}(aq)][F^-(aq)]^2.$$

Rather than constantly going through this clumsy approach of "find a value for K_{eq} and substitute in constant concentration values and finally combine all the constant terms", we shall **eliminate any concentrations which have a constant value in the equilibrium expression and only define K_{eq} in terms of concentrations which can be changed.**

This result can be generalized by stating that the following substances are ***NOT*** included in the equilibrium expression because they have a constant concentration.

1) **SOLIDS:** Solids cannot be appreciably compressed, so that their density cannot be changed. Therefore their molar concentrations cannot be changed; that is, more moles cannot be compressed into a given volume of solid.

2) **PURE LIQUIDS:** Liquids cannot be appreciably compressed, so that they have a constant density and molar concentration. However, if there is another liquid present which can dilute the first liquid then the liquid is not "pure" and CAN have its concentration changed by dilution. Therefore, **a liquid is said to be PURE if and only if IT IS THE ONLY LIQUID WHICH EXISTS ON BOTH SIDES OF THE ENTIRE EQUILIBRIUM EQUATION.**

All other substances MUST be included in the equilibrium expression. Gases, aqueous ions, gases in solution, and multiple liquids must therefore be included.

EXAMPLES:

a) The equilibrium equation $Br_2(l) + H_2(g) \rightleftharpoons 2\,HBr(g)$

has the equilibrium expression $K_{eq} = \dfrac{[HBr(g)]^2}{[H_2(g)]}$.

Since $Br_2(l)$ is the only liquid in the equation, it is PURE and is omitted. (Strictly speaking, the $[Br_2(l)]$ is "multiplied out" of the K_{eq} expression.)

b) The equilibrium equation $CH_3COCH_3(l) + Cl_2(g) \rightleftharpoons CH_3COCH_2Cl(l) + HCl(g)$

has the equilibrium expression $K_{eq} = \dfrac{[CH_3COCH_2Cl(l)]\,[HCl(g)]}{[CH_3COCH_3(l)]\,[Cl_2(g)]}$.

Since there are 2 liquids in the same reaction mixture, they dilute each other and are not pure. Hence, both liquids are included.

c) The equilibrium equation $Cl_2(g) + 8\,H_2O(l) \rightleftharpoons Cl_2{\bullet}8H_2O(s)$

has the equilibrium expression $K_{eq} = \dfrac{1}{[Cl_2(g)]}$.

The "only" liquid, $H_2O(l)$, is omitted (or "multiplied out" if preferred) and the solid is divided out, leaving a "1" behind as the numerator.

NOTE: In the equilibrium $Br_2(l) + H_2(g) \rightleftharpoons 2\ HBr(g)$ we omit the $[Br_2(l)]$ from the equilibrium expression because the concentration of pure liquid bromine is not changed by having more or less liquid bromine.

Because solids and pure liquids have constant concentrations, adding a reactant or product which is a solid or a pure liquid will have NO EFFECT on the equilibrium. That is, the equilibrium does not shift.

(There may be more or less of the solid or pure liquid but the concentration is unchanged and the equilibrium remains unshifted.)

EXERCISES:

31. Write the equilibrium expressions for the following.
   a) $2\ ICl(g) \rightleftharpoons I_2(g) + Cl_2(g)$
   b) $N_2(g) + O_2(g) \rightleftharpoons 2\ NO(g)$
   c) $3\ O_2(g) \rightleftharpoons 2\ O_3(g)$
   d) $2\ Bi^{3+}(aq) + 3\ H_2S(g) \rightleftharpoons Bi_2S_3(s) + 6\ H^+(aq)$
   e) $CaCO_3(s) \rightleftharpoons CaO(s) + CO_2(g)$
   f) $CaC_2(s) + 2\ H_2O(l) \rightleftharpoons C_2H_2(g) + Ca(OH)_2(s)$
   g) $C_6H_6(l) + Br_2(l) \rightleftharpoons C_6H_5Br(l) + HBr(g)$
   h) $Cu(s) + 2\ Ag^+(aq) \rightleftharpoons Cu^{2+}(aq) + 2\ Ag(s)$
   i) $4\ NH_3(g) + 5\ O_2(g) \rightleftharpoons 6\ H_2O(g) + 4\ NO(g)$
   j) $H_2(g) + 1/2\ O_2(g) \rightleftharpoons H_2O(l)$

32. Write the K_{eq} expressions for: a) $N_2O_4(g) \rightleftharpoons 2\ NO_2(g)$, and
   b) $2\ NO_2(g) \rightleftharpoons N_2O_4(g)$.

   Examine the relationship between the K_{eq} expressions for equations (a) and (b) of this question. If $K_{eq} = 10.0$ for equation (a), what would be the value of K_{eq} for equation (b)?

33. Write the K_{eq} expressions for: a) $SO_2(g) + 1/2\ O_2(g) \rightleftharpoons SO_3(g)$, and
   b) $2\ SO_2(g) + O_2(g) \rightleftharpoons 2\ SO_3(g)$.

   Examine the relationship which exists between the K_{eq} expressions for equations (a) and (b) of this question. If $K_{eq} = 3$ for equation (a), what would be the value of K_{eq} for equation (b)?

34. Which way will the equilibrium $CaCO_3(s) + CO_2(g) + H_2O(l) \rightleftharpoons Ca^{2+}(aq) + 2\ HCO_3^-(aq) + 40\ kJ$ shift if
   (a) more $CO_2(g)$ is added?
   (b) more $CaCO_3(s)$ is added?
   (c) $Ca^{2+}(aq)$ is removed?
   (d) heat is added?

35. Rearrange the following equations to solve in terms of the concentrations indicated in bold.

   (a) $K_{eq} = \dfrac{\mathbf{[H_3O^+][F^-]}}{[HF]}$

   (b) $K_{eq} = \dfrac{[H_3O^+][F^-]}{\mathbf{[HF]}}$

   (c) $K_{eq} = \dfrac{\mathbf{[NO_2]}^2}{[NO]^2[O_2]}$

   (d) $K_{eq} = \dfrac{[NO_2]^2}{\mathbf{[NO]}^2[O_2]}$

   (e) $K_{eq} = \dfrac{[NH_3]^2}{[N_2]\mathbf{[H_2]}^3}$

   (f) $K_{eq} = \dfrac{[N_2O_4]}{\mathbf{[NO_2]}^2}$

   (g) $K_{eq} = \dfrac{\mathbf{[NH_3]}^2}{[N_2][H_2]^3}$

   (h) $K_{eq} = \dfrac{[PCl_3]^4}{[P_4]\mathbf{[Cl_2]}^6}$

II.7. LE CHATELIER'S PRINCIPLE AND THE EQUILIBRIUM CONSTANT

When the concentration, pressure or surface area is changed, the reaction tends to counteract these "one–shot changes" and re–establish equilibrium. The equilibrium which is re–established has the same K_{eq} value. Increases in any of concentration, pressure or surface area correspond to increases in the number of reacting molecules per liter. In each case, the number of available species is increased ONCE and the system regains equilibrium. (If the concentration of reactants or products is CONTINUALLY INCREASED the [PRODUCT]/[REACTANT] ratio is continuously altered and the system does not reach equilibrium because it is an open system.) You have already seen evidence that K_{eq} has a tendency to remain unchanged. In Exercises 6 and 7 the ratio of [B] to [A] remains 5:1 (that is, $K_{eq} = 5$) before and after extra products are added.

When the temperature is **decreased and held** at a certain value, the equilibrium shifts to the product side:

$$2\,NO(g) + Cl_2(g) \rightleftharpoons 2\,NOCl(g) + 76\ kJ\ .$$

A decrease in temperature will then cause an increase in [PRODUCTS] and a decrease in [REACTANTS], and since

$$K_{eq} = \frac{[PRODUCTS]}{[REACTANTS]}\ , \quad \text{then } K_{eq} \text{ is increased.}$$

A sneaky way to predict the effect of temperature on the value of K_{eq} is as follows. If the equilibrium shift is

$$\text{REACTANTS} \rightleftharpoons \text{PRODUCTS}$$

then draw an arrow beside K_{eq} so that the arrow points

***FROM* REACTANTS *TO* PRODUCTS**

$$K_{eq} - \frac{[PRODUCTS]}{[REACTANTS]} \uparrow$$

and the UPWARD direction of the arrow indicates that the value of K_{eq} INCREASES.

SUMMARY: ONLY a temperature change can affect the value of K_{eq}.
Changes in concentration, pressure or surface area have ***no effect*** on K_{eq}.

THE MEANING OF THE SIZE OF K_{eq}

By this time the following may be obvious, but let's make sure you fully understand what the value of K_{eq} implies. Since

$$K_{eq} = \frac{[PRODUCTS]}{[REACTANTS]}$$

then: a ***LARGE*** value for K_{eq} implies that a ***LARGE*** amount of products is present at equilibrium.
a ***SMALL*** value for K_{eq} implies that a ***SMALL*** amount of products is present at equilibrium.

EXERCISES:

36. Consider the following equilibria.

i) $2\,NO_2(g) \rightleftharpoons N_2O_4(g)$; $K_{eq} = 2.2$

ii) $Cu^{2+}(aq) + 2\,Ag(s) \rightleftharpoons Cu(s) + 2\,Ag^{+}(aq)$; $K_{eq} = 1 \times 10^{-15}$

iii) $Pb^{2+}(aq) + 2\,Cl^{-}(aq) \rightleftharpoons PbCl_2(s)$; $K_{eq} = 6.3 \times 10^{4}$

iv) $SO_2(g) + 1/2\,O_2(g) \rightleftharpoons SO_3(g)$; $K_{eq} = 110$

a) Which equilibrium favours products to the greatest extent?
b) Which equilibrium favours reactants to the greatest extent?

37. In the reaction $A + B \rightleftharpoons C + D + 100\ kJ$, what happens to the value of K_{eq} if the temperature is INCREASED?

38. If the value of K_{eq} DECREASES when the temperature DECREASES, is the reaction EXOTHERMIC or ENDOTHERMIC?

39. In the reaction $P + Q + 150\ kJ \rightleftharpoons R + S$, what happens to the value of K_{eq} if the temperature is DECREASED?

40. In the reaction $W + X + 100\ kJ \rightleftharpoons Y + Z$, what happens to the value of K_{eq} if the [X] is INCREASED?

41. If the value of K_{eq} INCREASES when the temperature DECREASES, is the reaction EXOTHERMIC or ENDOTHERMIC?

42. In Exercises 21–23, describe the effect on K_{eq} of the changes indicated. Write **INC** for increase, **DEC** for decrease and **NC** for no change.

43. In Exercise 23, assume that the bold species is Sn(s) instead of $CO_2(g)$. Now redo the Exercise, describing the effect on the species in bold ***and*** the value of K_{eq} when the changes indicated occur.

44. In the equilibrium $KCl(s) + 17\ kJ \rightleftharpoons K^{+}(aq) + Cl^{-}(aq)$, which way will the equilibrium shift and what is the effect on the value of K_{eq} when
(i) more $K^{+}(aq)$ is added?
(ii) the temperature is decreased?
(iii) more KCl(s) is added?

45. An equilibrium $A(aq) + 2\,B(g) \rightleftharpoons 2\,C(aq) + 2\,D(aq)$ has

$K_{eq} = 0.25$ at 100°C and $K_{eq} = 0.15$ at 200°C

State whether the forward reaction is endothermic or exothermic and explain why.

46. Examine the following graphs for the equilibrium $3\ O_2 \rightleftharpoons 2\ O_3$.

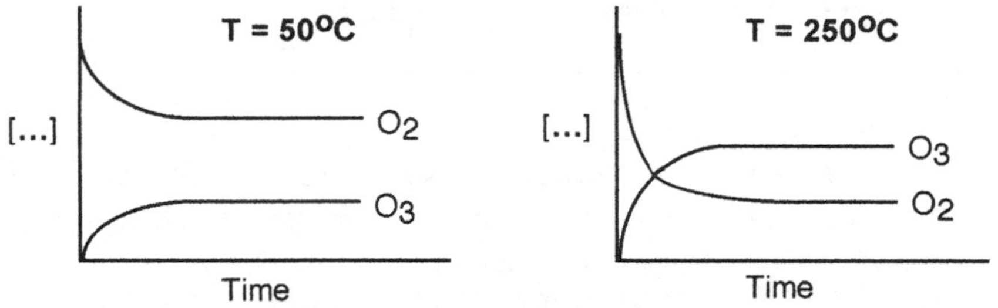

Is the equilibrium endothermic or exothermic, as written? Explain.

II.8. EQUILIBRIUM CALCULATIONS

Consider the equilibrium $2\ NO(g) + O_2(g) \rightleftharpoons 2\ NO_2(g)$. Determining the value of K_{eq} requires accurate information about the concentrations of NO(g), $O_2(g)$ and $NO_2(g)$ when the system is at equilibrium. Such information **CANNOT** be obtained without actually doing an experiment.

The following examples illustrate the various types of calculations which can be performed based on the equilibrium expression and some experimental data.

EXAMPLE A: **A 2.0 L bulb contains 6.00 mol of $NO_2(g)$, 3.0 mol of NO(g) and 0.20 mol of $O_2(g)$ at equilibrium. What is K_{eq} for $2\ NO(g) + O_2(g) \rightleftharpoons 2\ NO_2(g)$?**

First, determine the equilibrium expression: $K_{eq} = \dfrac{[NO_2(g)]^2}{[NO(g)]^2[O_2(g)]}$.

Next, use the data to calculate the concentrations required:

$[NO_2(g)] = \dfrac{6.0\ mol}{2.0\ L} = 3.0\ M$ $[NO(g)] = \dfrac{3.0\ mol}{2.0\ L} = 1.5\ M$

$[O_2(g)] = \dfrac{0.20\ mol}{2.0\ L} = 0.10\ M$

Substituting these values into the K_{eq} expression: $K_{eq} = \dfrac{(3.0)^2}{(1.5)^2(0.10)} = \mathbf{40}$.

> **Note:** Ignore the UNITS of K_{eq} since they depend on the particular equilibrium equation and have little or no significance at this time.

***EXAMPLE B*:** **4.00 mol of $NO_2(g)$ is introduced into a 2.00 L bulb. After a while equilibrium is attained according to the equation $2\ NO(g) + O_2(g) \rightleftharpoons 2\ NO_2(g)$. At equilibrium, 0.500 mol of NO(g) is found. What is the K_{eq} value?**

> **Preliminary analysis:** Go back and re–read the problem statement in Example A. Notice that there is no sense of time passing; that is, a situation simply exists and you are asked to find the value of K_{eq} which exists. Now re–read the problem statement in Example B. Notice that there is a distinct sense of time passing: NO_2 was put in a bulb, then time passed until equilibrium occurred. At equilibrium a certain amount of NO was formed. This means you have to distinguish between concentrations at the START and concentrations at EQUILIBRIUM, since starting concentrations will change as time passes and the reaction occurs.

First, determine the equilibrium expression: $$K_{eq} = \frac{[NO_2(g)]^2}{[NO(g)]^2[O_2(g)]}.$$

Next, calculate the concentrations which can be determined immediately from the data.

$$[NO_2(g)]_{START} = \frac{4.00\text{ mol}}{2.00\text{ L}} = 2.00\text{ M}$$

$$[NO(g)]_{EQUIL} = \frac{0.500\text{ mol}}{2.00\text{ L}} = 0.250\text{ M}$$

Now a data table is set up in the following manner. The unit symbol "M" is omitted from the entries so as to simplify the table usage; nevertheless the values put into such a table MUST **ALWAYS** HAVE UNITS OF **MOLES/L.**

	$2\ NO(g)$ +	$O_2(g)$	$\rightleftharpoons$ $2\ NO_2(g)$
START	0	0	2.00
+ Δ			
= EQUIL	0.250		

← assume that [NO] = $[O_2]$ = 0 at the start, since they were implied not to be present

Since "START + Δ = EQUIL" the Δ–value for NO must be +0.250.

IMPORTANT: the Δ–line represents how much the starting line has changed as a result of the reaction occurring. However, **the values in the Δ–line obey the stoichiometry of the reaction coefficients.** In this case, the changes must be in a 2:1:2 ratio for NO, O_2 and NO_2 respectively.

- Since O_2's coefficient ("1") is half of NO's coefficient ("2") then the change in $[O_2]$ must be half of the change in [NO].

  $\Delta[O_2] = 1/2\ \Delta[NO] = 1/2\ (0.250) = 0.125$

- Since NO_2's coefficient ("2") equals NO's ("2") then the change in $[NO_2]$ must equal the change in [NO].

  $\Delta[NO_2] = \Delta[NO] = 0.250$

After entering these Δ–values, the table now looks like:

	$2\,NO(g)$ +	$O_2(g)$ ⇌	$2\,NO_2(g)$	
START	0	0	2.00	
+ Δ	+0.250	+0.125	−0.250	← 0.250 : 0.125 : 0.250 equals a ratio of 2 : 1 : 2
= EQUIL	0.250			

Note that the Δ–value for NO_2 is negative. This makes sense because the reaction must have been **using** NO_2 and **producing** NO and O_2. Therefore, as the reaction shifted to the reactant side the $[NO_2]$ must have decreased and the [NO] and $[O_2]$ must have increased. **Because the Δ–values represent a shift, the Δ–values on one side of an equation will always be POSITIVE, while the Δ–values on the other side will always be NEGATIVE.**

Using the fact that "START + Δ = EQUIL", the table can be completed.

	$2\,NO(g)$ +	$O_2(g)$ ⇌	$2\,NO_2(g)$
START	0	0	2.00
+ Δ	+0.250	+0.125	−0.250
= EQUIL	0.250	0.125	1.75

Finally, substitute the equilibrium concentrations into the K_{eq} expression.

$$K_{eq} = \frac{(1.75)^2}{(0.250)^2(0.125)} = \mathbf{392}$$

EXAMPLE C: **A certain amount of $NO_2(g)$ was introduced into a 5.00 L bulb. When equilibrium was attained according to the equation $2\,NO(g) + O_2(g) \rightleftharpoons 2\,NO_2(g)$, the concentration of NO(g) was 0.800 M. If K_{eq} has a value of 24.0, how many moles of NO_2 were originally put into the bulb?**

The wording of the problem implies that "time is passing" and therefore a "START, Δ, EQUIL" table is required. Two pieces of information immediately concern us.

$[NO]_{EQUIL} = 0.800$ M
$[NO_2]_{START} = X$ (note that the $[NO_2]_{START}$ is unknown so a variable is used)

This information is placed in the table.

	$2\,NO(g)$ +	$O_2(g)$ ⇌	$2\,NO_2(g)$	
START	0	0	X	← $[NO] = [O_2] = 0$ can be assumed from the problem statement
+ Δ				
= EQUIL	0.800			

For NO, the equation "START + Δ = EQUIL" shows us that Δ[NO] = +0.800 M.

Again, the Δ–line must be in a 2:1:2 ratio, so that: $\Delta[NO_2] = \Delta[NO] = 0.800$ M, and
$\Delta[O_2] = 1/2\ \Delta[NO] = 0.400$ M

Filling in the rest of the table:

	$2\ NO(g)$ +	$O_2(g)$ ⇌	$2\ NO_2(g)$	
START	0	0	X	some of the starting amount of NO_2 reacts,
+ Δ	+0.800	+0.400	−0.800	⟵ so that $\Delta[NO_2]$ must represent a decrease
= EQUIL	0.800	0.400	X − 0.800	

Substituting the equilibrium values into the K_{eq} expression:

$$K_{eq} = \frac{[NO_2(g)]^2}{[NO(g)]^2[O_2(g)]} = 24.0 = \frac{(X - 0.800)^2}{(0.800)^2(0.400)}\ .$$

IMPORTANT: In this course you will NOT be required to solve a quadratic equation by using the quadratic formula, so let's take a clue from that statement. Whenever it looks as if a quadratic equation DOES have to be solved, you should be able to solve by simply taking the square root, as follows.

$(X - 0.800)^2 = (24.0)(0.800)^2(0.400) = 6.144$
$X - 0.800 = 2.479$
$X = 3.279\ M = [NO_2]_{START}$

The problem statement requires us to find the number of moles of NO_2 which were originally put in the 5.00 L bulb:

$$\#\text{ of moles } NO_2 = 3.279\ \frac{mol}{L} \times 5.00\ L = \mathbf{16.4\ mol}\ .$$

EXAMPLE D: **$K_{eq} = 49$ for $2\ NO(g) + O_2(g) \rightleftharpoons 2\ NO_2(g)$. If 2.0 mol of NO(g), 0.20 mol of $O_2(g)$ and 0.40 mol of $NO_2(g)$ are put into a 2.0 L bulb, which way will the reaction shift in order to reach equilibrium?**

Preliminary analysis: This question is NOT asking us to find a numerical value; rather, it is asking us for a DECISION. When dealing with numbers, decisions often are based on comparisons of two numbers: "Is A bigger than, less than, or equal to B?" Using the initial values for each species given in the problem statement, the following equation can be solved for Q.

$$Q = \frac{[NO_2]^2}{[NO]^2[O_2]}$$

, where **Q** = the **REACTION QUOTIENT** (Q = a "trial value" for K_{eq})

If $Q = K_{eq}$, then the system is at equilibrium.

If $Q < K_{eq}$, then $\frac{[PRODUCTS]}{[REACTANTS]}$ is **TOO SMALL** and the reaction must shift to produce more **PRODUCTS.**

If $Q > K_{eq}$, then $\frac{[PRODUCTS]}{[REACTANTS]}$ is **TOO BIG** and the reaction must shift to produce more **REACTANTS.**

First, determine the equilibrium expression: $K_{eq} = \frac{[NO_2(g)]^2}{[NO(g)]^2[O_2(g)]}$.

Next, calculate the starting concentrations.

$$[NO]_{START} = \frac{2.0\ mol}{2.0\ L} = 1.0\ M \qquad [O_2]_{START} = \frac{0.20\ mol}{2.0\ L} = 0.10\ M$$

$$[NO_2]_{START} = \frac{0.40\ mol}{2.0\ L} = 0.20\ M$$

Calculating the reaction quotient:

$$Q = \frac{(0.20)^2}{(1.0)^2(0.10)} = 0.40 = \frac{[PRODUCTS]}{[REACTANTS]} \uparrow < K_{eq} = 49.$$

Therefore, Q is too small and **THE REACTION MUST SHIFT TO THE PRODUCT SIDE** (notice the upward–pointing arrow) in order to **increase the value of Q up to the required value for K_{eq}.**

***EXAMPLE E*:** **K_{eq} = 3.5 for $SO_2(g) + NO_2(g) \rightleftharpoons SO_3(g) + NO(g)$. If 4.0 mol of $SO_2(g)$ and 4.0 mol of $NO_2(g)$ are placed in a 5.0 L bulb and allowed to come to equilibrium, what concentration of all species will exist at equilibrium?**

First, write out the equilibrium expression: $K_{eq} = \dfrac{[SO_3]\,[NO]}{[SO_2]\,[NO_2]}$.

Now set up a START, Δ, EQUIL table since there is a definite sense of time passing.

	$SO_2(g)$	+	$NO_2(g)$	$\rightleftharpoons$	$SO_3(g)$	+	$NO(g)$
START	0.80		0.80		0		0
+ Δ							
= EQUIL							

There is no more data to enter into the table EXCEPT the unknown. There are several ways to assign the variable when no information is available for both the Δ–line and EQUIL–line but one of the most straight–forward approaches is to let the variable be THE CHANGE IN CONCENTRATION of one of the chemical species involved. Since the reactants and products are in a 1:1:1:1 ratio, let the Δ-values all be "X" or "–X". The products obviously must GAIN in concentration (because they originally had a concentration of ZERO) and the reactants must LOSE, so that the table can be filled in as shown below.

	$SO_2(g)$	+	$NO_2(g)$	$\rightleftharpoons$	$SO_3(g)$	+	$NO(g)$
START	0.80		0.80		0		0
+ Δ	–X		–X		+X		+X
= EQUIL	0.80 – X		0.80 – X		X		X

and $$K_{eq} = 3.5 = \frac{X^2}{(0.80 - X)^2}.$$

This equation does NOT require the use of the quadratic formula – simply take the square root of both sides of the equation.

$$1.87 = \frac{X}{(0.80 - X)},$$ and solve to get: X = 0.52 M

Hence $[SO_3] = [NO] = X =$ **0.52 M** and $[SO_2] = [NO_2] = 0.80 - X =$ **0.28 M** .

EXAMPLE F: **A 1.0 L reaction vessel contained 1.0 mol of SO_2, 4.0 mol of NO_2, 4.0 mol of SO_3 and 4.0 mol of NO at equilibrium according to $SO_2(g) + NO_2(g) \rightleftharpoons SO_3(g) + NO(g)$. If 3.0 mol of SO_2 is added to the mixture, what will be the new concentration of NO when equilibrium is re–attained?**

> **Preliminary analysis:** The unknown is the final [NO] when equilibrium is re–established. Hence, all other concentrations must be given or be readily calculated AND you must have a value for K_{eq}. But, you are NOT given the value for K_{eq}. You ARE told the amount of each gas previously present at equilibrium. This information will then allow you to calculate a value for K_{eq}.

First find the value of K_{eq}: $K_{eq} = \dfrac{[SO_3]\,[NO]}{[SO_2]\,[NO_2]} = \dfrac{4.0 \times 4.0}{1.0 \times 4.0} = 4.0$.

Since there is no mention of the temperature having been changed, the value of K_{eq} will remain unchanged when the extra SO_2 is added.

> **IMPORTANT:** In ALL problems such as this one, in which a system was at equilibrium and then some species is added to or removed from the system, **any ADDITION (or REMOVAL) is shown on the "START" line.** The reasoning behind this procedure is simple: a system at equilibrium will not suddenly start to shift on its own; something has to cause the shift. By adding a chemical on the "START" line, the initial equilibrium situation is upset and must now shift so as to regain equilibrium.

Set up a START, Δ, EQUIL table as follows. Again, no values are available for either the Δ–line or the EQUIL-line so that the variable is assigned to be a CHANGE IN CONCENTRATION on the Δ–line. Since the equilibrium is upset by adding extra SO_2, the system will shift so as to use up some of the added SO_2 and the change in $[SO_2]$ put on the Δ–line will be "–X".

	SO_2	+	NO_2	$\rightleftharpoons$	SO_3	+	NO
START	1.0 + 3.0		4.0		4.0		4.0
+ Δ	–X		–X		+X		+X
= EQUIL	4.0 – X		4.0 – X		4.0 + X		4.0 + X

Substituting $$K_{eq} = 4.0 = \frac{(4.0 + X)^2}{(4.0 - X)^2}$$

Taking the square root $$2.0 = \frac{4.0 + X}{4.0 - X},$$ and solving gives $X = 1.33$

Finally $[NO] = 4.0 + X = \mathbf{5.3\ M}$

$\sqrt{\frac{(X-0.8^2)}{(X+0.4)^2(0.4)}} = \sqrt{24}$
∴ 1 = 2
You know, I always thought this stuff didn't make sense.
-ZimBoBwe

EXERCISES:

47. A 1.0 L reaction vessel contains 0.750 mol of CO(g) and 0.275 mol of $H_2O(g)$. After 1 h, equilibrium is reached according to the equation $CO(g) + H_2O(g) \rightleftharpoons CO_2(g) + H_2(g)$. Analysis shows 0.250 mol of CO_2 present at equilibrium. What is K_{eq} for the reaction?

48. A 5.0 L reaction vessel was initially filled with 6.0 mol of SO_2, 2.5 mol of NO_2 and 1.0 mol of SO_3. After equilibrium was established according to the equation $SO_2(g) + NO_2(g) \rightleftharpoons SO_3(g) + NO(g)$, the vessel was found to contain 3.0 mol of SO_3. What is K_{eq} for the reaction?

49. Consider the equilibrium $N_2(g) + 3\,H_2(g) \rightleftharpoons 2\,NH_3(g)$.
    a) At a certain temperature 3.0 mol of N_2 and 2.0 mol of H_2 are put into a 5.0 L container. At equilibrium the concentration of NH_3 is 0.020 M. Calculate K_{eq} for the reaction.
    b) At a different temperature, 6.0 mol of NH_3 were introduced into a 10.0 L container. At equilibrium 2.0 mol of NH_3 were left. Calculate K_{eq} for the reaction.

50. At a certain temperature, $K_{eq} = 4$ for the reaction $2\,HF(g) \rightleftharpoons H_2(g) + F_2(g)$. Predict the direction in which the equilibrium will shift, if any, when the following systems are introduced into a 5.0 L bulb.
    a) 3.0 mol of HF, 2.0 mol of H_2 and 4.0 mol of F_2
    b) 0.20 mol of HF, 0.50 mol of H_2 and 0.60 mol of F_2
    c) 0.30 mol of HF, 1.8 mol of H_2 and 0.20 mol of F_2

51. At a certain temperature, $K_{eq} = 75$ for the reaction $2\,O_3(g) \rightleftharpoons 3\,O_2(g)$. Predict the direction in which the equilibrium will shift, if any, when the following systems are introduced into a 10.0 L bulb.
    a) 0.60 mol of O_3 and 3.0 mol of O_2
    b) 0.050 mol of O_3 and 7.0 mol of O_2
    c) 1.5 mol of O_3 and no O_2

52. $K_{eq} = 5.0$ at a certain temperature for the reaction $2\,SO_2(g) + O_2(g) \rightleftharpoons 2\,SO_3(g)$. A certain amount of $SO_3(g)$ was placed in a 2.0 L reaction vessel. At equilibrium the vessel contained 0.30 mol of $O_2(g)$. What concentration of $SO_3(g)$ was originally placed in the vessel?

53. $K_{eq} = 35.0$ for the reaction $PCl_5(g) \rightleftharpoons PCl_3(g) + Cl_2(g)$. If you have $[PCl_5] = 1.34 \times 10^{-3}$ M and $[PCl_3] = 0.205$ M at equilibrium in a certain vessel, what is the equilibrium concentration of $Cl_2(g)$?

54. $K_{eq} = 125$ for $H_2(g) + I_2(g) \rightleftharpoons 2\,HI(g)$ at a certain temperature. If 0.15 mol of HI, 0.034 mol of H_2 and 0.096 mol of I_2 are introduced into a 10 L vessel, will the reaction proceed to the reactant side or product side as the reaction attempts to reach equilibrium?

55. A reaction mixture at equilibrium, $CO(g) + H_2O(g) \rightleftharpoons CO_2(g) + H_2(g)$, contains 1.00 mol of H_2, 2.00 mol of CO_2, 2.00 mol of CO and 2.00 mol of H_2O in a 2.00 L bulb. If 1.00 mol of H_2 is added to the system, calculate the [CO] which will exist when equilibrium is regained.

56. A student obtained the following data at 25°C while studying the equilibrium

$$2\,Tl^+(aq) + Cd(s) \rightleftharpoons 2\,Tl(s) + Cd^{2+}(aq).$$

Volume	Moles Tl^+	Moles Cd^{2+}
1.00 L	0.316	0.414
5.00 L	**?**	0.339

Calculate the number of moles of Tl^+ present in the second data set.

57. When 0.50 mol of NOCl(g) was put into a 1.0 L flask and allowed to come to equilibrium, 0.10 mol of $Cl_2(g)$ was found. What is K_{eq} for the reaction $2\,NOCl(g) \rightleftharpoons 2\,NO(g) + Cl_2(g)$?

58. $K_{eq} = 7.5$ for $2\,H_2(g) + S_2(g) \rightleftharpoons 2\,H_2S(g)$. A certain amount of H_2S was added to a 2.0 L flask and allowed to come to equilibrium. At equilibrium, 0.072 mol of H_2 was found. How many moles of H_2S were originally added to the flask?

59. A reaction mixture at equilibrium, $CO_2(g) + H_2(g) \rightleftharpoons CO(g) + H_2O(g)$, contained 4.00 mol of CO_2, 1.50 mol of H_2, 3.00 mol of CO and 2.50 mol of H_2O in a 5.0 L container. How many moles of CO_2 would have to be removed from the system in order to reduce the amount of CO to 2.50 mol?

60. $K_{eq} = 49.5$ for $H_2(g) + I_2(g) \rightleftharpoons 2\,HI(g)$ at a certain temperature. If 0.250 mol of $H_2(g)$ and 0.250 mol of $I_2(g)$ are placed in a 10.0 L vessel and permitted to react, what will be the concentration of each substance at equilibrium?

61. The equilibrium constant for the reaction $N_2(g) + 3\,H_2(g) \rightleftharpoons 2\,NH_3(g)$ is 3.0 at a certain temperature. Enough $NH_3(g)$ was added to a 5.0 L container such that at equilibrium the container was found to contain 2.5 mol of $N_2(g)$. How many moles of $NH_3(g)$ were put into the container?

62. $K_{eq} = 1.00$ for $N_2O_2(g) + H_2(g) \rightleftharpoons N_2O(g) + H_2O(g)$. If 0.150 mol of $N_2O(g)$ and 0.250 mol of $H_2O(g)$ were introduced into a 1.00 L bulb and allowed to come to equilibrium, what concentration of $N_2O_2(g)$ was present at equilibrium?

63. A reaction mixture at equilibrium, $H_2(g) + I_2(g) \rightleftharpoons 2\,HI(g)$, contains 0.150 mol of $H_2(g)$, 0.150 mol of $I_2(g)$ and 0.870 mol of HI(g) in a 10.0 L vessel. If 0.400 mol of HI(g) is added to this system and the system is allowed to come to equilibrium again, what will be the new concentrations of H_2, I_2 and HI?

64. A reaction mixture, $2\,NO(g) + O_2(g) \rightleftharpoons 2\,NO_2(g)$, contained 0.240 mol of NO(g), 0.0860 mol of $O_2(g)$ and 1.20 mol of $NO_2(g)$ when at equilibrium in a 2.00 L bulb. How many moles of $O_2(g)$ had to be added to the mixture to increase the number of moles of $NO_2(g)$ to 1.28 when equilibrium was re–established?

65. A reaction mixture, $2\,ICl(g) + H_2(g) \rightleftharpoons I_2(g) + 2\,HCl(g)$, was found to contain 0.500 mol of ICl(g), 0.0560 mol of $H_2(g)$, 1.360 mol of $I_2(g)$ and 0.800 mol of HCl(g) at equilibrium in a 1.00 L bulb. How many moles of ICl(g) would have to be removed in order to reduce the [HCl(g)] to 0.680 M when equilibrium is re–established?

66. **(Nasty!)** $K_{eq} = 100$ at a certain temperature for $CH_4(g) + 2\,H_2S(g) \rightleftharpoons CS_2(g) + 4\,H_2(g)$. Some CH_4 and H_2S were introduced into a 1.0 L bulb and at equilibrium 0.10 mol of CH_4 and 0.30 mol of H_2S were found. What was $[CS_2]$ at equilibrium?

UNIT III : SOLUBILITY EQUILIBRIUM

III.1. A REVIEW OF SOLUBILITY

Fact: Many barium compounds are extremely poisonous, yet barium sulphate is routinely swallowed by patients in order to get clearer X–ray pictures of their lower intestines. Why doesn't barium sulphate poison these patients?

Fact: It is possible to saturate a swimming pool with silver bromide and kill off all the nasty little micro–organisms such as algae and bacteria, so that the pool water remains clean and sparkling, yet the water is as pure as drinking water and harmless to people. Since silver ion is a heavy metal ion and hence dangerous to our health in large doses, how is it possible that water ***saturated*** with silver bromide doesn't harm us?

The answers to the questions posed above are tied to the concept of **SOLUBILITY.** In this unit you will examine what is meant when a compound is said to be "soluble" or a solution is said to be "saturated", how the solubility of compounds can be used to analyze solutions, how water can be purified, and how to selectively extract valuable metals from solution.

The main emphasis will be on solutions of aqueous ions, but some of the material covered will apply to non–ionic substances. As you may recall from Chem 11, there are three classes of compounds which form ionic solution: ACIDS, BASES and SALTS. **This unit will be concerned only with SALTS;** acids and bases will be thoroughly covered in Unit IV.

First, let's review some concepts from Chemistry 11.

Definition: An **ELECTROLYTE** is a substance which dissolves to give an electrically conducting solution containing ions.

Example: $(NH_4)_3PO_4(s) \longrightarrow 3\,NH_4^+(aq) + PO_4^{3-}(aq)$

$HCl(g) \longrightarrow H^+(aq) + Cl^-(aq)$

Definition: A **NON–ELECTROLYTE** is a substance which dissolves to give a non–conducting solution containing only neutral molecules.

Example: $C_2H_2(g) \longrightarrow C_2H_2(aq)$

$Br_2(l) \longrightarrow Br_2(aq)$

In summary, a **MOLECULAR SOLUTION** contains only neutral molecules and an **IONIC SOLUTION** contains ions.

The problem is: how can you predict whether a compound will form an ionic or molecular solution? The general rules below are GUIDELINES; there are some compounds which are exceptions to the rules. Don't worry about the exceptions, but be aware that a few exist.

GENERAL RULES FOR CLASSIFYING COMPOUNDS AS IONIC OR MOLECULAR

Ionic Compounds

- A compound made up of a **metal** and a **non–metal** is likely to be ionic in solution.

Example: $FeCl_3(s) \longrightarrow Fe^{3+}(aq) + 3\,Cl^-(aq)$.

- A compound made up of species which you know to be **polyatomic** ions will be ionic in solution. (For a list of ions which you should know, see the Table "Names, Formulae, and Charges of Some Common Ions" in the back of this book.)

Example: $(NH_4)_2Cr_2O_7(s) \longrightarrow 2\,NH_4^+(aq) + Cr_2O_7^{2-}(aq)$.

Note: In Chem 12 you will only encounter ionic solids made up of ONE TYPE OF POSITIVE ION and ONE TYPE OF NEGATIVE ION.

Examples: In $(NH_4)_2HPO_4$ you should recognize NH_4^+ as one ion present, so that HPO_4^{2-} must be the second ion.

$$(NH_4)_2HPO_4(s) \longrightarrow 2\,NH_4^+ + HPO_4^{2-}$$

In $NaH_3P_2O_7$ you should recognize Na^+ as one ion present, so that $H_3P_2O_7^-$ is the second ion.

$$NaH_3P_2O_7(s) \longrightarrow Na^+ + H_3P_2O_7^-$$

Molecular Compounds

- Covalent compounds (**non–metal + non–metal**), ***especially organic compounds***, generally form molecular solutions.

Example: $CH_3OH(l) \longrightarrow CH_3OH(aq)$ (CH_3OH is organic — it starts with a carbon atom)
$ClO_2(l) \longrightarrow ClO_2(aq)$

EXERCISES:

1. State whether each of the following substances is expected to form an IONIC or MOLECULAR solution.

a) $RbBr(s)$	c) $CsNO_3(s)$	e) $S_8(s)$	g) $NaCH_3COO(s)$	i) $HNO_3(l)$
b) $CHCl_3(l)$	d) $CuSO_4(s)$	f) $CrCl_3(s)$	h) $ICl(s)$	j) $CH_4(g)$

2. Write equations to show the dissolving of the following substances in water.

a) $(NH_4)_2SO_4(s)$ b) $CH_3CH_2OH(l)$ c) $K_2CO_3(s)$ d) $CaCl_2(s)$

Now, let's see what the term "solubility" means. A definition suitable for Chem 11 purposes was:

The **SOLUBILITY** of a substance is the maximum amount of the substance which can dissolve in a given amount of solvent at a given temperature.

A solution which has dissolved the "maximum amount" of a substance is said to be **SATURATED.** Once a solution has been saturated with a substance, the addition of more of the substance will simply cause this extra material to accumulate in undissolved form.

(An unstable situation called "supersaturation" also exists in which a concentrated solution contains more of a dissolved salt than it normally would when saturated but no solid crystals are able to form. Once a few ions eventually join together correctly and start to form a crystal, all the excess material quickly crystallizes out of solution. The remaining solution is then simply saturated. This situation will be of no concern to us in this unit.)

In keeping with your knowledge regarding chemical equilibrium, the following definitions of "saturated solution" and "solubility" are preferred in Chem 12.

A substance is said to form a **SATURATED SOLUTION** if the dissolved substance is in equilibrium with some of the undissolved substance.

(In contrast, an "unsaturated solution" contains less than the maximum amount of a substance which can dissolve, so there is no undissolved solid present and no equilibrium exists.)

The **SOLUBILITY** of a substance is the equilibrium concentration of the substance in solution at a given temperature.

The solubility is referred to as the **MOLAR SOLUBILITY** when the concentration is expressed in "moles/litre".

These equilibrium-based definitions show that to have a saturated solution two conditions must be met.

SATURATION exists when:

a) some undissolved material is present, and
b) equilibrium exists between the dissolved and the undissolved material.

You can show that a solution is saturated by writing an equation showing the substance in equilibrium with its aqueous products. For example:

$$AgBrO_3(s) \rightleftharpoons Ag^+(aq) + BrO_3^-(aq).$$

Such an equilibrium equation can also be interpreted in the following way.

- Solid $AgBrO_3$ dissolves and enters solution.

$AgBrO_3(s) \longrightarrow Ag^+(aq) + BrO_3^-(aq)$ = **DISSOLVING REACTION**

- Ag^+ and BrO_3^- ions come together and form $AgBrO_3$.

$Ag^+(aq) + BrO_3^-(aq) \longrightarrow AgBrO_3(s)$ = **CRYSTALLIZATION REACTION**

At first, there are few ions in solution and the dissolving reaction predominates. Later, as more ions accumulate in solution, there is an increased probability that an ion will leave the solution and re–attach itself to the solid crystals present. Eventually, the rate of the dissolving reaction equals the rate of the crystallization reaction and equilibrium occurs:

$$AgBrO_3(s) \rightleftharpoons Ag^+(aq) + BrO_3^-(aq).$$

EXERCISES:

3. Write the equation for the equilibrium reaction existing in each of the following saturated aqueous solutions.

   a) K_3PO_4 b) NH_4Cl c) $Al(NO_3)_3$

4. Write the crystallization reaction involving $MgBr_2(s)$.

5. Write the dissolving reaction involving $C_6H_{12}O_6(s)$.

6. A flask contains a saturated solution of NaCl in water. You carefully pour off 100 mL of the solution, taking care not to let any crystals of salt fall into the new container. Is the salt solution in the new container saturated? Why?

7. A student half–filled a 100 mL beaker with water and added a few grams of NaCl crystals. Seeing the crystals settle immediately to the bottom of the beaker, the student said the solution was saturated because some undissolved solid was present. Was the student correct? Why?

III.2. CALCULATING SOLUBILITY AND ION CONCENTRATIONS

Once the mass of a substance present in 1 L of a solution has been experimentally measured, it is straightforward to calculate the solubility of the substance.

EXAMPLE: It is experimentally found that 1 L of saturated $AgBrO_3(aq)$ contains 1.96 g of $AgBrO_3$. What is the **molar solubility** of $AgBrO_3$; that is, the solubility expressed in moles per litre?

$$[AgBrO_3] = 1.96\,\frac{g}{L} \times \frac{1\ mol}{235.8\ g} = \mathbf{8.31 \times 10^{-3}\ M}$$

EXAMPLE: The molar solubility of PbI_2 is 1.37×10^{-3} M. Express this value in grams per litre.

$$\text{Solubility (g/L)} = 1.37 \times 10^{-3}\,\frac{mol}{L} \times \frac{461.0\ g}{1\ mol} = \mathbf{0.632\ \frac{g}{L}}$$

A "Calculator Interlude":
When entering "1.37×10^{-3}" into your calculator, don't forget that the "EXP" or "EE" key on your calculator stands for "***10 to the power of***". The sequence of keystrokes needed to enter "1.37×10^{-3}" is:

1.37 EXP +/– 3
or 1.37 EE +/– 3 .

EXAMPLE: Experimentally it is found that 250 mL of saturated $CaCl_2$ contain 18.6 g of $CaCl_2$ at 20°C. What is the molar solubility of $CaCl_2$?

$$[CaCl_2] = \frac{18.6\ g}{0.250\ L} \times \frac{1\ mol}{111.1\ g} = \mathbf{0.670\ M}$$

Note: Assume all solutions are at a temperature of 25°C unless otherwise indicated.

EXERCISES:

8. Aluminum fluoride, AlF_3, has a solubility of 5.59 g/L of solution at 20°C. Express this solubility in moles per litre.

9. Lead (II) chloride, $PbCl_2$, has a solubility of 0.99 g/100.0 mL of solution at 20°C. Calculate the molar solubility of $PbCl_2$.

10. The molar solubility of $MgCO_3$ is 1.26×10^{-3} M at 25°C. Express this value in grams per litre.

11. The molar solubility of Ag_2CO_3 is 1.2×10^{-4} M at 25°C. Express this value in grams per 100.0 mL.

12. Chromium (VI) oxide, $CrO_3(s)$, has a solubility of 92.6 g in 150.0 mL of solution at 0°C. Calculate the molar solubility of CrO_3.

13. Silver chlorite, $AgClO_2$, has a molar solubility of 0.014 M at 25°C. What mass of $AgClO_2$ is contained in 50.0 mL of saturated $AgClO_2$?

14. Manganese (II) chloride, $MnCl_2$, has a molar solubility of 5.75 M at 0°C. If 125 mL of saturated $MnCl_2$ is evaporated to dryness, what mass of $MnCl_2$ will be left?

15. A chemistry student was assigned the task of determining the solubility of potassium chloride, KCl. She added an excess of solid KCl to water, stirred, and let the solution sit overnight. The next day, she pipetted a 25.00 mL portion of the saturated solution into a pre–weighed evaporating dish, determined the combined mass, carefully boiled off the water present, allowed the residue to cool and re–determined the mass of the evaporating dish and residue. The data obtained is given below.

temperature of solution	= 22.5°C
mass of evaporating dish	= 54.87 g
mass of solution and evaporating dish	= 84.84 g
mass of residue and evaporating dish	= 62.59 g

Calculate:

a) the mass of 25.00 mL of the solution.
b) the mass of KCl in 25.00 mL of solution.
c) the mass of water in 25.00 mL of solution.
d) the mass of KCl which can dissolve in 100.0 g of water at 22.5°C.
e) the molar solubility of KCl, expressed in moles of KCl per litre of solution.

16. The following data was obtained when a saturated solution of aqueous ammonium sulphate, $(NH_4)_2SO_4(aq)$, was poured into a beaker and evaporated to dryness.

temperature of solution	= 25°C
volume of solution used	= 70.0 mL
mass of beaker	= 87.23 g
mass of original solution and beaker	= 147.42 g
mass of beaker and dried $(NH_4)_2SO_4$	= 104.08 g

Calculate:

a) The mass of the solution.
b) The mass of ammonium sulphate in the solution.
c) The mass of water in the solution.
d) The mass of ammonium sulphate which could be dissolved in 100.0 g of water.
e) The molar concentration of the ammonium sulphate solution.

17. Examine the following diagram:

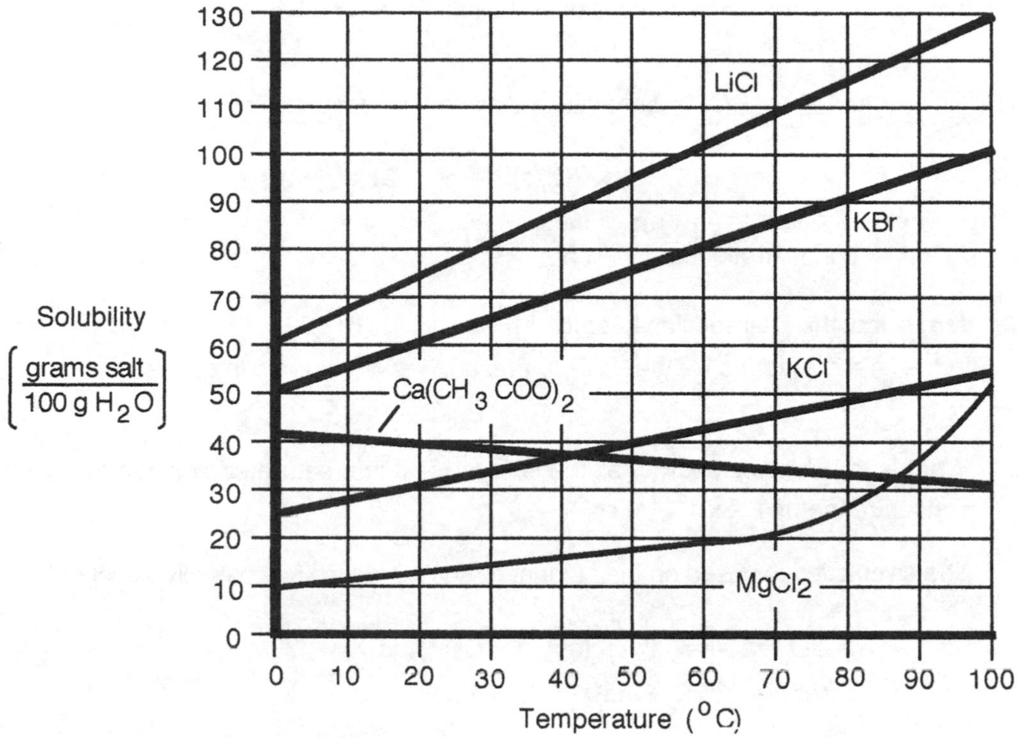

a) Which salt is the most soluble at 60°C?

b) If you put 40 g of KCl into 100 g of water at 90°C, will you be able to form a saturated solution? Explain your answer.

c) If you heat a saturated solution of calcium acetate, $Ca(CH_3COO)_2$, from 20°C to 80°C, what will you observe?

d) If you put 20 g of $MgCl_2$ into 100 g of water at 20°C and gradually heat the solution, what will you observe?

e) If you dissolve 90 g of both KBr and LiCl in 100 g of water at 90°C and then cool the mixture to 10°C, which salt will form crystals first?

f) A solution contains 20 g of KCl and 20 g of KBr in 100 g of water at 20°C. If the solution is left open to the air, which salt will form crystals first as the water evaporates?

g) Make a general statement regarding the change in solubility of LiCl(s) with a change in temperature. What does this imply about shifting the equilibrium

$$LiCl(s) \rightleftharpoons Li^+(aq) + Cl^-(aq)$$

when the temperature is increased? Is the dissolving of LiCl(s) an endothermic or exothermic process?

h) Is the dissolving of $Ca(CH_3COO)_2(s)$ endothermic or exothermic?

Having performed calculations relating to the solubility of a salt, a review of calculations involving the concentrations of ions in solution should be beneficial. Since a salt will dissociate into ions when it dissolves, you must be able to calculate the concentrations of all the ions in the solution.

EXAMPLE: When 1 mol of Na_3PO_4 is dissolved and diluted to a total volume of 1 L, one finds

	$Na_3PO_4(s)$	$\longrightarrow$	$3\ Na^+(aq)$	+	$PO_4^{3-}(aq)$
moles of particles (in 1 L):	1 mol	$\longrightarrow$	3 mol	+	1 mol
molar concentration:	1 M	$\longrightarrow$	3 M		1 M

Note that the final solution has: $[Na^+] = 3\ M$ and $[PO_4^{3-}] = 1\ M$ and **NO** particles of Na_3PO_4 in the final solution; all of the Na_3PO_4 present has dissociated into ions.

EXAMPLE: What is the concentration of all the ions present in a saturated solution of Ag_2CO_3 having a concentration of 1.2×10^{-4} M?

The calculation is based on the amount of Ag_2CO_3 which has actually dissolved.

$$Ag_2CO_3(s) \longrightarrow 2\ Ag^+(aq) + CO_3^{2-}(aq)$$

so that 1 mol $\longrightarrow$ 2 mol + 1 mol

It can be seen that if $[Ag_2CO_3]_{DISSOLVED} = 1.2 \times 10^{-4}$ M, then:

$$[CO_3^{2-}] = \mathbf{1.2 \times 10^{-4}\ M}$$

and

$$[Ag^+] = \frac{1.2 \times 10^{-4}\ \text{mol}\ Ag_2CO_3}{\text{L}} \times \frac{2\ \text{mol}\ Ag^+}{1\ \text{mol}\ Ag_2CO_3}$$

$$= 2.4 \times 10^{-4}\ \frac{\text{mol}\ Ag^+}{\text{L}} = \mathbf{2.4 \times 10^{-4}\ M}.$$

You also must be able to calculate the dilution occuring when solutions of ions are mixed with water or each other, as illustrated in the next example.

EXAMPLE: If 5.0 mL of 0.020 M Cl^- is added to 15.0 mL of 0.012 M Br^-, what is the molarity of the Cl^- and Br^- ions in the mixture?

The 5.0 mL of chloride solution is diluted by the 15.0 mL of liquid contained in the bromide solution, and vice versa. Recall that **dilution calculations** are performed as follows:

$$[\text{SUBSTANCE}]_{\text{DILUTED}} = [\text{SUBSTANCE}]_{\text{OLD}} \times \frac{\text{OLD VOLUME}}{\text{DILUTED VOLUME}}$$

so that

$$[Cl^-]_{\text{DILUTED}} = 0.020\ \text{M} \times \frac{5.0\ \text{mL}}{(5.0 + 15.0)\ \text{mL}} = \mathbf{0.0050\ M}$$

and

$$[Br^-]_{\text{DILUTED}} = 0.012\ \text{M} \times \frac{15.0\ \text{mL}}{(5.0 + 15.0)\ \text{mL}} = \mathbf{0.0090\ M}.$$

EXERCISES:

18. Calculate the concentration of each ion in each of the following solutions.
    a) 0.25 M $FeCl_3$
    b) 1.5×10^{-3} M $Al_2(SO_4)_3$
    c) 12.0 g of $(NH_4)_2CO_3$ in 2.50 L
    d) 0.41 g of $Ca(OH)_2$ in 500 mL of aqueous solution
    e) 2.50 g of KBr in 150 mL of aqueous solution

19. a) Write an equation showing the equilibrium in a saturated solution of lead (II) bromide, $PbBr_2$.
    b) The solubility of $PbBr_2$ is 0.844 g/100 mL. What is its molar solubility?
    c) Calculate the concentrations of Pb^{2+}(aq) and Br^- (aq) in a saturated solution of $PbBr_2$.

20. Calculate the concentration of each ion present when
    a) 25.0 mL of water is added to 20.0 mL of 0.35 M Fe^{3+}.
    b) 50.0 mL of 0.25 M Ag^+ is mixed with 100.0 mL of 0.10 M NO_3^-.
    c) 15.0 mL of 6.5×10^{-5} M Cu^{2+} is mixed with 40.0 mL of 3.2×10^{-3} M Cl^-.
    d) 55.0 mL of 0.185 M $MgCl_2$ is mixed with 25.0 mL of 4.8×10^{-2} M $CaBr_2$.
    e) 95.0 mL of 8.65×10^{-4} M $Al(NO_3)_3$ is mixed with 15.0 mL of 7.50×10^{-6} M Ag_2SO_4.
    f) 50.0 mL of 0.200 M $CaCl_2$ is mixed with 50.0 mL of 0.200 M NaCl.
    g) 25.0 mL of 0.360 M NH_4Br is mixed with 75.0 mL of 0.160 M $(NH_4)_2SO_4$.
    h) 10.0 mL of 0.100 M $Ba(NO_3)_2$ is mixed with 40.0 mL of 0.300 M $AgNO_3$.

III.3. PREDICTING THE SOLUBILITY OF SALTS

This section examines some of the general rules for predicting the solubility of salts and uses a Solubility Table to predict whether a specific salt is soluble in water.

First, let's establish what is meant when a salt is said to be "SOLUBLE" or to have a "LOW SOLUBILITY".

Strictly speaking, nothing is INSOLUBLE in water. For example, glass dissolves to an extremely small extent in water. Normally, the amount of glass which dissolves in water can be NEGLECTED and glass is said to have a **NEGLIGIBLE SOLUBILITY** in water.

Some compounds may dissolve SLIGHTLY, such that the amount which dissolves is extremely small but cannot be neglected. Such a substance is said to have **LOW SOLUBILITY.** For example, lead (II) chloride, $PbCl_2$, has a low solubility in water, but the amount which dissolves cannot always be neglected. For example, the small amount of Pb^{2+} ion present in saturated $PbCl_2$(aq) is toxic if swallowed.

Now the problem is: when has a compound dissolved to a sufficient extent that you cannot say it has LOW SOLUBILITY? This is like asking: "What is the least amount of money you need in order to be RICH?" All that can be done is to set an ***arbitrary value.***

Definition: A substance is said to have **LOW SOLUBILITY** if a saturated solution of the substance is less than 0.1 M.

Note: The phrase "having a solubility less than 0.1 M" is often used to indicate low solubility. Frequently you will see something like the following statement in a problem:

"Equal volumes of 0.2 M compound A and 0.2 M compound B are mixed."

After dilution, both compounds A and B are present as 0.1 M solutions. If a precipitate forms when A and B are mixed, the precipitate qualifies as having low solubility.

Let us illustrate how to use the table "SOLUBILITY OF COMMON COMPOUNDS IN WATER", found in the back of this book, by starting with the following small section of the table. (In the future this table will be referred to as the "Solubility Table" or simply the "Table".)

(Note that the term "Alkali ions" refers to the family of ions: Li^+, Na^+, etc. DO NOT FORGET THIS FACT when reading the Table.)

NEGATIVE IONS (Anions)	**POSITIVE IONS (Cations)**	**SOLUBILITY OF COMPOUNDS**
Phosphate, PO_4^{3-} or Carbonate, CO_3^{2-} or Sulphite, SO_3^{2-}	Alkali ions, H^+, NH_4^+	Soluble
	All others	LOW SOLUBILITY

EXAMPLE: Determine whether $FeCO_3(s)$ is soluble or has low solubility.

Using the Solubility Table in the back of this book, find the compound's negative ion (CO_3^{2-} in this case) and locate it in the "NEGATIVE ION" column (first column) – negative ions are written last in the chemical formula.

Find the other ion, Fe^{2+}, in the "POSITIVE ION" column. Since Fe^{2+} is not explicitly listed then it must be included in the category "**All others**".

Finally, look in the "SOLUBILITY OF COMPOUNDS" column (last column) to see that $FeCO_3(s)$ has "**LOW SOLUBILITY**".

When two ions form a compound having "LOW SOLUBILITY", the mixing of the two ions will cause a **PRECIPITATE** to form.

EXAMPLE: Will a precipitate form when 0.2 M solutions of CaS and Na_2SO_4 are mixed?

Look for combinations of ions which might form a precipitate.

The ions present are:

$$CaS = Ca^{2+} + S^{2-}$$

$$Na_2SO_4 = 2\,Na^+ + SO_4^{2-}.$$

Ignore the combinations: $Ca^{2+} + S^{2-}$ and $Na^+ + SO_4^{2-}$. (They must be soluble in order to allow us to obtain a 0.2 M solution of them.)

Examine the "cross–combinations" shown above:

$Na^+ + S^{2-}$: the Solubility Table indicates that this mixture is "Soluble"
$Ca^{2+} + SO_4^{2-}$: the Solubility Table indicates that this mixture has "LOW SOLUBILITY"

Therefore, mixing the solutions produces a precipitate of $CaSO_4$.

SPECIAL NOTES:

1. Copper forms TWO different ions: Cu^+ and Cu^{2+}.

   Cu^+ has "LOW SOLUBILITY" when combined with Cl^-, Br^- or I^-.
   Cu^{2+} is "Soluble" when combined with Cl^-, Br^- or I^-.

   No simple compounds exist which contain the Cu^+ ion and are soluble. (Copper(I) nitrate does not exist.) Therefore you can only be asked if a compound containing Cu^+ is or is not soluble. You cannot be asked if a precipitate of CuCl, say, is formed when two solutions are mixed because there is no easy way to get sufficient concentrations of Cu^+ ion into solution. [Copper(I) ions quickly react with water to form Cu(s) and Cu^{2+} — this point is not important for now but will be covered in Unit V.]

2. It will be assumed that you either have memorized the formulae and charges of the common ions or will be using the table "Names, Formulae, and Charges of Some Common Ions", found at the back of this book. **You MUST be able to write the chemical formula of a compound formed from two ions.**

EXERCISES:

21. Determine the solubility of the following ionic compounds from the table "SOLUBILITY OF COMMON COMPOUNDS IN WATER".

    a) AgCl c) FeS e) $Al_2(CO_3)_3$ g) Na_3PO_4 i) $CuCl_2$
    b) NaOH d) $FeSO_4$ f) $Fe(NO_3)_3$ h) CuI j) $PbBr_2$

22. Determine whether 0.2 M solutions of the following mixtures form a precipitate when mixed, and give the formula of any precipitate formed.

    a) $AgNO_3$ and NH_4Br c) KOH and $AlCl_3$ e) BaS and Na_2SO_4
    b) $SrBr_2$ and $NaNO_3$ d) NaI and $Pb(NO_3)_2$ f) CaS and NH_4Cl

23. Look at the two "Facts" on the first page of this unit. Suggest answers to the questions asked.

The Solubility Table allows us to make an important generalization.

Compounds containing **alkali metals, H^+, NH_4^+ or NO_3^-** will be soluble in water.

This generalization has two important consequences.

1. It is difficult (or impossible) to precipitate alkali metal ions, H^+, NH_4^+ or NO_3^- from solution.

2. If you have to write the formula for a **soluble compound** containing a specific ion, you should include an alkali metal ion, NH_4^+ or NO_3^- to help ensure the compound will be soluble. (We will omit H^+ from further consideration; acids will be discussed in more detail in Unit IV.)

   a) If you need to get a particular anion into solution **it is strongly suggested that you choose Na^+ to combine with your anion;** salts containing sodium are very common.

   Example: A soluble salt containing CO_3^{2-} would be Na_2CO_3.

   b) If you need to get a particular cation into solution **it is strongly suggested that you choose NO_3^- to combine with your cation;** salts containing nitrate are very common.

   Example: A soluble salt containing Fe^{3+} would be $Fe(NO_3)_3$.

EXERCISE:

24. You wish to make some precipitates. You will make up 0.2 M solutions of certain soluble salts, mix the solutions and filter off the resulting precipitates. Give the complete chemical formulae for the soluble salts you would select to make up the necessary solutions for the following precipitates.

    a) $PbCl_2$ b) $AgBr$ c) Cr_2S_3 d) $SrSO_4$

III.4. WRITING FORMULA, COMPLETE AND NET IONIC EQUATIONS

In this unit, every reaction which produces a precipitate will be a **DOUBLE REPLACEMENT REACTION.** Recall from Chemistry 11 that a double replacement reaction is written by using a FIVE–STEP procedure.

EXAMPLE: Write the double replacement reaction occuring when 0.2 M solutions of $Ca(NO_3)_2$ and Na_3PO_4 are mixed. (**Note:** It is conventional to assume that all ions and ionic solutions are aqueous unless told otherwise, so that the symbol "(aq)" can be omitted if desired.)

Step 1: **On the reactant side of an equation write the two compounds being mixed.**

Example: $Ca(NO_3)_2 + Na_3PO_4 \longrightarrow$

Step 2: **Identify the ions present and their charges in each reactant compound.**

Example: Using the table "Names, Formulae, and Charges of Some Common Ions", the ions present are: Ca^{2+}, NO_3^-, Na^+ and PO_4^{3-}.

Step 3: **Write two product molecules by "swapping" the negative ions in the reactant molecules.** (Allow a small space between the positive and negative ions to allow for possible subscripts.)

Example: $Ca(NO_3)_2 + Na_3PO_4 \longrightarrow Ca\ PO_4 + Na\ NO_3$

Step 4: **"Criss-cross" the charges to find the proper formula for each product molecule.** (This is the same procedure you used in Chem 11 to determine the proper formula for an ionic compound.)

Example: $Ca^{2+}_{3}\diagdown(PO_4^{3-})_2$ and $Na^+\diagdown NO_3^-$

equal charges

So that: $Ca(NO_3)_2 + Na_3PO_4 \longrightarrow Ca_3(PO_4)_2 + NaNO_3$

Step 5: **Balance the equation.**

Example: $3\,Ca(NO_3)_2 + 2\,Na_3PO_4 \longrightarrow Ca_3(PO_4)_2 + 6\,NaNO_3$

Once a precipitate is known to occur, you must be able to show the reaction equation in three different ways.

A FORMULA EQUATION is a balanced chemical equation in which all the reactants and products are given by their chemical formulae.

Example: $2\,AgNO_3 + Na_2CO_3 \longrightarrow Ag_2CO_3(s) + 2\,NaNO_3$

- The soluble species may be indicated by placing "(aq)" after the formula (this is optional); precipitates **must** be indicated by placing "(s)" after the formula.

- This way of expressing the reaction is used when you have to indicate the chemical formulae of the reactants and products.

A COMPLETE IONIC EQUATION shows all *soluble* ionic species broken into their respective ions.

Example: $2\,Ag^+ + 2\,NO_3^- + 2\,Na^+ + CO_3^{2-} \longrightarrow Ag_2CO_3(s) + 2\,Na^+ + 2\,NO_3^-$

- This way of writing an equation is not frequently used because it is cumbersome to write out. It is used whenever you want to emphasize the actual situation existing before and after a reaction: initially all reactants are broken into ions, after the reaction a precipitate forms and some unreacted ions remain.

- The unreacted ions shown on the product side are called **SPECTATOR IONS**. They take no part in the reaction. The spectator ions in the above reaction are Na^+ and NO_3^-.

- You should **NOT** write a complete ionic equation until you have first written a *balanced formula equation*; if you proceed directly to a complete ionic equation the result may be balanced but still may not represent the actual situation. For example:

$2\,Ag^+ + NO_3^- + Na^+ + CO_3^{2-} \longrightarrow Ag_2CO_3(s) + Na^+ + NO_3^-$

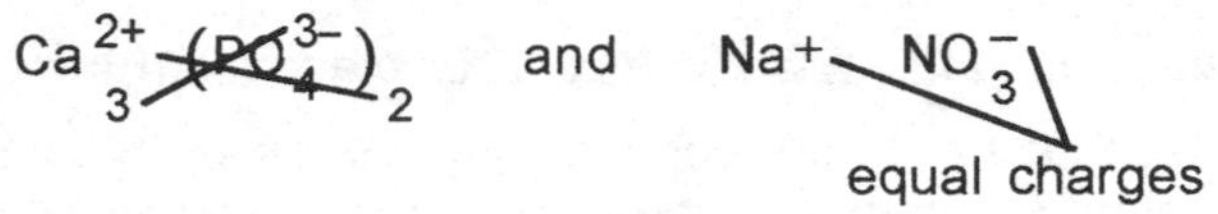

is balanced **BUT** wrongly indicates that $AgNO_3$ produces TWO silver ions and ONE nitrate ion and that Na_2CO_3 produces ONE sodium ion and ONE carbonate ion.

A NET IONIC EQUATION is an equation showing only the species which are actively involved in the reaction. ***The net ionic equation is formed by omitting the spectator ions from the complete ionic equation.***

Example: $2\ Ag^+(aq) + CO_3^{2-}(aq) \longrightarrow Ag_2CO_3(s)$

- In the example used to show a complete ionic equation, the spectator ions were $Na^+(aq)$ and $NO_3^-(aq)$. Deleting these ions from the complete ionic equation produces a net ionic equation. ("NET" implies "after deductions". Your net income is the income you have left after taxes . . . if any.)

The following is a modification of the procedure for writing the products in a double replacement reaction and works well for finding the formula, complete ionic and net ionic equations.

EXAMPLE: Write a formula equation, a total ionic equation and a net ionic equation for the reaction which occurs when 0.2 M solutions of $Pb(NO_3)_2(aq)$ and $FeCl_3(aq)$ are mixed.

a) **Identify any ion combinations which will form a precipitate.**

- if this step is not done first you could waste time writing equations only to find later that no precipitate occurs
- since the reactants are soluble (they form 0.2 M solutions) the possible ion combinations which must be checked are: (Pb^{2+} with Cl^-) and (Fe^{3+} with NO_3^-)
- a precipitate forms when Pb^{2+} and Cl^- are mixed

b) **If a precipitate forms, complete and balance the double replacement reaction equation.** Use "(s)" to indicate the precipitate. **This is the FORMULA EQUATION.**

$$3\ Pb(NO_3)_2 + 2\ FeCl_3 \longrightarrow 3\ PbCl_2(s) + 2\ Fe(NO_3)_3$$

c) **Write the balanced COMPLETE IONIC EQUATION.**

Break up the balanced formula equation into ions but note that

- the precipitate remains in molecular form.
- the number of ions produced by each molecule is found by multiplying the subscript after the ion by the coefficient in front of the molecule.
- the final equation must still be balanced (especially make sure that the spectator ions are balanced).

$$3\ Pb^{2+} + 6\ NO_3^- + 2\ Fe^{3+} + 6\ Cl^- \longrightarrow 3\ PbCl_2(s) + 2\ Fe^{3+} + 6\ NO_3^-$$

d) **Write the balanced NET IONIC EQUATION.**

- Eliminate the spectator ions from the complete ionic equation to leave the net ionic equation

$$3\ Pb^{2+} + 6\ Cl^- \longrightarrow 3\ PbCl_2(s)$$

which simplifies to $Pb^{2+} + 2\ Cl^- \longrightarrow PbCl_2(s)$.

SPECIAL NOTE: If you simply need to write the net ionic equation showing the formation of a precipitate (and don't have to show the formula and complete ionic equations), just use the following shortcut. On the products side write the precipitate and on the reactants side write the balanced set of ions which combine to form the precipitate. In the above example, you would simply write

$$Pb^{2+} + 2\,Cl^{-} \longrightarrow PbCl_2(s).$$

EXERCISE:

25. For each of the following combinations of equal volumes of 0.2 M aqueous solutions,
    i) identify the possible products by formula.
    ii) state which (if any) product has a low solubility.
    iii) if there IS a precipitate write the formula equation, total ionic equation, and net ionic equation for the reaction.

a) $MgS + Sr(OH)_2$
b) $CuBr_2 + Pb(NO_3)_2$
c) $FeBr_3 + SrI_2$
d) $Ba(NO_3)_2 + Li_2SO_4$
e) $K_3PO_4 + CuCl_2$
f) $(NH_4)_2SO_3 + Al_2(SO_4)_3$
g) silver nitrate and sodium phosphate
h) zinc sulphate and iron (II) chloride
i) cobalt (II) sulphate and lithium carbonate
j) iron (III) nitrate and magnesium sulphide
k) beryllium sulphate and ammonium carbonate
l) magnesium sulphate and strontium hydroxide

III.5. SEPARATING MIXTURES OF IONS BY PRECIPITATION METHODS

One important use of solubility is in the field of **QUALITATIVE ANALYSIS**. Qualitative analysis involves the use of experimental procedures to determine which elements or ions are present in a substance. Let's see how solubility differences can help to analyze a solution.

Here is the basic idea.

- Assume that an aqueous solution contains only one or both of the cations: Ag^+ and Sr^{2+}.
- Try to find some anion which could form a precipitate with ***only one*** of the two cations. If a precipitate is formed, you can assume that the ion being looked for is present; if no precipitate, the ion is absent.

The table below shows the reactions between the possible cations present in solution (on the left of the table) and the possible anions which could be added (along the top of the table). The five columns correspond to the five groups of ions in the first column of the Solubility Table which can produce a precipitate. A "—" indicates that no precipitate forms; "ppt" indicates that a precipitate forms when the ions are mixed.

	Cl^- (*)	SO_4^{2-}	S^{2-}	OH^-	PO_4^{3-} (*)
Ag^+	ppt	ppt	ppt	ppt	ppt
Sr^{2+}	—	ppt	—	—	ppt

* Only one member, say Cl^-, of the halide group (Cl^-, Br^- and I^-) and only one member, say PO_4^{3-}, of the group PO_4^{3-}, CO_3^{2-} and SO_3^{2-} needs to be used.

As can be seen, no anion can precipitate **ONLY** Sr^{2+}. For example, if SO_4^{2-} is added to the solution then both Ag^+ and Sr^{2+} will form precipitates and you cannot be certain which ion causes the precipitate.

On the other hand, if Cl^-, S^{2-}, or OH^- is added then only Ag^+ can be present if a precipitate forms. Assume that sufficient Cl^- is added to the solution, so that any Ag^+ present is precipitated out of solution. Now, one of SO_4^{2-} or PO_4^{3-} can be added. If one of these ions causes a precipitate to form then Sr^{2+} must be present, otherwise Sr^{2+} is absent.

NOTE: After a precipitate has formed, filter off the precipitate (or use a centrifuge) before adding more anions to the remaining solution.

EXAMPLE: A solution contains one or more of Ag^+, Ba^{2+} and Ni^{2+}. What ions could be added, and in what order, to determine which of these cations are present?

Set up a table of solubilities.

	Cl^-	SO_4^{2-}	S^{2-}	OH^-	PO_4^{3-}
Ag^+	ppt	ppt	ppt	ppt	ppt
Ba^{2+}	—	ppt	—	ppt	ppt
Ni^{2+}	—	—	ppt	ppt	ppt

Only Ag^+ can be precipitated if Cl^- is added. Therefore, first see if there is any Ag^+ present by adding Cl^- and filtering off any precipitate formed. If no precipitate is formed you can conclude that Ag^+ is absent.

At this point virtually no Ag^+ will be in solution. Cross out the horizontal line for Ag^+.

	Cl^-	SO_4^{2-}	S^{2-}	OH^-	PO_4^{3-}
~~Ag^+~~	~~ppt~~	~~ppt~~	~~ppt~~	~~ppt~~	~~ppt~~
Ba^{2+}	—	ppt	—	ppt	ppt
Ni^{2+}	—	—	ppt	ppt	ppt

Now a choice exists: either SO_4^{2-} or S^{2-} can be added.

- **If SO_4^{2-} is added,** any Ba^{2+} present will be precipitated. Any Ni^{2+} present can then be precipitated by adding one of S^{2-}, OH^- or PO_4^{3-}.
- **If S^{2-} is added,** any Ni^{2+} present will be precipitated. Any Ba^{2+} present can then be precipitated by adding one of SO_4^{2-}, OH^- or PO_4^{3-}.

The previous example can be re–written in the form of an experimental procedure.

Step 1: To 1 mL of a solution which might contain Ag^+, Ba^{2+} and/or Ni^{2+}, add a few drops of 1 M NaCl solution.

If there is NO PRECIPITATE then **Ag^+ is absent.** Proceed to Step 2.

If a PRECIPITATE FORMS then **Ag^+ is present.** Filter off and discard the precipitate. Proceed to Step 2 to test the rest of the solution.

Step 2: To the solution from Step 1, add a few drops of 1 M Na_2SO_4 solution. [To arbitrarily precipitate any Ba^{2+} first.]

If there is NO PRECIPITATE then **Ba^{2+} is absent.** Proceed to Step 3.

If a PRECIPITATE FORMS then **Ba^{2+} is present.** Filter off and discard the precipitate. Proceed to Step 3 to test the rest of the solution.

Step 3: To the solution from Step 2, add a few drops of 1 M NaOH.

If there is NO PRECIPITATE then **Ni^{2+} is absent.**

If a PRECIPITATE FORMS then **Ni^{2+} is present.**

Use the above model for writing up similar procedures. Notice that quite concentrated test solutions were used (1 M) to precipitate any metal cations as completely as possible with the few drops of added solution.

NOTE: The summary said "add Cl^- to precipitate any Ag^+ " but the experimental procedure had to specify a complete compound (NaCl), not just Cl^-.

EXERCISES:

26. When adding a salt to precipitate a cation from a mixture of ions, why must the salt be soluble?

27. What ions could be present in a solution if separate samples of it gave a precipitate when:
    a) either SO_4^{2-} or OH^- is added?
    b) SO_4^{2-} is added, but none when OH^- is added?

28. A solution contains only one of Ag^+ or Pb^{2+}. Is it possible to use a precipitation procedure based on your Solubility Table to determine which ion is present? If so, how? If not, why?

29. A solution contains Al^{3+} and Ag^+. What compounds could be added, and in what order, to separate these ions? You must specify the complete compound which will be added, not just the anion contained in the compound. Do not write out a complete experimental procedure.

30. A solution contains Sr^{2+}, Ca^{2+} and Ag^+. What compounds could be added, and in what order, to separate these ions?

31. A solution contains Mg^{2+}, Pb^{2+} and Zn^{2+}. What compounds could be added, and in what order, to separate these ions?

32. A solution contains Fe^{3+}, Ca^{2+}, Ag^+ and Be^{2+}. What compounds could be added, and in what order, to separate these ions?

33. Using your results from Exercise 29, write an experimental procedure for analyzing a solution which can only contain Ag^+ and Al^{3+}, but might contain one, both or neither of these ions.

34. Using your results from Exercise 30, write an experimental procedure for analyzing a solution which can only contain Sr^{2+}, Ca^{2+} and Ag^+, but might contain any number of these ions.

35. You are asked to identify the ions present in a particular solution. The ions which ***may*** be present are: I^-, SO_4^{2-} and OH^-.
    a) What is the name given to the process of identifying the chemical substances in a sample?
    b) You are to perform the identification using ***only*** the following reagents (that is, test chemicals): $AgNO_3$, $Ca(NO_3)_2$ and $Mg(NO_3)_2$. Which reagent must be added first? Explain why.
    c) How would you complete the analysis of the solution?

36. A solution is known to contain one or more of the ions: S^{2-}, OH^-, Cl^- and CO_3^{2-}. You are to identify the ions present using ***only*** the reagents: $AgNO_3$, $Ba(NO_3)_2$, $Cu(NO_3)_2$ and $Sr(NO_3)_2$. Briefly describe a procedure which could be used to analyze the anions in the solution.

The next topic shows how precipitation methods are used to find the actual concentration of ions in solution experimentally. Assume a solution contains Ba^{2+}. The Solubility Table shows that SO_4^{2-} forms a low solubility compound with Ba^{2+}. Precipitating the Ba^{2+} from solution in the form of $BaSO_4$, drying the precipitate and determining its mass, allows the $[Ba^{2+}]$ in the original solution to be calculated.

EXERCISES:

37. You have a sample of a solution which contains Ba^{2+}. You add Na_2SO_4 to the sample until no more $BaSO_4(s)$ will precipitate, then filter, dry and weigh the precipitate. Your results are as follows.

volume of sample	= 25.0 mL
mass of filter paper	= 1.21 g
mass of filter paper + $BaSO_4$ (dry)	= 3.75 g

Calculate: a) the moles of $BaSO_4$ produced.
b) the concentration of Ba^{2+} in the original solution.

38. A solution contains an unknown amount of Pb^{2+}. If 4.28 g of $PbSO_4(s)$ are obtained from 100.0 mL of the solution, what is the $[Pb^{2+}]$ in the solution?

39. Addition of phosphate ions to a 25.00 mL sample of a solution containing Ag^+ ions produces 1.57 g of $Ag_3PO_4(s)$. What is the $[Ag^+]$ in the original solution?

III.6. THE SOLUBILITY PRODUCT

The salt $CaF_2(s)$ is only slightly soluble in water, such that very little $CaF_2(s)$ is required to form a saturated aqueous solution having the EQUILIBRIUM EQUATION:

$$CaF_2(s) \rightleftharpoons Ca^{2+}(aq) + 2\,F^-(aq).$$

The equilibrium expression corresponding to the above equilibrium equation is called the **SOLUBILITY PRODUCT EXPRESSION.**

$K_{sp} = [Ca^{2+}][F^-]^2$ where K_{sp} is called the **Solubility Product constant.**

(K_{sp} is the special symbol given to K_{eq} when dealing with the dissociation reaction for a salt.)

IMPORTANT NOTE: If you simply have to predict whether a compound has a low solubility, use the table "SOLUBILITY OF COMMON COMPOUNDS IN WATER". If you have to calculate or compare relative solubilities, you MUST use a table such as "SOLUBILITY PRODUCT CONSTANTS AT 25°C", at the back of this book. We will refer to this latter table as the **K_{sp} Table.**

EXERCISE:

40. Write the EQUILIBRIUM EQUATION for a saturated solution of the following salts AND the corresponding SOLUBILITY PRODUCT EXPRESSIONS.
a) $BaSO_4(s)$ b) $MgF_2(s)$ c) $Ag_2S(s)$ d) $Cu(IO_3)_2(s)$

Since the value of K_{sp} depends on the concentrations of the ions in solution, a larger value of K_{sp} indicates a more soluble salt, while a smaller value of K_{sp} indicates a less soluble salt.

IMPORTANT: "***SOLUBILITY***" is the amount of a substance required to make a saturated solution.

"***MOLAR SOLUBILITY***" is the molar concentration of a saturated solution.

"***SOLUBILITY PRODUCT***" is the K_{sp} value obtained when the concentrations of the ions in a saturated solution are multiplied together.

SOLUBILITY and SOLUBILITY PRODUCT are **DIFFERENT CONCEPTS** – don't get them confused!

EXERCISE:

41. Which of the following salts is the most soluble? Which is the least?

AgCl ; $K_{sp} = 1.8 \times 10^{-10}$ AgI ; $K_{sp} = 8.5 \times 10^{-17}$ AgBr ; $K_{sp} = 5.4 \times 10^{-13}$

The solubility equilibrium for saturated CaF_2 is given by $CaF_2(s) \rightleftharpoons Ca^{2+} + 2\,F^-$,
and the K_{sp} expression is given by $K_{sp} = [Ca^{2+}][F^-]^2 = 1.46 \times 10^{-10}$
(the value is taken from a table of K_{sp} values).

If we take random amounts of $Ca(NO_3)_2(s)$ and NaF(s), dissolve them in water in different beakers, and mix the solutions together, a precipitate of $CaF_2(s)$ forms. The resulting mixture consists of $CaF_2(s)$ on the bottom of the beaker and Ca^{2+} and F^- ions in solution. The table below shows some examples of what we might find if we analyzed some solutions to find the $[Ca^{2+}]$ and $[F^-]$ present in the equilibrium mixtures.

Case	$[Ca^{2+}]$	$[F^-]$	$[Ca^{2+}][F^-]^2$
1	4.46×10^{-3}	1.81×10^{-4}	1.46×10^{-10}
2	1.21×10^{-3}	3.47×10^{-4}	1.46×10^{-10}
3	**3.32×10^{-4}**	**6.64×10^{-4}**	1.46×10^{-10}
4	9.65×10^{-5}	1.23×10^{-3}	1.46×10^{-10}

Some observations can be made.

1. The last column, which shows the result of multiplying the $[Ca^{2+}]$ by $[F^-]^2$, is just the K_{sp} value. As expected, these values are equal for all cases because K_{sp} is a constant.

2. The values for $[F^-]$ increase going down the table, while the values for $[Ca^{2+}]$ get smaller going down the table. This should make sense because if two numbers have to multiply together to give a specific K_{sp} value then an increase in one number must be accompanied by a decrease in the other number so as to keep the K_{sp} value constant.

3. In case 3, the value for $[F^-]$ is exactly double the value for $[Ca^{2+}]$. Such a situation can happen coincidentally as we have described: throw some Ca^{2+} and F^- ions separately into solution, let a precipitate form and find the $[Ca^{2+}]$ and $[F^-]$ remaining in solution. However, another way to get a saturated solution which contains Ca^{2+} and F^- in a 1:2 ratio is to simply throw some solid CaF_2 into water and wait until the solution is saturated. The process of dissolving CaF_2 automatically gives us the same 1:2 ratio found by randomly putting Ca^{2+} and F^- ions into solution:

$$CaF_2(s) \longrightarrow Ca^{2+} + 2\,F^- .$$

There is nothing fundamentally different between the two ways to get a saturated solution having a 1:2 ratio for the concentrations of Ca^{2+} and F^-, as seen from the fact that they give identical results.

In both of these situations, the $[Ca^{2+}]$ and $[F^-]$ in solution can be found and placed directly into the K_{sp} expression. The only difference is that:

- **if a saturated solution is made by separately putting Ca^{2+} and F^- into solution, we have to be given separate values for $[Ca^{2+}]$ and $[F^-]$. These values are placed directly into the K_{sp} expression.**

- **if a saturated solution is made by putting $CaF_2(s)$ into water and letting it dissolve, then once we know the molarity of the dissolved CaF_2, we are assured that**

  $$[Ca^{2+}] = [CaF_2]_{dissolved}$$
  and
  $$[F^-] = 2 \times [CaF_2]_{dissolved} .$$

  These values are placed directly into the K_{sp} expression.

INITIAL ANALYSIS OF PROBLEMS

Calculations involving K_{sp} are simpler than previous equilibrium problems because the reactant is a solid and therefore is omitted from the equilibrium expression. There are really only two types of problems which must be solved in this section when dealing with a solubility product expression of the form:

$$K_{sp} = [Ca^{2+}][F^-]^2$$

1. The values for $[Ca^{2+}]$ and $[F^-]$ may be given or you may have to find the values from the mass of salt which dissolves to produce the ions. You will be required to find the value of K_{sp}.

2. The value for K_{sp} may be given, requiring you to find the individual concentrations of the ions or the solubility of the salt.

NOTE: It is very strongly suggested that for EVERY problem involving K_{sp} you

- write out the equilibrium equation showing the dissolving of the salt, and
- write out the solubility product expression.

Some problems can be tricky. By writing the above, thinking about what information you are given and what you have to find, you can greatly improve your chances of success.

EXAMPLE: A solution in equilibrium with a precipitate of BaF_2 contains 4.59×10^{-2} M Ba^{2+} and 2.00×10^{-3} M F^-. What is K_{sp} for BaF_2?

The equilibrium equation and K_{sp} expression are

$$BaF_2(s) \rightleftharpoons Ba^{2+}(aq) + 2\,F^-(aq)\,; \qquad K_{sp} = [Ba^{2+}][F^-]^2.$$

Simply substitute the given concentrations into the K_{sp} expression

$$K_{sp} = (4.59 \times 10^{-2})(2.00 \times 10^{-3})^2 = \mathbf{1.84 \times 10^{-7}}.$$

EXAMPLE: A saturated solution of BaF_2 contains 3.58×10^{-3} mol of BaF_2 in 1.00 L of solution. What is K_{sp} for BaF_2?

Write the equilibrium equation and K_{sp} expression. The equilibrium equation is used as a table heading to show the concentration of the ions produced when 3.58×10^{-3} mol/L of BaF_2 dissolves and dissociates.

$BaF_2(s)$	$\rightleftharpoons$	$Ba^{2+}(aq)$	+	$2\,F^-(aq)$	; $K_{sp} = [Ba^{2+}][F^-]^2$
3.58×10^{-3} M		3.58×10^{-3} M		7.16×10^{-3} M	

Now $\quad K_{sp} = [Ba^{2+}][F^-]^2 = (3.58 \times 10^{-3})(7.16 \times 10^{-3})^2 = \mathbf{1.84 \times 10^{-7}}.$

EXAMPLE: What is the $[Mg^{2+}]$ in a saturated solution of $Mg(OH)_2$?

Since the value of $[Mg^{2+}]$ is not known, nor indeed how much $Mg(OH)_2(s)$ was able to dissolve, a variable is assigned. Let $X = [Mg(OH)_2]$dissolved

$Mg(OH)_2(s)$	$\longrightarrow$	$Mg^{2+}(aq)$	+	$2\,OH^-(aq)$	; $K_{sp} = [Mg^{2+}][OH^-]^2$
X		X		2X	

Now $\quad K_{sp} = [Mg^{2+}][OH^-]^2 = (X)(2X)^2$

$4X^3 = 5.6 \times 10^{-12}$ (Using the value of K_{sp} found in the K_{sp} Table)

$X^3 = 1.4 \times 10^{-12}$

$X = 1.12 \times 10^{-4}$ M (see "Calculator Interlude", below)

and: $\quad [Mg^{2+}] = \mathbf{1.1 \times 10^{-4}\ M.}$

Another "Calculator Interlude"

If you are having trouble taking the cube root with your calculator, try the following sequence of key–strokes.

Enter the number you want to use (1.4×10^{-12} in the above case). Then use:

INV, Y^X, 3, = or 2nd function, Y^X, 3, =

EXAMPLE: What mass of $Mg(OH)_2$ will dissolve in 250 mL of water?

Assume the previous example has been solved.

letting $X = [Mg^{2+}]_{EQ} = [Mg(OH)_2]_{dissolved}$

then $\text{mass } Mg(OH)_2 = 1.12 \times 10^{-4} \frac{mol}{L} \times 0.250\ L \times \frac{58.3\ g}{1\ mol} = \mathbf{1.6 \times 10^{-3}\ g.}$

EXERCISES:

42. A solution in equilibrium with a precipitate of $FeCO_3$ contains 5.0×10^{-6} M Fe^{2+} and 6.0×10^{-6} M CO_3^{2-}. Calculate K_{sp} for $FeCO_3$.

43. What is the concentration of Zn^{2+} ions in a saturated solution made by shaking ZnS(s) with water?

44. How many grams of $PbSO_4$(s) will dissolve in 5.0 L of water?

45. How many grams of $BaCrO_4$ are present in 10.0 L of a saturated solution of $BaCrO_4$?

46. An experiment shows that a maximum of 7.35 g of silver acetate, $AgCH_3COO$(s) can dissolve in 1.00 L of water at 25°C. What is K_{sp} for $AgCH_3COO$?

47. Calculate the molar solubility of Ag_2CrO_4.

48. Calculate the solubility of $CaSO_4$ in grams per litre.

49. Calculate the solubility of $Fe(OH)_2$ in grams per litre.

50. A solution in equilibrium with a precipitate of Ag_2S contained 1.6×10^{-16} M S^{2-} and 2.6×10^{-17} M Ag^+. Calculate the solubility product of Ag_2S.

51. A small piece of the mineral smithsonite, $ZnCO_3$, with a mass of 0.000 14 g just barely dissolves in 100.0 mL of water. Calculate K_{sp} for $ZnCO_3$.

52. What is the concentration of OH^- in a saturated solution of $Zn(OH)_2$? $K_{sp} = 4.1 \times 10^{-17}$ for $Zn(OH)_2$.

53. What is the concentration of Cd^{2+} ions in saturated $Cd(OH)_2$? $K_{sp} = 5.3 \times 10^{-15}$ for $Cd(OH)_2$.

54. What mass of Pb^{2+} is present in 5.0 L of saturated $Pb(IO_3)_2$(aq)?

55. The data below was obtained when a student combined various solutions of $Mn(NO_3)_2$ and KOH.

Trial	$[Mn^{2+}]$	$[OH^-]$
1	2.1×10^{-5} M	1.0×10^{-4} M
2	7.8×10^{-4} M	**?**

What is the value of the $[OH^-]$ in Trial 2?

III.7. PREDICTING WHETHER A PRECIPITATE WILL FORM

Whenever two solutions containing ions are mixed, we can ask whether a precipitate will form. For example, if Ag^+ (aq) and Cl^-(aq) are mixed, you have to consider whether there is a sufficient concentration of both ions to establish the equilibrium:

$$AgCl(s) \rightleftharpoons Ag^+ (aq) + Cl^- (aq) ; \quad K_{sp} = [Ag^+][Cl^-] = 1.8 \times 10^{-10} .$$

Define the **ION PRODUCT** or **TRIAL ION PRODUCT ("TIP")** as: $Q = [Ag^+]_{START} [Cl^-]_{START}$.

The values of K_{sp} and Q for a sparingly soluble salt can be thought of as follows.

Q = the product of the ion concentrations which actually exist in solution
= **"what we have"**

K_{sp} = the product of ion concentrations required to establish a solubility equilibrium
= **"what we need to form a saturated solution"**

If two solutions are mixed there are three possible outcomes.

CASE 1: $Q < K_{sp}$

In this case **"what we have" is less than "what we need to form a saturated solution"** so that there are not enough ions in solution to form a precipitate.

Conclusion: **A PRECIPITATE CANNOT FORM IF Q < K_{sp}.**

CASE 2: $Q = K_{sp}$

In this case **"what we have" is just equal to "what we need to form a saturated solution"**. The minimum possible amount of precipitate forms at this point.

Conclusion: **A BARELY SATURATED SOLUTION IS FORMED IF Q = K_{sp}.**

CASE 3: $Q > K_{sp}$

In this case **"what we have" is greater than "what we need to form a saturated solution"** and there is an excess of ions, over and above the amount needed to form a precipitate. Therefore a precipitate must form **and will continue to form** until the excess ions have been removed from solution and the value of Q has been reduced down to the value of K_{sp}.

Conclusion: **A PRECIPITATE WILL FORM IF Q > K_{sp}.**

EXAMPLE: Will a precipitate form when 5.0 mL of 6.0×10^{-5} M Ag^+ mixes with 10.0 mL of 4.2×10^{-6} M Cl^-?

First write the equilibrium equation and solubility product expression for AgCl.

$$AgCl(s) \rightleftharpoons Ag^+(aq) + Cl^-(aq)\,;\ K_{sp} = [Ag^+][Cl^-] = 1.8 \times 10^{-10} \text{ (from the } K_{sp} \text{ Table)}$$

When the two solutions are mixed they dilute each other, so that the concentration of the ions in the mixture must first be calculated:

$$[Ag^+]_{DIL} = 6.0 \times 10^{-5}\ M \times \frac{5.0\ mL}{15.0\ mL} = 2.0 \times 10^{-5}\ M$$

$$[Cl^-]_{DIL} = 4.2 \times 10^{-6}\ M \times \frac{10.0\ mL}{15.0\ mL} = 2.8 \times 10^{-6}\ M$$

Now calculate the trial ion product and compare it to K_{sp}.

$$Q = [Ag^+]_{DIL}[Cl^-]_{DIL} = (2.0 \times 10^{-5})(2.8 \times 10^{-6}) = 5.6 \times 10^{-11} < K_{sp} = 1.8 \times 10^{-10}$$

Since $Q < K_{sp}$ then a **PRECIPITATE WILL NOT FORM**.

EXAMPLE: If 25.0 mL of 4.50×10^{-3} M $Pb(NO_3)_2$ is mixed with 35.0 mL of 2.80×10^{-3} M MgI_2, will a precipitate form?

The only possible precipitate formed is PbI_2.

$$PbI_2(s) \rightleftharpoons Pb^{2+}(aq) + 2\,I^-(aq)\ ;\quad K_{sp} = [Pb^{2+}][I^-]^2$$

First perform the dilution calculations.

$$[Pb(NO_3)_2]_{DIL} = 4.50 \times 10^{-3}\ M \times \frac{25.0\ mL}{60.0\ mL} = 1.88 \times 10^{-3}\ M$$

$$[MgI_2]_{DIL} = 2.80 \times 10^{-3}\ M \times \frac{35.0\ mL}{60.0\ mL} = 1.63 \times 10^{-3}\ M$$

Since you are given entire compounds in solution, write the dissociation equations for the compounds to find $[Pb^{2+}]_{DIL}$ and $[I^-]_{DIL}$.

$$\begin{array}{cccc} Pb(NO_3)_2(s) & \longrightarrow & Pb^{2+}(aq) & + & 2\,NO_3^-(aq) \\ 1.88 \times 10^{-3}\ M & & \mathbf{1.88 \times 10^{-3}\ M} & & 3.76 \times 10^{-3}\ M \end{array}$$

and

$$\begin{array}{cccc} MgI_2(s) & \longrightarrow & Mg^{2+}(aq) & + & 2\,I^-(aq) \\ 1.63 \times 10^{-3}\ M & & 1.63 \times 10^{-3}\ M & & \mathbf{3.26 \times 10^{-3}\ M} \end{array}$$

An acceptable short–cut to writing these dissociation equations is to show

$$[Pb^{2+}] = [Pb(NO_3)_2] = 1.88 \times 10^{-3}\ M$$
$$[I^-] = 2 \times [MgI_2] = 3.26 \times 10^{-3}\ M.$$

Now calculate the trial ion product and compare it to K_{sp}.

$$Q = [Pb^{2+}]_{DIL}[I^-]^2_{DIL} = (1.88 \times 10^{-3})(3.26 \times 10^{-3})^2 = 2.00 \times 10^{-8} > K_{sp} = 8.5 \times 10^{-9}$$

Since $Q > K_{sp}$, then **A PRECIPITATE WILL FORM.**

A different type of problem relies on the fact that a precipitate just starts to form when $Q = K_{sp}$.

EXAMPLE: What $[Cl^-]$ is required to just start precipitation of AgCl(s) from a 3.6×10^{-3} M solution of Ag^+?

$$AgCl(s) \rightleftharpoons Ag^+(aq) + Cl^-(aq) \; ; \qquad K_{sp} = [Ag^+][Cl^-] = 1.8 \times 10^{-10}$$

When precipitation just starts to occur: $Q = K_{sp}$. Rearrange the solubility product expression and solve for $[Cl^-]$.

$$[Cl^-] = \frac{K_{sp}}{[Ag^+]} = \frac{1.8 \times 10^{-10}}{3.6 \times 10^{-3}} = \mathbf{5.0 \times 10^{-8}\ M.}$$

EXERCISES:

56. Will a precipitate form if 1.0 L of 3.0×10^{-10} M Fe^{2+} is added to 1.0 L of 1.2×10^{-8} M S^{2-}?

57. What concentration of S^{2-} is required to just start precipitation of CuS from a 0.20 M solution of $CuCl_2$?

58. What F^- concentration must be present to just start precipitating CaF_2 from a 3.0×10^{-3} M solution of $Ca(NO_3)_2$? $K_{sp} = 1.5 \times 10^{-10}$ for CaF_2.

59. Will a precipitate form when 10.0 mL of 1.0×10^{-3} M $Pb(NO_3)_2$ is added to 40.0 mL of 1.5×10^{-4} M Na_2SO_4?

60. A precipitate barely forms when 20.0 mL of 3.00×10^{-3} M Ni^{2+} is added to 60.0 mL of 2.52×10^{-4} M CO_3^{2-}. What is K_{sp} for $NiCO_3$?

61. Does a precipitate form when 25.0 mL of 1.0×10^{-4} M $Zn(NO_3)_2$ is added to 45.0 mL of 2.4×10^{-5} M $Ca(OH)_2$? $K_{sp} = 4.1 \times 10^{-17}$ for $Zn(OH)_2$.

62. When 100.0 mL of 4.0×10^{-2} M $CaCl_2$ is added to 150.0 mL of 2.9×10^{-2} M NaOH, a precipitate of $Ca(OH)_2$ just starts to form. What is K_{sp} for $Ca(OH)_2$?

63. Will a precipitate form if 1 drop (0.050 mL) of 5.0 M Pb^{2+} is added to 100.00 mL of 3.0×10^{-5} M I^-?

64. Predict whether a precipitate will form when 20.0 mL of 5.0×10^{-5} M Ca^{2+} is added to 35.0 mL of 2.5×10^{-4} M $C_2O_4^{2-}$ and the resulting solution is boiled down to a total volume of 25.0 mL.

65. If a precipitate can be detected as soon as it begins to form, what is the minimum concentration of CO_3^{2-} that can be detected in a solution having $[Ag^+] = 0.050$ M?

66. A precipitate just starts to form if 5.0 mL of 1.0×10^{-9} M Na_2S is diluted to 1.0 L and 10.0 mL of the resulting solution is added to 90.0 mL of 2.0×10^{-16} M Pb^{2+}. What is K_{sp} for PbS?

67. The solubility of $Mn(IO_3)_2$ in water is 4.78×10^{-3} M. What $[Mn^{2+}]$ is required to just start precipitation of $Mn(IO_3)_2$ from a 0.0200 M solution of KIO_3?

68. If 0.1 M Pb^{2+} is added dropwise to a solution having 0.10 M Cl^-, 0.10 M I^- and 0.10 M SO_4^{2-}, which precipitate will form first?

69. If 0.02 M $AgNO_3$ is added to a solution containing 1.0 M CO_3^{2-}, 1.0 M IO_3^- and 1.0 M CrO_4^{2-}, which precipitate will form first?

III.8. APPLYING SOLUBILITY PRINCIPLES TO CHLORIDE TITRATIONS

Definition: A **TITRATION** is a process in which a measured amount of a solution is reacted with a known volume of another solution (one of the solutions has an unknown concentration) until a desired **EQUIVALENCE POINT** (or "**STOICHIOMETRIC POINT**") is reached.

The **PURPOSE** of carrying out a titration is to find the concentration of a particular solution.

The concentration of chloride ions in a solution can be determined by using a titration procedure which adds silver ions to the chloride ions and forms a precipitate of silver chloride.

$$Ag^+(aq) + Cl^-(aq) \longrightarrow AgCl(s)$$

In order to signal the point at which the titration is complete, chromate ions are added to the solution being titrated. Let us see how chromate ions can act as an indicator.

Assume you use a burette to add a 0.10 M solution of Ag^+ into a beaker containing 0.10 M Cl^- and 0.010 M chromate ion, CrO_4^{2-}. The slow addition of Ag^+ steadily increases the $[Ag^+]$ in the beaker, starting from 0.0 M. Both Cl^- and CrO_4^{2-} eventually can form a precipitate with the added Ag^+.

$$\underset{\text{white}}{AgCl(s)} \rightleftharpoons Ag^+ + Cl^- \ ; \qquad K_{sp} = [Ag^+][Cl^-] = 1.8 \times 10^{-10}$$

$$\underset{\text{red}}{Ag_2CrO_4(s)} \rightleftharpoons 2\,Ag^+ + \underset{\text{yellow}}{CrO_4^{2-}} \ ; \qquad K_{sp} = [Ag^+]^2[CrO_4^{2-}] = 1.1 \times 10^{-12}$$

Rearranging the K_{sp} expressions allows us to solve for the minimum $[Ag^+]$ required to form a precipitate.

$$[Ag^+] = \frac{K_{sp}}{[Cl^-]} = \frac{1.8 \times 10^{-10}}{0.10} = 1.8 \times 10^{-9}\ \text{M} \quad \text{(for AgCl)}$$

$$[Ag^+] = \sqrt{\frac{K_{sp}}{[CrO_4^{2-}]}} = \sqrt{\frac{1.1 \times 10^{-12}}{0.010}} = 1.0 \times 10^{-5}\ \text{M} \quad \text{(for } Ag_2CrO_4\text{)}$$

The first precipitate to form is AgCl(s) since a smaller [Ag^+] is required. As more Ag^+ is added from the burette, the Cl^- in solution is steadily precipitated in the form of AgCl(s). When virtually all the Cl^- has been reacted and removed, the next drop of Ag^+ will form a precipitate of Ag_2CrO_4(s). The red colour of the Ag_2CrO_4 signals us to stop the titration. At this point, the moles of Ag^+ added will **equal** the moles of Cl^- originally present.

The fact that $K_{sp} = [Ag^+][Cl^-]$ has a constant value means the steady **decrease** in [Cl^-] has been accompanied by a steady **increase** in [Ag^+]. By the time [Ag^+] has risen from 0.0 M (initially) to 1.0×10^{-5} M (where Ag_2CrO_4 starts to precipitate), the [Cl^-] has dropped to:

$$[Cl^-] = \frac{K_{sp}}{[Ag^+]} = \frac{1.8 \times 10^{-10}}{1.0 \times 10^{-5}} = 1.8 \times 10^{-5}\ M.$$

At this point the percentage of Cl^- left is

$$\frac{1.8 \times 10^{-5}\ M\ \text{(when } Ag_2CrO_4 \text{ precipitates)}}{0.10\ M\ \text{(initially)}} \times 100\ \% = 0.018\ \%$$

and 99.98 % of the Cl^- has been reacted, which agrees with the above statement that "virtually all Cl^- has been reacted and removed".

IN SUMMARY: When the moles of Cl^- used in the reaction is equal to the moles of Ag^+ added, the titration is said to have arrived at the **"EQUIVALENCE POINT"** (or "**STOICHIOMETRIC POINT**").

$$Ag^+(aq) + Cl^-(aq) \longrightarrow AgCl(s)$$

and moles Ag^+ added = moles Cl^- originally present

Also, at this same point, it is clear that virtually all the Cl^- has reacted because further addition of Ag^+ causes a red precipitate of Ag_2CrO_4(s) to form. In practice, only a very small amount of Ag_2CrO_4(s) is present when the first drop of excess Ag^+ is added so that a faint trace of ORANGE is seen above the white precipitate of AgCl(s). (The orange colour is a mixture of yellow CrO_4^{2-} and red Ag_2CrO_4.)

Although the discussion above may look a bit complicated, in practice the calculations associated with such a titration are straightforward. Don't worry about the chromate indicator; it is simply regarded as being "in the background" to allow us to accurately detect the "equivalence point" of the titration.

EXAMPLE: In order to find the [Cl^-] in a sea water sample, a 25.0 mL sample was titrated with 0.500 M $AgNO_3$ solution, using sodium chromate as an indicator. At the equivalence point 26.8 mL of $AgNO_3$ solution had been added. What was the [Cl^-] in the sea water?

$$\text{moles } AgNO_3 \text{ used} = 0.500\ \frac{mol}{L} \times 0.0268\ L = 0.0134\ mol$$

since $Ag^+(aq) + Cl^-(aq) \longrightarrow AgCl(s)$

then moles Cl^- = moles $AgNO_3$ used = 0.0134 mol

hence $[Cl^-] = \dfrac{0.0134\ mol}{0.0250\ L} = \mathbf{0.536\ M}$

EXAMPLE: What volume of 0.125 M $AgNO_3$ will be required to titrate 50.0 mL of 0.0550 M Cl^- solution, using chromate indicator?

$$\text{moles } Cl^- = 0.0550\ \frac{\text{mol}}{\text{L}} \times 0.0500\ \text{L} = 0.00275\ \text{mol}$$

$$\text{moles } Ag^+ = \text{moles } Cl^- = 0.00275\ \text{mol}$$

$$\text{volume } AgNO_3 = \frac{0.00275\ \text{mol}}{0.125\ \text{mol/L}} = \mathbf{0.0220\ L\ \ (22.0\ mL)}$$

EXAMPLE: A 5.29 g sample of impure sodium chloride was dissolved and diluted to a total volume of 250.0 mL. If 25.0 mL of the sodium chloride solution required 28.5 mL of 0.300 M $AgNO_3$ solution to reach the equivalence point, using chromate indicator, what was the percentage purity of the original sodium chloride?

First, find the $[Cl^-]$ which exists in the solution.

$$\text{moles } Ag^+ = 0.300\ \frac{\text{mol}}{\text{L}} \times 0.0285\ \text{L} = 0.00855\ \text{mol} = \text{moles } Cl^-$$

$$[Cl^-] = \frac{0.00855\ \text{mol}}{0.0250\ \text{L}} = 0.342\ \text{M} \quad \text{(this is the actual } [Cl^-] \text{ existing in solution)}$$

Now, calculate the $[Cl^-]$ expected if the NaCl had been pure.

$$[Cl^-] = \frac{5.29\ \text{g}}{0.250\ \text{L}} \times \frac{1\ \text{mol}}{58.5\ \text{g}} = 0.362\ \text{M}$$

Finally, since $$\%\ \text{purity} = \frac{\text{actual } [Cl^-]}{\text{expected } [Cl^-]} \times 100\%$$

then $$\%\ \text{purity} = \frac{0.342\ \text{M}}{0.362\ \text{M}} \times 100\% = \mathbf{94.6\%}\ .$$

EXERCISES:

70. When 25.0 mL of NaCl solution having an unknown concentration is titrated with 0.100 M $AgNO_3$, using chromate ion as an indicator, 36.8 mL of the $AgNO_3$ solution are required to reach the equivalence point. What is the $[Cl^-]$?

71. What volume of 0.0988 M Cl^- solution is required to titrate 25.0 mL of 0.0750 M $AgNO_3$, using chromate indicator?

72. A solution of potassium chloride is made by dissolving 3.25 g of KCl in water and diluting to 500.0 mL. If 9.48 mL of $AgNO_3$ solution are required to titrate 25.00 mL of the KCl solution, what is the molar concentration of the $AgNO_3$?

73. A student is assigned the task of finding the K_{sp} value for silver acetate, $AgCH_3COO$. Several grams of $AgCH_3COO(s)$ are added to distilled water and stirred overnight. The next day a 50.0 mL sample of the saturated $AgCH_3COO$ solution is titrated with 30.6 mL of 0.100 M NaCl. What is the value of K_{sp} for $AgCH_3COO$?

74. A 4.75 g silver coin was dissolved in nitric acid and the resulting solution diluted to 250 mL. When a 25.0 mL sample of 0.200 M NaCl was titrated with the silver solution, using chromate indicator, 28.8 mL of silver solution was required. What was the percentage purity of the silver in the coin, assuming any impurities present were unreactive?

75. A 95.6 g sample of hamburger meat from the Brand X Hamburger Palace was tested for the presence of Cl^- (in the form of NaCl) as follows. The meat sample was put into a blender with some water, blended and suction filtered. The solution obtained from the meat was then diluted to 1.00 L. A 25.0 mL sample of the solution was titrated with 0.0200 M $AgNO_3$ solution, using chromate indicator, and 15.3 mL was found to be needed.
a) What was the $[Cl^-]$ in the solution obtained from the meat?
b) How many grams of NaCl were extracted from the meat, altogether?
c) What was the percentage of NaCl in the original meat sample?

III.9. REMOVING POLLUTION AND HARDNESS FROM WATER BY PRECIPITATION METHODS

A. Removing Metal Ion Pollutants By Precipitation Methods

Although biological systems can generally tolerate common lighter ions such as sodium and magnesium, heavier metal ions such as Cu^{2+}, Hg^{2+} and Pb^{2+} interfere with their chemical reactions and are therefore toxic to the organism ingesting them. The toxicity of heavy metal ions is proportional to their concentrations: the greater the concentration, the greater the toxicity. The use of the precipitation process allows us to lower the concentrations of unwanted metal ions.

EXAMPLE: Waste water in the "tailings" pond of a mining operation had a cadmium ion concentration of about 0.005 M. Before discharging the waste water into an adjacent river, the mine had to lower the $[Cd^{2+}]$ to at most 1.0×10^{-5} M. What $[OH^-]$ would be required to bring the $[Cd^{2+}]$ to acceptable values? $K_{sp} = 5.3 \times 10^{-15}$ for $Cd(OH)_2$

$$Cd(OH)_2(s) \rightleftharpoons Cd^{2+}(aq) + 2\,OH^-(aq)\,;\; K_{sp} = [Cd^{2+}][OH^-]^2 = 5.3 \times 10^{-15}$$

Solving for $[OH^-]$: $$[OH^-]^2 = \frac{K_{sp}}{[Cd^{2+}]} = \frac{5.3 \times 10^{-15}}{1.0 \times 10^{-5}} = 5.3 \times 10^{-10}$$

$[OH^-]$ = **2.3×10^{-5} M**.

B. Hardness In Water: Where It Comes From And How To Get Rid Of It

THE ORIGINS OF HARDNESS IN WATER

"HARDNESS" in water results from the presence of Ca^{2+} and/or Mg^{2+}.

Many areas in our country contain deposits of limestone ($CaCO_3$). When acid rain or the acids naturally present in humus–containing soils make contact with the limestone, the acids react with and dissolve the $CaCO_3(s)$.

$$CaCO_3(s) + 2\,H^+(aq) \rightleftharpoons Ca^{2+}(aq) + CO_2(g) + H_2O(l) + heat \qquad ...(1)$$

In addition, atmospheric carbon dioxide dissolves in water to a small extent to produce an acidic solution of "carbonic acid". This acidic solution will also react with limestone deposits.

$$CaCO_3(s) + CO_2(g) + H_2O(l) \rightleftharpoons Ca^{2+}(aq) + 2\,HCO_3^-(aq) + heat \qquad ...(2)$$

In either case, the ground water and much of the runoff water contain noticeable amounts of Ca^{2+} ion (and lesser amounts of Mg^{2+} ion produced by the action of acids on $MgCO_3$ in rocks).

Because rocks contain minute cracks which extend several hundred metres below the surface, acidic water is able to penetrate to limestone layers buried far below the surface. The action of the acid on the limestone can eat away substantial volumes of limestone. If the limestone layer is just below the surface, the overburden of soil may collapse into the cavity produced, creating a "sinkhole". If the cavity is well below the surface, a limestone cavern is produced. Water from surface cracks continually drips from the cavern roof. The action of dilute carbonic acid solutions ($CO_2(g)$ dissolved in H_2O) on limestone produces a solution of $Ca^{2+}$and HCO_3^- ions, as shown in equation (2) above.

Because the air in a cavern has a relatively low $[CO_2(g)]$ – most of the $CO_2(g)$ present has reacted with the limestone – and because water evaporates as droplets of solution fall from the ceiling through air currents, the above equilibrium tends to proceed in reverse according to Le Chatelier's principle.

$$Ca^{2+}(aq) + 2\,HCO_3^-(aq) \rightleftharpoons CaCO_3(s) + CO_2(g) + H_2O(l)$$

The resulting precipitate forms stalactites at the roof of the cavern and stalagmites on the floor. Nevertheless, the great majority of the dissolved Ca^{2+} (and Mg^{2+}) ions remains in the water.

GETTING RID OF HARDNESS IN WATER

The effect of hardness in water is three–fold. First, the water has a somewhat bitter taste which many people find objectionable. The presence of Ca^{2+} and/or Mg^{2+} causes the bitterness.

Second, the dissolved material present in hard water leaves white deposits of $CaCO_3/MgCO_3$ whenever the water evaporates or is heated.

$$Ca^{2+}(aq) + 2\,HCO_3^-(aq) + heat \rightleftharpoons CaCO_3(s) + CO_2(g) + H_2O(l)$$

These deposits can accumulate inside steam pipes and kettles as rock–hard material which can clog the steam lines and interfere with the heating coils in kettles.

Third, the hardness inhibits the cleaning action of soaps. The effective "cleaning ingredient" in many soaps is a large organic ion called the stearate ion: $C_{17}H_{35}COO^-$. Since calcium and magnesium stearate are quite insoluble:

$$K_{sp} = 1 \times 10^{-12} \text{ for } Ca(C_{17}H_{35}COO)_2$$
$$K_{sp} = 5 \times 10^{-13} \text{ for } Mg(C_{17}H_{35}COO)_2$$

the presence of Ca^{2+} or Mg^{2+} in "soapy" water causes a gray–white curd–like precipitate of calcium or magnesium stearate to form. This removes the unwanted ions by using relatively expensive soap to precipitate the Ca^{2+} and Mg^{2+}. Even more soap is then required to build up a sufficient concentration of stearate ion to permit proper cleansing action.

The problem is: how can Ca^{2+} and Mg^{2+} be removed from "hard" water by less expensive ways, so as to "soften" the water?

One of the most common methods of softening water is to add **WASHING SODA,** which is simply sodium carbonate, Na_2CO_3. [Strictly speaking, washing soda is $Na_2CO_3 \cdot 10H_2O$.] The Solubility Table indicates that $CaCO_3$ and $MgCO_3$ both have low solubilities in water, so that the addition of the carbonate ion precipitates the unwanted calcium and magnesium ions.

If water **contains Ca^{2+} and/or Mg^{2+} and DOES NOT CONTAIN HCO_3^-**, the water is said to be **PERMANENTLY HARD.** The term "permanent hardness" refers to the fact that the only way to get rid of the offending Ca^{2+}/Mg^{2+} ions is to carry out a precipitation reaction.

If hard water **also** contains hydrogen carbonate ions, the HCO_3^- can be decomposed by heat.

$$Ca^{2+}(aq) + 2\,HCO_3^-(aq) + \textbf{heat} \rightleftharpoons CaCO_3(s) + CO_2(g) + H_2O(l)$$

Since $CaCO_3(s)$ is quite insoluble in water, the act of boiling the water will effectively remove most of the Ca^{2+} present, and hence the hardness. Therefore, water **containing HCO_3^- and Ca^{2+}/Mg^{2+}** is said to be **TEMPORARILY HARD** since the hardness can be removed by boiling the water.

EXERCISES:

76. A new kettle was used to make tea using "temporarily hard" water. After a few weeks there was a thin layer of white "kettle scale" on the inside of the kettle. Suggest the chemical formula for the "kettle scale".

77. What simple procedure could you use to determine whether a sample of hard water was temporarily hard or permanently hard?

78. Is it possible to distinguish between temporarily and permanently hard water by seeing if a precipitate forms when washing soda is added? Explain your answer.

79. Many statues are made of marble, which is a beautiful white variety of limestone (calcium carbonate). What effect would acid rain have on such statues?

80. Towns which have some temporary hardness in their water supplies often have trouble with hot water pipes. What problem would you expect to occur inside pipes through which such hot water flows?

III.10. THE COMMON ION EFFECT AND OTHER WAYS TO ALTER THE SOLUBILITY OF A SALT

The solubility of an ionic compound, such as AgCl, in **PURE WATER** cannot change. If pure water is **not** used to dissolve AgCl(s), it is possible to INCREASE or DECREASE the solubility (but NOT the solubility product constant) by applying Le Chatelier's Principle to the equilibrium.

First, let us see what it means TO INCREASE OR DECREASE THE SOLUBILITY OF A SALT.

Recall that in section 1 of this unit

the reaction $AgCl(s) \longrightarrow Ag^+(aq) + Cl^-(aq)$ is called the DISSOLVING REACTION, and
the reaction $Ag^+(aq) + Cl^-(aq) \longrightarrow AgCl(s)$ is called the CRYSTALLIZATION REACTION.

Therefore, **if we can increase the rate of dissolving** more than the rate of crystallization

$$AgCl(s) \rightleftharpoons Ag^+(aq) + Cl^-(aq)$$

then **more** AgCl(s) will leave the solid phase and enter the aqueous phase and we can say the SOLUBILITY OF AgCl(s) INCREASES. (Recall that a substance is said to be highly soluble if it dissolves to a great extent.)

Similarly, **if we can increase the rate of crystallization** more than the rate of dissolving

$$AgCl(s) \rightleftharpoons Ag^+(aq) + Cl^-(aq)$$

then **more** $Ag^+(aq)$ and $Cl^-(aq)$ will leave the aqueous phase and enter the solid phase and we can say the SOLUBILITY OF AgCl(s) DECREASES. (Recall that a substance is said to have a very low solubility if almost none of it dissolves.)

Both INCREASING and DECREASING the solubility of a salt work on a similar principle.

According to Le Chatelier's principle, **changing the concentration of the dissolved ions** in the equilibrium

$$AgCl(s) \rightleftharpoons Ag^+(aq) + Cl^-(aq)$$

will **shift the equilibrium** either to the solid side (decreasing the solubility of the solid) or to the ions side (increasing the solubility of the solid).

In other words, "INCREASING and DECREASING the solubility" refers to the SOLID SALT, but the changes in solubility are accomplished by altering the concentration of the DISSOLVED IONS.

A. DECREASING THE SOLUBILITY OF A SALT

If we **INCREASE** the concentration of ONE of the ions in solution, then by Le Chatelier's Principle the equilibrium will shift so as to use up some of the added ions and cause more solid to form.

EXAMPLE: In the equilibrium $AgCl(s) \rightleftharpoons Ag^+(aq) + Cl^-(aq)$ we can either

- increase the $[Ag^+]$ by adding a soluble salt containing Ag^+, such as $AgNO_3$,

$$AgCl(s) \rightleftharpoons \mathbf{Ag^+}(aq) + Cl^-(aq)$$

or

- increase the $[Cl^-]$ by adding a soluble salt containing Cl^-, such as NaCl,

$$AgCl(s) \rightleftharpoons Ag^+(aq) + \mathbf{Cl^-}(aq).$$

Note: If we attempt to add a solution containing large concentrations of both $Ag^+(aq)$ and $Cl^-(aq)$, a precipitate of AgCl will immediately form in the solution being added. The precipitate reduces the concentrations of one or both of the Ag^+ and Cl^- ions and prevents the added solution from containing large concentrations of both ions.

The lowering of the solubility of a salt by adding a second salt which has one ion "IN COMMON" with the first salt is called the COMMON ION EFFECT.

In the first part of our example above, the **Ag**Cl and **Ag**NO_3 had the **Ag^+ ion in common.**

$$AgCl(s) \rightleftharpoons \mathbf{Ag^+} + Cl^-$$
$$AgNO_3 \longrightarrow \mathbf{Ag^+} + NO_3^-.$$

In the second part the Ag**Cl** and Na**Cl** had the **Cl^- ion in common.**

$$AgCl(s) \rightleftharpoons Ag^+ + \mathbf{Cl^-}$$
$$NaCl \longrightarrow Na^+ + \mathbf{Cl^-}.$$

The common ion effect is frequently used in chemistry to deliberately prevent a particular salt from dissolving to any great extent or to force a particular dissolved ion to leave a solution.

EXAMPLE: In the industrial Solvay Process for making sodium hydrogen carbonate ($NaHCO_3$ or "baking soda") a saturated solution of $NaHCO_3$ is produced in solution. In order to increase the yield of the solid $NaHCO_3$ produced, a saturated solution of NaCl is added.

$$NaHCO_3(s) \rightleftharpoons \mathbf{Na^+} + HCO_3^-$$
$$NaCl(s) \rightleftharpoons \mathbf{Na^+} + Cl^-$$

The molar solubility of NaCl is much larger (6.1 M) than that of $NaHCO_3$ (0.82 M). As a result of the common ion effect, the large [Na^+] present in the mixture will remove virtually all the HCO_3^- in the solution and form the desired $NaHCO_3(s)$.

B. INCREASING THE SOLUBILITY OF A SALT

If we **DECREASE** the concentration of one of the ions in solution, then the equilibrium will shift so as to dissolve more of the solid and bring the concentration of the ions back up again.

EXAMPLE: In the equilibrium $AgCl(s) \rightleftharpoons Ag^+(aq) + Cl^-(aq)$ we can either

- **decrease the [Ag^+] by adding some ion which precipitates the Ag^+ present.** Looking at the Solubility Table, we see that any of SO_4^{2-} , S^{2-}, OH^- or CO_3^{2-} will form a precipitate with Ag^+ (we don't consider adding Cl^- because the equilibrium already involves Cl^-); arbitrarily, let us choose S^{2-} and add the soluble salt Na_2S. (The Na^+ acts as a spectator.)

$$AgCl(s) \rightleftharpoons Ag^+ + Cl^-$$
$$+$$
$$S^{2-}$$
$$\updownarrow$$
$$Ag_2S(s)$$

  As the above set of equilibria show, adding S^{2-} lowers the [Ag^+] by precipitating the Ag^+ as $Ag_2S(s)$. This decrease in [Ag^+] shifts the equilibrium involving AgCl(s) so as to dissolve more AgCl. The net result of adding S^{2-} is to increase the solubility of AgCl(s).

or

- **decrease the [Cl^-] by adding some ion which precipitates the Cl^- present.** Again, looking at the Solubility Table, we see that either of Pb^{2+} or Cu^+ will form a precipitate with Cl^- (we don't consider adding Ag^+ because the equilibrium already involves Ag^+). We will choose Pb^{2+}, in the form of the soluble salt $Pb(NO_3)_2$. (Again, the NO_3^- acts as a spectator.)

$$AgCl(s) \rightleftharpoons Ag^+ + Cl^-$$
$$+$$
$$Pb^{2+}$$
$$\updownarrow$$
$$PbCl_2(s)$$

  As the above set of equilibria show, the addition of Pb^{2+} lowers the [Cl^-] by precipitating the Cl^- as $PbCl_2(s)$. This decrease in [Cl^-] shifts the equilibrium involving AgCl(s) so as to dissolve more AgCl. The net result of adding Pb^{2+} is to increase the solubility of AgCl(s).

EXERCISES:

81. The solubility of $Sr(OH)_2$ is about 0.5 M at 25°C. State two ways of INCREASING the solubility of $Sr(OH)_2$ in water. State two ways to DECREASE the solubility of $Sr(OH)_2$ in water.

82. Why can't the solubility of $BaCO_3$ be increased by adding more $BaCO_3(s)$ to saturated $BaCO_3(aq)$?

83. A metal plate had an unwanted coating of $CaCO_3(s)$. How might you dissolve the coating?

84. State two different ways in which you could increase the solubility of $PbCl_2$. State two different ways in which you could decrease the solubility of $PbCl_2$.

85. In which solution would $SrCl_2(s)$ be most soluble? In which solution would $SrCl_2(s)$ be least soluble? Explain your choices.

    (A) 1 M $NaNO_3$ (B) 1 M Na_2SO_4 (C) 1 M $Sr(NO_3)_2$ (D) 1 M $MgCl_2$

86. Arrange the following solutions such that NaBr has a decreasing solubility in them. Explain your choices.

    (A) 1 M NaCl (B) 1 M $AgNO_3$ (C) 1 M KNO_3 (D) 1 M Na_2SO_4 (E) 2 M $AgNO_3$

UNIT IV : ACIDS, BASES AND SALTS

In this unit you will study two theories about acids and bases. The first theory will cover most of what you already understand about acids and bases and the second one will be "built from scratch", based on your knowledge of equilibrium reactions. By the end of this unit you should appreciate the variety of effects that acid–base chemistry has on your life and be able to answer such questions as: How do our bodies protect us from the potentially lethal effects of eating pickles or tomatoes? (Aha! Now you're curious!) What causes "acid rain" and how might the damage it causes be prevented? Why do chickens who drink Perrier™ water give better eggs than chickens who drink ordinary water? How can you deal with a power–crazed Chemistry student who threatens to turn all the waters of the world into super–concentrated acid? Well, you'll never know the answers until you learn more, so let's get on with it.

IV.1. THE ARRHENIUS THEORY OF ACIDS AND BASES

This theory of acids and bases is the first theory proposed to explain the actions of acids and bases, and is still valuable in many circumstances. The theory is named after Svante Arrhenius who did such outstanding work in developing the theory of electrolytes that he received the Nobel Prize in Chemistry in 1903. The following is actually a summary of the main ideas of his theory.

Definitions: An **ACID** is any substance which releases H^+ (aq) in water.

A **BASE** is any substance which releases OH^- (aq) in water.

A **SALT** is the neutralization product which results when an acid and a base react.

$$\underset{\text{acid}}{HCl(aq)} + \underset{\text{base}}{NaOH(aq)} \longrightarrow \underset{\text{"salt"}}{NaCl(aq)} + \underset{\text{water}}{H_2O(l)}$$

In other words, a ***SALT*** is any ***ionic*** compound which is neither an acid nor a base.

OK, let's simplify this stuff a bit. The formal definitions are fine, but a little clumsy to use. The following is a simpler way to think of acids, bases and salts.

An **ACID** is any **ionic** species whose formula starts with an "H".

EXAMPLES: HCl, HNO_3, H_2SO_4

A **BASE** is any **ionic** species whose formula ends with an "OH".

EXAMPLES: $NaOH$, KOH, $Ca(OH)_2$, $Zn(OH)_2$

(There are exceptions to the idea that a formula which ends in "OH" must be a base, as will be seen later, but this is a reasonable way to recognize bases for now.)

The simplest way to recognize that a chemical is a salt is as follows. If the chemical is seen to be ionic because it contains species that you have come to recognize as being IONS, and if the formula DOES NOT START WITH "H" OR END WITH "OH", then you are dealing with a SALT.

EXAMPLES: **KBr, $FePO_4$** and **Li_2CO_3**. These compounds contain species which are recognized as being ionic, such as K^+, Br^-, Fe^{3+}, PO_4^{3-}, Li^+ and CO_3^{2-}. Also, none of the three compounds start with a "H" or end with an "OH", so ... these compounds are SALTS.

EXERCISE:

1. Which of the following are ACIDS, which are BASES, which are SALTS and which are NONE of these three categories?

a) KNO_3	c) CH_4	e) H_2CO_3	g) $Ba(OH)_2$
b) $HC_2H_3O_2$	d) LiOH	f) Na_2CO_3	h) SO_2

Next, we need to review how to write and balance an acid–base neutralization reaction. A general equation for the reaction between an acid and a base is:

$$\text{ACID} + \text{BASE} \longrightarrow \text{SALT} + \text{WATER}.$$

All neutralization reactions are based on the fact that acids produce H^+ and bases produce OH^-. The net ionic equation for every acid–base reaction just shows the production of water.

$$H^+ + OH^- \longrightarrow H_2O$$

The following balancing procedure is used.

1. Check to see how many H's and OH's are in the formulae for the acid and base. For example, in the reaction:

   $$HCl + Ca(OH)_2 \longrightarrow ?$$

   HCl can supply one H and $Ca(OH)_2$ can supply two OH's.

2. In front of the HCl and $Ca(OH)_2$ put the smallest coefficients which will give the same number (in this case, 2 and 1) of H's as OH's.

   $$\underline{\mathbf{2}}\ HCl + \underline{\mathbf{1}}\ Ca(OH)_2 \longrightarrow ?$$

3. Since: $\underline{1}\ H^+ + \underline{1}\ OH^- \longrightarrow \underline{1}\ H_2O$, there are the same number of H_2O's as H's (or OH's).

   $$\underline{2}\ HCl + \underline{1}\ Ca(OH)_2 \longrightarrow \underline{\mathbf{2}}\ H_2O + ?$$

4. Finally, write down the formula for the salt produced by combining the remaining ions. The base contains Ca^{2+} and the acid contains Cl^-, and since the positive ion is ALWAYS written first in an ionic compound, start by writing: Ca Cl. Then, since 1 Ca atom and 2 Cl atoms exist on the reactant side, put these numbers after the appropriate atoms to create the formula for the salt: Ca_1Cl_2, or more correctly, $CaCl_2$. The final equation then becomes:

   $$\mathbf{2\ HCl + Ca(OH)_2 \longrightarrow CaCl_2 + 2\ H_2O}.$$

EXERCISE:

2. Balance the following neutralization equations.

a) H_2SO_4 reacts with NaOH	d) HCl reacts with $Sn(OH)_4$
b) H_2SO_4 reacts with $Fe(OH)_3$	e) H_2S reacts with $Ca(OH)_2$
c) H_3PO_4 reacts with KOH	f) $H_4P_2O_7$ reacts with NaOH

Now to finish examining the Arrhenius theory of acids and bases. Early chemists did not properly understand the nature of acids and bases. They decided if a substance was an acid or base by resorting to a method which works on the principle that "if it looks like a duck, quacks like a duck, flies like a duck and eventually produces more little ducks, then the thing is probably a duck". The following are termed **DESCRIPTIVE DEFINITIONS** of acids and bases.

The presence of H^+ accounts for the following properties of those substances which are traditionally called "acids".

a) acids react with bases
b) acids are electrolytes
c) acids act on some metals to produce $H_2(g)$ (for example: $Mg(s) + 2\,HCl(aq) \longrightarrow MgCl_2(aq) + H_2(g)$)
d) acids turn litmus paper RED
e) acids taste SOUR (for example: vinegar, lemon juice)

The presence of OH^- accounts for the following properties of those substances which are traditionally called "bases".

a) bases react with acids
b) bases are electrolytes
c) bases feel slippery (they react with your skin and fat to make soap)
d) bases turn litmus paper BLUE
e) bases taste BITTER (for example: baking soda)

Some comments on the above definitions are required.

1. Chemists DO NOT go around tasting everything they make in the lab (unless they have suicidal tendencies!), but early chemists ***would*** put a little of a particular chemical on their tongues to determine the taste, and then, without swallowing, rinse their mouths out before they poisoned themselves. What they did not appreciate is that some chemicals are ***directly absorbed through the skin*** ... and unfortunately early deaths among chemists were quite frequent. Moral: DON'T TASTE ANYTHING THAT ISN'T RECOGNIZED AS "FOOD".

2. Some metals, such as gold and platinum, are effectively unreactive with acids while other metals, such as sodium and potassium, are so reactive that they react with water. Magnesium is used to test for the presence of acids because it is just sufficiently reactive to produce $H_2(g)$ when put into acids.

3. Remember that "BASES FEEL SLIPPERY"! If you ever get an unknown chemical on your hands and your hands feel slippery afterward, there is an excellent chance that you spilled a base on your hands. You must quickly wash ***and*** scrub your hands since the base starts to eat away the skin and form an outer layer which does not easily wash away. You have to scrub lightly to get to the base which is eating away ***underneath*** the "protective" outer layer.

4. A sneaky way to remember the litmus colours is shown below.

Litmus is: **RED in ACID** **and** **BLUE in BASE**

EXERCISES:

3. Which of the following are properties of acids only, which are properties of bases only, which are properties of both, and which are not properties of either?
   a) form electrically conducting solutions in water
   b) react with metals to produce $O_2(g)$
   c) make skin feel slippery
   d) turn litmus paper red
   e) taste sour
   f) react with salts

4. You have been given a solution and are told that it contains either an acid or base. What tests would you perform to help decide if the solution is acidic or basic?

IV.2. SOME COMMON ACIDS AND BASES

This Section outlines some common properties and uses of several important acids and bases.

ACIDS

a) Sulphuric Acid: H_2SO_4 ***Commercial names***: oil of vitriol, "battery acid"

Properties:
- good dehydrating agent (i.e. removes water from substances)
- strongly exothermic reaction when mixed with water
- concentrated form chars some types of organic material (e.g. sugars) as a result of dehydrating action
- reacts with some metals, but often slowly
- good electrolyte (conducts electricity)
- concentrated sulphuric acid is 98% H_2SO_4 and 2% water (18 M H_2SO_4)

Common uses:
- production of sulphates
- manufacturing fertilizers, explosives, dyes, insecticides, detergents, plastics
- used to absorb water and keep chemicals/nonaqueous solutions free of water
- used in car batteries as an electrolyte

b) Hydrochloric Acid: HCl ***Commercial name***: muriatic acid

Properties:
- good electrolyte
- concentrated solutions have a choking odour
- reacts with some metals, but often slowly
- concentrated hydrochloric acid is 37% HCl in water (12 M HCl)

Common uses:
- production of chlorides
- cleaning metal products (removes metal oxides) and bricks
- catalyst in some chemical reactions
- "stomach acid" is a dilute solution of HCl; stomach acid activates a protein–digesting biological catalyst called an "enzyme"
- removing "boiler scale", which consists of calcium and magnesium carbonate

c) Nitric Acid: HNO_3 ***Commercial name***: (none, other than "nitric acid")

Properties:
- colours protein yellow (this is a nonspecific test for the presence of protein). Hence, turns skin yellow on contact.
- very reactive, quickly attacks almost all metals
- concentrated nitric acid is 69% HNO_3 in water (16 M HNO_3)

Common uses:
- production of nitrates
- manufacturing fertilizers, explosives, dyes

d) Acetic Acid: CH_3COOH ***Commercial name***: 5% aqueous solution is called "vinegar"

Properties:
- non–electrolyte when concentrated (99 – 100%, 17 M); weak electrolyte when diluted
- only affects highly reactive metals

Common uses:
- making acetates
- food preservation ("pickles")
- manufacturing textiles and plastics

BASES

a) Sodium Hydroxide: NaOH ***Commercial names***: caustic soda, lye

Properties:
- very corrosive (caustic) to animal and plant tissues
- highly exothermic reaction when mixed with water
- rapidly "deliquesces"; that is, absorbs H_2O from the air
- rapidly absorbs $CO_2(g)$ from the air to form carbonates: $NaOH(s) + CO_2(g) \longrightarrow NaHCO_3(s)$

Common uses:
- making sodium salts
- making soap and other cleaning products such as oven cleaner, drain cleaner
- manufacturing glass, pulp and paper, plastics, aluminum
- neutralizing acids during industrial reactions

b) Potassium Hydroxide: KOH ***Commercial name***: caustic potash

Properties:
- much the same as NaOH, but melts at a lower temperature

Common uses:
- manufacturing liquid soap (potassium soaps have a lower melting temperature than sodium soaps)
- absorbing $CO_2(g)$
- making potassium salts
- electrolyte in alkaline batteries

c) Ammonia: NH_3 ***Commercial name***: $NH_3(aq)$ is called "ammonium hydroxide"

Properties:
- colourless, alkaline, highly toxic, corrosive gas with pungent odour
- highly soluble in water
- exothermic reaction when dissolved in water

Common uses:
- manufacturing nitric acid
- manufacturing explosives, fertilizers, synthetic fibres
- used as a refrigeration gas

EXERCISES:

5. Why must containers of NaOH and KOH be tightly closed when not in use?
6. Which of the above acid and bases are useful in making: a) fertilizers? b) plastics?
7. Which acid or base is used:
   a) in car batteries? c) as a refrigerant? e) for cleaning fireplace bricks?
   b) in making pickles? d) in alkaline batteries?
8. Which of the above acids and bases could be used as drying agents?
9. Which of the above acids is the most reactive?

IV.3. THE TRUE NATURE OF H^+ (aq) : (BACKGROUND THEORY)

The hydrogen atom consists of a proton surrounded by a single electron. If the electron is removed, so as to create H^+, a "naked" proton is left. Since this tiny nuclear particle has an enormous charge concentration (it has a +1 charge concentrated in a very small region of space — the diameter of a proton is 5×10^{-14} cm), this highly concentrated ***positive*** charge is ***very strongly attracted*** to any region where ***negative*** charges exist.

A water molecule has its electrons distributed as follows.

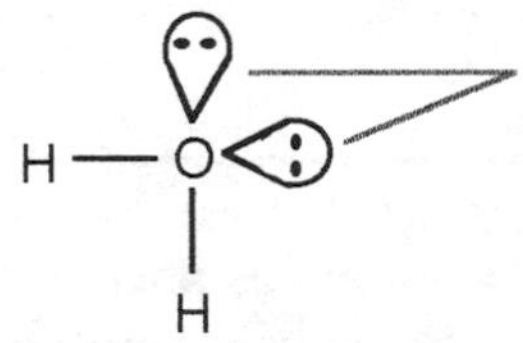

region of space called a "non-bonding orbital", in which are stored the electrons not being used in bonds. The electrons stored here are very vulnerable to attack by H^+.

The attraction between H^+ and the electrons in the non–bonding orbitals causes ***all*** the H^+ ions present to attach themselves to available water molecules.

$H^+ + H_2O \longrightarrow H_3O^+$, where H_3O^+ is:

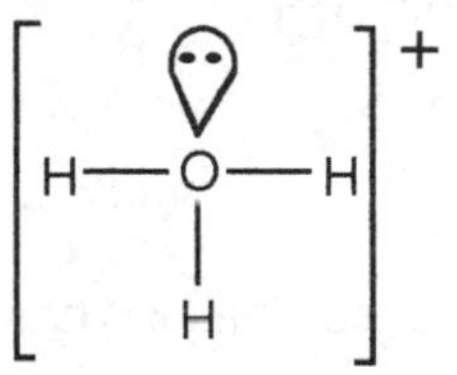

Definition: H^+ is called the **proton.** (REMEMBER THIS !)
H_3O^+ is called the **hydronium ion,** or the **hydrated proton.**

Therefore, what has previously been called H^+(aq) is actually H_3O^+(aq). Using H_3O^+(aq) instead of H^+(aq) will mean having to write the IONIZATION of an acid in another way.

EXAMPLE: When HCl(g) is added to water to produce HCl(aq), the previous way of writing the dissociation:

$$HCl(g) \longrightarrow H^+(aq) + Cl^-(aq),$$

is now rewritten as $HCl(g) + H_2O(l) \longrightarrow H_3O^+(aq) + Cl^-(aq)$.

Notice that the second equation results from adding H_2O to both sides of the first equation, but on the right side the added H_2O combines with H^+ to produce H_3O^+.

EXERCISE:

10. Write equations which show how the following acids dissociate in water to give H_3O^+ (aq).
    a) HNO_3(aq) b) $HClO_4$(aq)

IV.4. THE BRØNSTED–LOWRY THEORY OF ACIDS AND BASES

The Brønsted–Lowry theory is more ***general*** than the Arrhenius theory, and incorporates all of the Arrhenius theory into a larger scheme. The need to have another theory of acids and bases arose because of the existence of **EQUILIBRIUM** reactions, which were not considered when the original Arrhenius theory was proposed. Therefore, the Brønsted–Lowry theory is an expansion of the Arrhenius theory which allows for the existence of equilibrium reactions and an extension of the idea of acids and bases to a wider range of species and reactions.

Definitions:

> An **ACID** is a substance which **DONATES A PROTON** to another substance.
> A **BASE** is a substance which **ACCEPTS A PROTON** from another substance.

In other words: **an ACID is a PROTON DONOR** (gives away an H^+), and
a BASE is a PROTON ACCEPTOR (receives an H^+).

Let's look at a typical Brønsted–Lowry acid–base reaction equation.

$$NH_3 + H_2O \rightleftharpoons NH_4^+ + OH^-$$

You should observe that the NH_3 reacts to become NH_4^+. Hence, the NH_3 has gained an extra "H" and a "+" charge, so that the NH_3 **is acting as a BASE:** it has "accepted a proton" (H^+).

WAIT, THERE'S MORE. If NH_3 accepted a proton (H^+) then H_2O must have donated a proton and acted as an ACID. If you examine the above equation again, you will see that the H_2O ***has lost*** (that is, donated) an H^+, and produced an OH^- in the process. Overall, then:

$$\underset{\text{base}}{NH_3} + \underset{\text{acid}}{H_2O} \rightleftharpoons NH_4^+ + OH^-.$$

THE "TRICK" TO DECIDING WHETHER A SUBSTANCE IS ACTING AS AN ACID OR A BASE IS THIS: look at a particular chemical on the "REACTANT SIDE" of the equation and then look for a SOMEWHAT SIMILAR LOOKING chemical on the "PRODUCT SIDE". If the chemical on the PRODUCT side has ONE MORE H ATOM, then the REACTANT chemical must have GAINED (ACCEPTED) an H^+. If the chemical on the PRODUCT side has ONE LESS H ATOM, then the REACTANT chemical must have LOST (DONATED) an H^+.

Let's look at a second example.

$$CH_3COOH + H_2O \rightleftharpoons CH_3COO^- + H_3O^+.$$

The CH_3COOH donates (loses) an H^+ to become CH_3COO^- and therefore CH_3COOH must be acting as an ACID. (The fact that ***acetic acid*** acts as an acid should make sense!) The H_2O accepted a proton to become H_3O^+ and hence H_2O must be acting as a BASE in this equation.

Definitions: A **MONOPROTIC ACID** is an acid which can supply only **one** proton.
A **DIPROTIC ACID** is an acid which can supply up to **two** protons.
A **TRIPROTIC ACID** is an acid which can supply up to **three** protons.
A **POLYPROTIC ACID** is a general term for an acid which can supply **more than one** proton.

EXERCISES:

11. In the following reactions, which reactant acts as an acid and which acts as a base?
    a) $HNO_3 + H_2O \rightleftharpoons NO_3^- + H_3O^+$
    b) $HCO_3^- + SO_3^{2-} \rightleftharpoons CO_3^{2-} + HSO_3^-$
    c) $HS^- + H_2PO_4^- \rightleftharpoons H_2S + HPO_4^{2-}$
    d) $H_3PO_4 + CH_3COO^- \rightleftharpoons H_2PO_4^- + CH_3COOH$
    e) $CO_3^{2-} + HF \rightleftharpoons HCO_3^- + F^-$

12. Consider the acids: H_3PO_4, HF, H_2S, $H_4P_2O_7$, H_2CO_3, HCN.
    a) Which of the acids are MONOPROTIC?
    b) Which of the acids are DIPROTIC?
    c) Which of the acids are TRIPROTIC?
    d) Which of the acids are POLYPROTIC?

Let's go back a bit and look at the above two example equations.

$$\underset{\text{base}}{NH_3} + \underset{\text{acid}}{H_2O} \rightleftharpoons NH_4^+ + OH^-$$

$$\underset{\text{acid}}{CH_3COOH} + \underset{\text{base}}{H_2O} \rightleftharpoons CH_3COO^- + H_3O^+$$

Oh, Oh ... this just got confusing: according to the Arrhenius theory, H_2O is neither an acid nor a base. But water acts as an **ACID** when it reacts with NH_3 (in the first example) and as a **BASE** when it reacts with CH_3COOH (in the second example). Consider this question: when it comes to birthday presents, do you give or receive presents? It depends on whose birthday it is, doesn't it?

CONCLUSION: In some circumstances a substance acts as a Brønsted–Lowry acid, while in other circumstances the same substance acts as a Brønsted–Lowry base. Water acts as a Brønsted–Lowry base when it reacts with an acid and as an acid when it reacts with a base.

Water is an example of a substance which is said to be **AMPHIPROTIC.**

Some amphiprotic substances are: H_2O, $H_2PO_4^-$, HS^- and HCO_3^-. Apart from H_2O, amphiprotic species are ions derived from POLYPROTIC ACIDS which have lost at least one proton. As shown in the example below, each ion can either lose another proton or regain one.

EXAMPLE: $H_3PO_4 \xleftarrow{+H^+} H_2PO_4^- \xrightarrow{-H^+} HPO_4^{2-}$

$H_2S \xleftarrow{+H^+} HS^- \xrightarrow{-H^+} S^{2-}$

CONCLUSION: If a substance	**a) possesses a NEGATIVE CHARGE, and** **b) still has an easily removable HYDROGEN,**
	then the substance will be AMPHIPROTIC.

(Apart from hydrogens attached to carbon, assume that all hydrogens on a negatively–charged ion are "easily removable".)

Examine another pair of Brønsted–Lowry acid–base reactions.

$$\underset{\text{acid}}{NH_4^+} + \underset{\text{base}}{OH^-} \longrightarrow NH_3 + H_2O$$

$$\underset{\text{base}}{CH_3COO^-} + \underset{\text{acid}}{H_3O^+} \longrightarrow CH_3COOH + H_2O$$

These reactions are the same as the two reactions at the start of this section, except that they are reversed. Since the reactions are reversible, the net result is:

$$\underset{\text{base}}{NH_3} + \underset{\text{acid}}{H_2O} \rightleftharpoons \underset{\text{acid}}{NH_4^+} + \underset{\text{base}}{OH^-}$$

$$\underset{\text{acid}}{CH_3COOH} + \underset{\text{base}}{H_2O} \rightleftharpoons \underset{\text{base}}{CH_3COO^-} + \underset{\text{acid}}{H_3O^+}.$$

In every Brønsted–Lowry reaction there is an acid and a base on both sides of the equation.

To save time deciding which species is which in a Brønsted–Lowry reaction, use the following procedure. In order to illustrate what is happening look at the example equation:

$$CH_3COOH + H_2O \rightleftharpoons CH_3COO^- + H_3O^+.$$

- First, determine the identity of one species on the reactant side, by seeing whether it gains or loses a proton. For example, CH_3COOH here is acting as an acid since it is losing a proton.

- Second, you can now determine the identity of the "similar species" on the product side. It is the opposite (for example, BASE) of the first species you identified (for example, ACID).

  To this point: $$\underset{\text{acid}}{CH_3COOH} + H_2O \rightleftharpoons \underset{\text{base}}{CH_3COO^-} + H_3O^+.$$

- Finally, use the fact that ***each side must have both an ACID and a BASE*** to complete the assignment. For example:

$$\underset{\text{acid}}{CH_3COOH} + \underset{\textbf{base}}{H_2O} \rightleftharpoons \underset{\text{base}}{CH_3COO^-} + \underset{\textbf{acid}}{H_3O^+}.$$

EXERCISES:

13. Identify each species in the following equations as being an acid or base.
    a) $HF + SO_3^{2-} \rightleftharpoons F^- + HSO_3^-$
    b) $H_2O + HCO_3^- \rightleftharpoons H_3O^+ + CO_3^{2-}$
    c) $NO_2^- + H_2O \rightleftharpoons OH^- + HNO_2$
    d) $H_2PO_4^- + S^{2-} \rightleftharpoons HS^- + HPO_4^{2-}$
    e) $N_2H_5^+ + SO_4^{2-} \rightleftharpoons N_2H_4 + HSO_4^-$

14. Which of the following would be expected to exhibit amphiprotic behaviour?
    Se^{2-}, HSe^-, H_2Se, H_3PO_4, HPO_4^{2-}, HSO_3^-

IV.5. CONJUGATE ACIDS AND BASES

Definitions: A **CONJUGATE ACID–BASE PAIR** (or **CONJUGATE PAIR**) is a pair of chemical species which differ by only one proton.

A **CONJUGATE ACID** is the member of a conjugate pair which ***HAS*** the extra proton.

A **CONJUGATE BASE** is the member of a conjugate pair which ***LACKS*** the extra proton.

EXAMPLE: In the equilibrium reaction $NH_4^+ + H_2O \rightleftharpoons NH_3 + H_3O^+$ there are two conjugate pairs.

Conjugate pair	Conjugate acid	Conjugate base
NH_4^+, NH_3	NH_4^+	NH_3
H_2O, H_3O^+	H_3O^+	H_2O

EXERCISE:

15. Write the appropriate species, taken from each conjugate pair, in the blanks provided.

	Conjugate pair	Conjugate acid	Conjugate base
a)	CH_3COOH / CH_3COO^-		
b)	HSO_4^- / SO_4^{2-}		
c)	PH_3 / PH_4^+		

NOTE: You can interpret the question "what is the conjugate base of X?"
as "what base is the conjugate of X?"
or **"what is the base counterpart of X?".**

All these statements imply that **X is an ACID.**

If you are asked to find the CONJUGATE ACID of NH_3, you should give the formula of the acid which has one MORE proton than NH_3 (which is assumed to be a base).

Therefore, you add H^+ to NH_3 to get NH_4^+.

If you are asked to find the CONJUGATE BASE of NH_3, then you must give the formula of the base which has one LESS proton than NH_3 (which is assumed to be an acid).

Therefore, you take away an H^+ from NH_3 to get NH_2^-.

SPECIAL NOTE: Simple **organic acids** end with a **COOH** group, and the H at the end of the group is acidic.

EXAMPLE: $CH_3CH_2COOH \longrightarrow CH_3CH_2COO^- + H^+$

Organic bases contain an **NH_2** group or an **NH** group. The **nitrogen** atom accepts H^+.

EXAMPLE: $CH_3CH_2NH_2 + H^+ \longrightarrow CH_3CH_2NH_3^+$

$(CH_3)_2NH + H^+ \longrightarrow (CH_3)_2NH_2^+$

Using Lewis structures, the equilibrium reaction between water and NH_3 is shown below.

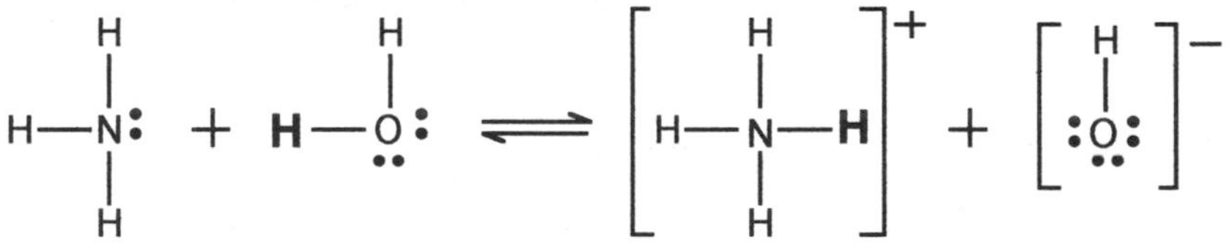

Aha! Now you can see what is going on. There is an H^+ which is just being tossed back and forth: from H_2O to NH_3 and then from NH_4^+ back to OH^-. You can imagine this "back–and–forth" motion by pretending that each of your hands is a different "base" molecule and that a can of "Chemi–Cola" is a proton. Take the can in your left hand. Since the left hand has the "proton", it is now an "acid" molecule. Toss the can over to your right hand. The left hand has lost its "proton" and is now a "base", whereas the right hand has gained a "proton" and is now an "acid". Each time the can is tossed back and forth, the "conjugate acid form" of a molecule turns into the "conjugate base form" of the molecule, and vice versa.

CONCLUSION: A Brønsted–Lowry acid–base reaction just involves an equilibrium proton transfer.

(CONJUGATE ACID FORM of A) + (CONJUGATE BASE FORM of B) ⇄ (CONJUGATE BASE FORM of A) + (CONJUGATE ACID FORM of B)

EXAMPLE: Write the acid–base equilibrium which occurs when H_2S and CO_3^{2-} are mixed in solution.

The CO_3^{2-} has no protons so it acts as a base. Since CO_3^{2-} is the base then H_2S will be the acid:

$$H_2S + CO_3^{2-} \rightleftharpoons HS^- + HCO_3^- .$$

H_2S donates a proton to become its conjugate base: HS^-.

CO_3^{2-} accepts a proton to become its conjugate acid: HCO_3^-.

EXERCISES:

16. Write the formula for each of the following.
    a) the conjugate base of HSO_4^-
    b) the conjugate acid of HSO_4^-
    c) the conjugate base of OH^-
    d) the conjugate acid of OH^-

17. Write the conjugate acid of each of the following.
    a) F^- b) HTe^- c) Te^{2-} d) CH_3NH_2 e) $HC_2O_4^-$ f) $H_2PO_3^-$ g) H^- h) N_2H_4

18. Write the conjugate base of each of the following.
    a) H_2CO_3 b) $C_5H_5NH^+$ c) HPO_4^{2-} d) H_2O_2 e) HN_3 f) HNO_2 g) HS^- h) C_6H_5COOH

19. Write the Brønsted–Lowry acid–base equilibria which occur when the following pairs of substances are mixed in solution.
    a) HCN and F^-
    b) S^{2-} and HCOOH
    c) HPO_4^{2-} and SO_4^{2-}
    d) HIO_3 and $C_2O_4^{2-}$
    e) NO_2^- and HSO_3^-
    f) HPO_4^{2-} and CH_3COO^-

IV.6. "STRONG AND WEAK" ACIDS AND BASES

Definitions: A **STRONG** acid or base is **100% ionized** in solution.

EXAMPLE:
$NaOH(s) \longrightarrow Na^+(aq) + OH^-(aq)$
$HCl(g) \longrightarrow H^+(aq) + Cl^-(aq)$

A **WEAK** acid or base is ***LESS THAN*** **100% ionized** in solution.

EXAMPLE:
$NH_3(aq) + H_2O(l) \rightleftharpoons NH_4^+(aq) + OH^-(aq)$
$HF(aq) + H_2O(l) \rightleftharpoons H_3O^+(aq) + F^-(aq)$

NOTE: a) Equilibrium reactions involve **weak** acids and bases, ***NOT*** **strong** acids and bases.

b) The definition of a weak acid implies that an acid which is 99% ionized is "weak", while an acid which is 100% ionized is "strong". This fine distinction won't cause any problems ***in practice*** because weak acids and bases are always less than 50% ionized.

c) In everyday life the terms "**strong**" and "**concentrated**" are used interchangeably. For example: "I diluted the lemon juice because it was too strong". However, chemistry requires more precise terminology. Specifically . . .

The terms WEAK and STRONG refer to the percentage of ionization.
The terms DILUTE and CONCENTRATED refer to the molarity of a solution.

EXAMPLE:
10.0 M HF(aq) is CONCENTRATED and WEAK
0.001 M HCl(aq) is DILUTE and STRONG

EXERCISE:

20. Suggest an experimental procedure to determine whether a 1 M aqueous solution of an unknown acid is strong or weak. (Hint: What you need is a method which can determine the difference between a solution which is 100% ionized and one which is less than 100% ionized. Titration won't work; whether or not the acid is weak or strong there is still 1 mol of acid in 1 L of the 1 M solution.)

At this point it is appropriate to introduce a table which will be very important in this unit. Look at the table of "Relative Strengths of Brønsted–Lowry Acids and Bases" at the back of this book as you read the following. (From now on we will refer to the table as "Relative Strengths of Acids" or occasionally as the "Table".

THE STRONG ACIDS

The strong acids are the **top six acids** on the **left** side of the table "Relative Strengths of Acids", namely:

$HClO_4$
HI
HBr
HCl
HNO_3
H_2SO_4 **Note**– H_2SO_4 is only strong for the first dissociation: $H_2SO_4 \longrightarrow H^+ + HSO_4^-$.

Notice that the top six reactions have ONE–WAY reaction arrows, pointing to the product side. This means the **REVERSE REACTIONS DO NOT OCCUR AT ALL.**

The 7th entry from the top, $H_3O^+ \rightleftharpoons H^+ + H_2O$, just shows that "$H^+(aq)$" is equivalent to "$H_3O^+(aq)$". **This equilibrium is the net result of putting ANY strong acid in water:**

$$H^+\text{(from dissociation of strong acid)} + H_2O \rightleftharpoons H_3O^+.$$

THE STRONG BASES

The **bottom two bases** listed on the **right** side of the table "Relative Strengths of Acids" are strong bases; that is, O^{2-} **and** NH_2^- **are strongly dissociated in water.**

The 3rd entry from the bottom, $H_2O \rightleftharpoons H^+ + OH^-$, **is the result of adding ANY strong base to water:**

$$OH^-\text{(from dissociation of strong base)} + H^+\text{(from any available acid)} \rightleftharpoons H_2O.$$

The most common strong bases are metal hydroxides, which are 100% dissociated in water. For example:

$NaOH$ KOH $Mg(OH)_2$ $Ca(OH)_2$ $Fe(OH)_3$ $Zn(OH)_2$.

Notice that the bottom two reactions on the Table have ONE–WAY reaction arrows, pointing BACKWARDS to the reactant side. This means the **FORWARD REACTIONS DO NOT OCCUR.**

THE WEAK ACIDS

The **weak acids** are the species on the **left** side of the Table from HIO_3 down to H_2O. (H_3O^+ is the result of adding a strong acid to water.)

$$HIO_3 \rightleftharpoons H^+ + IO_3^-$$
$$\vdots$$
$$H_2O \rightleftharpoons H^+ + OH^-$$

The weak acids on the left are always separated by equilibrium arrows from their conjugate bases on the right. **The last two species at the bottom left of the Table, OH^- and NH_3, NEVER act as acids in aqueous solutions.** (OH^- and NH_3 can only be formed from the strong bases opposite them.)

THE WEAK BASES

The **weak bases** are the species on the **right** side of the Table from $\mathbf{H_2O}$ down to $\mathbf{PO_4^{3-}}$. (OH^- is the result of adding a strong base to water.)

$$H_3O^+ \rightleftharpoons H^+ + \mathbf{H_2O}$$
$$\vdots$$
$$HPO_4^{2-} \rightleftharpoons H^+ + \mathbf{PO_4^{3-}}$$

The weak bases on the right are separated by equilibrium arrows from their conjugates acids on the left. **The six species (ClO_4^- to HSO_4^-) on the right of the top section of the Table NEVER act as bases in aqueous solutions;** they are the conjugates of strong acids.

A SPECIAL NOTE ON READING THE TABLE "RELATIVE STRENGTHS OF ACIDS"

Looking at the Table you find, for example: $\mathbf{H_2S \rightleftharpoons H^+ + HS^-}$.

This equation, being an equilibrium, may proceed forward or backward. When using the equation to refer to H_2S acting as an acid in water, the equation should be written as:

$$H_2S(aq) + H_2O(l) \rightleftharpoons H_3O^+(aq) + HS^-(aq).$$

The equation $H_2S \rightleftharpoons H^+ + HS^-$ is a simplified way to show what happens to H_2S. The complete reaction is shown below.

	$H_2S \rightleftharpoons H^+ + HS^-$	(H_2S gives off H^+)
added to	$H_2O + H^+ \rightleftharpoons H_3O^+$	(H_2O accepts the H^+ given off by H_2S)
gives	$H_2S + H_2O \rightleftharpoons H_3O^+ + HS^-$	(overall reaction when H_2S acts as an acid with H_2O)

When a substance acts as an acid with water, H_3O^+ is always produced. The stronger the acid, the greater the $[H_3O^+]$ produced.

When using the equation to refer to HS^- acting as a base, write the reaction in reverse, showing how HS^- acts as a base with water:

$$HS^-(aq) + H_2O(l) \rightleftharpoons H_2S(aq) + OH^-(aq).$$

The equation $H_2S \rightleftharpoons H^+ + HS^-$ is read in reverse to show what happens to HS^-. The complete reaction is shown below.

	$HS^- + H^+ \rightleftharpoons H_2S$	(HS^- accepts H^+ from H_2O)
added to	$H_2O \rightleftharpoons H^+ + OH^-$	(H_2O donates H^+ to H_2S)
gives	$HS^- + H_2O \rightleftharpoons H_2S + OH^-$	(overall reaction when H_2S acts as a base with H_2O)

When a substance acts as a base with water, OH^- is always produced. The stronger the base, the greater the $[OH^-]$ produced.

SOME OTHER RELATIONSHIPS FOUND IN THE TABLE

- **The higher an acid is on the left side of the Table, the stronger the acid.**
  Example: HNO_2 is higher on the left side than HF, so HNO_2 is a stronger acid than HF.
- **The lower a base is on the right side of the Table, the stronger the base.**
  Example: HPO_4^{2-} is lower on the right side than HCO_3^-, so HPO_4^{2-} is a stronger base than HCO_3^-.
- **The stronger an acid, the weaker its conjugate base, and vice versa.**
  Example: HIO_3 is relatively strong for a "weak acid" **but** its conjugate base, IO_3^-, is very weak.

  NOTE: It is ***NOT CORRECT*** to say that, for example, since IO_3^- is a very weak base then it is a relatively strong acid — IO_3^- doesn't have any protons! It ***IS CORRECT*** to say that since IO_3^- is a very weak base then **its conjugate acid, HIO_3, is a relatively strong acid.**

IMPORTANT: HPO_4^{2-} and HCO_3^- can be found on BOTH the left side AND the right side of the Table.
When comparing relative **ACID** strengths, look at the **left** (**acid side**) of the Table.

Higher on left and **stronger** ⟶ $\mathbf{HCO_3^-} \rightleftharpoons H^+ + CO_3^{2-}$

$\mathbf{HPO_4^{2-}} \rightleftharpoons H^+ + PO_4^{3-}$

When comparing relative **BASE** strengths, look at the **right** (**base side**) of the Table.

$H_2CO_3 \rightleftharpoons H^+ + \mathbf{HCO_3^-}$

$H_2PO_4^- \rightleftharpoons H^+ + \mathbf{HPO_4^{2-}}$ ⟵ Lower on right and **stronger**

Water is amphiprotic: if mixed with a stronger acid than itself, water acts as a base; if mixed with a stronger base than itself, water acts as an acid.

"THE LEVELLING EFFECT"

Examine the following results of preparing 1 M aqueous solutions of four different acids.

1 M $HClO_4$ produces:	1 M H_3O^+ + 1 M ClO_4^- (and **NO undissociated $HClO_4$**)
1 M HCl produces:	1 M H_3O^+ + 1 M Cl^- (and **NO undissociated HCl**)
1 M HF produces:	0.97 M HF + 0.03 M H_3O^+ + 0.03 M F^-
1 M CH_3COOH produces:	0.996 M CH_3COOH + 0.004 M H_3O^+ + 0.004 M CH_3COO^-

The following points should be noticed.

- The weak acids (HF and CH_3COOH) only dissociate to a small extent: the solutions still contain 0.97 mol of undissociated HF and 0.996 mol of undissociated CH_3COOH.
- On the other hand, the strong acids ($HClO_4$ and HCl) produce solutions containing ***NO*** undissociated molecules of $HClO_4$ or HCl.
- HF and CH_3COOH are both WEAK, but HF is "stronger" than CH_3COOH, as can be seen from the fact that more H_3O^+ is formed with HF than with CH_3COOH.
- $HClO_4$ and HCl BOTH produce 1 M solutions of H_3O^+; in effect the $HClO_4$ and HCl solutions have been replaced by 1 M H_3O^+ and another ion.

A look at the table of Relative Strengths of Acids shows that all the strong acids are 100% dissociated to form $H_3O^+(aq)$. Water is said to have "levelled" all the strong acids to the same strength; they are all solutions of $H_3O^+(aq)$. Therefore, H_3O^+ is the strongest acid which can exist in aqueous solution:

$$H_3O^+ \rightleftharpoons H^+ + H_2O\,.$$

Because the table of Relative Strengths of Acids refers to ***AQUEOUS SOLUTIONS***, do not make the mistake of thinking that the six acids at the top have different strengths. In fact, they have ***IDENTICAL STRENGTHS*** in aqueous solution and are equivalent to solutions of $H_3O^+(aq)$.

Similarly, the strongest base which can exist in aqueous solution is OH^-: all strong bases are 100% ionized to form OH^-. For example, the two strong bases shown at the bottom cannot exist in solution; they immediately undergo the following reactions on contact with water:

$$O^{2-} + H_2O \longrightarrow 2\,OH^-$$

and

$$NH_2^- + H_2O \longrightarrow NH_3 + OH^-\,.$$

Do not make the mistake of thinking that O^{2-} and NH_2^- have different strengths in aqueous solutions.

Definition: **THE LEVELLING EFFECT** is the term describing the fact that all strong acids are 100% dissociated in aqueous solution and are equivalent to solutions of $H_3O^+(aq)$, while all strong bases are 100% dissociated in aqueous solution and are equivalent to solutions of $OH^-(aq)$.

Therefore, the central portion of the Table from:

$$H_3O^+ \rightleftharpoons H^+ + H_2O$$

to

$$H_2O \rightleftharpoons H^+ + OH^-$$

shows the reactions which can actually occur in aqueous solution: the top six reactions are levelled to produce H_3O^+ and the bottom two reactions are levelled to produce OH^-.

EXERCISES:

21. Which member of each of the following pairs is the stronger acid?
   a) HIO_3 or CH_3COOH b) H_2O_2 or HSO_3^- c) $H_2PO_4^-$ or HCN

22. Which member of each of the following pairs is the stronger base?
   a) HCO_3^- or PO_4^{3-} b) HPO_4^{2-} or HS^- c) OH^- or NH_3 d) $HCOO^-$ or HSO_3^-

23. H_2Te is a stronger acid than H_2S.
   a) Write the formulae of the conjugate bases of the above two acids.
   b) Which conjugate base is the stronger?

24. Use the table "Relative Strengths of Acids" to write equations which show how the following reactions occur in water.
   a) F^- acts as a base
   b) HNO_2 acts as an acid
   c) $Fe(H_2O)_6^{3+}$ acts as an acid
   d) HCO_3^- acts as a base
   e) HCO_3^- acts as an acid
   f) $Al(H_2O)_5(OH)^{2+}$ acts as a base

25. What is wrong with each of the following statements?
   a) I^- is on the right side of the table "Relative Strengths of Acids" (2nd entry from the top), and hence I^- acts as a base.
   b) OH^- is 2nd from the bottom on the acid side of the Table and 3rd from the bottom on the base side, and hence OH^- can act as either an acid or a base.
   c) $HClO_4$ is stronger than HBr and therefore a 1 M solution of $HClO_4(aq)$ is a stronger acid than a 1 M solution of $HBr(aq)$.

26. Although HI is higher on the Table than HCl, explain clearly why 0.10 M HI(aq) and 0.10 M HCl(aq) both contain 0.10 M H_3O^+ (aq).

27. How is it possible for a solution of a weak acid to have the same conductivity as a solution of a strong acid?

IV.7. THE EQUILIBRIUM CONSTANT FOR THE IONIZATION OF WATER

Definitions: A **NEUTRAL** solution is a solution having $[H_3O^+] = [OH^-]$.
An **ACIDIC** solution is a solution having $[H_3O^+] > [OH^-]$.
A **BASIC** solution is a solution having $[H_3O^+] < [OH^-]$.

When a strong acid and a strong base react, a great deal of heat is released. For example:

$$HCl(aq) + NaOH(aq) \rightleftharpoons NaCl(aq) + H_2O(l) + 59\ kJ.$$

Re–writing this equation in complete ionic form gives

$$H^+(aq) + Cl^-(aq) + Na^+(aq) + OH^-(aq) \rightleftharpoons Na^+(aq) + Cl^-(aq) + H_2O(l) + 59\ kJ.$$

Eliminating the Na^+ (aq) and Cl^- (aq) spectator ions gives the net ionic equation

$$H^+(aq) + OH^-(aq) \rightleftharpoons H_2O(l) + 59\ kJ.$$

This net ionic equation applies to the reaction between any strong acid and strong base. The reverse of this latter reaction is called the SELF–IONIZATION of water.

$$H_2O(l) + 59\ kJ \rightleftharpoons H^+(aq) + OH^-(aq).$$

The equilibrium expression corresponding to the self–ionization reaction is

$$K_w = [H^+][OH^-] = 1.00 \times 10^{-14} \quad (\text{at } 25^\circ C).$$

(Recall that $[H_2O(l)]$ is a constant and is eliminated from the K_w expression.)

NOTE: The self–ionization of water can also be written as $2\,H_2O(l) + 59\ kJ \rightleftharpoons H_3O^+(aq) + OH^-(aq)$ so that the equilibrium expression is

$$K_w = [H_3O^+][OH^-] = 1.00 \times 10^{-14} \quad (\text{at } 25^\circ C).$$

The equilibrium expression shows that $[H_3O^+][OH^-]$ has a small, constant value: as $[H_3O^+]$ increases, $[OH^-]$ decreases, and vice versa.

IMPORTANT: Unless you are told otherwise, from now on you should always assume that the temperature is 25°C, and therefore the value of K_w is 1.00×10^{-14}.

EXERCISES:

28. What is $[H_3O^+]$ in pure, neutral water? What is $[OH^-]$?

29. a) When water is heated, what happens to the $[H_3O^+]$?
    b) Is hot water acidic, basic or neutral?
    c) What happens to the value of K_w when water is heated?

In 1 M HCl(aq), the HCl will be 100% ionized into 1 M $H_3O^+(aq)$ and 1 M $Cl^-(aq)$:

$$HCl(aq) + H_2O(l) \longrightarrow H_3O^+(aq) + Cl^-(aq).$$

The concentrations of H_3O^+ and OH^- in neutral water are very low: $[H_3O^+] = [OH^-] = 1.0 \times 10^{-7}$ M . The addition of excess $H_3O^+(aq)$, from the HCl, neutralizes most of the OH^- present and shifts the equilibrium to form more water:

$$2\,H_2O \rightleftharpoons H_3O^+ + OH^-.$$

Nevertheless, even in acidic solutions a small amount of OH^- is always present. The added acid is not used up significantly by the small amount of OH^- initially present, so that the $[H_3O^+]$ in the resulting solution remains at 1 M.

The equilibrium expression for water will play a major role in much of the remaining material in this section. One of the most common usages for the expression will be to solve for $[H_3O^+]$ once $[OH^-]$ is known, and vice versa.

EXAMPLE: What is $[H_3O^+]$ and $[OH^-]$ in 0.0010 M HCl(aq)?

Since HCl is a strong acid, then $[H_3O^+] = [HCl] = \mathbf{1.0 \times 10^{-3}\ M}$

and $$[OH^-] = \frac{K_w}{[H_3O^+]} = \frac{1.00 \times 10^{-14}}{1.0 \times 10^{-3}} = \mathbf{1.0 \times 10^{-11}\ M.}$$

EXERCISE:

30. Determine both $[H_3O^+]$ and $[OH^-]$ in each of the following solutions.
    a) 10.0 M HCl b) 4.0 M NaOH c) 2.5×10^{-4} M HNO_3 d) 6.00×10^{-3} M $Ca(OH)_2$

IV.8. K_a AND K_b

The **ACID IONIZATION** reaction of a WEAK acid such as CH_3COOH with water is shown by

$$CH_3COOH(aq) + H_2O(l) \rightleftharpoons CH_3COO^-(aq) + H_3O^+(aq).$$

The equilibrium expression for the ionization is $K_a = \frac{[CH_3COO^-][H_3O^+]}{[CH_3COOH]} = 1.76 \times 10^{-5}$.

(The equilibrium expression assumes that the solutions are sufficiently dilute that $[H_2O]$ remains constant.)

The value of K_a is called the **ACID IONIZATION CONSTANT.**

The **BASE IONIZATION** reaction of a WEAK base such as NH_3 with water is shown by

$$NH_3(aq) + H_2O(l) \rightleftharpoons NH_4^+(aq) + OH^-(aq).$$

The equilibrium expression for the ionization is $K_b = \frac{[NH_4^+][OH^-]}{[NH_3]} = 1.79 \times 10^{-5}$.

The value of K_b is called the **BASE IONIZATION CONSTANT.**

The table of Relative Strengths of Acids shows that the greater the value of K_a, the stronger the acid. For a STRONG ACID, the value of K_a is not defined since the acid is 100% ionized and the concentration of the unionized acid in the denominator of the K_a expression is zero.

Similarly, the greater the K_b value for a base, the stronger the base. The table of Relative Strengths of Acids does not list K_b values but the next section shows the procedure for calculating K_b values using K_a values in the Table.

EXERCISES:

31. Write the K_a expression for the reaction in which each of the following acts as an acid with water.
    a) HCN b) HPO_4^{2-} c) HNO_2

32. Write the K_b expression for the reaction in which each of the following acts as a base with water.
    a) HS^- b) CH_3NH_2 c) F^-

33. You have a 1 M solution of an acid with $K_a = 1 \times 10^{-5}$ and a 1 M solution of an acid with $K_a = 1 \times 10^{-10}$. Which solution contains the greater concentration of H_3O^+ ?

34. You have a 1 M solution of a base with $K_b = 5 \times 10^{-12}$ and a 1 M solution of a second base with $K_b = 7 \times 10^{-6}$. Which solution contains the greater concentration of OH^- ?

IV.9. THE RELATIONSHIP BETWEEN K_a AND K_b FOR A CONJUGATE PAIR

Experimentally, it is found that the **ACID IONIZATION** equation $NH_4^+ + H_2O \rightleftharpoons NH_3(aq) + H_3O^+$

has the acid ionization constant $K_a = \frac{[NH_3][H_3O^+]}{[NH_4^+]} = 5.59 \times 10^{-10}$,

while the **BASE IONIZATION** equation $NH_3 + H_2O \rightleftharpoons NH_4^+ + OH^-$

has the base ionization constant $K_b = \frac{[NH_4^+][OH^-]}{[NH_3]} = 1.79 \times 10^{-5}$.

Since both equations involve NH_3 and NH_4^+, you might suspect that there is some relationship between K_a and K_b for these species. In fact

$$K_a \times K_b = \frac{[NH_3][H_3O^+]}{[NH_4^+]} \times \frac{[NH_4^+][OH^-]}{[NH_3]} = [H_3O^+][OH^-].$$

CONCLUSION: for a **CONJUGATE PAIR**

$$K_a\text{(conjugate acid)} \times K_b\text{(conjugate base)} = K_w.$$

This equation allows you to find K_b values for weak bases on the table of Relative Strengths of Acids.

EXAMPLE: **To FIND the K_a value for $H_2PO_4^-$** look down the ***LEFT*** side (that is, the ***ACID*** side) of the Table until you find $H_2PO_4^-$.

$\mathbf{H_2PO_4^-} \rightleftharpoons H^+ + HPO_4^{2-}$ .... 6.2×10^{-8}

The K_a for $H_2PO_4^-$ is immediately seen to be 6.2×10^{-8}.

To CALCULATE the K_b value for $H_2PO_4^-$ look down the ***RIGHT*** side (that is, the ***BASE*** side) of the Table until you find $H_2PO_4^-$.

$H_3PO_4 \rightleftharpoons H^+ + \mathbf{H_2PO_4^-}$ .... 7.5×10^{-3}

Since this equation should be read as $H_2PO_4^- + H_2O \rightleftharpoons H_3PO_4 + OH^-$ when $H_2PO_4^-$ acts as a base, the base ionization constant can be calculated from:

$$K_b(H_2PO_4^-) = \frac{K_w}{K_a(H_3PO_4)} = \frac{1.00 \times 10^{-14}}{7.5 \times 10^{-3}} = \mathbf{1.3 \times 10^{-12}}.$$

***EXERCISES*:**

35. Use your table of Relative Strengths of Acids to calculate K_b for the following bases.
    a) SO_4^{2-} c) HCO_3^- e) HSO_3^-
    b) $Al(H_2O)_5(OH)^{2+}$ d) HPO_4^{2-} f) HS^-

36. Given that $K_b = 1.7 \times 10^{-6}$ for N_2H_4, what is K_a for $N_2H_5^+$?

37. If a substance has a K_b value of 2×10^{-10}, is the substance a weak acid, a strong acid, a weak base or a strong base? Explain your answer.

IV.10. THE RELATIVE STRENGTHS OF ACIDS AND BASES

If solutions containing H_2CO_3 and SO_3^{2-} are mixed, the SO_3^{2-} can only act as a base since it has no protons.

$$H_2CO_3 + SO_3^{2-} \rightleftharpoons HCO_3^- + HSO_3^-$$

so that there are again 2 conjugate pairs in solution.

NOTE: All the Brønsted–Lowry reactions studied in Chem 12 will only involve the transfer of a single proton. There will ***NOT*** be two–proton transfers such as

$$H_2CO_3 + SO_3^{2-} \rightleftharpoons CO_3^{2-} + H_2SO_3.$$

Now consider what happens when CO_3^{2-} and $H_2PO_4^-$ are mixed.

$$CO_3^{2-} + H_2PO_4^- \rightleftharpoons HCO_3^- + HPO_4^{2-}$$

A "proton competition" is now set up in solution. There are two acids in equilibrium, $H_2PO_4^-$ and HCO_3^-, each of which can donate a proton. Conversely, there are two bases in solution, each of which can accept a proton. Reasonably, the stronger of the two acids involved will be more successful in donating a proton than the weaker. From the table of Relative Strengths of Acids it can be seen that $H_2PO_4^-$ ($K_a = 6.2 \times 10^{-8}$) is stronger than HCO_3^- ($K_a = 5.6 \times 10^{-11}$), so that:

$$\begin{array}{rcl} H_2PO_4^- & \longrightarrow & HPO_4^{2-} + H^+ \quad \text{(stronger)} \\ CO_3^{2-} + H^+ & \longleftarrow & HCO_3^- \\ \hline CO_3^{2-} + H_2PO_4^- & \rightleftharpoons & HCO_3^- + HPO_4^-. \end{array}$$

As a result, $H_2PO_4^-$ has a greater tendency to donate a proton than does HCO_3^-. Therefore, there will be more products than reactants ("products are favoured").

To Summarize: In a Brønsted–Lowry acid–base equilibrium, the side of the equilibrium which has the WEAKER ACID will be "favoured".

There is also a different way to show that products are favoured in the above reaction. [You are not required to know both methods. Both methods can be used to describe whether reactants or products are favoured in a reaction, so pick the method you like better.]

Since the above reaction is an equilibrium, the equilibrium expression for it is:

$$K_{eq} = \frac{[HCO_3^-][HPO_4^{2-}]}{[CO_3^{2-}][H_2PO_4^-]} .$$

This expression can be rewritten as follows

$$K_{eq} = \frac{[H^+][HPO_4^{2-}]}{[H_2PO_4^-]} \times \frac{[HCO_3^-]}{[H^+][CO_3^{2-}]} = K_a(H_2PO_4^-) \times \frac{1}{K_a(HCO_3^-)}$$

or simply $$K_{eq} = \frac{K_a(H_2PO_4^-)}{K_a(HCO_3^-)} .$$

Evaluating this expression: $$K_{eq} = \frac{6.2 \times 10^{-8}}{5.6 \times 10^{-11}} = 1.1 \times 10^3 = \frac{[products]}{[reactants]} .$$

This value agrees with the prediction: there should be more products than reactants if $K_{eq} > 1$.

NOTE: A general expression for calculating the equilibrium value can be derived, based on the K_a values of the acids involved in the reaction.

Let K_a(reactant acid) = the K_a value of the acid on the reactant side, **HReact**
K_a(product acid) = the K_a value of the acid on the product side, **HProd**

Then for the reaction: **HReact + Prod⁻ ⇌ React⁻ + HProd** the equilibrium expression is:

$$K_{eq} = \frac{K_a(\text{reactant acid})}{K_a(\text{product acid})} .$$

Important: Be sure that you understand the significance of the above expression. **K_{eq} is the ratio of [products] to [reactants],** and its value ***ALSO*** can be calculated as the ratio of the K_a value for the reactant acid to the K_a value for the product acid.

$$\frac{[products]}{[reactants]} = K_{eq} = \frac{K_a(\text{reactant acid})}{K_a(\text{product acid})} .$$

EXAMPLE: When HS^- and HCO_3^- are mixed, does the resulting equilibrium favour reactants or products?

Since HCO_3^- is a stronger acid than HS^-, then HS^- acts as a base and the equilibrium is written as

$$HCO_3^- + HS^- \rightleftharpoons CO_3^{2-} + H_2S\,.$$

The two acids are HCO_3^- and H_2S; H_2S is a stronger acid than HCO_3^-.

$$\begin{array}{lcll} HCO_3^- & \longrightarrow & CO_3^{2-} + H^+ & \\ HS^- + H^+ & \longleftarrow & H_2S & \text{(stronger)} \\ \hline HCO_3^- + HS^- & \rightleftharpoons & CO_3^{2-} + H_2S & \end{array}$$

Since H_2S has a greater tendency to donate protons and form its conjugate base, HS^-, then there will be more reactants than products when equilibrium is established (reactants are favoured).

Alternately, the equilibrium constant can be calculated for this reaction.

$$K_{eq} = \frac{K_a(HCO_3^-)}{K_a(H_2S)} = \frac{5.6 \times 10^{-11}}{9.1 \times 10^{-8}} = 6.2 \times 10^{-4} = \frac{[\text{products}]}{[\text{reactants}]}$$

Since $K_{eq} < 1$, this agrees with the prediction that there will be more reactants than products.

The weak acids could see they weren't going to win this competition
NITRIC
SULPHURIC
OXALIC
H+
CITRIC
-ZimBoBwe

EXERCISES:

38. Write the Brønsted–Lowry acid–base equilibria which occur when the following pairs of substances are mixed in solution. Identify the conjugate pairs formed.

a) HNO_2 and NH_3 c) HS^- and H_3PO_4 e) HCOOH and CN^- g) HSO_3^- and OH^-

b) CO_3^{2-} and HF d) HCO_3^- and S^{2-} f) H_3BO_3 and HO_2^- h) H_2O and H_2SO_3

39. In the following equilibria, predict whether reactants or products are favoured.

a) $H_2S + NH_3 \rightleftharpoons HS^- + NH_4^+$

b) $H_2PO_4^- + HS^- \rightleftharpoons HPO_4^{2-} + H_2S$

c) $NH_4^+ + OH^- \rightleftharpoons NH_3 + H_2O$

d) $H_2O_2 + SO_3^{2-} \rightleftharpoons HO_2^- + HSO_3^-$

e) $CH_3COOH + PO_4^{3-} \rightleftharpoons CH_3COO^- + HPO_4^{2-}$

40. Write the major equilibrium reactions which occur when the following substances are put into water. Ignore reactions between the ions and water. All salts are 100% dissociated in water. Do the resulting equilibria favour reactants or products?

a) HSO_4^- and NO_2^-

b) H_3PO_4 and HPO_4^{2-}

c) HCO_3^- and HSO_3^-

d) NH_4F

e) HSO_3^- and $HC_2O_4^-$

f) H_2O_2 and HS^-

g) $(NH_4)_2CO_3$

h) H_2S and NO_2^-

i) $Cr(H_2O)_6^{3+}$ and $H_2PO_4^-$

j) $H_2C_6H_5O_7^-$ and HSO_3^-

41. K_{eq} = 14 for the equilibrium: $H_2Te + HSe^- \rightleftharpoons HTe^- + H_2Se$.

a) Which acid is stronger: H_2Te or H_2Se?
b) Which base is stronger?
c) Based on your answers for parts (a) and (b), fill in the blanks in the following using the terms:

STRONGER ACID, weaker acid, STRONGER BASE and **weaker base.**

____________ + ____________ $\rightleftharpoons$ ____________ + ____________

42. Will K_{eq} be greater than or less than 1 for the equilibrium: $HSO_4^- + NH_3 \rightleftharpoons SO_4^{2-} + NH_4^+$?

43. Consider the following equilibrium which favours ***reactants***: $X^- + HA \rightleftharpoons HX + A^-$.

a) Give the formula of the two bases.
b) Which base must be weaker? Why?

44. The following equilibrium favours products: $Se^{2-} + HSO_4^- \rightleftharpoons HSe^- + SO_4^{2-}$.

a) Which is the stronger of the two acids in the equation?
b) If NaHSe were added to the solution, how would the above equilibrium be affected?

45. Given:

$HOI + H_2GeO_4^- \rightleftharpoons OI^- + H_3GeO_4$; $K_{eq} = 8.8 \times 10^{-3}$

$HOCl + OBr^- \rightleftharpoons OCl^- + HOBr$; $K_{eq} = 14$

$HOBr + H_2GeO_4^- \rightleftharpoons OBr^- + H_3GeO_4$; $K_{eq} = 7.9 \times 10^2$.

Arrange the four acids involved in order from strongest to weakest.

46. You are given three different acids: H_2SO_3, H_3PO_4 and HCOOH. Which of these acids would form an equilibrium with F^- in which the reactants are favoured? Explain your answer.

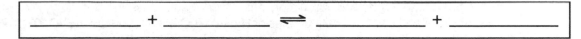

IV.11. pH AND pOH

Definitions:

$$pH = -\log_{10}[H_3O^+]$$

$$pOH = -\log_{10}[OH^-]$$

A Digression on Logarithms (or "logs")

Since this is NOT a math course (although you may occasionally wonder about that statement), "logarithms" will not be explored to any great extent. Nevertheless, you must know a bit about them, so get ready for some math.

"**$\mathbf{Log_{10}(X)}$**" translates as "**the logarithm to the base 10 of X**". O.K., what does that mean?

A **LOGARITHM TO THE BASE 10** is the power of 10 used to represent a number. (From now on, Chem 12 will always use the base 10 and will omit any further reference to the base.) Let's see how to use logarithms.

EXAMPLE: What is the logarithm of 1000?

The "logarithm of 1000" is written as: log(1000)

Since the logarithm is the power of 10 used to represent "1000", and: $1000 = 10^3$

then representing 1000 as 10 to the power of 3, means

$$\log(1000) = 3 .$$

(Try this yourself: grab your calculator, enter "1000" and press the "log" key. You should see the answer "3". If your calculator does not have a "LOG" key, you are in ***BIG TROUBLE*** so sell it to your little brother and buy a proper scientific calculator!)

The process of determining the logarithm of a number is called "taking the log" of the number.

EXAMPLE: What is log(0.01)?

In exponential terms: $0.01 = 10^{-2}$. The process of "taking the log" simply requires you to write down the power of 10 used to express the number.

Therefore: $\log(0.01) = \log(10^{-2}) = -2$.

Try this on your calculator: enter "0.01", press the "log" key, and read the answer "–2".

EXERCISE:

47. Take the log of each of the following.
    a) 100 b) 10^{-7} c) 0.001 d) 5.59×10^{-6} e) 1.0 f) 3.67×10^{-11}

The ***reverse*** procedure to "taking the log" is called "**taking the antilog**". The antilog function involves writing a number as a power of 10. In other words:

$$\text{antilog}(X) = 10^X.$$

EXAMPLE: What is the antilog of 4?

Write "the antilog of 4" as: antilog(4)

and since "antilog(X)" means "10 to the power of X", then: antilog(4) = 10^4 = 10 000 .

(Again, try this on your calculator: enter "4", then press the keys "INV" (or "2nd") and then "LOG". You should get the answer "10000".)

NOTE: It is very important to get enough significant digits in your answers. (You will learn more about significant digits in a logarithm later.) When you take the antilog of numbers such as "–8.72" or "–6.72" (try them), your calculator might show something like "0.000000001" or "0.0000002". It is important to make your calculator re–express answers in scientific notation or severe round–off errors will occur in your calculations. If you put these previous answers into "scientific mode" on your calculator, you should see "**1.905×10^{-9}**" and "**1.905×10^{-7}**", respectively. You should always express "antilogs" in scientific notation.

EXERCISE:

48. Take the antilog of each of the following.
    (a) 2 (b) –3 (c) 1 (d) 2.369 (e) –6.155 (f) –8.908

NOTES: a) "LOG" and "ANTILOG" cancel each other's effect, in the same way that adding 5 to a number and then subtracting 5 from the result will give back the original number.

EXAMPLES: (Check these calculations on your calculator)

antilog(log(3)) = antilog(0.4771) = 3
log(antilog(0.5)) = log(3.162) = 0.5

b) The "log" of a number is an easy way to keep track of powers of 10:

EXAMPLES: $\log(10^{-7}) = -7$ $\log(10^{30}) = 30$ $\log(10^{-6}) = -6$ $\log(10^{31}) = 31$

You can take the log of a power of 10 mentally by simply stating the power. Notice that **THE LOGARITHM OF A NUMBER CHANGES BY 1 WHENEVER THE NUMBER CHANGES BY A FACTOR OF 10.** The logarithm just records the powers of 10.

One more piece of information is needed about logarithms:

$$\log(10^X \cdot 10^Y) = \log(10^X) + \log(10^Y)$$

or, letting $A = 10^X$ and $B = 10^Y$ then **$\log(A \cdot B) = \log(A) + \log(B)$** .

This can be seen to be true as follows.

Since $10^3 \times 10^4 = 10^{(3+4)}$, it follows that

$$\log(10^3 \times 10^4) = \log(10^{(3+4)}) = 3 + 4 = \log(10^3) + \log(10^4)$$

and hence $\log(10^3 \times 10^4) = \log(10^3) + \log(10^4)$.

Now you have the math background to deal with pH and pOH calculations. (Incidentally, the term "pH" was coined by the Danish chemist S.P.L. Sorenson: the "p" is an abbreviation for "potenz", which means "potency" or "power" in German. Hence, pH represents "powers of 10 of $[H_3O^+]$".)

Converting from $[H_3O^+]$ and $[OH^-]$ to pH and pOH

EXAMPLE: If $[H_3O^+] = 3.94 \times 10^{-4}$ M, what is pH?

$$pH = -\log[H_3O^+] = -\log(3.94 \times 10^{-4}) = -(-3.405) = \mathbf{3.405}$$

EXAMPLE: If $[OH^-] = 9.51 \times 10^{-12}$ M, what is pOH?

$$pOH = -\log[OH^-] = -\log(9.51 \times 10^{-12}) = -(-11.022) = \mathbf{11.022}$$

Converting from pH and pOH to $[H_3O^+]$ and $[OH^-]$

This process is more involved than finding pH and requires a bit of simplification. Since $pH = -\log[H_3O^+]$ then sequentially "undoing" all the procedures which have been applied to $[H_3O^+]$ leaves you with the value of $[H_3O^+]$ on the right–hand side. Working from the outside, first remove the negative sign by changing the sign of the entire equation.

$$-pH = \log[H_3O^+]$$

Next remove the "log" by taking the antilog of the entire equation.

$$\text{antilog}(-pH) = \text{antilog}(\log[H_3O^+]) = [H_3O^+]$$

Overall, the new procedure is: $\mathbf{[H_3O^+] = antilog(-pH)}$, or $\mathbf{[H_3O^+] = 10^{-pH}}$.

Another "Calculator Interlude"
Perform the procedure "antilog(–pH)" on your calculator with this series of keypresses:
enter the negative of pH, then press "INV" and "LOG"
or press "10", "Y^X", enter the negative of pH, and finally press "=" .

EXAMPLE: If pH = 3.405, what is $[H_3O^+]$?

$[H_3O^+]$ = antilog(–3.405) (Enter "–3.405", then "INV", "LOG")
= $\mathbf{3.94 \times 10^{-4}}$ (or: "10", "Y^X", "–3.405", "=")

EXAMPLE: If pOH = 11.682, what is $[OH^-]$?

$[OH^-]$ = antilog(–11.682) = $\mathbf{2.08 \times 10^{-12}}$

Before going farther, an important relationship must be derived. Starting with the K_w expression

$$[H_3O^+][OH^-] = 1.00 \times 10^{-14},$$

take the logarithm of both sides of the equation:

$$\log([H_3O^+][OH^-]) = \log(1.00 \times 10^{-14}).$$

But $\log(A \times B) = \log(A) + \log(B)$

so that $\log([H_3O^+][OH^-]) = \log[H_3O^+] + \log[OH^-]$.

Since $\log(1.00 \times 10^{-14}) = -14$,

then $\log[H_3O^+] + \log[OH^-] = -14$.

Multiplying by –1 $\quad -\log[H_3O^+] - \log[OH^-] = 14$.

Finally, since $\quad pH = -\log[H_3O^+]$, and $pOH = -\log[OH^-]$, then

$$\boxed{\mathbf{pH + pOH = 14}}$$

You can now work back and forth between any of $[H_3O^+]$, $[OH^-]$, pH and pOH as shown in the following scheme.

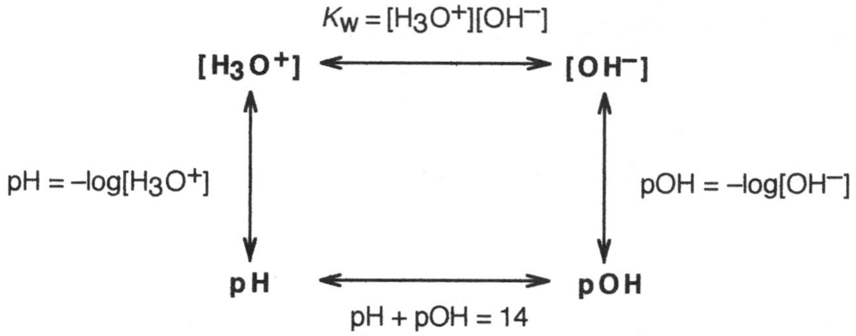

Any of the values in bold type can be calculated, given any of the other values, by using the relationships connecting the values.

EXAMPLE: If pH = 9.355, what is pOH?

Since: pH + pOH = 14.000

then: pOH = 14.000 – pH = 14.000 – 9.355 = **4.645**

EXAMPLE: If pH = 6.330, what is $[OH^-]$?

pOH = 14.000 – pH = 14.000 – 6.330 = 7.670

$[OH^-]$ = antilog(–7.670) = $\mathbf{2.14 \times 10^{-8}}$

Before continuing, recall the definitions $pH = -\log[H_3O^+]$, and $pOH = -\log[OH^-]$. These imply that other "powers" can be defined in similar terms. For example, pK_w can be defined as follows.

$$\mathbf{pK_w = -\log(K_w)} = -\log(1.00 \times 10^{-14}) \quad \text{so that} \quad \mathbf{pK_w = 14.000\ ,\ at\ 25^\circ C.}$$

Wait, there's more. Recall that the expression $\quad [H_3O^+][OH^-] = 1.00 \times 10^{-14}$

eventually becomes $\quad pH + pOH = 14$.

Let's take a slightly different approach this time.

$$-\log(\,[H_3O^+][OH^-]\,) = -\log[H_3O^+] - \log[OH^-] = pH + pOH$$

But $\quad pK_w = -\log(K_w) = -\log(\,[H_3O^+][OH^-]\,)$

Combining these relationships: $\boxed{\mathbf{pK_w = pH + pOH}}$

A Special Note on Significant Digits

Since $[H_3O^+] = \mathbf{5.28} \times 10^{-5}$ M   has 3 significant digits

          ↑

        3 significant digits

then the pH also must have 3 significant digits. To actually see which digits are "significant", examine the pH calculation in more detail.

$$pH = -\log(5.28 \times 10^{-5}) = -\log(\mathbf{5.28}) - \log(10^{-5})$$

                         ↑   ↑

             3 significant digits   not significant

$$= -0.\mathbf{723} - (-5) = 4.\mathbf{277}$$

> **Conclusion: In a pH *only* the digits *after* the decimal are significant digits.**

(The digits *before* the decimal come from the "nonsignificant" power of 10 in the original $[H_3O^+]$.)

EXERCISES:

49. Calculate pH *and* pOH, to the correct number of significant digits, in the following solutions.

    a) $[H_3O^+] = 1.0 \times 10^{-5}$ M   d) $[H_3O^+] = 12.5$ M   g) $[H_3O^+] = 5.2 \times 10^{-9}$ M
    b) $[OH^-] = 7.53 \times 10^{-3}$ M   e) $[OH^-] = 0.0125$ M   h) $[OH^-] = 8.51 \times 10^{-15}$ M
    c) $[OH^-] = 4.9 \times 10^{-6}$ M   f) $[H_3O^+] = 1.0$ M

50. Calculate $[H_3O^+]$ *and* $[OH^-]$, to the correct number of significant digits, in the following solutions.

    (a)   pH = 3.0   (c)   pH = 6.413   (e)   pH = -0.55   (g)   pOH = 9.561
    (b)   pOH = 5.633   (d)   pH = 8.50   (f)   pOH = 11.542   (h)   pH = 2.65

51. Recall that: $2 H_2O(l) + 59 kJ \rightleftharpoons H_3O^+(aq) + OH^-(aq)$. Assume a system is not at 25°C but rather involves a sample of pure water at its boiling temperature.

    a)   What happens to the pH of the water as the temperature increases?
    b)   What happens to the pOH of the water as the temperature increases?
    c)   What happens to the value of pK_w as the water temperature increases?

52. At 60°C, the value of pK_w is 13.018. Calculate pH, pOH, $[H_3O^+]$ and $[OH^-]$ in water at 60°C.

53. You have 0.5 M solutions of two weak acids. The pH of HA is 3.75 and the pH of HB is 5.84. Which solution will have the greater conductivity: HA or HB?

54. A representative of the Radical Chemistry Students of Canada (RCSC) has delivered an ultimatum to the Prime Minister. The RCSC demands 1 mol of dollars (in small unmarked bills) or they will put 1 drop (0.050 mL) of 5.0×10^{-7} M NaOH into the Pacific Ocean, and stir. As a result of adding the drop of NaOH, the oceans of the world will turn into an incredibly concentrated acid solution, having a pH of −17.7, therefore destroying the earth. In order to convince an unbelieving world, the RCSC has supplied the following calculations to back up their demands. You have 24 hours to meet their demands!

$$\text{moles of NaOH added} = 5.0 \times 10^{-7}\ \frac{\text{mol}}{\text{L}} \times 5.0 \times 10^{-5}\ \text{L} = 2.5 \times 10^{-11}\ \text{mol}$$

The estimated volume of the oceans is 1.37×10^{21} L (this number is correct)

Now $$[\text{NaOH}]_{\text{DILUTED}} = \frac{2.5 \times 10^{-11}\ \text{mol}}{1.37 \times 10^{21}\ \text{L}} = 1.82 \times 10^{-32}\ \text{M} = [\text{OH}^-]$$

But $[H_3O^+][OH^-] = K_w$ so that the $[H_3O^+]$ in the oceans will be

$$[H_3O^+] = \frac{K_w}{[OH^-]} = \frac{1.00 \times 10^{-14}}{1.82 \times 10^{-32}} = \mathbf{5.48 \times 10^{17}\ M} \quad \text{and} \quad \text{pH} = -\log[H_3O^+] = \mathbf{-17.7}\ .$$

Support or reject the above argument and state your reasons.

The pH Scale

The relationships between $[H_3O^+]$, $[OH^-]$, pH and pOH are shown on the following diagram.

pH:	0	1	2	3	4	5	6	7	8	9	10	11	12	13	14
$[H_3O^+]$:	1	10^{-1}	10^{-2}	10^{-3}	10^{-4}	10^{-5}	10^{-6}	10^{-7}	10^{-8}	10^{-9}	10^{-10}	10^{-11}	10^{-12}	10^{-13}	10^{-14}
$[OH^-]$:	10^{-14}	10^{-13}	10^{-12}	10^{-11}	10^{-10}	10^{-9}	10^{-8}	10^{-7}	10^{-6}	10^{-5}	10^{-4}	10^{-3}	10^{-2}	10^{-1}	1
pOH:	14	13	12	11	10	9	8	7	6	5	4	3	2	1	0

You should note the following about the diagram.

a) The pH scale INCREASES as the pOH scale DECREASES.

b) A solution is ACIDIC when its pH is LESS THAN 7; a solution is BASIC when its pOH is LESS THAN 7. Conversely, a solution is BASIC when its pH is GREATER THAN 7; a solution is ACIDIC when its pOH is GREATER THAN 7. A NEUTRAL solution has pH = pOH = 7.

c) At any point along the horizontal scale it is found, as expected, that pH + pOH = 14
and $[H_3O^+][OH^-] = 10^{-14}$.

d) While it is possible for pH to have a value of −1 or 15, say, the pH scale is meant for use in the range 0 to 14. A pH of −1.00 is better handled in terms of its molar concentration: $[H_3O^+] = 10$ M.

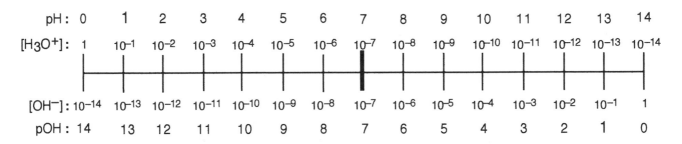

NOTE: The logarithmic "pH scale" is VERY nonlinear, as can be seen when comparing the pH and decimal scales.

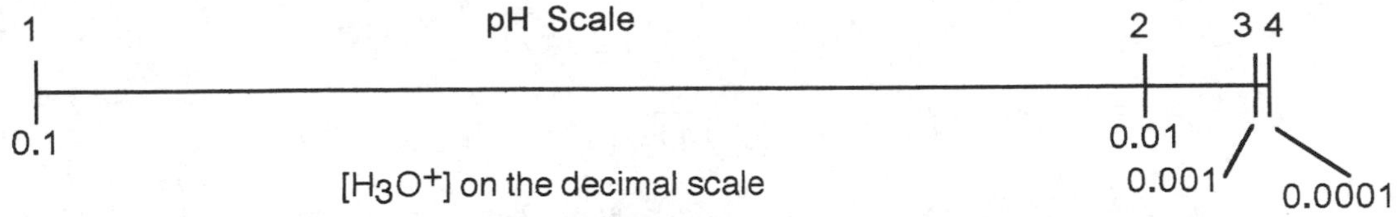

Going from 0.1 to 0.01 is a ten times decrease on the decimal scale, but is represented by a change of 1 unit on the pH scale. Also, going from 0.001 to 0.0001 is a ten times decrease on the decimal scale, but is again represented by a change of 1 on the pH scale.

When the pH is *increased* by 1, the $[H_3O^+]$ is *decreased* by 10.

***EXERCISES*:**

55. State whether the following represent conditions which are ACIDIC, NEUTRAL or BASIC.
    a) pH = 4
    b) pOH = 9
    c) $[H_3O^+] = 1 \times 10^{-10}$ M
    d) $[OH^-] = 1 \times 10^{-2}$ M
    e) pOH = 7
    f) $[H_3O^+] = 5 \times 10^{-7}$ M
    g) pH = 8
    h) $[OH^-] = 0.008$ M
    i) $[OH^-] = 1 \times 10^{-7}$ M
    j) pOH = 7.5
56. a) If the pH of a solution is increased by 2, what happens to the $[H_3O^+]$?
    b) If the pH of a solution is decreased by 3, what happens to the $[H_3O^+]$?
    c) If the pOH of a solution is increased by 1, what happens to the $[H_3O^+]$?
    d) If the pH of a solution is decreased by 2, what happens to the $[OH^-]$?
57. What happens to the pH of a 0.2 M solution of NaOH when a 0.2 M solution of $Zn(NO_3)_2$ is added?

IV.12. MIXTURES OF STRONG ACIDS AND BASES

Mixing an acid and a base produces a solution which can be acidic, basic or neutral depending on the relative amounts of reactants involved.

***EXAMPLE*:** If 10.0 mL of 0.100 M HCl is added to 90.0 mL of 0.100 M NaOH, what is the pH of the mixture?

First, perform dilution calculations on the $[H_3O^+]$ and $[OH^-]$ to find the starting concentrations (after dilution, but before reaction), $[H_3O^+]_{ST}$ and $[OH^-]_{ST}$.

$$[H_3O^+]_{ST} = 0.100 \text{ M} \times \frac{10.0 \text{ mL}}{100.0 \text{ mL}} = 0.0100 \text{ M}$$

$$[OH^-]_{ST} = 0.100 \text{ M} \times \frac{90.0 \text{ mL}}{100.0 \text{ mL}} = 0.0900 \text{ M}$$

Since the neutralization reaction $H_3O^+ + OH^- \longrightarrow 2\,H_2O$ involves a 1:1 ratio between H_3O^+ and OH^-, the OH^- is present in excess.

$$[OH^-]_{XS} = [OH^-]_{ST} - [OH^-]_{REACTED} \qquad \text{(where } [OH^-]_{XS} \text{ is the excess } [OH^-]\text{)}$$

But $[OH^-]_{REACTED} = [H_3O^+]_{REACTED}$

and since virtually all of the H_3O^+ originally present reacted with the added OH^- then

$$[H_3O^+]_{REACTED} = [H_3O^+]_{ST}.$$

Putting this all together gives

$$\boxed{[OH^-]_{XS} = [OH^-]_{ST} - [H_3O^+]_{ST}}$$

so that $[OH^-]_{XS} = [OH^-]_{ST} - [H_3O^+]_{ST} = 0.0900 - 0.0100 = 0.0800\ M$

and $pOH = -\log(0.0800) = 1.097$.

Finally $pH = 14.000 - pOH = 14.000 - 1.097 =$ **12.903**

A pH of 12.903 implies that $[H_3O^+] = 1.25 \times 10^{-13}$, which is very small as assumed in the statement "virtually all of the H_3O^+ originally present reacted".

Note that if H_3O^+ had been in excess, the equation would have been:

$$\boxed{[H_3O^+]_{XS} = [H_3O^+]_{ST} - [OH^-]_{ST}}$$

NOTE: You may prefer to find the value of $[OH^-]_{XS}$ by a "moles method". The above example would give

$$\text{moles } H^+ \text{ present} = 0.100\ \frac{mol}{L} \times 0.0100\ L = 0.00100\ mol$$

$$\text{moles } OH^- \text{ present} = 0.100\ \frac{mol}{L} \times 0.0900\ L = 0.00900\ mol$$

moles OH^- (in excess) = 0.00900 – 0.00100 = 0.00800 mol

total volume = 0.0100 + 0.0900 = 0.1000 L

$$[OH^-]_{XS} = \frac{0.00800\ mol}{0.1000\ L} = 0.0800\ M.$$

EXAMPLE: How many moles of HCl(g) must be added to 40.0 mL of 0.180 M NaOH to produce a solution having pH = 12.500, if it is assumed that there is no change in volume when the HCl is added?

The pH given indicates this is actually a ***basic*** solution, so the $[OH^-]$ is calculated.

$$pOH = 14.000 - pH = 14.000 - 12.500 = 1.500$$

$$[OH^-] = \text{antilog}(-1.500) = 0.03162 \text{ M}$$

The problem requires the mixing of HCl and NaOH to produce a basic solution; that is, to produce an excess of OH^-. The equation:

$$[OH^-]_{XS} = [OH^-]_{ST} - [H_3O^+]_{ST},$$

is rearranged to find $[H_3O^+]$, since the amount of HCl used is the unknown.

$$[H_3O^+]_{ST} = [OH^-]_{ST} - [OH^-]_{XS} = 0.180 - 0.0316 = 0.1484 \text{ M}.$$

Since the volume of the solution will be the volume of the NaOH, then

$$\text{moles HCl added} = 0.1484 \frac{\text{mol}}{\text{L}} \times 0.0400 \text{ L} = \mathbf{5.94 \times 10^{-3} \text{ mol}}.$$

EXERCISES:

58. Calculate the pH resulting from mixing 50.0 mL of 0.150 M NaOH with 50.0 mL of 0.200 M HCl.

59. Calculate the pOH resulting from mixing 75.0 mL of 0.200 M HBr with 225.0 mL of 0.150 M KOH.

60. Calculate the pH resulting from mixing 25.0 mL of 0.0420 M $Ba(OH)_2$ with 125.0 mL of 0.0120 M HCl.

61. Calculate the pOH resulting from the mixture of 50.0 mL of 0.0185 M $Sr(OH)_2$ with 35.0 mL of a solution containing 0.130 g of HCl.

62. Calculate the pH produced when 100.0 mL of a solution containing 5.00 g of KOH is mixed with 100.0 mL of a solution containing 6.00 g of HCl?

63. What is the pOH of the solution produced by mixing 250.0 mL of a solution containing 6.08 g of $Sr(OH)_2$ with 100.0 mL of a solution containing 8.09 g of HBr?

64. Calculate the pH which results when 0.450 g of LiOH are added to 200.0 mL of water containing 9.50 g of HI. Assume the volume of the final mixture is 200.0 mL.

In the next three exercises assume that no volume change occurs.

65. A chemist had 2.000 L of a 0.00120 M KOH solution. What mass of HCl(g) would have to be added to the KOH solution to produce a solution having a pH of 10.875?

66. What mass of LiOH must be added to 750.0 mL of 0.0550 M HCl to create a mixture having a pH of 2.500?

67. What mass of $Ca(OH)_2$ must be added to 500.0 mL of 0.0150 M HBr to create a solution with pH = 2.750?

68. Calcium hydroxide has a low solubility: $Ca(OH)_2(s) \rightleftharpoons Ca^{2+} + 2\,OH^-$; $K_{sp} = 3.88 \times 10^{-5}$.

a) What is the pH of a saturated solution of $Ca(OH)_2$?

b) A saturated solution of $Ca(OH)_2$ contains several grams of $Ca(OH)_2(s)$ on the bottom of a 1 L container. Why would the $Ca(OH)_2(s)$ dissolve if HCl were added to the solution?

IV.13. HYDROLYSIS

Definition: The **HYDROLYSIS OF A SALT** is a reaction between water and the cation or anion (or both) contained in the salt so as to produce an acidic or basic solution.

NOTE: All salts are considered to be 100% ionized in water. Hence, the ions making up the salt are of concern, not the salt itself.

In this section, only the reactions between ions and water are being considered. Reactions between ions, although they might occur, are not being examined.

Before dealing with ions that react with water, you must know which ions DON'T react with water: spectator ions.

Definition: The conjugates of strong acids and bases are **SPECTATOR IONS.**

(Note that "spectator ions" are always defined as "ions which do not participate in the reaction being considered". The nature of the reaction then determines the ions which are spectators: in precipitations, spectators always remain in solution; in acid–base reactions, spectators do not react with water to produce acidic or basic solutions; in the next unit (Electrochemistry), spectators will have somewhat different properties.)

EXAMPLE:

$NaOH \longrightarrow Na^+ + OH^-$ The Na^+ cannot re–form NaOH in an equilibrium (NaOH is 100 % ionized), so that **a reaction between Na^+ and water *CANNOT* occur**

$$Na^+ + H_2O \not\rightarrow NaOH + H^+$$ and therefore Na^+ is a **SPECTATOR.**

$HCl \longrightarrow H^+ + Cl^-$ The Cl^- cannot reform HCl in an equilibrium (HCl is 100 % ionized), so that **a reaction between Cl^- and water *CANNOT* occur**

$$Cl^- + H_2O \not\rightarrow HCl + OH^-$$ and Cl^- is a **SPECTATOR.**

CONCLUSION: SPECTATOR CATIONS will be the ions of the alkali metals (column I of the periodic table) and the ions of the alkaline earth metals (column II).

SPECTATOR ANIONS will be the first five anions found at the top right of the table of Relative Strengths of Acids:

ClO_4^-, I^-, Br^-, Cl^- and NO_3^- (HSO_4^- is not a spectator since it is a weak acid).

It is strongly suggested that you memorize the spectators – you will be using them quite frequently from now on.

The procedure for determining the behaviour of a salt in water is straightforward.

a) Determine the ions produced when the salt dissociates.
b) Discard from further consideration any spectators.
c) Any remaining ions will act as acids if they are on the acid (left) side of the Table and/or as bases if they are on the base (right) side.

EXAMPLE 1: **NaCl**

- The dissociation process gives: $NaCl(s) \longrightarrow Na^+(aq) + Cl^-(aq)$; both Na^+ and Cl^- are spectators
- Since no ions are available to react with water, solutions of NaCl will be ***NEUTRAL*** and ***NO HYDROLYSIS REACTION OCCURS.***

EXAMPLE 2: **NH_4Cl**

- The dissociation process gives: $NH_4Cl(s) \longrightarrow NH_4^+ + Cl^-(aq)$; Cl^- is a spectator
- NH_4^+ is on the acid side of the Table, so that the hydrolysis reaction is:

$$NH_4^+ + H_2O \rightleftharpoons H_3O^+ + NH_3.$$

Because H_3O^+ is produced, the resulting solution is **ACIDIC.**

EXAMPLE 3: **NaF**

- The dissociation process gives: $NaF(s) \longrightarrow Na^+(aq) + F^-(aq)$; Na^+ is a spectator
- F^- is found on the base side of the Table, so that the hydrolysis reaction is:

$$F^- + H_2O \rightleftharpoons HF + OH^-.$$

Because OH^- is produced, the resulting solution is **BASIC.**

(***Note***: While it is true that the solution produces HF, an acid, the solution is still BASIC because no H_3O^+ is produced in the equilibrium reaction.)

EXAMPLE 4: **$NaHC_2O_4$**

- The dissociation process gives: $NaHC_2O_4(s) \longrightarrow Na^+(aq) + HC_2O_4^-(aq)$; Na^+ is a spectator

Chemistry 12 will not consider any cases where a salt dissociates into **more than two different species** in solution. As a result, $NaHC_2O_4$ *NEVER* initially dissociates in a reaction such as:

$$NaHC_2O_4 \longrightarrow Na^+ + H^+ + C_2O_4^{2-}$$

- Now there is a problem: $HC_2O_4^-$ is an ***AMPHIPROTIC*** ion, and as such is found on both the acid ***and*** base side of the Table. A decision must be made as to whether $HC_2O_4^-$ acts preferentially as an acid or a base.

For $HC_2O_4^-$ acting as an acid

$$HC_2O_4^- + H_2O \rightleftharpoons H_3O^+ + C_2O_4^{2-} \ ; \quad K_a(HC_2O_4^-) = 6.4 \times 10^{-5}$$

For $HC_2O_4^-$ acting as a base

$$HC_2O_4^- + H_2O \rightleftharpoons H_2C_2O_4 + OH^- ; \ K_b(HC_2O_4^-) = \frac{K_w}{K_a(H_2C_2O_4)} = \frac{1.0 \times 10^{-14}}{5.9 \times 10^{-2}} = 1.7 \times 10^{-13}$$

Since $HC_2O_4^-$ is a stronger acid ($K_a = 6.4 \times 10^{-5}$) than it is a base ($K_b = 1.7 \times 10^{-13}$), then $HC_2O_4^-$ is **ACIDIC** in solution.

Note: A small amount of $HC_2O_4^-$ ***will*** undergo base ionization, but the ACIDIC character of $HC_2O_4^-$ will completely dominate the BASIC character.

EXAMPLE 5: **NH_4NO_2**

- The dissociation process gives: $NH_4NO_2(s) \longrightarrow NH_4^+(aq) + NO_2^-(aq)$.
- Neither of the ions are spectators, so both ions undergo hydrolysis in solution:

$$NH_4^+ + H_2O \rightleftharpoons H_3O^+ + NH_3$$

$$NO_2^- + H_2O \rightleftharpoons HNO_2 + OH^-$$

One ion is producing H_3O^+ in solution and the other is producing OH^-. To find whether more H_3O^+ or OH^- is produced, check the K_a and K_b values again.

$$K_a(NH_4^+) = 5.6 \times 10^{-10}$$

$$K_b(NO_2^-) = \frac{K_w}{K_a(HNO_2)} = \frac{1.0 \times 10^{-14}}{4.6 \times 10^{-4}} = 2.2 \times 10^{-11}$$

Since $K_a(NH_4^+) > K_b(NO_2^-)$, then NH_4^+ produces more H_3O^+ than NO_2^- does OH^- and the solution is **ACIDIC.**

EXAMPLE 6: **$Fe(H_2O)_6Cl_3$**

- The dissociation process gives: $Fe(H_2O)_6Cl_3(s) \longrightarrow Fe(H_2O)_6^{3+}(aq) + 3\,Cl^-(aq)$.

  (Look on your Table for $Fe(H_2O)_6^{3+}$. Note that any time you see a metal ion with water molecules attached, that ion will be on the Table. ***NEVER*** split off the H_2O's and attempt to show the metal ion separately.)

- Cl^- is a spectator
- $Fe(H_2O)_6^{3+}$ is found on the acid side of the Table so that the hydrolysis reaction is:

$$Fe(H_2O)_6^{3+} + H_2O \rightleftharpoons H_3O^+ + Fe(H_2O)_5(OH)^{2+}.$$

Because H_3O^+ is produced, the resulting solution is **ACIDIC.**

NOTE: Highly charged metal ions strongly attract the negative end (oxygen end) of the dipolar water molecule. As a result, Fe^{3+}, Cr^{3+} and Al^{3+} ions form species such as:

$$Fe(H_2O)_6^{3+},\ Cr(H_2O)_6^{3+} \text{ and } Al(H_2O)_6^{3+}.$$

The positive charge on the metal atom attracts electrons away from the water's oxygen atoms, pulling electrons in the O–H bonds closer to the oxygen and weakening the O–H bond. This weakened O–H bond has a large tendency to release H^+ from the attached H_2O's so that:

$$Fe(H_2O)_6^{3+} + H_2O \rightleftharpoons H_3O^+ + Fe(H_2O)_5(OH)^{2+}.$$

EXAMPLE 7: **$Al(H_2O)_5(OH)(NO_3)_2$**

- The dissociation process gives: $Al(H_2O)_5(OH)(NO_3)_2(s) \longrightarrow Al(H_2O)_5(OH)^{2+}(aq) + 2\,NO_3^-(aq)$.

  Note that again there is a metal ion with attached H_2O's, but this time the species is found on the base (right) side of the Table.

- NO_3^- is a spectator
- $Al(H_2O)_5(OH)^{2+}$ is on the base side of the Table so that the hydrolysis reaction is:

$$Al(H_2O)_5(OH)^{2+} + H_2O \rightleftharpoons Al(H_2O)_6^{3+} + OH^-.$$

Because OH^- is produced, the resulting solution is **BASIC.**

EXERCISES:

69. Write the hydrolysis reaction for the following salts in water and state whether the resulting solution is acidic, basic or neutral. Note that two steps are involved for each reaction: first you must write an equation to show how the salt dissociates in water, and then write a reaction equation for the predominant reaction (if any) which occurs between the **ions** and **water.** (Ignore any reactions between ions.) For some of the salts you will have to perform a calculation to decide whether the solution produced is acidic or basic.

a) Na_2SO_3	c) LiBr	e) NH_4CH_3COO	g) $K_2C_2O_4$	i) $Al(H_2O)_6Cl_3$
b) Na_2HPO_4	d) K_2CO_3	f) $Na_2HC_6H_5O_7$	h) $Ca(NO_3)_2$	j) NH_4F

70. Predict whether the following salts are acidic, basic, or neutral in solution.

a) $NaNO_2$	c) NH_4I	e) $Cr(H_2O)_5(OH)Br_2$	g) $NaHSO_3$	i) Na_3PO_4
b) $Ba(NO_3)_2$	d) KBr	f) Na_2CO_3	h) Na_2HPO_4	j) $(NH_4)_3C_6H_5O_7$

71. You have the following solutions: A = 0.1 M $NaNO_2$, B = saturated $Fe(OH)_3$.
Why are both solutions only slightly basic?

72. You have two solutions: 1 M KF and 1 M HF. Which solution has the greater conductivity? Explain your answer.

73. Arrange the following 1.0 M solutions from highest to lowest pH.

NH_4Cl, HCl, $NaCH_3COO$, NH_4CH_3COO, NaOH

IV.14. CALCULATIONS INVOLVING K_a

When a weak acid, HA, is put into water, some of the acid ionizes. As a result of the ionization, a certain amount of H_3O^+ is produced; the smaller the K_a value for the acid, the less H_3O^+ is formed. Since it is assumed that none of the acid ionizes until it reacts with the water, it is appropriate to use a "ST, Δ, EQ" approach to allow the incorporation of the "sense of time passing" implied by the ionization process.

There are three major pieces of information which a completely solved problem contains.

- [HA], the original concentration of the weak acid
- K_a for the acid
- $[H_3O^+]$ or pH of the acid solution

The only equation used to solve the problems is the acid ionization expression. Therefore, there are three types of problems to be solved:

- given [HA] and K_a, find $[H_3O^+]$ (or pH)
- given [HA] and $[H_3O^+]$ (or pH), find K_a
- given $[H_3O^+]$ (or pH) and K_a, find [HA]

You should ***ALWAYS*** check the information available in order to understand the type of problem. The easiest way to decide is to determine what you are asked to find. Since you will ***not*** be given a value for the unknown, values ***must*** be available for the other two pieces of required information.

EXAMPLE: If $K_a = 1.8 \times 10^{-5}$ for CH_3COOH, what is the pH of a 0.500 M solution of CH_3COOH?

The problem gives values for $[CH_3COOH]$ and K_a ; the $[H_3O^+]$ and pH must be found. First write the acid ionization equation for CH_3COOH and set up a "ST, Δ, EQ" table.

	$CH_3COOH + H_2O$	$\rightleftharpoons$	$CH_3COO^- +$	H_3O^+
ST	0.500		0	0
+Δ	−X		+X	+X
= EQ	0.500 − X		X	X

$$\text{Now:} \quad K_a = \frac{[CH_3COO^-][H_3O^+]}{[CH_3COOH]} = \frac{X^2}{0.500 - X} = 1.8 \times 10^{-5}$$

This equation requires the use of the quadratic formula to solve it. Since the use of the quadratic formula is not required in Chemistry 12, we make a simplifying assumption. Assume that the WEAK acid is sufficiently weak that the amount of acid which ionizes will not significantly affect the original concentration of the acid. That is, assume that:

$$[CH_3COOH]_{EQ} = 0.500 - X \cong 0.500 \text{ .}$$

This assumption reduces the equation to

$$K_a = \frac{X^2}{0.500} = \mathbf{1.8 \times 10^{-5}} \text{ .}$$

Solving: $X = 3.0 \times 10^{-3}$ M $= [H_3O^+]$ and pH = **2.52** .

NOTE: (a) Since $0.50 >> 3.0 \times 10^{-3}$, the assumption that

$$0.50 - X = 0.50 - 3.0 \times 10^{-3} \cong 0.50$$

was justified. This is a good way to check your answer. More specifically, the assumption is justified if the **"PERCENTAGE DISSOCIATION" IS NOT MORE THAN 5%** .

Percentage dissociation refers to the amount of H_3O^+ produced as a percentage of the original amount of acid present.

$$\% \text{ dissociation} = \frac{[H_3O^+]_{EQ}}{[HA]_{ST}} \times 100\%$$

In the example above: $$\% \text{ dissociation} = \frac{3.0 \times 10^{-3} \text{ M}}{0.50 \text{ M}} \times 100\% = \mathbf{0.60\%} \text{ .}$$

(b) You **MUST** state your simplifying assumption when solving such a problem as this. If you don't state your assumption, and simply ignore the "X" in the term "0.50 – X", it will be considered that you have made a mistake in solving the problem. A satisfactory way to state your assumption is:

" **Assume 0.50 – X ≅ 0.50** " .

(c) **A calculation requiring the use of a K_a value from the table of Relative Strengths of Acids is restricted to a maximum of 2 significant digits in the final answer. (All K_a values in the Table are only good to 2 significant digits.)**

EXAMPLE: If pH = 1.70 for a 0.100 M solution of an unknown weak acid, HA, what is K_a for HA?

The concentration and pH of the acid are given; the value of K_a must be found.

First convert the pH to $[H_3O^+]$: pH = 1.70 gives $[H_3O^+]$ = antilog(–1.70) = 0.0200 M.

Next set up a "ST, Δ, EQ" table for acid ionization.

	$HA + H_2O \rightleftharpoons$	H_3O^+ +	A^-
ST	0.100	0	0
+ Δ	–0.0200	+0.0200	+0.0200
= EQ	0.100 – 0.0200	0.0200	0.0200

In this case ***don't assume that the amount of ionization is negligible*** (0.0200 is actually 20% of 0.100). Also, even if the amount of ionization is small the subtraction can be performed easily to give a more accurate answer.

Hence [HA] = 0.100 – 0.0200 = 0.080 M

and $$K_a = \frac{[H_3O^+][A^-]}{[HA]} = \frac{(0.0200)^2}{0.080} = 5.0 \times 10^{-3}.$$

EXAMPLE: What mass of NH_4Cl will produce 1.50 L of a solution having a pH of 4.75?

First dissociate the salt: $NH_4Cl \longrightarrow NH_4^+ + Cl^-$.

The Cl^- is a spectator, and NH_4^+ acts as an acid.

$$NH_4^+ + H_2O \rightleftharpoons H_3O^+ + NH_3$$

Since K_a for NH_4^+ is in the Table and pH is given, then $[NH_4^+]$ must be found. The $[NH_4^+]$ and volume of solution is then used to find moles and mass of NH_4Cl.

Convert the pH into $[H_3O^+]$: pH = 4.75 gives $[H_3O^+]$ = antilog(–4.75) = 1.78×10^{-5} M.

Next set up a "ST, Δ, EQ" table for acid ionization.

	$NH_4^+ + H_2O \rightleftharpoons$	H_3O^+ +	NH_3
ST	X	0	0
+ Δ	-1.78×10^{-5}	$+1.78 \times 10^{-5}$	$+1.78 \times 10^{-5}$
= EQ	$X - 1.78 \times 10^{-5}$	1.78×10^{-5}	1.78×10^{-5}

Assume $X - 1.78 \times 10^{-5} \cong X$,

so that $K_a = \dfrac{[H_3O^+][NH_3]}{[NH_4^+]} = \dfrac{(1.78 \times 10^{-5})^2}{X} = 5.6 \times 10^{-10}$.

Solving $X = [NH_4^+] = [NH_4Cl] = 0.565\ M$

Note that the assumption was valid: $X - 1.78 \times 10^{-5} = 0.565 - 1.78 \times 10^{-5} = 0.565$.

Finally mass $NH_4Cl = 0.565\ \dfrac{mol}{L} \times 1.50\ L \times \dfrac{53.5\ g}{mol} = \mathbf{45\ g}$

NOTES:

1. In all the calculations, consider only the first proton of a polyprotic acid to be given off during the ionization process. For example, in $H_2C_2O_4$ the only important ionization is:

$$H_2C_2O_4 + H_2O \rightleftharpoons H_3O^+ + HC_2O_4^- .$$

The amount of $C_2O_4^{2-}$ which is actually produced in the second ionization:

$$HC_2O_4^- + H_2O \rightleftharpoons H_3O^+ + C_2O_4^{2-} ,$$

is a very small fraction of the small amount of $HC_2O_4^-$ produced by the first ionization. As a result, the amount of $C_2O_4^{2-}$ produced from $H_2C_2O_4$ can be neglected.

2. **TWO OF THE ACIDS IN YOUR TABLE DO NOT EXIST!** When $CO_2(g)$ is put in water, an acidic solution results due to the reaction:

$$CO_2(aq) + 2\,H_2O(l) \rightleftharpoons HCO_3^-(aq) + H_3O^+(aq) .$$

For many years it was thought that the molecule "H_2CO_3", carbonic acid, was produced when CO_2 combined with H_2O, and that the resulting H_2CO_3 then underwent ionization:

$$CO_2(aq) + H_2O(l) \rightleftharpoons H_2CO_3(aq), \qquad \text{followed by}$$
$$H_2CO_3(aq) + H_2O(l) \rightleftharpoons HCO_3^-(aq) + H_3O^+(aq) .$$

However, numerous studies have failed to find evidence for the existence of H_2CO_3. Nevertheless, it is often convenient to pretend that the molecule "H_2CO_3" exists. Solutions of CO_2 are therefore called "carbonic acid" and the ionization reaction is assumed to be:

$$H_2CO_3(aq) + H_2O(l) \rightleftharpoons HCO_3^-(aq) + H_3O^+(aq) .$$

Similarly, there is little or no experimental evidence for the existence of sulphurous acid, H_2SO_3, which was thought to result from solutions of $SO_2(g)$ in water. The H_2SO_3 molecule is treated similarly to H_2CO_3.

EXERCISES:

74. What is the $[H_3O^+]$ in a 0.050 M solution of H_2S?
75. What is the pH of a 0.20 M solution of H_2O_2?
76. What concentration of HCOOH is required to produce a pH of 1.93?
77. The pH of a 0.250 M solution of HX is 1.357. What is K_a for HX?
78. What concentration of $CO_2(aq)$, that is "H_2CO_3", is required to produce a pH of 4.18?
79. Calculate the pH of a 0.30 M solution of NH_4NO_3.
80. A 0.100 M solution of HOBr has a pH of 5.343. What is K_a for HOBr?
81. What is the pH of a 3.0 M solution of $Fe(H_2O)_6Cl_3$?
82. The pH of a 0.010 M solution of HBr is 2.00. What is K_a for HBr?
83. Red blood cells undergo "haemolysis" (rupture of the cell walls) at a pH of 3.00. In an effort to minimize damage to the cell contents, a biochemist added acetic acid to 100 mL of a suspension of red blood cells in blood plasma so as to gently rupture the cell walls. What mass of acetic acid was required?

IV.15. CALCULATIONS INVOLVING K_b

When a weak base, A^-, is put into water, some of the base ionizes. As a result of the ionization, a certain amount of OH^- will be produced; the smaller the K_b value for the base, the less OH^- formed.

Calculations involving weak bases are similar to the calculations involving weak acids, with two important changes:

- the K_b value will have to be calculated; it can't be taken directly from the Table.
- the resulting solution will be basic, not acidic, which means using $[OH^-]$ rather than $[H_3O^+]$.

EXAMPLE: What is the pH of a 0.10 M solution of NaCN?

First dissociate the salt: $NaCN \longrightarrow Na^+ + CN^-$. Na^+ is a spectator and CN^- acts as a weak base.

The [NaCN] is given and $K_b(CN^-)$ can be calculated from the K_a value of HCN found in the Table. The $[OH^-]$ and then the pH must be found. First write out the base ionization equation for CN^- and set up a "ST, Δ, EQ" table.

	CN^- + H_2O ⇌	HCN +	OH^-
ST	0.10	0	0
+ Δ	−X	+X	+X
= EQ	0.10 − X	X	X

Assume this base is sufficiently weak to approximate: $0.10 - X \cong 0.10$.

Then $K_b(CN^-) = \dfrac{K_w}{K_a(HCN)} = \dfrac{1.0 \times 10^{-14}}{4.9 \times 10^{-10}} = 2.04 \times 10^{-5}$

and $K_b = \dfrac{[HCN][OH^-]}{[CN^-]} = \dfrac{X^2}{0.10} = 2.04 \times 10^{-5}$. Solving: $X = [OH^-] = 1.43 \times 10^{-3}$ M

so that $pOH = -\log[OH^-] = 2.845$, and $pH = 14.00 - pOH = \mathbf{11.15}$.

EXAMPLE: The pOH of a 0.50 M solution of the weak acid HA is 10.64. What is K_b for A^-?

Do not be tricked into assuming you can go directly to K_b from the starting data. In this problem you are given the concentration of an **acid** and the pOH of its solution, and are asked to find the K_b value for the conjugate base. Since this is actually an acidic solution ("the weak acid"), the data must be put into an appropriate form.

First, convert the pOH to $[H_3O^+]$.

$pH = 14.00 - pOH = 14.00 - 10.64 = 3.36$
$[H_3O^+] = \text{antilog}(-3.36) = 4.37 \times 10^{-4}$ M.

Next, set up a "ST, Δ, EQ" table for acid ionization.

	$HA + H_2O \rightleftharpoons$	H_3O^+	+ A^-
ST	0.50	0	0
+ Δ	-4.37×10^{-4}	$+4.37 \times 10^{-4}$	$+4.37 \times 10^{-4}$
= EQ	$0.50 - 4.37 \times 10^{-4}$	4.37×10^{-4}	4.37×10^{-4}

Since $0.50 - 4.37 \times 10^{-4} \cong 0.50$

then $K_a(HA) = \dfrac{[H_3O^+][A^-]}{[HA]} = \dfrac{(4.37 \times 10^{-4})^2}{0.50} = 3.81 \times 10^{-7}$

and $K_b(A^-) = \dfrac{K_w}{K_a(HA)} = \dfrac{1.00 \times 10^{-14}}{3.81 \times 10^{-7}} = \mathbf{2.6 \times 10^{-8}}$.

EXERCISES:

84. What concentration of SO_3^{2-} is required to produce a pH of 9.69?

85. Calculate $[H^+]$, $[OH^-]$, pH and pOH for a 0.20 M solution of NH_3.

86. $K_b = 1.7 \times 10^{-6}$ for hydrazine, N_2H_4. If a solution of N_2H_4 has a pH of 10.50, what is the $[N_2H_4]$ in the solution?

87. A 0.750 M solution of Te^{2-} had a pH of 12.438 What is K_b for Te^{2-}?

88. Calculate the pH of a 0.50 M solution of NaCN.

89. A 0.600 M solution of the weak base hydroxylamine, NH_2OH, has a pH of 9.904. What is K_a for NH_3OH^+ ?

90. What is the pH of a 0.80 M solution of sodium phenate, NaC_6H_5O?

91. Calculate the original $[NH_3]$ in a solution in which 1.30 % of the NH_3 is ionized, and also calculate $[OH^-]$ in the equilibrium mixture.

92. Calculate the pH of a saturated solution of CaF_2. ($K_{sp} = 1.46 \times 10^{-10}$ for CaF_2)

93. The pH of a saturated solution of $Na_2C_2O_4$ is 8.82. What is the K_{sp} for $Na_2C_2O_4$?

IV.16. ACID–BASE TITRATIONS

Definition: A **TITRATION** is a process in which a measured amount of a solution is reacted with a known volume of another solution (one of the solutions has an unknown concentration) until a desired **EQUIVALENCE POINT** (or "**STOICHIOMETRIC POINT**") is reached. [We previously used this definition in unit III.]

In the reaction: $aA + bB \longrightarrow cC + dD$, the EQUIVALENCE POINT (or STOICHIOMETRIC POINT) of the reaction occurs when:

$$\frac{\text{moles A}}{\text{moles B}} = \frac{a}{b}.$$

In other words, the equivalence point occurs when the mole ratio in the reaction exactly equals the mole ratio required by the stoichiometry of the reaction.

Before proceeding to titration calculations, recall that $c = \frac{n}{V}$

where: c = molar concentration

n = moles in solution

V = volume of solution.

All titration problems involve at least FIVE PARAMETERS.

concentration of acid	**concentration of base**	**base/acid mole ratio**
volume of acid	**volume of base**	

If the reaction equation is given, the base/acid mole ratio is read directly from the balanced equation so that one of the concentrations or volumes must be the unknown. These problems always have three parts to the calculation.

- Use $c = n/V$ to calculate the moles of the first substance present, starting with the substance for which you are given both the concentration and volume.
- Use the base/acid mole ratio to calculate the moles of the second substance present.
- Use $c = n/V$ to combine the moles of the second substance with either the concentration or the volume given for the second substance to find the unknown volume or concentration.

NOTE: Pay special attention to significant digits with titration calculations. The purpose of a titration is to get accurate and precise values for unknown concentrations.

EXAMPLE: In the reaction $H_2SO_4 + 2\,NaOH \longrightarrow Na_2SO_4 + 2\,H_2O$ an equivalence point occurs when 23.10 mL of 0.2055 M NaOH is added to a 25.00 mL portion of H_2SO_4. What is the $[H_2SO_4]$?

NOTE: The use of the unit "mmol" (millimole) will save having to convert back and forth between litres and millilitres — the following ratios are equal:

$$\mathbf{1\ M} = \frac{\mathbf{1\ mol}}{\mathbf{L}} = \frac{\mathbf{1\ mmol}}{\mathbf{mL}}\ .$$

$$\text{moles NaOH} = n = c \cdot V = 0.2055\ \frac{\text{mmol}}{\text{mL}} \times 23.10\ \text{mL} = 4.7471\ \text{mmol}$$

$$\text{moles } H_2SO_4 = 4.7471\ \text{mmol NaOH} \times \frac{1\ \text{mmol } H_2SO_4}{2\ \text{mmol NaOH}} = 2.3735\ \text{mmol}$$

$$\text{Hence:}\quad [H_2SO_4] = c = \frac{n}{V} = \frac{2.3735\ \text{mmol}}{25.00\ \text{mL}} = \mathbf{0.09494\ M}$$

Partial Neutralization:

One mole of the polyprotic acid molecule $H_4P_2O_7$ has 4 mol of removable protons. In the neutralization reaction $H^+ + OH^- \longrightarrow H_2O$, 1 mol of OH^- can neutralize 1 mol of H^+. Therefore, one H^+ after another can be removed from the $H_4P_2O_7$, in a series of "partial neutralization" reactions:

$$H_4P_2O_7 + 1\,OH^- \longrightarrow H_3P_2O_7^- + 1\,H_2O$$

$$H_4P_2O_7 + 2\,OH^- \longrightarrow H_2P_2O_7^{2-} + 2\,H_2O$$

$$H_4P_2O_7 + 3\,OH^- \longrightarrow HP_2O_7^{3-} + 3\,H_2O$$

$$H_4P_2O_7 + 4\,OH^- \longrightarrow P_2O_7^{4-} + 4\,H_2O$$

Note that each time another OH^- is added, the number of H's left on the $H_4P_2O_7$ decreases by ***one*** and the number of water molecules formed increases by ***one***. In addition, each time another H^+ is removed, the $H_4P_2O_7$ gains an extra NEGATIVE charge.

If the reaction equation involves not just OH^- but rather NaOH, the partial neutralization reactions become:

$$H_4P_2O_7 + 1\,NaOH \longrightarrow NaH_3P_2O_7 + 1\,H_2O$$

$$H_4P_2O_7 + 2\,NaOH \longrightarrow Na_2H_2P_2O_7 + 2\,H_2O$$

$$H_4P_2O_7 + 3\,NaOH \longrightarrow Na_3HP_2O_7 + 3\,H_2O$$

$$H_4P_2O_7 + 4\,NaOH \longrightarrow Na_4P_2O_7 + 4\,H_2O$$

Note that both H^+ and Na^+ have a +1 charge. These reactions are double replacement reactions in which the H's are systematically replaced by the Na's. In each case the number of H's and Na's add up to 4. (The original acid contains 4 removable H's.) The number of NaOH's added equals the number of H_2O's formed and the number of Na's in the salt.

Partial neutralization calculations involve five parameters. In addition to "standard" calculations in which the concentration or volume of one substance is the unknown, the base/acid mole ratio itself can be the unknown. In this case, the volumes and concentrations of both the acid and base are given, allowing the moles of acid and base to be found. The resulting moles are then made into a ratio to calculate the unknown base/acid mole ratio.

EXAMPLE: An equivalence point is reached by reacting 25.00 mL of 0.1255 M NaOH with 38.74 mL of 0.02700 M $H_4P_2O_7$. How many protons are removed from the $H_4P_2O_7$ on the average and what is the balanced equation for the reaction?

$$\text{moles NaOH used} = 0.1255\ \frac{\text{mmol}}{\text{mL}} \times 25.00\ \text{mL} = 3.1375\ \text{mmol}$$

$$\text{moles } H_4P_2O_7 \text{ used} = 0.02700\ \frac{\text{mmol}}{\text{mL}} \times 38.74\ \text{mL} = 1.0460\ \text{mmol}$$

$$\frac{\text{moles NaOH}}{\text{moles } H_4P_2O_7} = \frac{3.1375\ \text{mmol}}{1.0460\ \text{mmol}} = \frac{3.000\ \text{mmol NaOH}}{1\ \text{mmol } H_4P_2O_7}$$

Therefore the reaction stoichiometry requires 3 NaOH for every 1 $H_4P_2O_7$:

$$\mathbf{3\ NaOH + H_4P_2O_7 \longrightarrow Na_3HP_2O_7 + 3\ H_2O}$$ and 3 protons are removed, on the average.

Percentage Purity

Titrations are often performed to determine the percentage purity of a solid acid or base. There are numerous ways to perform such calculations, but most students find the following procedure simple to follow.

- Calculate the concentration of the acid (or base) using the concentrations, volumes and base/acid mole ratio given. The concentration calculated here is the ACTUAL CONCENTRATION of the acid/base in solution – a titration will only react the moles of substances actually present.
- Use the mass of impure solid acid/base and its molar mass to calculate the EXPECTED CONCENTRATION of the impure acid/base which is created when the solid is dissolved in the stated volume of solution.
- Calculate the percentage purity from the equation:

$$\textbf{Percentage purity} = \frac{\textbf{Actual concentration}}{\textbf{Expected concentration}} \times \mathbf{100\%}\ .$$

EXAMPLE: A 3.4786 g sample of impure $NaHSO_4$ is diluted to 250.0 mL . A 25.00 mL sample of the solution is titrated with 26.77 mL of 0.09974 M NaOH. What is the percentage purity of the $NaHSO_4$?

First, find the moles of NaOH used in the titration.

$$\text{moles NaOH} = 0.09974\ \frac{\text{mmol}}{\text{mL}} \times 26.77\ \text{mL} = 2.6700\ \text{mmol}$$

$NaHSO_4$ is monoprotic, so that: moles $NaHSO_4$ used = moles NaOH used = 2.6700 mmol .

Next, find the concentration of pure $NaHSO_4$ in the 25.00 mL sample.

$$[NaHSO_4] = \frac{2.6700\ \text{mmol}}{25.00\ \text{mL}} = 0.10680\ \text{M (actual)}$$

Now calculate the expected $[NaHSO_4]$ if the original sample were 100% pure.

$$[NaHSO_4] = \frac{3.4786\ \text{g}}{0.2500\ \text{L}} \times \frac{1\ \text{mol}}{120.1\ \text{g}} = 0.11586\ \text{M (expected)}$$

Finally $$\%\ \text{purity} = \frac{[NaHSO_4]\ \text{(actual)}}{[NaHSO_4]\ \text{(expected)}} \times 100\% = \frac{0.10680\ \text{M}}{0.11586\ \text{M}} \times 100\% = \mathbf{92.18\%}\ .$$

Molar Mass Determination

Titration methods can be used to find the molar mass of an unknown solid acid (or base), if it is known whether the acid/base is monoprotic, diprotic, etc. To experimentally determine the molar mass of an unknown acid, say, dilute a known mass of the acid to a known volume. Titrating a known volume of the unknown solution with a known concentration of base allows the concentration of the unknown acid to be found. By combining this acid concentration with the original volume of the acid solution, the moles of acid used to make the original acid solution is found. The molar mass is found by dividing the mass of acid used by this number of moles.

EXAMPLE: A 3.2357 g sample of unknown monoprotic acid is diluted to 250.0 mL. A 25.00 mL sample of the acid solution is titrated with 16.94 mL of 0.1208 M KOH. What is the molar mass of the acid?

Start by finding the moles of KOH used.

$$\text{moles KOH} = 0.1208\,\frac{\text{mmol}}{\text{mL}} \times 16.94\ \text{mL} = 2.0464\ \text{mmol}$$

Since the acid is monoprotic, then

$$\text{moles acid} = \text{moles KOH} = 2.0464\ \text{mmol}\,.$$

The concentration of the unknown acid is now calculated.

$$[\text{acid}] = \frac{2.0464\ \text{mmol}}{25.00\ \text{mL}} = 0.081854\ \text{M}$$

Next, calculate the moles of acid in the original 250 mL volume:

$$\text{moles acid} = 0.081854\,\frac{\text{mol}}{\text{L}} \times 0.2500\ \text{L} = 0.020464\ \text{mol}$$

Finally, the molar mass is known to have units of "grams/mol":

$$\text{molar mass} = \frac{3.2357\ \text{g}}{0.020464\ \text{mol}} = \mathbf{158.1\ g/mol}\,.$$

EXPERIMENTAL NOTE:

A titration must be repeated as an accuracy check. If the volumes added from the burette agree with each other to within ± 0.02 mL (or ± 0.1 mL for beginning students), then you have satisfactorily determined the equivalence point in the titration. Very often, however, solutions are not stirred well or pipetting accuracy is poor, so that the volumes obtained from the first two titrations do not agree within the desired uncertainty. In this case the titration is repeated until good agreement on volumes is found. For example, if the volumes obtained were:

volume added in	1st titration	= 21.55 mL
	2nd titration	= 21.82 mL
	3rd titration	= 21.81 mL

then the first titration seems to give a poor value relative to the second and third titrations. In this case, discard the results from the first titration and average the other two results.

$$\text{average volume} = \frac{(21.82 + 21.81)}{2} = 21.815\ \text{mL}\,,\ \text{which rounds to } 21.82\ \text{mL}\,.$$

EXERCISES:

94. A solution of NaOH having an unknown concentration is titrated using 0.125 M HCl. The equivalence point is reached after 15.3 mL of HCl is added to a 25.0 mL portion of the base. What is the [NaOH]?

95. A solution of H_2SO_4 is titrated according to the equation $H_2SO_4 + 2\,KOH \longrightarrow K_2SO_4 + 2\,H_2O$ using 0.0635 M KOH. The equivalence point in the reaction is reached when 28.2 mL of KOH is added to a 25.0 mL portion of the acid. What is the $[H_2SO_4]$?

96. What volume of 0.0350 M NH_3 will be required to reach the equivalence point in the titration of 50.0 mL of 0.0275 M HCl?

97. What volume of 0.230 M NaOH is required to bring 25.0 mL of 0.175 M H_2SO_4 to the equivalence point represented by the equation $H_2SO_4 + 2\,NaOH \longrightarrow Na_2SO_4 + 2\,H_2O$?

98. A 35.0 mL portion of 0.0475 M citric acid, abbreviated H_3Cit (triprotic), is titrated to a particular equivalence point with 27.8 mL of 0.120 M NaOH. How many protons (on the average) are neutralized on each H_3Cit molecule at the equivalence point? If the resulting solution is boiled to dryness, what is the formula of the salt produced?

99. A 28.7 mL portion of 0.0136 M pyrophosphoric acid, $H_4P_2O_7$, is titrated to a certain equivalence point using 40.3 mL of 0.0387 M KOH. How many protons (on the average) are removed from the $H_4P_2O_7$ molecules at the equivalence point? If the resulting solution is evaporated to dryness, what is the formula of the resulting salt?

100. A 5.000 g sample of impure benzoic acid, C_6H_5COOH, is dissolved and diluted to a volume of 250.0 mL. A 25.00 mL portion of the benzoic acid solution is titrated using 31.84 mL of 0.1236 M NaOH. What is the percentage purity of the benzoic acid?

101. A 3.857 g sample of an unknown monoprotic acid is diluted to 100.0 mL. A 25.00 mL portion of the solution is titrated using 23.61 mL of 0.2000 M KOH. What is the molar mass of the unknown acid?

102. A solution of sodium hydroxide is made by diluting 0.470 g of NaOH to exactly 50.0 mL. If it requires 37.5 mL of 0.288 M HCl to titrate the entire NaOH solution, what is the percentage purity of the NaOH?

103. A 1.021 g sample of a monoprotic weak base is dissolved and diluted to 100.0 mL. The results of titrating three 25.00 mL portions of the base solution with 0.05023 M HCl are:

volume of HCl used in	1st titration	= 17.98 mL
	2nd titration	= 17.79 mL
	3rd titration	= 17.83 mL.

What is the molar mass of the unknown base?

104. A 1.50 g sample of impure $Ca(OH)_2$ is diluted to 1.00 L. A 25.0 mL portion of the base solution is titrated to neutrality by adding 19.1 mL of 0.0500 M HCl. What is the percentage purity of the $Ca(OH)_2$?

105. A 2.500 g sample of an unknown diprotic acid is dissolved and diluted to 250.0 mL. Three different 25.00 mL samples of the acid solution are titrated using 0.1328 M NaOH. The volumes obtained are:

Titration #1: 39.67 mL
Titration #2: 39.32 mL
Titration #3: 39.65 mL.

What is the molar mass of the unknown acid?

106. A 0.10 M solution of HCl has a pH of 1.00. A 0.10 M solution of CH_3COOH has a pH of 2.87. You are given 25 mL of 0.10 M HCl and 25 mL of 0.10 M CH_3COOH. Which acid solution requires a greater volume of 0.10 M NaOH in order to neutralize the acid?

107. A student titrates 25.0 mL of 0.100 M $Ba(OH)_2$ with 0.100 M H_2SO_4.

(a) What is the equation for the neutralization reaction?
(b) What happens to the ***conductivity*** of the $Ba(OH)_2$ solution as the first few millilitres of H_2SO_4 are added? (Hint: check the solubility of the products using your solubility table.)
(c) What volume of H_2SO_4 is required to reach the equivalence point in the titration? What is true about the conductivity at the equivalence point?
(d) What happens to the conductivity if extra H_2SO_4 is added after the equivalence point is reached?
(e) Make a sketch of the "conductivity" (vertical axis) versus "volume of H_2SO_4 added" (horizontal axis) behaviour expected for the titration.

IV.17. INDICATORS

An **INDICATOR** is a weak organic acid or base with different colours for its conjugate acid and base forms.

(Indicators are such complex molecules that their names are represented by an abbreviation. An indicator molecule might be abbreviated as "HIn" to denote that it is an acid and an indicator.)

EXAMPLE: $\underset{\text{yellow}}{HIn} + H_2O \rightleftharpoons \underset{\text{red}}{In^-} + H_3O^+$

When an indicator is put into an acid, the excess of H_3O^+ shifts the equilibrium

$\underset{\text{yellow}}{HIn} + H_2O \leftleftharpoons In^- + H_3O^+$ (by Le Chatelier's Principle)

causing the solution to turn YELLOW.

Conclusion:	**An indicator is in its CONJUGATE ACID form when in HIGHLY ACIDIC solutions.**

In basic solutions, the $[H_3O^+]$ is very low so that the equilibrium shifts to the In^- side and the solution turns RED.

$HIn + H_2O \rightrightharpoons \underset{\text{red}}{In^-} + H_3O^+$

Conclusion:	**An indicator is in its CONJUGATE BASE form when in HIGHLY BASIC solutions.**

In summary: In acidic solutions $[HIn] > [In^-]$ (that is, there are more YELLOW than RED molecules, and the solution appears YELLOW).

In basic solutions $[In^-] > [HIn]$ (that is, there are more RED than YELLOW molecules, and the solution appears RED).

Now, if a base is added to an acidic solution then at some point $[HIn] = [In^-]$ and an equal number of YELLOW and RED molecules give an ORANGE solution. The point at which an indicator is half way through its colour change is called the **END POINT** or **TRANSITION POINT.**

At the END POINT: $K_a = \frac{[H_3O^+][In^-]}{[HIn]} = [H_3O^+]$ (since $[HIn] = [In^-]$)

> **Conclusion: The $[H_3O^+]$ at which an indicator changes colour equals the value of K_a for the indicator.**

Similar to the way that pK_w was defined, we can let $pK_a = -\log K_a$.

Then, at the indicator's end point:

$$K_a = [H_3O^+]$$
$$-\log K_a = -\log [H_3O^+]$$
$$pK_a = pH$$

> **Conclusion: An indicator is at the midpoint of its colour change when the pH of the solution equals the pK_a of the indicator.**

NOTE: 1. The END POINT is the point in the titration where the colour of the indicator changes. The EQUIVALENCE POINT is the point in the titration where the stoichiometry of the reaction is exactly satisfied. If the indicator is chosen correctly, the indicator should change colour at or very close to the equivalence point, and there will be a negligible difference between the END POINT and the EQUIVALENCE POINT. If the indicator is poorly chosen, it will change colour at some point substantially different from the EQUIVALENCE POINT.

2. At the back of this book is a table called "Acid–Base Indicators". The table shows that an indicator doesn't change colour instantly at some magic pH value; the colour changes over a range of about 2 pH units. If an indicator changes colour in the pH range 4.5 to 6.7, the midpoint pH is estimated as the average of the values given (5.6 in this example).

EXAMPLE: Ethyl orange is red at pH < 3.4, yellow at pH > 4.8 and an intermediate orange at pH = 4.1. What is the approximate value of K_a for ethyl orange?

At the midpoint of the colour change: $pK_a = pH = 4.1$.

So that: $K_a = \text{antilog}(-4.1) = \mathbf{8 \times 10^{-5}}$.

EXAMPLE: Alizarin Yellow R changes from yellow to red at pH = 11.0. If $Aliz^-$ ion is red, what colour is Alizarin Yellow R in 1×10^{-5} M NaOH?

From the information given: $HAliz + H_2O \rightleftharpoons Aliz^- + H_3O^+$.
yellow red

Before proceeding, a few points must be established.

- at pH = 11 $[HAliz] = [Aliz^-]$
- at pH < 11 $[HAliz] > [Aliz^-]$ That is, **at a pH below its transition point (on its "acidic side") an indicator is mainly in its conjugate acid form.**
- at pH > 11 $[HAliz] < [Aliz^-]$ That is, **at a pH above its transition point (on its "basic side") an indicator is mainly in its conjugate base form.**

Now, the problem gives $[OH^-] = 1 \times 10^{-5}$ M
so that $[H^+] = 1 \times 10^{-9}$ M, and the solution's pH is 9.0.

The diagram below describes the overall situation. As can be seen, the solution's pH (9) is on the "acid" side of the pH where the colour changes (11). Therefore the conjugate acid of the indicator will be the dominant species present and Alizarin Yellow R is **YELLOW** in 10^{-5} M NaOH.

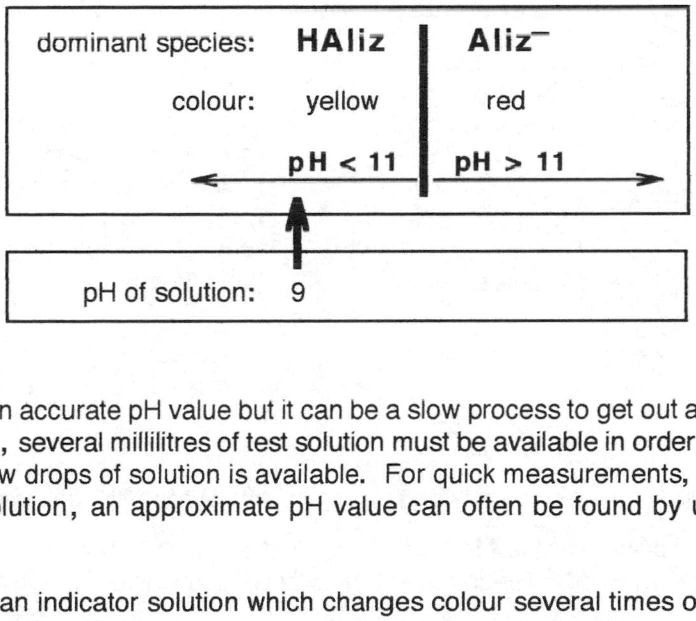

A pH meter can be used to get an accurate pH value but it can be a slow process to get out a meter, calibrate it and determine a pH. In addition, several millilitres of test solution must be available in order to use a pH meter and in some instances only a few drops of solution is available. For quick measurements, or measurements involving limited amounts of solution, an approximate pH value can often be found by using a "universal indicator".

A **UNIVERSAL INDICATOR** is an indicator solution which changes colour several times over a range of pH values.

The colour changes in a universal indicator are sufficiently distinct that it is possible to estimate the pH of a solution to within ± 0.5 pH unit (or within ± 0.1 pH unit with special "short–range" solutions). In order to be even more convenient, sometimes universal indicator solution is placed on absorbent paper and the solvent is evaporated. In order to test the pH of a given solution, a small strip of this "universal indicator test paper" is then dipped in the solution (or a drop of solution is put on the paper) and the pH is determined by the colour produced.

EXAMPLE: A **UNIVERSAL** indicator solution was made by mixing the following indicators

Indicator	pK_a	Acid form colour	Base form colour
Methyl orange	3.8	red	yellow
Bromthymol blue	6.8	yellow	blue
Phenolphthalein	9.1	colourless	pink

The diagram below helps to interpret the colour–vs–pH behaviour expected from this solution.

pH range ⟶	0 – 3.8	3.8 – 6.8	6.8 – 9.1	9.1 – 14
Methyl orange	red	yellow	yellow	yellow
Bromthymol blue	yellow	yellow	blue	blue
Phenolphthalein	colourless	colourless	colourless	pink
Combined colour ⟶	ORANGE	YELLOW	GREEN	PURPLE

The methyl orange changes to yellow at pH's above 3.8, then at 6.8 the bromthymol blue changes colour and finally the phenolphthalein changes colour at 9.1. The following colour associations can now be made:

pH	colour
3	orange
4	yellow–orange
5	yellow
6	yellow–green
7	green–yellow
8	green
9	yellow brown
10	red–purple

⟵ For example: at pH = 4 the solution will be a mixture of orange (methyl orange is in the middle of its colour change) plus yellow (bromthymol blue) plus colourless (phenolphthalein) to produce "yellow–orange."

EXERCISES:

108. An indicator, HIn, is red in acids and blue in bases. What is the colour of the anion, In^-?

109. Bromocresol purple is yellow in its acid form and purple in its base form. If its colour changes between pH 5.2 and 6.8, what is the colour of bromocresol purple in 0.01 M HCl?

110. The indicator Clayton Yellow changes from yellow to amber at pH = 12.7. What is K_a for the indicator?

111. The indicator 2,4–dinitrophenol changes colour in the pH range 2.8 to 4.0, such that it is halfway through the change at pH = 3.4. Estimate the K_a value of the indicator.

112. If an indicator has the equilibrium $HIn \rightleftharpoons H^+ + In^-$ and $K_a = 1 \times 10^{-5}$ is [HIn] greater than, less than or equal to $[In^-]$ at a pH of 8? Explain your answer.

113. Alizarin turns from yellow to red at about pH = 6.4 and turns from red to purple at about pH = 11.7. What can you conclude about the number of acidic groups in the Alizarin molecule and their acidic strengths?

114. Ethyl Red, HEth ($K_a = 1 \times 10^{-5}$), undergoes a colour change from colourless to red. If Eth^- is red, what colour is a solution of Ethyl Red in pure water?

115. Ethyl orange changes from red to yellow at pH = 4.1 (HEth is red) and bromthymol blue changes colour from yellow to blue at pH = 6.8 ($Brom^-$ is blue). A mixed indicator containing ethyl orange and bromthymol blue was added to a solution having a pH of 6. What colour did the mixed indicator solution turn?

116. A mixture of thymol blue and alizarin yellow is put in a solution with $[OH^-] = 1.0 \times 10^{-4}$ M. Use your table of Acid–Base Indicators to determine the colour of this mixed indicator.

117. A solution gave the following results when tested with three indicators.

Indicator	colour
Methyl orange	yellow
Thymol blue	yellow
Bromthymol blue	yellow

Give the pH range of the solution.

118. A solution gave the following results when tested with three indicators.

Indicator	colour
Methyl Red	yellow
Phenol Red	red
Phenolphthalein	colourless

Give the pH range of the solution.

119. You have a 0.10 M solution which contains either an acid or a base. Further, you do not know whether the acid/base is weak or strong. What tests could you perform and how would you interpret the results of the tests in order to determine whether you had an acid or a base and whether it was strong or weak?

120. You have 4 unlabelled bottles containing 0.1 M solutions of H_3PO_4 , NaH_2PO_4 , Na_2HPO_4 and Na_3PO_4. The results of testing the solutions with litmus, alizarin yellow and methyl orange are shown below.

Bottle	Litmus	Alizarin yellow	Methyl orange
1	blue	red	yellow
2	pink	yellow	yellow
3	pink	yellow	red
4	blue	yellow	yellow

Identify the contents of each bottle and explain your answer.

IV.18. PRACTICAL ASPECTS OF TITRATION

STANDARD SOLUTIONS

In order to carry out a titration, you must have a solution with an accurately known concentration. Such a solution is called a **STANDARD SOLUTION** or a **STANDARDIZED SOLUTION.** A standard solution is used to titrate other solutions and determine their concentrations. There are two main ways to prepare a standard solution.

a) Use a substance which can be obtained in a pure and stable form, which does not absorb water or carbon dioxide from the air, and which has a known molar mass such that it can be used to prepare a solution of known concentration. Such a substance is called a **PRIMARY STANDARD.**

***EXAMPLE*:** Potassium hydrogen phthalate ($KHC_8H_4O_4$; molar mass = 204.22) is used as an acidic primary standard: 20.422 g of $KHC_8H_4O_4$ is diluted to 1.000 L, to give a 0.1000 M solution.

b) Titrate a base, say, with an acidic primary standard. Once the concentration of the base is known, it can then be used as a "standard" for titrating "unknown" acid solutions.

***EXAMPLE*:** NaOH cannot easily be used as a primary standard because solid NaOH is generally about 95–98 % pure and absorbs water carbon dioxide rapidly upon exposure to the atmosphere. However, solutions of NaOH can be made which are known to be close to 0.1 M, say. A primary standard (0.1000 M potassium hydrogen phthalate) is then titrated against the NaOH solution to find the EXACT [NaOH]. The resulting solution is said to be a "standardized solution of NaOH". The NaOH solution can now be used in turn to titrate several different HCl solutions and find their concentrations.

PREPARATION OF PRIMARY STANDARDS

The following chemicals are most commonly used as primary acidic or basic standards; other acids and bases are used occasionally. (Do not memorize this information; just know the identity of the three primary acids and bases.)

1. Acidic Primary Standards

a) Potassium hydrogen phthalate, $KHC_8H_4O_4$ (MW = 204.22)

This substance acts as a monoprotic acid in its reaction with NaOH

$$KHC_8H_4O_4 + NaOH \longrightarrow NaKC_8H_4O_4 + H_2O\ .$$

Potassium hydrogen phthalate is the most widely used acidimetric primary standard. The preferred indicator is either phenolphthalein or thymol blue.

b) Oxalic acid dihydrate, $H_2C_2O_4 \cdot 2H_2O$ (MW = 126.07)

This substance acts as a diprotic acid in its reaction with NaOH

$$H_2C_2O_4 \cdot 2H_2O + 2\ NaOH \longrightarrow Na_2C_2O_4 + 4\ H_2O\ .$$

Again, the preferred indicator is phenolphthalein.

2. Basic Primary Standard

Sodium carbonate, Na_2CO_3 (MW = 105.99)

Anhydrous sodium carbonate is diprotic in its reaction with HCl

$$Na_2CO_3 + 2\,HCl \longrightarrow 2\,NaCl + H_2O + CO_2.$$

Methyl orange is a suitable indicator for this titration.

The procedure for using one of these chemicals is to:

- obtain very pure chemical ("Analytical Reagent"),
- dry a sample of the chemical in an oven and store the dried sample in a "desiccator" (which is a sealed vessel containing a drying agent such as anhydrous calcium chloride or concentrated sulphuric acid),
- use an analytical balance to weigh a portion of the dried chemical accurately (normally, sufficient chemical is used to make a 0.1000 M solution),
- quantitatively transfer the weighed portion of the chemical to a volumetric flask, and
- dilute the chemical to the exact volume required.

EXERCISES:

121. Some properties of barium hydroxide, $Ba(OH)_2 \cdot 8H_2O(s)$, are:

melting point = 78°C,
reacts with CO_2 in the air,
available in high purity.

Would $Ba(OH)_2 \cdot 8H_2O(s)$ be suitable for use as a primary standard? Why?

122. A sample of dried, high purity borax, $Na_4B_4O_7$, was weighed out and dissolved to make a 0.1000 M solution. A solution of high purity HCl was titrated against the borax solution and the concentration of HCl was found to be 0.1012 M. The HCl solution was then used to titrate a series of NaOH solutions. Which of the three substances, $Na_4B_4O_7$, HCl or NaOH:

a) served as a standard solution? b) served as a primary standard?

123. What procedure could you use to experimentally standardize a solution of HCl? Suggest an appropriate indicator. What data would you need to obtain and what calculations would you need to perform?

TYPES OF TITRATION CURVES

These sections look at the details of the shapes of titration curves and establish some "rules of thumb" which allow you to predict the approximate pK_a values of the indicators needed to help find the equivalence point of titrations.

A. THE TITRATION OF A *STRONG ACID* WITH A *STRONG BASE*

The following two tables give the result of slowly adding 1.000 M NaOH to 1.000 L of 1.000 M HCl.

Volume of NaOH added (L)	$[H^+]$ after NaOH addition	pH
0.0000	1.000	0.00
0.2500	0.600	0.22
0.5000	0.333	0.48
0.7500	0.143	0.85
0.9000	5.26×10^{-2}	1.28
0.9900	5.03×10^{-3}	2.30
0.9990	5.00×10^{-4}	3.30
0.9999	5.00×10^{-5}	4.30
1.0000	1.00×10^{-7}	7.00

At this point, the solution is neutral. Any further addition of NaOH will give a basic solution.

Volume of NaOH added (L)	$[OH^-]$ after NaOH addition	pOH	pH
1.0001	5.00×10^{-5}	4.30	9.70
1.0010	5.00×10^{-4}	3.30	10.70
1.0100	4.98×10^{-3}	2.30	11.70
1.1000	4.76×10^{-2}	1.32	12.68
1.2500	0.111	0.95	13.05
1.5000	0.200	0.70	13.30
1.7500	0.273	0.56	13.44
2.0000	0.333	0.48	13.52

***EXERCISE*:**

124. (a) Plot the above pH–vs–(volume of NaOH) data on the graph below.

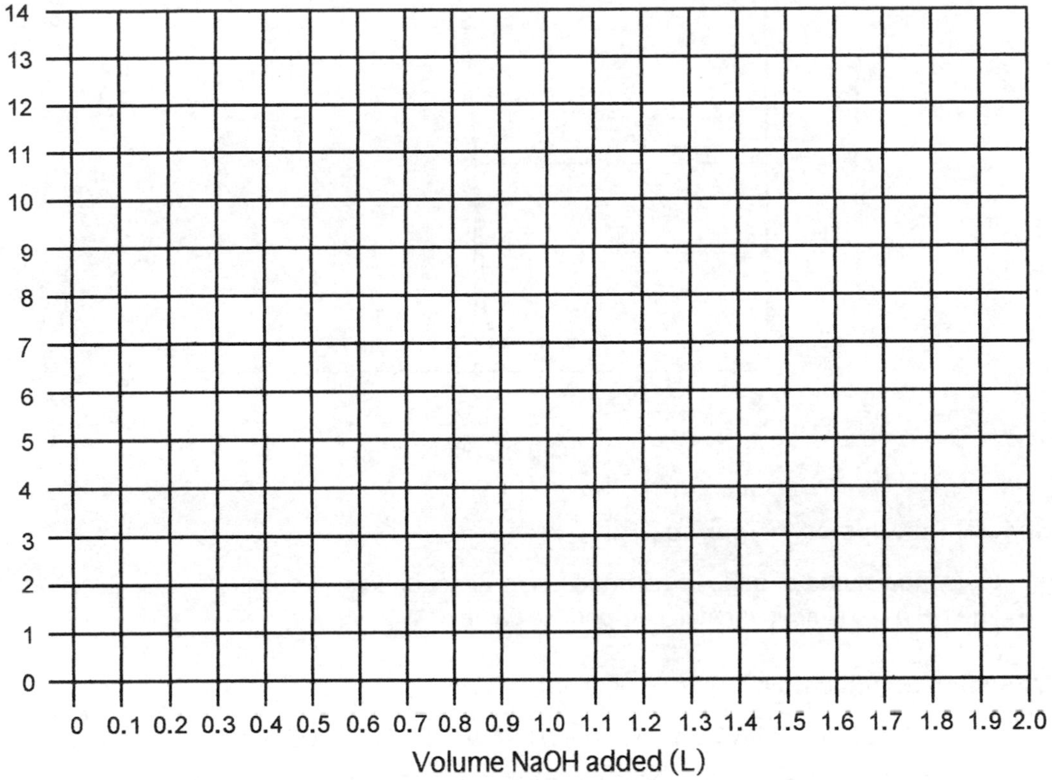

(b) What volume of 1.000 M NaOH was required to attain the equivalence point in the above titration?

(c) In what pH range is the pH changing most rapidly?

(d) Was the solution acidic, basic or neutral at the equivalence point of the titration?

(e) Look at the graph you plotted in part (a). At what pH should an indicator change colour for this titration? A chemistry student titrated HCl with NaOH, with phenolphthalein ($pK_a = 9.1$) as an indicator. Why was the student able to get good results for the equivalence point when using phenolphthalein as an indicator, even though its pK_a value differs from the pH value which "should exist"?

In general, the pH behaviour observed when titrating a STRONG ACID with a STRONG BASE resembles the graph below.

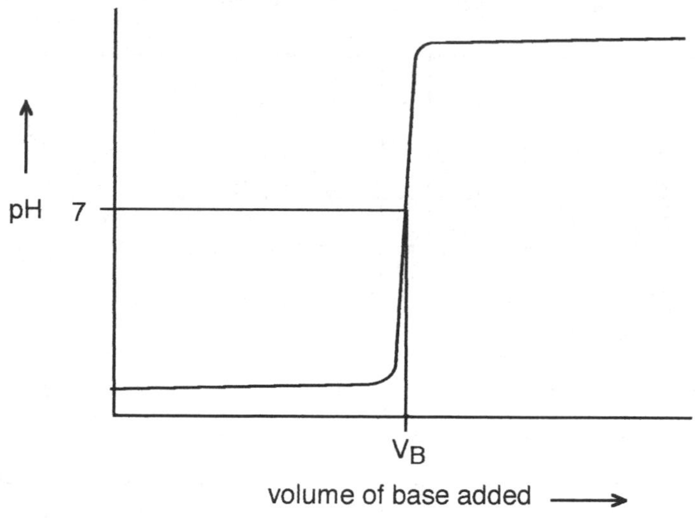

Special features of the curve:

- V_B is the volume of base required to get to the equivalence point.
- The pH rises almost vertically around the value of V_B.

Choosing an indicator:

- The ***SALT*** of a ***STRONG ACID*** and a ***STRONG BASE*** is **NEUTRAL** in solution.

  For example: $HCl + NaOH \longrightarrow NaCl + H_2O$; NaCl(aq) has a pH of 7.

- The titration requires an indicator which changes colour around pH = 7; that is, has $pK_a = 7$.

B. THE TITRATION OF A *weak acid* WITH A *STRONG BASE*

In general, the pH behaviour observed when titrating a weak acid with a strong base resembles the graph below.

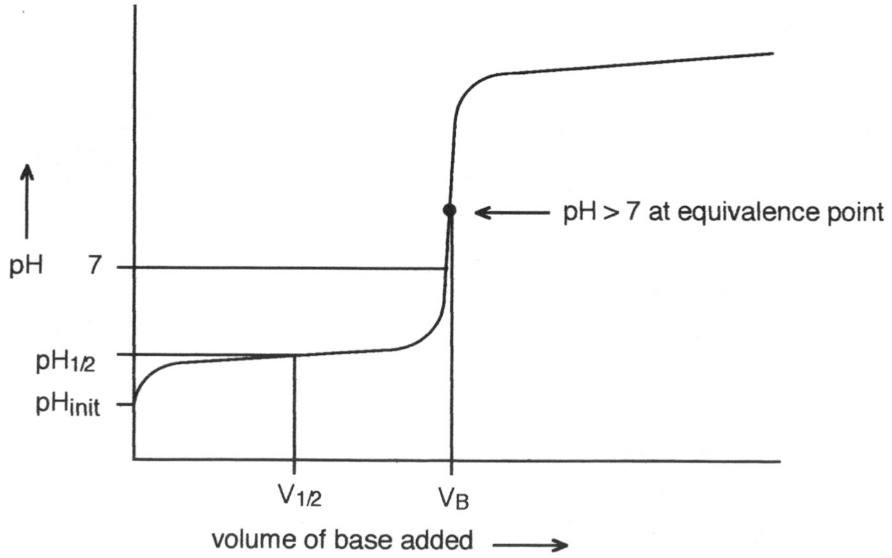

Special features of the curve:

- There is an initial upswing in the pH at the start of the titration.
- V_B is the volume of base required to get to the equivalence point, and $V_{1/2} = \frac{1}{2} V_B$; that is, $V_{1/2}$ is the point on the graph which is half the value of V_B.
- The equivalence point occurs above pH = 7.

Calculating The Concentration of the Acid from the Volume of NaOH at the Equivalence Point

In the titration of a monoprotic acid (CH_3COOH) with NaOH, three out of four of the following pieces of data are available.

V_A	= the volume of the acid used	V_B	= the volume of the base added
[HA]	= the concentration of acid used	$[OH^-]$	= the concentration of base added

The normal titration calculation will then be used. For example, if [HA] was unknown

then moles OH^- added = $[OH^-] \times V_B$
moles HA used = moles OH^- added

and $$[HA] = \frac{\text{moles HA used}}{V_A}.$$

Calculating K_a and the Concentration of the Weak Acid

Although the acid concentration can be found using the volume of NaOH added at the equivalence point, it is also possible to find the acid concentration when the base concentration is ***not known.***

Assume NaOH is being added to CH_3COOH and that the above graph has been plotted to show the "pH–vs–volume of NaOH added" behaviour which occurs during the titration.

On the above graph two special pH's can be defined:

- $pH_{1/2}$ = the pH at which the volume equals $V_{1/2}$.
- pH_{init} = the initial pH of the weak acid solution (before any NaOH is added).

***Step 1*: Use $pH_{1/2}$ to determine the K_a value for the weak acid**

The K_a expression relates $[H_3O^+]$, $[CH_3COO^-]$ and $[CH_3COOH]$. Assume you start with 0.100 mol of CH_3COOH in 1.00 L of solution. At the equivalence point 0.100 mol of NaOH is added, and at the "half–volume" point (where V = $V_{1/2}$ and pH = $pH_{1/2}$ on the graph) 0.050 mol of NaOH is added. The "ST, Δ, EQ" table below shows the situation existing at the half–volume point. Since CH_3COOH is in excess, all the added NaOH is used up.

	CH_3COOH +	OH^-	$\longrightarrow$ $CH_3COO^- + H_2O$
ST	0.100	0.050	0
+ Δ	−0.050	−0.050	+0.050
= EQ	0.050	≈ 0	0.050

As can be seen from the table, at exactly halfway to the equivalence point half of the initial CH_3COOH is neutralized and converted to CH_3COO^-.

Therefore $[CH_3COOH] = [CH_3COO^-]$ (see the EQ–line in the above table)

and $$K_a = \frac{[H_3O^+][CH_3COO^-]}{[CH_3COOH]} = [H_3O^+]_{1/2}$$

so that $\boxed{pK_a = pH_{1/2}}$, at the point $pH_{1/2}$ on the above graph .

Therefore, the value of K_a can be determined by using the pH value at point $pH_{1/2}$.

***Step 2*: Combine the K_a value with pH_{init} to determine the concentration of the weak acid**

Let $[CH_3COOH]$ = the initial concentration of CH_3COOH which is introduced into a solution.
X = the amount of CH_3COOH which dissociates
$[CH_3COOH]_{EQ}$ = the concentration of CH_3COOH which exists at equilibrium

	$CH_3COOH + H_2O \rightleftharpoons$	CH_3COO^- +	H_3O^+
ST	$[CH_3COOH]$	0	0
+Δ	−X	+X	+X
= EQ	≈ $[CH_3COOH]_{EQ}$	X	X

The initial pH ("pH_{init}") is measured before any base is added to the initial solution, allowing calculation of the initial $[H_3O^+]$ in solution. As the table shows, the ionization of CH_3COOH produces a solution having

$$X = [H_3O^+] = [CH_3COO^-]$$

so that $$K_a = \frac{[H_3O^+][CH_3COO^-]}{[CH_3COOH]_{EQ}} = \frac{[H_3O^+]^2}{[CH_3COOH]_{EQ}}$$

which rearranges to $$[CH_3COOH]_{EQ} = \frac{[H_3O^+]^2}{K_a}.$$

Since the value of K_a has previously been found from "$pH_{1/2}$" and the value of $[H_3O^+]$ can be found from "pH_{init}", the value for $[CH_3COOH]_{EQ}$ can be calculated. Finally, the initial molarity of the CH_3COOH, $[CH_3COOH]$, can be calculated from the equation

$$[CH_3COOH] = [CH_3COOH]_{EQ} + X.$$

Choosing an indicator

- The salt of a ***weak acid*** and a ***STRONG BASE*** is **BASIC** in solution, as can be seen from the pH at the equivalence point on the graph. (The fact that the resulting salt produces a basic solution also can be seen from the reaction equation:

  $$CH_3COOH + NaOH \longrightarrow Na^+ + CH_3COO^- + H_2O.$$

  The Na^+ is a spectator and CH_3COO^- is a weak base which produces a basic solution in water.)

- An indicator is required which changes colour in the basic range. If the acid being titrated is very weak, the pK_a of the indicator should be several pH units above 7; the stronger the acid, the closer to 7 the pK_a value should be. For most situations in Chem 12, an indicator with a pK_a value in the range 8–10 suffices.

A SUMMARY OF IMPORTANT POINTS FOR *weak acid–STRONG BASE* TITRATIONS

1. The pH at the equivalence point is GREATER THAN 7 .
2. The value of K_a can be found from the equation

   $K_a = [H_3O^+]_{1/2}$ . . . (1) where $[H_3O^+]_{1/2}$ is found from $pH_{1/2}$.
3. The molarity of a weak acid, [HA], can be found from the equation

   $$[HA] = \frac{[H_3O^+]^2}{K_a} \quad \ldots (2)$$

   where $[H_3O^+]$ is found from pH_{init}

   and K_a is previously found from equation (1) .

EXAMPLE: The following data is obtained when a solution of furoic acid, $(C_4H_3O)COOH$, is titrated with NaOH.

25.0 mL = volume of furoic acid solution
28.8 mL = volume of NaOH required to get to equivalence point
2.021 = initial pH of furoic acid solution
3.170 = pH at 14.4 mL point of titration

a) Calculate the K_a value for furoic acid.
b) Calculate the initial concentration of the furoic acid solution.
c) Calculate the concentration of the NaOH used.
d) Is the titration mixture acidic, basic or neutral at the equivalence point?
e) Suggest a suitable indicator for the titration.

a) Since the concentrations of furoic acid and NaOH are unknown, K_a must be found first.

$pK_a = pH_{1/2} = 3.170$ (at 14.4 mL; that is, half–way to the equivalence point)

and $\mathbf{K_a = 6.76 \times 10^{-4}}$.

b) Next, use $K_a = \frac{[H_3O^+]^2}{[\text{Furoic acid}]_{EQ}}$. The initial pH is given in the data statement: $pH_{init} = 2.021$

so that $[H_3O^+] = 9.53 \times 10^{-3}$ M .

Solving for $[\text{Furoic acid}]_{EQ}$: $$[\text{Furoic acid}]_{EQ} = \frac{[H_3O^+]^2}{K_a} = \frac{(9.53 \times 10^{-3})^2}{6.76 \times 10^{-4}} = 0.134 \text{ M}.$$

WAIT! This isn't quite the answer. This [Furoic acid] is the EQUILIBRIUM CONCENTRATION but the question wanted the ORIGINAL CONCENTRATION. To find the original concentration of furoic acid, the amount of furoic acid which dissociates must be added onto the equilibrium concentration:

$[\text{Furoic acid}] = 0.134 + 9.53 \times 10^{-3} = \mathbf{0.144\ M}.$

c) The initial concentration of the furoic acid and the volumes of NaOH and furoic acid are known, so the concentration of the NaOH can now be found.

$$\text{moles of furoic acid} = 0.144 \frac{\text{mmol}}{\text{mL}} \times 25.0 \text{ mL} = 3.60 \text{ mmol} = \text{moles NaOH}$$

$$[NaOH] = \frac{3.60 \text{ mmol}}{28.8 \text{ mL}} = \mathbf{0.125\ M}$$

d) The graph drawn above for "pH–versus–volume of base added" indicates that the pH at equivalence point is greater than 7. Therefore, the titration mixture will be basic at the equivalence point.

e) For titrations involving the addition of a strong base to a moderately weak acid, the pH at equivalence point will typically be in the range 8–10. Using the table of Acid–Base Indicators at the back of this book, a suitable indicator would be any of thymol blue, phenolphthalein or thymolphthalein.

C. THE TITRATION OF A *weak base* WITH A *STRONG ACID*

In general, the pH behaviour observed when titrating a weak base with a strong acid resembles the graph below.

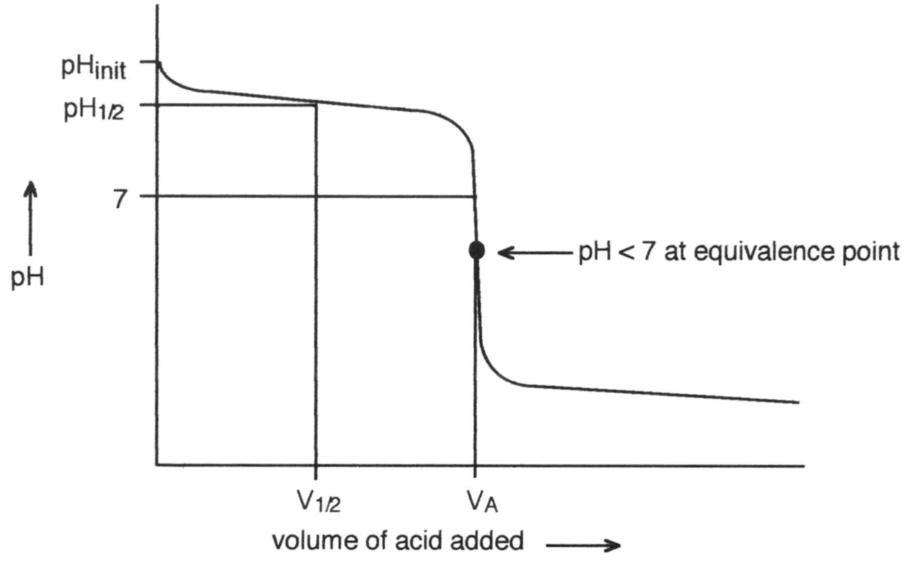

NOTE: This case is very similar to the case of a weak acid and a strong base, except that the curve looks like it has been flipped upside down.

IMPORTANT: The above graph gives pH values BUT pOH values are required for all calculations. Therefore, the first step in using the pH values MUST BE TO CONVERT pH to pOH.

Calculating K_b and the Concentration of the Weak Base

Assume HCl is being added to NH_3 and that a graph has been plotted which shows the "pH–vs–volume of HCl added" behaviour occurring during the titration (as shown above).

On the above graph two special pH's are shown.

- $pH_{1/2}$ = the pH at which the volume equals $V_{1/2}$.
- pH_{init} = the initial pH of the weak base solution (before any HCl is added).

***Step 1*: Use $pH_{1/2}$ to determine the K_b value for the weak base**

The K_b expression relates $[OH^-]$, $[NH_4^+]$ and $[NH_3]$. Assume you start with 0.100 mol of NH_3 in 1.00 L of solution. At the equivalence point 0.100 mol of HCl is added, and at the "half–volume" point (where $V = V_{1/2}$ and $pH = pH_{1/2}$ on the graph) 0.050 mol of HCl is added. Set up a "ST, Δ, EQ" table showing the situation at the half–volume point. Since NH_3 is in excess, all the added HCl is used up.

	NH_3 +	H_3O^+ $\rightleftharpoons$	$NH_4^+ + H_2O$
ST	0.100	0.050	0
+ Δ	−0.050	−0.050	+0.050
= EQ	0.050	≈ 0	0.050

As can be seen from the table, at exactly halfway to the equivalence point half of the initial NH_3 is neutralized and converted to NH_4^+.

Therefore $[NH_3] = [NH_4^+]$ (see the EQ–line in the above table)

Because NH_3 is a weak base, the K_b expression is

$$K_b = \frac{[NH_4^+][OH^-]_{1/2}}{[NH_3]} = [OH^-]_{1/2}$$

(where $[OH^-]_{1/2}$ is the concentration of OH^- at the half–volume point)

so that $\boxed{\mathbf{p}K_b = \mathbf{pOH_{1/2}}}$

(where $pOH_{1/2} = 14 - pH_{1/2}$ and $pH_{1/2}$ is found from the above graph).

As a result, the value of K_b can be determined by using the value of the pH at point "$pH_{1/2}$".

NOTE: be sure to change the pH to a pOH before determining K_b.

Step 2**: Combine the K_b value with pH_{init} to find the concentration of the weak base**

Let $[NH_3]$ = the initial concentration of NH_3 which is introduced into a solution
X = the amount of NH_3 which dissociates
$[NH_3]_{EQ}$ = the concentration of NH_3 which exists at equilibrium

	$NH_3 + H_2O \rightleftharpoons$	NH_4^+ +	OH^-
ST	$[NH_3]$	0	0
+ Δ	−X	+X	+X
= EQ	≈ $[NH_3]$	X	X

The initial pH ("pH_{init}") is measured before any acid is added to the initial solution.
Using $pOH_{init} = 14 - pH_{init}$ the value of pOH_{init} is calculated and the value of $[OH^-]$ is found. As the table shows, the ionization of NH_3 produces a solution having

$$X = [NH_4^+] = [OH^-]$$

so that
$$K_b = \frac{[NH_4^+][OH^-]}{[NH_3]_{EQ}} = \frac{[OH^-]^2}{[NH_3]_{EQ}}$$

which rearranges to
$$[NH_3]_{EQ} = \frac{[OH^-]^2}{K_b}.$$

Since the value of K_b has previously been found from "$pH_{1/2}$" and the value of $[OH^-]$ can be determined from point "pH_{init}" (after converting to pOH_{init}), the value for $[NH_3]_{EQ}$ can be calculated. Finally, the initial molarity of the NH_3, $[NH_3]$, can be calculated from the equation

$$[NH_3] = [NH_3]_{EQ} + X .$$

Choosing an indicator

- The salt of a ***STRONG ACID*** and a ***weak base*** is **ACIDIC** in solution, as can be seen from the pH at the equivalence point on the graph. (You can also deduce that the salt is acidic from the reaction:

$$NH_3 + HCl \longrightarrow NH_4^+ + Cl^-,$$

since the Cl^- is a spectator and the NH_4^+ is a weak acid in solution.)

- An indicator is required which changes colour in the acidic range: if the base is very weak, the pK_a of the indicator should be several pH units below 7; the stronger the base, the closer to 7 the pK_a value should be. For most situations in Chem 12, an indicator having a pK_a value in the range 4–6 suffices.

A SUMMARY OF IMPORTANT POINTS FOR *weak base–STRONG ACID* TITRATIONS

1. The pH at the stoichiometric point is LESS THAN 7 .
2. The value of K_b can be found from the equation

   $K_b = [OH^-]_{1/2}$ ...(1) where $[OH^-]_{1/2}$ is found by converting $pH_{1/2}$ to $pOH_{1/2}$ and then converting to $[OH^-]_{1/2}$.

3. The molarity of a weak base, B^-, can be found from the equation

   $[B^-] = \dfrac{[OH^-]^2}{K_b}$ ...(2) where $[OH^-]$ is found by converting pH_{init} to pOH_{init} and then converting to [OH−]

   and K_b is previously found from equation (1) .

Sneaky Trick: In order to remember whether a titration gives an acidic, basic or neutral solution at the equivalence point, use the following memory aids.

The salt of a ***STRONG ACID*** and a ***STRONG BASE*** is **NEUTRAL.**
(two **STRONG** reactants produce a "tie"; the result is NEUTRAL)

The salt of a ***STRONG ACID*** and a ***weak base*** is **ACIDIC.**
(the stronger reactant "wins out", so solution is ACIDIC)

The salt of a ***weak acid*** and a ***STRONG BASE*** is **BASIC.**
(the stronger reactant "wins out", so solution is BASIC)

Alternately: A reaction between a **STRONG ACID** and a **STRONG BASE** produces spectator ions at the equivalence point, and therefore will be **NEUTRAL.**

A reaction between a **STRONG ACID** and a **weak base** produces spectator ions and a weak conjugate acid at the equivalence point, and therefore will be **ACIDIC.**

A reaction between a **weak acid** and a **STRONG BASE** produces spectator ions and a weak conjugate base at the equivalence point, and therefore will be **BASIC.**

A FINAL COMMENT ON THE SELECTION OF AN INDICATOR

The equivalence point in a titration between a:

STRONG ACID and a ***STRONG BASE*** requires an indicator which changes colour close to pH = 7.

STRONG ACID and a ***weak base*** requires an indicator which changes colour in the range pH = 4–6.

weak acid and a ***STRONG BASE*** requires an indicator which changes colour in the range pH = 8–10.

Indicators which change colour between pH = 0 – 3 are only used for VERY weak bases, and indicators which change between pH = 11 – 14.0 are only used for VERY weak acids – none of which are used in Chem 12.

EXAMPLE: The following data was obtained when titrating ethylamine, a monoprotic weak base, with HCl.

25.00 mL = volume of ethylamine solution titrated
19.22 mL = volume of HCl required too get to the equivalence point
11.855 = initial pH of the ethylamine solution
10.807 = pH at 9.60 mL point of titration

(a) Calculate the K_b value for ethylamine.
(b) Calculate the initial [ethylamine].
(c) Calculate the concentration of the HCl used.
(d) Suggest a suitable indicator for the reaction.

(a) Since [ethylamine] is not given, [HCl] can't be found until [ethylamine] is known. But, [ethylamine] cannot be found until the K_b for ethylamine is known. Therefore, the value of K_b has to be found first.

Using: $K_b = [OH^-]_{1/2}$, where $[OH^-]_{1/2}$ is found from the "half–volume" point.

$pOH_{1/2} = 14.000 - pH_{1/2} = 14.000 - 10.807 = 3.193$; $[OH^-]_{1/2} = 6.412 \times 10^{-4}$ M

$K_b = [OH^-]_{1/2} = \mathbf{6.41 \times 10^{-4}}$.

(b) Next, use: $K_b = \dfrac{[OH^-]^2}{[\text{ethylamine}]_{EQ}}$.

The value of K_b is now available, but a value for $[OH^-]$ is required. Since this equation refers to the situation existing before the titration starts, the value of pH_{init} is used to find $[OH^-]$.

$pOH_{init} = 14.000 - pH_{init} = 14.000 - 11.855 = 2.145$; $[OH^-] = 7.161 \times 10^{-3}$ M

$$[\text{ethylamine}]_{EQ} = \frac{[OH^-]^2}{K_b} = \frac{(7.161 \times 10^{-3})^2}{6.412 \times 10^{-4}} = \mathbf{0.0800\ M}$$

Again, this isn't quite the answer yet. This $[\text{ethylamine}]_{EQ}$ is the EQUILIBRIUM CONCENTRATION but the question wanted the ORIGINAL CONCENTRATION. To find the original concentration of ethylamine, the amount of ethylamine which dissociates must be added onto the equilibrium concentration:

$[\text{ethylamine}] = [\text{ethylamine}]_{EQ} + [OH^-] = 0.0800 + 0.00716 = \mathbf{0.0872\ M}$.

(c) The [HCl] is found using a standard titration calculation.

$$\text{moles ethylamine} = 0.0872\ \frac{\text{mmol}}{\text{mL}} \times 25.00\ \text{mL} = 2.18\ \text{mmol}$$

moles HCl = moles ethylamine = 2.18 mmol

$$[\text{HCl}] = \frac{2.18\ \text{mmol}}{19.22\ \text{mL}} = \mathbf{0.113\ M}$$

(d) Since ethylamine is a weak base and HCl is a strong acid, the equivalence point will be in the acidic range (pH = 4–6), so that a suitable indicator (chosen from the Acid–Base Indicators table) would be any of methyl orange, bromcresol green, methyl red or chlorophenol red.

EXERCISES:

125. Some indicators and their pK_a values are:

Indicator	pK_a value
Methyl Red	5.4
Bromthymol Blue	6.8
Phenolphthalein	9.1

The acids and bases below are titrated against each other. Are the solutions acidic, neutral or basic when the titrations are at equivalence point? Which of the above indicators are best to use in the titrations?

a) HF + NaOH
b) NH_3 + HI
c) LiOH + HBr
d) $C_6H_5COOH + Ca(OH)_2$
e) $NH_3 + CH_3COOH$
f) HNO_3 + KOH

126. The following data is obtained during the titration of 25.0 mL of propanoic acid (C_2H_5COOH, monoprotic) with 0.100 M NaOH.

initial pH = 2.950
volume of NaOH used = 23.8 mL
pH at 11.9 mL = 4.873

a) What is K_a for propanoic acid?
b) What is the concentration of the propanoic acid, based on the [NaOH] and the volumes of the reactants?
c) What is the concentration of the propanoic acid, as calculated from your value of K_a, found in part a, and the initial pH value?

127. The following data is obtained during the titration of an organic base called aniline, $C_6H_5NH_2$, with 0.100 M HCl.

initial pH = 8.72
volume of HCl used = 16.32 mL
pH at 8.16 mL = 4.63

a) What is K_b for aniline?
b) What is the original concentration of the aniline?

128. If both the concentration of the aniline and the concentration of the HCl in the previous exercise were ten times larger, what effect would changing the concentration of aniline have on the pH at the "half–volume point"? Why does this occur?

129. The titration of a solution of benzoic acid (C_6H_5COOH) requires 28.4 mL of 0.125 M NaOH. The initial pH of the benzoic acid solution is 2.628 and the pH is 4.191 after 14.2 mL of the NaOH is added.
   a) What is K_a for benzoic acid?
   b) What is the original concentration of the benzoic acid solution?

130. A solution of a monoprotic organic base, imidazole ($C_3H_4N_2$), has a pH of 10.104. When 25.0 mL of the solution of imidazole is titrated with 0.0986 M HCl, the pH of the mixture is 7.047 after 18.4 mL of HCl is added. A total of 36.8 mL of HCl is required to reach the stoichiometric point.
   a) What is K_b for imidazole?
   b) What is the concentration of imidazole, based on the [HCl] and volumes of HCl and imidazole used?
   c) What is the concentration of imidazole, as calculated from the value of K_b, found in part a, and the initial pH?

IV.19. BUFFERS

Definition: A **BUFFER** is a solution containing appreciable amounts of a ***weak acid*** and its conjugate ***weak base.***

EXAMPLE: $CH_3COOH + H_2O \rightleftharpoons CH_3COO^- + H_3O^+$
1 M 1 M

Writing the K_a expression for CH_3COOH, and using the fact that this buffer has $[CH_3COOH] = [CH_3COO^-]$,

then: $$K_a = \frac{[CH_3COO^-][H_3O^+]}{[CH_3COOH]} = [H_3O^+] = 1.8 \times 10^{-5} \text{ and } pH = pK_a.$$

Conclusion:	When **equal** concentrations of a weak acid and its conjugate base are added to water, the pH of the resulting buffer will equal the pK_a value of the weak acid.

At first, it may seem strange that a solution can contain large amounts of both an acid and a base. Let's see what happens when a buffer is made.

The ionization of CH_3COOH gives: $CH_3COOH + H_2O \rightleftharpoons CH_3COO^- + H_3O^+$; $K_a = 1.8 \times 10^{-5}$.

If a solution is made by adding CH_3COOH to water, there will be a small amount of both CH_3COO^- and H_3O^+ present. Adding **extra** CH_3COO^- to the CH_3COOH solution causes the equilibrium to shift to the CH_3COOH side due to Le Chatelier's Principle. As a result, there is a large relative decrease in the $[H_3O^+]$, but only a very small amount of the added CH_3COO^- will be used up because there was very little H_3O^+ available in the initial solution to react with the added CH_3COO^-. Overall, a buffer will then have a relatively large concentration of both a weak acid and its conjugate base, and a small concentration of H_3O^+.

NOTE: A solution of CH_3COOH, by itself, is ***NOT*** a buffer. There may be large amounts of CH_3COOH present, but the amount of CH_3COO^- present is very small and does not satisfy the buffer definition. A buffer requires substantial amounts of ***both*** the conjugate acid and conjugate base.

When acids and bases are diluted their concentrations and pH's are changed. If a buffer is diluted, the concentrations of the conjugate acid base are diluted equally. Let's examine the result of this equal dilution.

If $[CH_3COOH] = [CH_3COO^-] = 1.0\ M,$

then $$K_a = \frac{[CH_3COO^-][H_3O^+]}{[CH_3COOH]} = \frac{(1.0)[H_3O^+]}{(1.0)} = [H_3O^+]$$

whereas after diluting the solution tenfold: $[CH_3COOH] = [CH_3COO^-] = 0.1\ M,$ and

$$K_a = \frac{(0.1)[H_3O^+]}{(0.1)} = [H_3O^+].$$

In general, when water is added to a buffer the value of the ratio $\frac{[\text{conjugate base}]}{[\text{conjugate acid}]}$

in the K_a expression $$K_a = \frac{[\text{conjugate base}][H_3O^+]}{[\text{conjugate acid}]}$$

is unchanged because both [conjugate base] and [conjugate acid] are diluted equally.

Conclusion: Diluting a buffer has no effect on its pH.

What is the purpose of creating a buffer?

Note: In the following discussion some calculations will be used to show the effect of adding H_3O^+ or OH^- on the pH of a buffer. You will not be required to perform calculations concerned with buffers; the calculations are shown so that you can see some of the special features of buffers.

Assume a buffer contains 1 mol of CH_3COOH and 1 mol of CH_3COO^- in 1 L. If 0.1 mol of H_3O^+ is added, the equilibrium shifts to use up 0.1 mol of the CH_3COO^- present and produce an extra 0.1 mol of CH_3COOH

$$CH_3COOH + H_2O \rightleftharpoons CH_3COO^- + H_3O^+.$$

The diagram below shows the effect of adding H_3O^+.

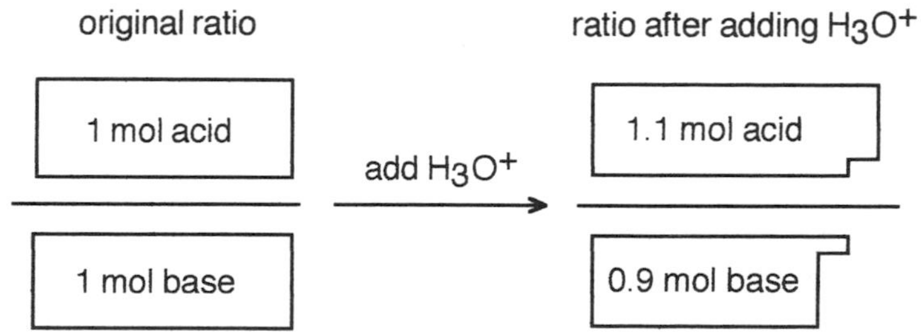

where the little "chunk" taken out of "1 mol base" and added to the "1 mol acid" (under the heading "ratio after adding H_3O^+ ") represents the amount of conjugate base neutralized by the added H_3O^+ and converted to the conjugate acid form.

The original value of the ratio is $$\frac{[CH_3COOH]}{[CH_3COO^-]} = \frac{1.0}{1.0} = 1.0.$$

Afterward, the ratio is $\dfrac{[CH_3COOH]}{[CH_3COO^-]} = \dfrac{1.1}{0.9} = 1.22$.

Rearranging the K_a expression $[H_3O^+] = K_a \cdot \dfrac{[CH_3COOH]}{[CH_3COO^-]}$.

Substituting the values of the above ratios into the rearranged K_a expression gives the following pH values.

Originally $[H_3O^+] = 1.8 \times 10^{-5} \times 1.0 = 1.8 \times 10^{-5}$ M and pH = **4.74**

after adding H_3O^+ $[H_3O^+] = 1.8 \times 10^{-5} \times 1.22 = 2.2 \times 10^{-5}$ M and pH = **4.66**

Enough H_3O^+ is added to neutralize 10% of the conjugate base, yet the pH only changes by **0.08** units.

In contrast, if there were no buffer present, adding 0.1 mol of H_3O^+ to 1 L of pure water would change the pH of the water by **6** pH units!

Similarly, if 0.1 mol of OH^- is added to the buffer, the equilibrium shifts to use up 0.1 mol of the CH_3COOH present and produce an extra 0.1 mol of CH_3COO^-.

$$CH_3COOH + OH^- \rightleftharpoons CH_3COO^- + H_2O$$

The diagram below shows the effect of adding OH^-.

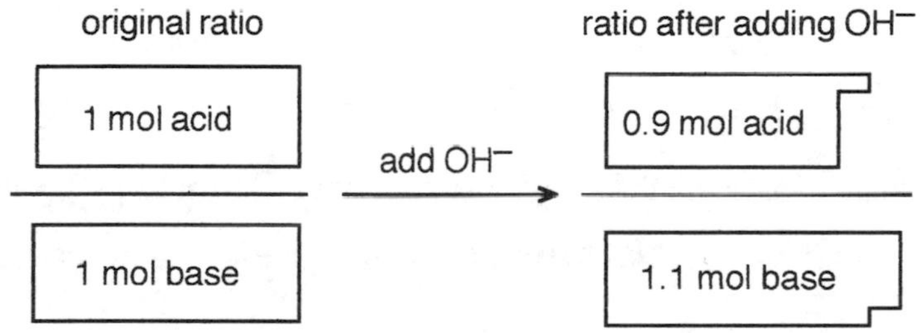

The original value of the ratio is $\dfrac{[CH_3COOH]}{[CH_3COO^-]} = \dfrac{1.0}{1.0} = 1.0$.

Afterward, the ratio is $\dfrac{[CH_3COOH]}{[CH_3COO^-]} = \dfrac{0.9}{1.1} = 0.82$.

Substituting the values of the above ratios into the rearranged K_a expression gives the following pH values.

originally $[H_3O^+] = 1.8 \times 10^{-5} \times 1.0 = 1.8 \times 10^{-5}$ M and pH = **4.74**

after adding OH^- $[H_3O^+] = 1.8 \times 10^{-5} \times 0.82 = 1.47 \times 10^{-5}$ M and pH = **4.83**

Again, enough OH^- is added to neutralize 10% of the conjugate acid present and yet the pH only changes by **0.09** units.

The foregoing discussion reveals the purpose of a buffer.

A buffer prevents the addition of either an acid or base from changing the pH of a solution to any great extent.

The "buffering effect" is due to the fact that the value of the ratio

$$\frac{[\text{conjugate acid}]}{[\text{conjugate base}]}$$

does not change much when one reacts a buffer with small amounts of either an acid or a base. The conjugate acid present can react with added OH^- and the conjugate base present can react with added H_3O^+.

$$CH_3COO^- + H_3O^+ \longrightarrow CH_3COOH + H_2O \qquad \text{(buffers can neutralize added } H_3O^+\text{)}$$

$$CH_3COOH + OH^- \longrightarrow CH_3COO^- + H_2O \qquad \text{(buffers can neutralize added } OH^-\text{)}$$

Thus the pH of a solution can be "stabilized" by using a buffer with an appropriate pH (governed by the pK_a value of the conjugate acid present).

EXAMPLE of an "ACIDIC BUFFER"

Mix 1.0 mol of acetic acid (CH_3COOH) and 1.0 mol of sodium acetate ($NaCH_3COO$) and dilute to 1.0 L of solution.

Note: When making up a buffer, be certain that any salts used are ***soluble.***

Since $NaCH_3COO(s) \longrightarrow Na^+ + CH_3COO^-$, and Na^+ is a spectator, the following equilibrium is set up

$$CH_3COOH + H_2O \rightleftharpoons CH_3COO^- + H_3O^+ ; \qquad K_a = 1.8 \times 10^{-5}$$

and this solution "buffers" or holds the pH almost constant at $pH = pK_a = -\log(1.8 \times 10^{-5}) = \mathbf{4.74}$.

This solution is referred to as an **ACIDIC BUFFER** since it buffers the pH in the **ACIDIC** region.

EXAMPLE of a "BASIC BUFFER"

Mix 1.0 mol of ammonia (NH_3) and 1.0 mol of ammonium nitrate (NH_4NO_3) and dilute to 1.0 L of solution.

Since $NH_4NO_3(s) \longrightarrow NH_4^+ + NO_3^-$, and NO_3^- is a spectator, the following equilibrium is set up

$$NH_4^+ + H_2O \rightleftharpoons NH_3 + H_3O^+ ; \qquad K_a = 5.6 \times 10^{-10}$$

and this solution "buffers" the pH at $pH = pK_a = -\log(5.6 \times 10^{-10}) = \mathbf{9.25}$.

This solution is referred to as a **BASIC BUFFER** since it buffers the pH in the **BASIC** region.

Note: This last equilibrium can also be set up as: $NH_3 + H_2O \rightleftharpoons NH_4^+ + OH^-$ and the solution's buffering pH can be calculated from:

$$K_b(NH_3) = \frac{K_w}{K_a(NH_4^+)} = \frac{1.0 \times 10^{-14}}{5.6 \times 10^{-10}} = 1.79 \times 10^{-5}$$

so that $pOH = pK_b = 4.75$, and $pH = 14.00 - 4.75 = \mathbf{9.25}$. The same result occurs whether the equilibrium is set up as an acid ionization or a base ionization.

A moment's thought should convince you that there is a limit to the amount of H_3O^+ or OH^- which can be neutralized by a buffer. If there is 1 mol of conjugate base present, a maximum of 1 mol of H_3O^+ can be neutralized. Similarly, 1 mol of conjugate acid can only neutralize 1 mol of added OH^-. It can be shown easily that by the time you have neutralized 50% of the available conjugate acid or conjugate base, the pH is starting to change to a noticeable extent and by 80% neutralization the pH has moved by almost 1 unit.

The buffering effect can be seen by examining the pH behaviour of a CH_3COOH/CH_3COO^- buffer when H_3O^+ or OH^- is added.

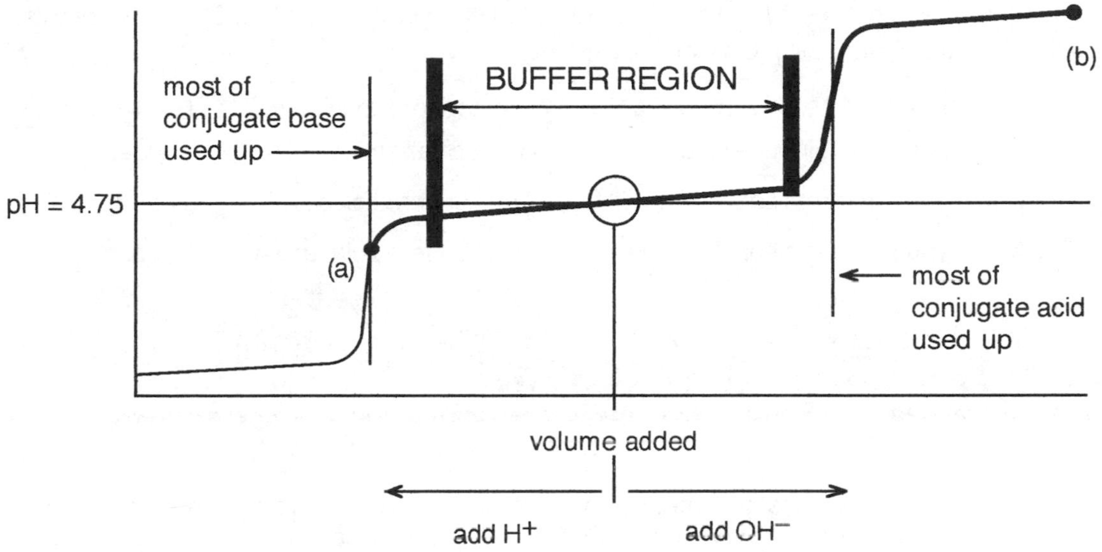

This graph should look somewhat familiar, the heavy curved line between points (a) and (b) is the titration curve seen previously for CH_3COOH reacting with NaOH. Aha! The central circle on the above diagram represents the pH of 1:1 CH_3COOH/CH_3COO^- mixture when nothing has been added to it. But in the titration of CH_3COOH with NaOH this point occurred when half of the CH_3COOH had been neutralized and converted to CH_3COO^- — that is, when equal amounts of CH_3COOH and CH_3COO^- were present, PRODUCING A BUFFER SOLUTION! (Recall that the pH at this central point on the curves for both the buffer and the titration is given by pH = pK_a.)

Conclusion:	**Whenever a weak acid or base is titrated, a buffer solution will occur in the middle portion of the titration curve.**

***EXERCISES*:**

131. You are given two buffer solutions: 1 M NH_3 mixed with 1 M NH_4Cl, and 0.1 M NH_3 mixed with 0.1 M NH_4Cl.

   Will the pH of these buffers differ from each other? Why?

132. Which of the following solutions will be buffers? Explain your answer in each case.

   a) 0.10 M KCN mixed with 0.10 M HCN
   b) 1.0 M HNO_2 mixed with 1.0 M HF
   c) 1.0 M NaOH mixed with 1.0 M NaCl
   d) 1.5 M $NaHCO_3$ mixed with 1.2 M Na_2CO_3

133. What happens to the pH of a buffer if you add some NaOH to it? What happens to the pH if HCl is added?

134. Many chemical laboratories contain bottles labelled "Emergency Neutralizing Solution", which are placed in a prominent place with other safety equipment. Often, the bottle contains 0.1 M CH_3COOH and 0.1 M $NaCH_3COO$. Under what conditions might the contents of the bottle be used? Why wouldn't a 0.1 M solution of CH_3COOH serve just as well?

135. What experimental procedure could be used to decide whether or not a given solution contains a buffer?

136. A solution consists of 1 M HNO_3 mixed with 1 M $NaNO_3$. Is this solution a buffer? Why?

137. You have a buffer made by mixing 0.10 mol of NH_3 and 0.10 mol of NH_4Cl in 1.0 L of water. Will this buffer be able to neutralize 0.15 mol of OH^-? Why?

138. A buffer consists of 1 M NH_4Cl and 1 M NH_3. What happens to the $[NH_4^+]$ and $[NH_3]$ when:
(a) a small amount of HCl is added? (b) a small amount of NaOH is added?

139. How would you prepare a solution in which the pH is buffered close to a value of 7.2?

140. How would you prepare a solution in which the pH is buffered close to a value of 2.1?

IV.20. BUFFERS IN BIOLOGICAL SYSTEMS

Biological systems exist in a constantly changing environment. Some chemical species which are vital or neutral to a system's survival may change concentration to the point where they harm the system. Buffers are very important in biological systems because they provide a way to prevent the systems from being overwhelmed by changes in the acidity or basicity of their environment. Let's look at a few examples which illustrate how buffers accomplish their task.

Haemoglobin is the oxygen carrier in blood and is involved in the equilibrium

$$\underset{\text{haemoglobin}}{HHb} + O_2 + H_2O \rightleftharpoons H_3O^+ + \underset{\text{oxyhaemoglobin}}{HbO_2^-}.$$

The optimum pH for blood is 7.35; that is, slightly alkaline (basic).

If the pH is too low ("ACIDOSIS"; pH < 7.20) then $[H_3O^+]$ is too high and the equilibrium shifts sufficiently to the left that the $[HbO_2^-]$ is too low. As a result of this shift, O_2 does not react to the same extent with haemoglobin; that is, it won't bind properly to haemoglobin.

If the pH is too high ("ALKALOSIS"; pH > 7.50) then $[H_3O^+]$ is too low and the equilibrium shifts sufficiently to the right that the $[HbO_2^-]$ is too high, preventing the release of O_2.

To prevent acidosis or alkalosis, two important buffers regulate the $[H_3O^+]$ at a more or less constant value. If no buffers were present in our bodies, the act of eating a tomato or drinking lemon juice would affect the pH of the blood so drastically as to cause death.

a) **The CO_2 / HCO_3^- System**

The main buffer present in the blood is a solution of CO_2 and HCO_3^-. When $CO_2(aq)$ is produced during metabolism, two equilibria come into play:

$$CO_2(aq) + 2\,H_2O \rightleftharpoons H_3O^+ + HCO_3^- \qquad \ldots(1)$$

$$CO_2(g) \rightleftharpoons CO_2(aq). \qquad \ldots(2)$$

Breathing out $CO_2(g)$ in (2) upsets the $[H_3O^+]$ in (1). Since the presence of $CO_2(aq)$ and HCO_3^- in (1) creates a buffer, the loss of CO_2 (or build–up of HCO_3^-) has a minimal effect on the pH of the blood.

("Hyperventilating", or excessive and rapid inhaling and exhaling, will lower the $[CO_2]$ in the blood to such an extent that the blood's pH is raised to the point where a person may "black out" or have hallucinations.)

b) **The $H_2PO_4^-$ / HPO_4^{2-} System**

Both $H_2PO_4^-$ and HPO_4^{2-} are present in the blood to a smaller extent and in cells to a greater extent, as a result of being critical components in bone, tooth and DNA maintenance. The buffer

$$H_2PO_4^- + H_2O \rightleftharpoons H_3O^+ + HPO_4^{2-}$$

stabilizes the pH of cells to a large degree. This "nutrient buffer" is also used extensively in cell–culture studies: the metabolic byproducts of cell growth are acidic and the buffer prevents a build–up of acid.

EXERCISES:

141. A solution containing HCO_3^- is sometimes injected directly into the blood of people who have stopped breathing in order to jolt the body into breathing again. What effect would such an injection have on the pH of the blood?

142. Write suitable reactions to show how the species present in a $H_2PO_4^-$ / HPO_4^{2-} buffer react with added H_3O^+ or OH^-.

143. The following is true. A few years ago, a farmer's son in the mid–western United States adopted a chicken as a pet and one day playfully gave the chicken some soda pop. The chicken loved it and soon looked forward to her daily "pop" ration. The farmer then noticed that whereas most of his chickens laid eggs with very thin and fragile shells during the hot summer months, his son's pet laid eggs having relatively thick shells which were less prone to cracking. Since handling eggs with thin shells gave substantial economic losses due to excess breakage, the farmer consulted a chemist who prescribed a steady diet of "carbonated water" (such as Perrier water) for the chickens. Let's see what caused the thin shells and how soda pop corrected the defect. The following equilibria are set up when $CO_2(g)$ is put into water.

$$CO_2(g) \rightleftharpoons CO_2(aq) \qquad \ldots(1)$$

$$CO_2(aq) + 2\,H_2O(l) \rightleftharpoons H_3O^+(aq) + HCO_3^-(aq) \qquad \ldots(2)$$

$$HCO_3^-(aq) + H_2O(l) \rightleftharpoons H_3O^+(aq) + CO_3^{2-}(aq) \qquad \ldots(3)$$

When an egg forms inside a chicken, a protective shell composed of $CaCO_3(s)$ is formed on the outside of the egg. Hence the solubility equilibrium must also be considered:

$$CaCO_3(s) \rightleftharpoons Ca^{2+}(aq) + CO_3^{2-}(aq). \qquad ...(4)$$

You should know one more thing: like a dog, a chicken has no sweat glands, so that when a chicken gets hot it has to "pant" to cool off. When a chicken "pants", it exhales large amounts of $CO_2(g)$.

(a) What effect would the loss of $CO_2(g)$ have on equilibrium (1)? What effect would this have on equilibria (2), (3) and (4)? (Disregard any changes in $[H_3O^+]$ – the buffering present in the system prevents $[H_3O^+]$ from changing appreciably.)

(b) What effect would the shifting of equilibrium (4) have on the thickness of the shells around the eggs laid by a "panting" chicken?

(c) If a chicken drinks large amounts of $CO_2(aq)$ what effect will this have on equilibrium (2)? What effects will this have on equilibria (3) and (4)? What effect will this shifting of equilibrium (4) have on the thickness of the egg shells?

IV.21. APPLIED ACID/BASE CHEMISTRY

A. AQUEOUS SOLUTIONS OF METAL AND NON–METAL OXIDES

Metal Oxides

When a **metal oxide** is added to water there is an initial dissociation such as

$$Na_2O(s) \longrightarrow 2\,Na^+(aq) + O^{2-}(aq), \quad \text{and} \quad CaO(s) \longrightarrow Ca^{2+}(aq) + O^{2-}(aq).$$

But, these metal ions are spectators and the oxide ion, O^{2-}, is a strong base (found on the bottom right side of the Table). The hydrolysis of the oxide ion is then given by

$$O^{2-} + H_2O \longrightarrow 2\,OH^-,$$ producing a **BASIC** solution.

EXAMPLE: Write the molecular equation for the reaction between Na_2O and water.

The actual reaction is $O^{2-} + H_2O \longrightarrow 2\,OH^-$.

Since sodium forms Na^+, the neutral product molecule formed when Na^+ combines with the OH^- is NaOH. Therefore, Na_2O and H_2O react to form NaOH.

$$Na_2O + H_2O \longrightarrow NaOH$$

Completing the balancing: $Na_2O + H_2O \longrightarrow 2\,NaOH$.

NOTE: Strictly speaking, only ***ionic metal oxides*** form ***basic*** solutions. The oxides of the Group I and II metals (apart from Be) are highly ionic and are the only metal oxides considered in Chem 12. Therefore a less accurate rule is used which states that METAL oxides are BASIC in solution. (To see why the "metal oxide" rule is not always correct, you should be aware of the fact that experiments show that $CrO_3(aq)$ is acidic, $Cr_2O_3(aq)$ is amphoteric, and $CrO(aq)$ is basic!)

Nonmetal Oxides

When a **nonmetal oxide** reacts with water, the water bonds to the existing oxide molecule to produce an **ACIDIC** solution.

EXAMPLE: $SO_3 + H_2O \longrightarrow$ 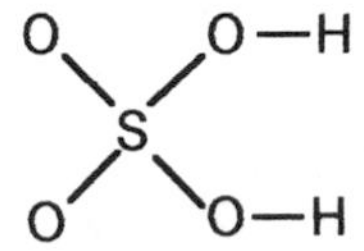 (that is, H_2SO_4)

$N_2O_5 + H_2O \longrightarrow 2$ 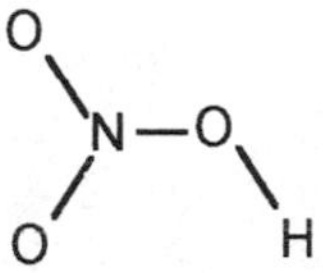 (that is, HNO_3)

NOTE: i) Again, strictly speaking, it is COVALENT OXIDES which form ACIDIC solutions. Since the nonmetals form covalent oxides, it is quite valid to say that nonmetal oxides form ACIDIC solutions.

ii) The only reactions between NONMETAL OXIDES and water that you should know are:

$$CO_2 + H_2O \longrightarrow H_2CO_3$$

$$SO_2 + H_2O \longrightarrow H_2SO_3$$

and

$$SO_3 + H_2O \longrightarrow H_2SO_4.$$

EXERCISE:

144. Write the reaction of the following oxides with water.

a) Li_2O b) MgO c) CO_2 d) BaO e) SO_2 f) K_2O

145. Which of the oxides in the previous exercise form solutions having pH > 7?

B. ACID RAIN

Because of dissolved CO_2, rain is naturally slightly acidic with a pH of about 5.6.

$$CO_2 + 2\,H_2O \rightleftharpoons H_3O^+ + HCO_3^-.$$

Any precipitation with pH < 5.6 is called "acid rain".

Sources of the acidity in acid rain

Most fuels, including coal and oil, are mixtures of many different hydrocarbons, some of which contain sulphur. When fuels containing sulphur are burned, the sulphur present forms sulphur dioxide.

$$S + O_2 \longrightarrow SO_2$$

Subsequent reaction of the SO_2 with air gives

$$2\,SO_2 + O_2 \rightleftharpoons 2\,SO_3$$ (dust and water act as catalysts for this reaction).

When the gases SO_2 and SO_3 join with water vapour, acids are formed.

$$SO_2 + H_2O \longrightarrow H_2SO_3$$ ("sulphurous acid")

$$SO_3 + H_2O \longrightarrow H_2SO_4$$ ("sulphuric acid")

The mixture of SO_2 and SO_3 is often referred to as "SO_X".

Similarly, combustion reactions (such as in an automobile) cause small amounts of N_2 to react with oxygen in the air.

$$N_2 + O_2 \longrightarrow 2\,NO$$
$$N_2 + 2\,O_2 \longrightarrow 2\,NO_2$$

Subsequently, some of the NO reacts with atmospheric O_2.

$$2\,NO + O_2 \rightleftharpoons 2\,NO_2$$

In addition, some of the NO_2 also reacts with water vapour.

$$2\,NO_2 + H_2O \longrightarrow HNO_2 + HNO_3$$

Similar to sulphur oxides, mixtures of NO and NO_2 are referred to as "NO_X".

The combined "soup" of H_2SO_3, H_2SO_4, HNO_2 and HNO_3 constitutes "acid rain".

It should be noted that nature also contributes to the acid rain problem with volcanic eruptions, gases given off by rotting vegetation, etc. For example, nitric oxide, NO, is produced in relatively large quantities by lightning and sulphur dioxide is spewed out in massive amounts by some volcanic eruptions.

Natural Protection Against Acid Rain

Most lakes have a moderate CO_2 / HCO_3^- buffering capacity, but once a lake receives large amounts of acid rain, the buffering capacity is exceeded and the lake ecosystems begin to be harmed. However, if the acid rain is halted, the absorption of CO_2 from the atmosphere eventually reverses most, if not all, of the effects of acid rain.

In addition, some lakes are in limestone–rich areas. The limestone ($CaCO_3$) can neutralize the acidity of acid rain. For example:

$$H_2SO_4(aq) + CaCO_3(s) \longrightarrow CaSO_4(s) + CO_2(aq) + H_2O(l).$$

Eventually, however, even the available limestone may be used up. In some cases, lakes may have powdered limestone dumped into them from airplanes to reverse some of the effects of acid rain.

Some Environmental Problems Associated with Acid Rain

1. Fish and plant growth is seriously affected in acidified water and soil. Many lakes are now "fishless" and contain little or no algae. Forests begin to die whenever their soil is sufficiently acidified. The devastation of the sugar maples in Quebec, the Black Forest in Germany and much of the forests of Scandinavia is evidence of the killing effects of acid rain. The question then becomes: how much is the heritage of a people worth?

2. Acid rain leaches minerals out of rocks and soils. For example, poisonous substances such as aluminum ions are leached out of rocks, while beneficial nutrients are leached out of the topsoil and down to the subsoils where these nutrients are generally unavailable for plant growth.

3. Metal and stone structures, especially buildings made of limestone (which has been much favoured as a building material in the past), are damaged by acid rain. The facings of many ancient buildings are now completely destroyed and many statues are unrecognizable.

Other Problems Related to Acid Rain

1. Acid rain often falls to earth far from the region in which it was created. Until international agreements were reached, nations often didn't bother to clean up their pollution because they didn't suffer directly from the effects of the acid rain they create. The cost of cleaning up industrial processes, using different fuels or alternate engines in cars is ENORMOUS and may require industries to be closed down if they can't afford to comply with strict pollution regulations. It is often considered to be political suicide to spend vast sums of money when the average person sees no immediate benefit. Who should pay for the cleanup?
2. People's health suffers directly and indirectly from water contaminated by acid rain, and water contaminated by chemicals leached from rocks.
3. Food crops such as radishes, tomatoes and apples are easily destroyed by acid rain.

Glimmers of Hope

An upsurge in public awareness on many environmental issues, including acid rain, has started a wave of well–publicized international conferences and agreements concerned with overcoming such problems and halting pollution. Abandoning our technology is not the answer, for then nothing could reverse some of the problems which have been set in motion. However, new technologies offer a way to bring many of the problems to a halt.

- Alternate nonpolluting energy sources are increasingly being used.
- Industrial processes are being modernized to cut down on pollution and to recycle harmful waste products.
- International cooperation on pollution problems is proceeding at an accelerating rate; people are making their governments listen to their concerns.

EXERCISES:

146. Some of the most acidic rain ever observed had a pH of 2.2. If 2.5 cm of such rain fell into a small lake having a surface area of 25 hectares ($2.5 \times 10^5 m^2$) over a 24 hr period, how many kilograms of limestone ($CaCO_3$) would be required to neutralize the effects of this single rainfall? ($10^3 L = 1 m^3$) The neutralization equation is

$$CaCO_3 + 2\,H_3O^+ \longrightarrow Ca^{2+} + CO_2 + 3\,H_2O\,.$$

147. The aluminum ions leached out of rocks by acid rain will be in the form: $Al(H_2O)_6^{3+}$. Why will these ions add to the problem of groundwater acidity?

UNIT V : ELECTROCHEMISTRY

V.1. INTRODUCTION

Acids have a bad reputation. Ask the average person what will happen if acid is placed on a metal and it is likely you will be told that the acid "eats" through the metal. Perhaps, but consider the following two demonstrations of the power of acids.

a) Place a strip of copper into a beaker containing concentrated hydrochloric acid, HCl(aq). Nothing happens.

b) Put a strip of copper into a beaker containing concentrated nitric acid, HNO_3(aq). The solution starts to produce red–brown bubbles of gas at the surface of the copper, the solution starts to turn green and the metal starts to dissolve.

Well, the nitric acid acted as might be expected, but why didn't the hydrochloric acid do anything? In this unit, you will discover the answer to this and many other curious questions, such as: why do large ships apply an electric current to their hulls? How can you clean silverware with aluminum foil? Why are copper refineries sometimes able to sell their left–over "sludge" for substantial profits? The answers to these questions are all based on ELECTROCHEMISTRY.

ELECTROCHEMISTRY is the branch of chemistry which is concerned with the conversion of chemical energy to electrical energy, and vice versa.

It is highly appropriate to introduce the subject of electrochemistry by considering the action of acids, because there is a substantial overlap between dealing with acids and bases and dealing with electrochemistry. You will work with a table which is remarkably similar to the now–familiar table of Relative Strengths of Acids and use many concepts first learned in acid–base theory.

In order to start investigating electrochemistry, consider this. A coil of copper wire is put in silver nitrate solution, $AgNO_3$(aq). The colourless solution slowly becomes blue while, at the same time, long crystals of pure, shining silver grow on the copper coil. The chemical equation for this reaction is

$$2\ Ag^{+}(aq) + Cu(s) \longrightarrow 2\ Ag(s) + Cu^{2+}(aq).$$

The same reaction can be produced in the following experimental setup.

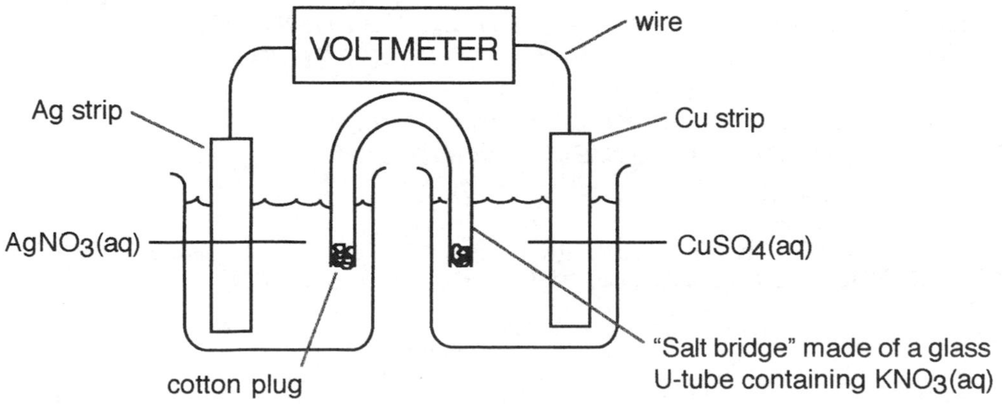

The above setup is an example of a chemical system called an **ELECTROCHEMICAL CELL** — a system which produces electrical energy.

The voltmeter reveals that electrons are flowing through the wire, from the copper strip to the silver strip. The electrochemical process will be analyzed in more detail later, but some preliminary definitions are required first.

The reaction $2\ Ag^{+}(aq) + Cu(s) \longrightarrow 2\ Ag(s) + Cu^{2+}(aq)$ only involves the loss and gain of electrons. The reaction has been split up so that the Ag^{+} is reacting in the left half of the electrochemical cell

$$2\ Ag^{+}(aq) + 2\ e^{-} \longrightarrow 2\ Ag(s)$$

while the Cu(s) is reacting in the right half

$$Cu(s) \longrightarrow Cu^{2+}(aq) + 2\ e^{-}.$$

Each half of the electrochemical cell is called a **HALF–CELL** and the reaction which occurs in a half–cell is called a **HALF–CELL REACTION,** or simply a **HALF–REACTION.**

If the "salt bridge" is removed, the reaction stops in the same abrupt way that an electric switch turns off a light. If the salt bridge is replaced with a piece of bent wire, such that one end of the wire dips into the left hand solution and the other end of the wire dips into the right hand solution, there is still no reaction. Whatever the salt bridge is doing, it seems essential that there be a salt solution connecting the two half–cells.

Definitions: An **OXIDATION REACTION** is a half–reaction in which a species loses electrons.

A **REDUCTION REACTION** is a half–reaction in which a species gains electrons.

MEMORY AID: "LEO the lion says GER"

"LEO" = **L**oss of **E**lectrons is **O**xidation
"GER" = **G**ain of **E**lectrons is **R**eduction

For every reduction reaction there must be an accompanying oxidation reaction. This makes sense because a substance can't accept electrons if another substance won't give off electrons in the first place.

A reaction involving the loss and gain of electrons is called a **REDUCTION–OXIDATION** reaction, or **REDOX** reaction.

In the reaction $2\ Ag^{+}(aq) + Cu(s) \longrightarrow 2\ Ag(s) + Cu^{2+}(aq)$, Ag^{+} is said to be the "agent" which causes Cu to become oxidized, and therefore Ag^{+} is called the **OXIDIZING AGENT.** Similarly, Cu is the "agent" which causes Ag^{+} to become reduced, and Cu is called the **REDUCING AGENT.**

Note: The **OXIDIZING AGENT** is **REDUCED** during the reaction.
The **REDUCING AGENT** is **OXIDIZED** during the reaction.

ANY TIME YOU SEE THAT AN ATOM OR ION HAS CHANGED ITS CHARGE DURING A REACTION, YOU CAN BE CERTAIN YOU ARE DEALING WITH A REDOX REACTION.

How can you tell which species is being oxidized and which is being reduced?

General rules emerge if some oxidation and reduction reactions are examined.

In each of the following OXIDATION REACTIONS

$$Zn \longrightarrow Zn^{2+} + 2\,e^-$$
$$U^{3+} \longrightarrow U^{4+} + e^-$$
$$2\,Cl^- \longrightarrow Cl_2 + 2\,e^-$$
$$Cl^- \longrightarrow Cl^{4+} + 5\,e^-,$$

the charge on the atoms involved gets MORE POSITIVE on the mathematical number line. In a neutral atom, the number of negative charges due to electrons exactly cancels the number of positive charges due to protons in the nucleus. When an electron is taken away, a greater amount of positive charge from the nucleus is allowed to "show through", producing a species with a more positive charge. The act of TAKING AWAY A NEGATIVE CHARGE is equivalent to ADDING A POSITIVE CHARGE. Therefore, **a species being oxidized becomes more positively charged (or, equivalently, less negatively charged).**

A frequently–encountered situation involving oxidation is the attachment of oxygen to metals such as iron. (This is the situation which originally gave rise to the term "oxidation".)

$$4\,Fe(s) + 3\,O_2(g) \longrightarrow 2\,Fe_2O_3(s)$$

In this case, the charge on the iron goes from zero to +3. You may have heard it said that the surface of a corroded metal was "heavily oxidized".

Similarly, in each of the following REDUCTION REACTIONS

$$Cu^{2+} + 2\,e^- \longrightarrow Cu$$
$$V^{3+} + e^- \longrightarrow V^{2+}$$
$$F_2 + 2\,e^- \longrightarrow 2\,F^-$$
$$I^{3+} + 4\,e^- \longrightarrow I^-,$$

the charge on the atoms gets MORE NEGATIVE on the mathematical number line. When an electron is added, more negative charge is added. Therefore, **a species being reduced becomes more negatively charged (or, equivalently, less positively charged).**

When an ore containing a metal is smelted, it is said that the ore is "reduced" to the metal or that the metal is produced in its "reduced form". The reduction process removes the oxygen from the metal compounds, leaving more or less pure metal behind. For example:

$$Fe_2O_3(s) + C(s) \longrightarrow CO_2(g) + Fe(s)\,.$$

Metallic iron is also called "reduced iron". If you examine the side panels of cereal packages, you will see that many of them have "reduced iron" listed as one of their ingredients. That's right — many cereals contain finely powdered iron metal! (The iron reacts with the hydrochloric acid in your stomach to produce Fe^{2+}, which is an essential nutrient. If Fe^{2+} were added directly to the food, the oxygen in the air would quickly convert the Fe^{2+} to Fe^{3+}, which cannot be used as a nutrient.)

EXAMPLE: In the equation $Zn^{2+} + Mg \longrightarrow Zn + Mg^{2+}$, two species are changing their electrical charge during the course of the reaction:

$$Mg \longrightarrow Mg^{2+} + 2\,e^- \quad \text{and} \quad Zn^{2+} + 2\,e^- \longrightarrow Zn$$

Since Mg is losing electrons (becoming more positively charged), it is being oxidized.
Since Zn^{2+} is gaining electrons (becoming less positively charged), it is being reduced.

Finally, since Mg is being oxidized it is the REDUCING AGENT, and since Zn^{2+} is being reduced it is the OXIDIZING AGENT.

EXERCISES:

1. In the following reactions, indicate the:

   i) species oxidized ii) species reduced iii) oxidizing agent iv) reducing agent.

   a) $Hg^{2+} + Mn \longrightarrow Hg + Mn^{2+}$
   b) $H_2 + Sn^{4+} \longrightarrow 2\,H^+ + Sn^{2+}$
   c) $2\,Li + F_2 \longrightarrow 2\,Li^+ + 2\,F^-$
   d) $Br_2 + 2\,Cr^{2+} \longrightarrow 2\,Br^- + 2\,Cr^{3+}$
   e) $2\,Fe^{2+} + Sn^{4+} \longrightarrow Sn^{2+} + 2\,Fe^{3+}$

2. When cesium metal is exposed to chlorine gas, a bright flash occurs as the elements react. The product, cesium chloride, is a white solid composed of cesium ions and chloride ions.

   a) Write the balanced overall reaction which occurs between chlorine and cesium.
   b) Write the half–reactions which occur and identify which half–reaction is the reduction and which is the oxidation.
   c) Identify the reducing and oxidizing agents.

V.2. OXIDATION NUMBERS

An **OXIDATION NUMBER** is the charge that an atom would possess if the species containing the atom were made up of ions.

Since molecules are usually held together by covalent bonds, not ionic bonds, oxidation numbers often are a somewhat fictitious concept. Nevertheless, they are a useful idea.

To assign oxidation numbers to the atoms in a molecule, make the following assumptions regarding the charges of ions, based on their position in the periodic table:

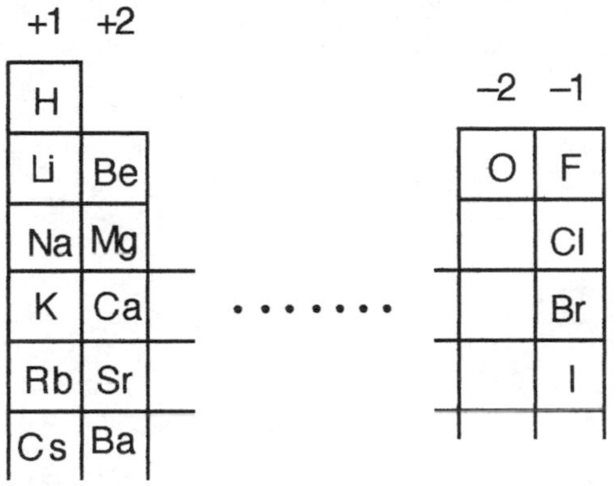

NOTE: although the halogens are NORMALLY −1, there are MANY exceptions.

The rule which governs the calculation of oxidation numbers is simply

THE SUM OF THE POSITIVE CHARGES AND THE NEGATIVE CHARGES MUST EQUAL THE OVERALL CHARGE ON THE SPECIES.

Other important concepts relating to oxidation numbers will be found as further examples are examined.

EXAMPLES:

a) What is the oxidation number of P in the molecule $H_4P_2O_7$?

Write out your work on two lines below the formula for the molecule.

	H_4	P_2	O_7	
individual charge for an atom ⟶	+1	"x"	−2	
total charge (all atoms) ⟶	+4	2x	−14	= 0

Each H has a charge of +1, so that 4 H's contribute +4 to the total charge. Since you don't know the charge on P, let the individual charge on P be "x" and the total charge on 2 P's be "2x". Each O has a charge of −2, so the total contribution from the 7 O's is −14. The molecule is neutral, so that its overall charge must be zero.

Solving $4 + 2x - 14 = 0$ produces $x = +5$. Therefore, **the oxidation number of P is +5.**

b) What is the oxidation number of P in P_4?

Since the molecule is neutral, then $4x = 0$ and $x = 0$.

Conclusion: The oxidation number of an atom in its elemental form is ZERO.

c) What is the oxidation number of Cr in Cr^{3+} ?

This one is obvious: the oxidation number (charge on the atom) is +3.

Conclusion: The oxidation number of a monatomic ion is the charge on the ion.

d) What is the oxidation number of S in SO_4^{2-} ?

$$\begin{array}{rcc} & S & O_4 \ ^{2-} \\ \text{individual charge for an atom} \longrightarrow & x & -2 \\ \text{total charge (all atoms)} \longrightarrow & x & -8 = \mathbf{-2} \end{array}$$

The ion has a 2– charge overall, requiring the solution of the equation:

$x - 8 = -2$, which gives $x = +6$.

Therefore, **the oxidation number of S is +6.**

EXERCISES:

3. Calculate the oxidation number of the atom in **bold** type.

a) $H\mathbf{N}O_3$	e) $\mathbf{N}H_4^+$	i) $\mathbf{Al}(OH)_4^-$	m) $H\mathbf{Cl}O_3$	q) $K_2\mathbf{U}O_4$
b) $\mathbf{N}O_2^-$	f) $\mathbf{N}_3^-$	j) $\mathbf{S}_2F_{10}$	n) $\mathbf{N}_2H_5^+$	r) $\mathbf{C}_3H_6O$
c) $\mathbf{Cr}O_4^{2-}$	g) $\mathbf{C}_2H_6$	k) $\mathbf{N}_2O_3$	o) $\mathbf{N}H_2OH$	s) $\mathbf{S}_8$
d) $\mathbf{Cr}_2O_7^{2-}$	h) $\mathbf{C}_3H_8$	l) $H\mathbf{Cl}O_4$	p) $\mathbf{C}_2O_4^{2-}$	t) $\mathbf{C}_4H_6$

4. Assign oxidation numbers to the **bold** species in each of the following unbalanced reaction equations. Then determine which species undergoes oxidation in each reaction.

a) $\mathbf{ClO_2} + \mathbf{C} \longrightarrow \mathbf{ClO_2^-} + \mathbf{CO_3^{2-}}$

b) $\mathbf{Sn^{2+}} + Cl^- + \mathbf{BrO_3^-} \longrightarrow \mathbf{SnCl_6^{2-}} + \mathbf{Br^-}$

c) $\mathbf{MnO_4^-} + \mathbf{C_2O_4^{2-}} \longrightarrow \mathbf{MnO_2} + \mathbf{CO_2}$

d) $\mathbf{NO_3^-} + H_2\mathbf{Te} \longrightarrow \mathbf{NO} + \mathbf{TeO_4^{2-}}$

5. Which of the following are redox reactions?

a) $I_2 + 5\,HOBr + H_2O \longrightarrow 2\,IO_3^- + 5\,Br^- + 7\,H^+$

b) $4\,Ag^+ + Cr_2O_7^{2-} + H_2O \longrightarrow 2\,Ag_2CrO_4 + 2\,H^+$

c) $KHCO_3 + HI \longrightarrow KI + CO_2 + H_2O$

d) $2\,H_2O \longrightarrow 2\,H_2 + O_2$

e) $H_2SO_4 + BaCl_2 \longrightarrow BaSO_4 + 2\,HCl$

f) $Fe + H_2SO_4 \longrightarrow FeSO_4 + H_2$

SNEAKY TRICK!

You will sometimes find that the solution to a problem only requires you to determine which species have been oxidized and which have been reduced. Look at the following oxidations and reductions.

i) $ClO_3^- \longrightarrow ClO_4^-$ (oxidation: $Cl^{5+} \longrightarrow Cl^{7+}$)

ii) $H_2O_2 \longrightarrow H_2O$ (reduction: $O^- \longrightarrow O^{2-}$)

iii) $Cr^{3+} \longrightarrow CrO_4^{2-}$ (oxidation: $Cr^{3+} \longrightarrow Cr^{6+}$)

iv) $NO_2 \longrightarrow N_2O_3$ (reduction: $N^{4+} \longrightarrow N^{3+}$)

In each of these cases, **THE NUMBER OF ATTACHED OXYGEN ATOMS INCREASES DURING AN OXIDATION,** and **THE NUMBER OF ATTACHED OXYGENS DECREASES DURING A REDUCTION.** In the last example, (iv), the number of oxygens go from 2 O's per N–atom to 1.5 O's per N–atom.

EXERCISE:

6. (a) Which of Cl_2, ClO_4^-, Cl^-, ClO_3^- and Cl_2O can be produced by reducing ClO_2^-?

   (b) Which of NO_3^-, N_2, NO_2^-, N_2O and N_2O_3 can be produced by oxidizing NO?

V.3. PREDICTING THE SPONTANEITY OF A REDOX REACTION

The table of Standard Reduction Potentials is constructed as shown below. As you examine the table, you should notice the similarity between it and the table of Relative Strengths of Acids.

INCREASING TENDENCY TO REDUCE that is, INCREASING STRENGTH AS AN OXIDIZING AGENT	$F_2 + 2e^- \rightleftharpoons 2F^-$ $\vdots$ $Ag^+ + e^- \rightleftharpoons Ag$ $\vdots$ $Cu^{2+} + 2e^- \rightleftharpoons Cu$ $\vdots$ $Zn^{2+} + 2e^- \rightleftharpoons Zn$ $\vdots$ $Li^+ + e^- \rightleftharpoons Li$	INCREASING TENDENCY TO OXIDIZE that is, INCREASING STRENGTH AS A REDUCING AGENT

NOTE: Look at the table of Standard Reduction Potentials found at the back of this book and observe the following. (These observations will help you find a given half–reaction much more quickly when you are looking for it on the table.)

a) In general, metals are found in the bottom half of the Table, on the right. The exceptions are: Cu, Ag, Hg and Au. These latter metals are clustered together on the periodic table.

b) In general, the halogens and oxyanions (anions containing oxygen) are found in the top half of the Table, on the left.

c) Some metals, such as Fe, Sn, Cr, Hg and Cu have more than one common oxidation number. In these cases, there will be MORE THAN ONE HALF–REACTION on the Table involving these metals. Remember this point because it means that a given ion may be found on either side of the Table.

   For example: $Cu^+ + e^- \rightleftharpoons Cu(s)$
   $Cu^{2+} + 2e^- \rightleftharpoons Cu(s)$
   $Cu^{2+} + e^- \rightleftharpoons Cu^+$

   The Cu^+ ion is found on both the left AND right sides. Similarly, Sn^{2+} and Fe^{2+} are also found on both sides of the Table.

d) H_2O_2 is found at the top **left** side of the Table (at +1.78 V) **AND** lower down on the **right** side of the Table (at +0.70 V).

The table of Standard Reduction Potentials is used in a similar way to the table of Relative Strengths of Acids; the species at the upper left have a great tendency to "go forward" while the species at the lower right have a great tendency to "go backward". Each of the reactions in the table of Standard Reduction Potentials can go either forward or backward.

For example, if there is a piece of Zn(s) in a solution of Zn^{2+}, you can write either:

$$Zn^{2+} + 2\,e^- \longrightarrow Zn \quad \text{(written as a reduction)}$$

or

$$Zn \longrightarrow Zn^{2+} + 2\,e^- \quad \text{(written as an oxidation).}$$

> **NOTE:** When referring to an isolated half–reaction, use equilibrium arrows to show that the reaction can go forward or backward.
>
> **Example:** $Ag^+ + e^- \rightleftharpoons Ag$
>
> If the half–reaction is made to undergo either reduction or oxidation as a result of being part of a redox reaction, then use a one–way reaction arrow.
>
> **Example:** $Ag^+ + e^- \longrightarrow Ag$

Since you cannot simply lift the reaction equation $Zn^{2+} + 2\,e^- \longrightarrow Zn$ off the paper and turn it around backward, you will have to get used to the idea of thinking of an oxidation as "running backward" on the Table.

$$Zn^{2+} + 2\,e^- \longleftarrow Zn \quad \text{(implied to be an oxidation)}$$

Now, assume there are two half–cells such that in one half–cell there is a piece of Zn in a solution of Zn^{2+} and in the other half–cell there is a piece of Cu in a solution of Cu^{2+}. The half–reactions can be written as

$$Cu^{2+} + 2\,e^- \rightleftharpoons Cu$$

and

$$Zn^{2+} + 2\,e^- \rightleftharpoons Zn\,.$$

Of the two species which can reduce (Cu^{2+} and Zn^{2+}), the Cu^{2+} is higher on the left side of the Table and has a greater tendency to reduce. The actual reduction reaction will then be

$$Cu^{2+} + 2\,e^- \longrightarrow Cu\,.$$

Of the two species which can oxidize (Cu and Zn), the Zn is lower on the right side of the Table and has a greater tendency to oxidize. The reaction on the Table is then thought of as going in reverse:

$$Zn^{2+} + 2\,e^- \longleftarrow Zn\,.$$

When actually writing down the oxidation reaction, put the Zn on the reactants side:

$$Zn \longrightarrow Zn^{2+} + 2\,e^-.$$

The overall redox reaction which will spontaneously occur is found by adding the two half–reactions.

$$\begin{array}{rcl} Cu^{2+} + 2\,e^- & \longrightarrow & Cu \\ Zn & \longrightarrow & Zn^{2+} + 2\,e^- \\ \hline Cu^{2+} + Zn & \longrightarrow & Cu + Zn^{2+} \end{array}$$

OK. Let's see what can be concluded from the above discussion.

> **If two half–cells are joined, the higher half–reaction on the Table will undergo reduction and the lower one will undergo oxidation.**

For example: $\boxed{Cu^{2+}} + 2\,e^- \longrightarrow Cu$

$Zn^{2+} + 2\,e^- \longleftarrow \boxed{Zn}$

The species in the boxes will react, forming the species on the opposite side of the equation.

Note: (1) **When a species reacts, it moves to the other side of the reaction equation. Therefore, a species on the left side before the reaction will form the species on the right side after a reaction, and vice versa.** This point might seem trivial and obvious, but many students take a while to get used to "reading an equation backwards". (See example above)

(2) **If only one species in a half–reaction is present, the other species in the half-reaction are *NOT* present (unless you have been EXPLICITLY told that the other species are present)!** Again, this point might seem obvious but assume you are told that a solution contains Cl^-. The table of Standard Reduction Potentials shows the half–reaction

$$Cl_2 + 2\,e^- \longrightarrow 2\,Cl^-.$$

Just because the reduction reaction shows that Cl_2 can be reduced to Cl^- does not mean you are free to assume Cl_2 is present. (Solutions of sodium chloride don't give off chlorine gas!)

Now, if you are only given two potential reactants, rather than complete half–reactions, a reaction may or may not occur. The following procedure is used to determine whether a reaction actually happens.

First, locate each reactant on the Table.

a) If both reactants are only found on the left or both reactants are only found on the right then NO REACTION IS POSSIBLE.

Example: Assume the **ONLY** reactants present are **Zn** and **Cu.**

$Cu^{2+} + 2\,e^- \longleftarrow \boxed{Cu}$

$Zn^{2+} + 2\,e^- \longleftarrow \boxed{Zn}$

Both Cu and Zn can only oxidize (the reaction can only go backward, as shown) and since there is nothing present which can reduce, a complete redox reaction is impossible. Therefore, **NO REACTION.**

Example: Assume the **ONLY** reactants present are $\mathbf{Zn^{2+}}$ and $\mathbf{Cu^{2+}}$.

$\boxed{Cu^{2+}} + 2\,e^- \longrightarrow Cu$

$\boxed{Zn^{2+}} + 2\,e^- \longrightarrow Zn$

Both Cu^{2+} and Zn^{2+} can only reduce (the reaction can only go forward, as shown) and since there is nothing present which can oxidize, a complete redox reaction is impossible. Therefore, **NO REACTION.**

b) If one reactant is on the left hand side and one is on the right hand side then there are TWO POSSIBLE CASES.

CASE 1: The reactant to be **reduced** (left side) is **HIGHER** on the Table than the reactant to be **oxidized** (right side).

For example, assume the reactants given are $\mathbf{Cu^{2+}}$ and **Zn.**

$\boxed{Cu^{2+}} + 2\,e^- \longrightarrow Cu$

$Zn^{2+} + 2\,e^- \longleftarrow \boxed{Zn}$

In this case, a **SPONTANEOUS REACTION** is experimentally found to occur.

$$Cu^{2+} + Zn(s) \longrightarrow Cu(s) + Zn^{2+}$$

The reaction goes 100% to completion.

CASE 2: The reactant to be **reduced** (left side) is **LOWER** on the Table than the reactant to be **oxidized** (right side).

For example, assume the reactants given are **Zn^{2+}** and **Cu**.

$$Cu^{2+} + 2\,e^- \longleftarrow \boxed{Cu}$$

$$\boxed{Zn^{2+}} + 2\,e^- \longrightarrow Zn$$

In this case, **NO REACTION** occurs.

Note that this is the ***reverse*** of CASE 1. Since CASE 1 stated that

$$Cu^{2+} + Zn(s) \longrightarrow Cu(s) + Zn^{2+}$$

had a 100% tendency to go forward, then the reverse reaction (CASE 2) must have 0% tendency to react.

IN SUMMARY :

A REACTION WILL BE SPONTANEOUS IF AND ONLY IF THERE IS A REACTANT TO BE REDUCED (on the left side) WHICH IS <u>ABOVE</u> A REACTANT TO BE OXIDIZED (on the right side).

EXAMPLES: Look at the Standard Reduction Potentials table while working through these examples. To help find the half–reactions more quickly, the number on the Table beside the half–reaction is given.

Predict whether or not a reaction will occur when the following are mixed.

a) **Cl_2** is mixed with **Br^-** :

$$\boxed{Cl_2} + 2\,e^- \longrightarrow 2\,Cl^- \quad \ldots\ldots \quad 1.36$$

$$Br_2 + 2\,e^- \longleftarrow \boxed{2\,Br^-} \quad \ldots\ldots \quad 1.09$$

This reaction will **OCCUR SPONTANEOUSLY** because the reactant to be reduced (Cl_2, on the left) is above the reactant to be oxidized (Br^-, on the right).

b) **Sn** is mixed with **Mn** :

$$Sn^{2+} + 2\,e^- \longleftarrow \boxed{Sn} \quad \ldots\ldots \quad -0.14$$

$$Mn^{2+} + 2\,e^- \longleftarrow \boxed{Mn} \quad \ldots\ldots \quad -1.19$$

This reaction will **NOT OCCUR** because both reactants can only oxidize, and there is nothing available to reduce.

c) **Ni^{2+}** is mixed with **Pb** :

$$Pb^{2+} + 2\,e^- \longleftarrow \boxed{Pb} \quad \ldots\ldots \quad -0.13$$

$$\boxed{Ni^{2+}} + 2\,e^- \longrightarrow Ni \quad \ldots\ldots \quad -0.26$$

This reaction will **NOT OCCUR** because the reactant to be reduced (Ni^{2+}, on the left) is **BELOW** the reactant to be oxidized (Pb, on the right).

A FINAL COMMENT ON H^+

When H^+ is present, it must be treated like any other reactant. For example, if you are asked whether the SO_4^{2-} in a solution of Na_2SO_4 will reduce:

$$SO_4^{2-} + 4\,H^+ + 2\,e^- \longrightarrow H_2SO_3 + 2\,H_2O \quad \ldots\ldots\ldots \quad +0.17$$

your answer should be **"there is no reaction UNLESS H^+ is present also"**, or equivalently, that the solution is "ACIDIC". In the same way that the reduction doesn't occur if SO_4^{2-} is absent, there is no reaction if H^+ is absent.

Note that H^+ is a necessary reactant in many reduction reactions. However, there is only ONE reaction in which H^+ is the only substance involved in the reduction half–reaction:

$$2\,H^+ + 2\,e^- \longrightarrow H_2(g) \quad \ldots\ldots\ldots \quad 0.00\,.$$

EXERCISES:

7. Using the Standard Reduction Potential table, state whether the following species
   - can only undergo reduction, or
   - can only undergo oxidation, or
   - cannot react at all, or
   - can undergo **either** reduction **or** oxidation (because it is found on both sides of the Table).

   (a) Na^+ (c) Cu^+ (e) NO_3^- (g) Fe^{2+} (i) Se(s) (k) Al(s)
   (b) I^- (d) Sn^{4+} (f) Hg(l) (h) Co^{2+} (j) Sn^{2+} (l) acidic $Cr_2O_7^{2-}$

8. Classify as **spontaneous** or **no reaction.** If spontaneous, write out the complete reaction.
   a) Ni^{2+} + Ag(s) c) Ag(s) + I^- e) H^+ + Fe(s) g) Sn^{2+} + Co(s) i) Al^{3+} + Ni(s)
   b) Zn^{2+} + Li(s) d) H^+ + Cu(s) f) Sn^{4+} + Au(s) h) Cu^+ + Sn(s) j) Hg^{2+} + $H_2(g)$

9. Which member of each of the following pairs is the stronger oxidizing agent?
   a) Zn^{2+} or Ca^{2+} b) Cr^{3+} or Cu^{2+} c) Br_2 or I_2

10. Which member of each of the following pairs is the stronger reducing agent?
    a) Mn or Pb b) Cu^+ or Sn^{2+} c) Cr^{2+} or Fe^{2+}

11. Predict whether a spontaneous reaction is expected when the following are mixed, and state the products of any spontaneous reactions.
    a) Zn(s) and $H_2(g)$
    b) Sn(s) and Sn^{4+}
    c) H^+ is added to Mn(s)
    d) Fe^{2+} is added to $Cr_2O_7^{2-}$
    e) Fe^{2+} is added to acidic $Cr_2O_7^{2-}$
    f) Cu(s) and H^+
    g) A mixture of $MnO_2(s)$ and H^+ is added to I^-
    h) SO_4^{2-} is added to Sn(s)

12. a) Which of Cr, I_2, Al and Fe^{3+} will oxidize Co?
    b) Which of H_2, Cl_2, Hg^{2+} and H_2O_2 will reduce Ag^+?
    c) Which of I^-, Pb, Br_2 and Sn^{2+} will act as reducing agents for Sn^{4+}?
    d) Which of Cu^{2+}, Zn, acidic NO_3^- and Cl^- will act as oxidizing agents for aqueous SO_2 (i.e. H_2SO_3)?
    e) Which substance(s) can be oxidized by I_2 but not by acidic SO_4^{2-}?
    f) Which substance(s) can be reduced by I^- but not by Fe^{2+}?
    g) Which substance(s) can act as an oxidizing agent for Pb but not for Sn^{2+}?
    h) Which substance(s) will oxidize Co and reduce H^+?

13. An electrochemical cell was made by joining a half–cell containing 1 M $Pb(NO_3)_2$ and a lead electrode to a half–cell consisting of 1 M $Zn(NO_3)_2$ and a zinc electrode. As the cell continues to operate, what happens to the $[Pb^{2+}]$? What happens to the $[Zn^{2+}]$?

14. You have been given three half–reactions:

$$A^{2+} + 2\,e^- \rightleftharpoons A(s)$$
$$B^{2+} + 2\,e^- \rightleftharpoons B(s)$$
$$C^{2+} + 2\,e^- \rightleftharpoons C(s).$$

The reactions are not in any order of tendency to reduce. The following experimental data is found:

A^{2+} reacts with C(s) but not with B(s) .

Arrange the half–reactions in decreasing order of tendency to reduce (greatest tendency first).

15. You have been given four half–reactions:

$$D^{2+} + 2\,e^- \rightleftharpoons D(s)$$
$$E^{2+} + 2\,e^- \rightleftharpoons E(s)$$
$$F^{2+} + 2\,e^- \rightleftharpoons F(s)$$
$$G^{2+} + 2\,e^- \rightleftharpoons G(s).$$

Experimentally, it was found that: F^{2+} reacts with D(s), E(s) and G(s)
no reaction occurs between D^{2+} and any of the metals
G^{2+} only reacts with D(s) .

Arrange the half–reactions in decreasing strength as oxidizing agents (greatest strength first).

16. You have been given five half–reactions:

$$H^{2+} + 2\,e^- \rightleftharpoons H(s)$$
$$I^{2+} + 2\,e^- \rightleftharpoons I(s)$$
$$J^{2+} + 2\,e^- \rightleftharpoons J(s)$$
$$K^{2+} + 2\,e^- \rightleftharpoons K(s)$$
$$L^{2+} + 2\,e^- \rightleftharpoons L(s).$$

Experimentally, it was found that: K^{2+} only reacted with I(s) and H(s)
L^{2+} did not react with J(s)
I^{2+} reacted with H(s) .

Arrange the half–reactions in decreasing tendency to reduce (greatest tendency first).

17. Use your Table of Reduction Potentials to complete the following table. Omit the spaces on the diagonal and use "RX" to indicate that a reaction occurs between the metal and ion or use "–" to indicate that no reaction occurs.

	Fe^{2+}	Au^{3+}	Ni^{2+}	Pb^{2+}
Fe				
Au				
Ni				
Pb				

18. Given the following data

	V^{2+}	Cd^{2+}	Ti^{2+}	Ga^{3+}
V		Rx	—	Rx
Cd	—		—	—
Ti	Rx	Rx		Rx
Ga	—	Rx	—	

where: "**RX**" means a reaction occurred and "—" means no reaction occurred

Arrange the metal ions in decreasing strength as oxidizing agents.

V.4. BALANCING HALF–REACTIONS

A half–reaction must be balanced for mass and charge. The balancing procedure for a half–reaction is easy BUT if you are sloppy about writing the charges on ions, you will make many mistakes until you correct your sloppy habits.

Typically, when you are required to balance a half–reaction, you will be given a "skeleton equation" containing the major atoms involved. It is up to you to complete the balancing by supplying other species as follows.

a) Balance the **MAJOR** atoms by inspection. (The "major atoms" are any atoms other than O and H.)
b) Balance the **OXYGEN** atoms by adding H_2O molecules. (The reactions normally occur in water.)
c) Balance the **HYDROGEN** atoms by adding H^+. (The reactions are initially treated as if they occur in acidic solution.)
d) Balance the overall **CHARGE** by adding electrons.

Note: ***NEVER*** vary the order in which the above steps are carried out because –

- The major atoms are often joined to oxygen atoms, so there is no point in balancing the oxygens before the major species are settled.
- The water molecules contain hydrogen, so there is no point in balancing the hydrogens until H_2O's are added to balance the oxygens.
- H^+ carries an electric charge, so there is no point in balancing the charge until H^+'s are added.

The following memory aid summarizes the procedure.

The officer's name was: **MAJOR HYDROXIDE.**

"MAJOR HYDROXIDE" translates as "MAJOR OH^-"

1. Balance the MAJOR species. (MAJOR)
2. Balance the O atoms. (O)
3. Balance the H atoms. (H)
4. Balance the charge, using e^- (–)

Now read the examples below to learn some of the "tricks" associated with balancing half–reactions.

EXAMPLE: Balance the half–reaction $RuO_2 \rightleftharpoons Ru$. The half–reaction occurs in acidic solution.

Step 1: Balance the major atoms by inspection.

- In this case, there is only one major atom, Ru, and it is already balanced.

Step 2: Balance the O's by adding H_2O's.

- Since there are two O's on the left, add two H_2O's to the right (to end up with two O's on both sides).

$$RuO_2 \rightleftharpoons Ru + 2\,H_2O$$

Step 3: Balance the H's by adding H^+'s.

- Since there are 4 H's on the right (2 H_2O's, each containing 2 H's) then add 4 H^+ to the left.

$$4\,H^+ + RuO_2 \rightleftharpoons Ru + 2\,H_2O$$

Step 4: Balance the charge by adding e^-'s.

- Since there is a +4 charge on the left and zero charge on the right, add 4 e^-'s to the left (see below) to finish.

$$4\,e^- + 4\,H^+ + RuO_2 \rightleftharpoons Ru + 2\,H_2O$$

Note: By adding **negative** charges (electrons), the charge on a given side of an equation can only be decreased (on the mathematical number line, in which +1 is greater than –3). Therefore, you must determine which side of an equation has the greater charge and add electrons to that side until its charge equals the smaller charge on the other side. The following procedure works very well.

a) Find the charge on both sides.
b) Find the difference in charge between the two sides.
c) To the side with the **greater** charge add a number of electrons equal to the difference in charge.

For example: i) $\mathbf{Z^{6+} \longrightarrow Z^{2+}}$: the difference in charge is 4, and the left side has the greater charge, so add 4 e^-'s to the left:

$$Z^{6+} + 4\,e^- \longrightarrow Z^{2+}$$

ii) $\mathbf{X^{2-} \longrightarrow X^{+}}$: the charge difference is 3, and the right side has the greater charge, so add 3 e^-'s to the right:

$$X^{2-} \longrightarrow X^{+} + 3\,e^-$$

***EXAMPLE*:** Balance the half–reaction $Cr_2O_7^{2-} \rightleftharpoons Cr^{3+}$ (The half–reaction occurs in acidic solution.)

Step 1: Balance the major atoms. $Cr_2O_7^{2-} \rightleftharpoons 2\,Cr^{3+}$

Step 2: Balance the O's. $Cr_2O_7^{2-} \rightleftharpoons 2\,Cr^{3+} + 7\,H_2O$

Step 3: Balance the H's. $14\,H^+ + Cr_2O_7^{2-} \rightleftharpoons 2\,Cr^{3+} + 7\,H_2O$

Step 4: Balance the charge.

- on the left: 14 x (+1) –2 = +12
- on the right: 2 x (+3) = +6
- the difference in charges = 12 – 6 = 6 ; therefore 6 e^-'s must be added to the left side:

$$6\,e^- + 14\,H^+ + Cr_2O_7^{2-} \rightleftharpoons 2\,Cr^{3+} + 7\,H_2O$$

***EXAMPLE*:** Balance the half–reaction $Pb \rightleftharpoons HPbO_2^-$, which occurs in **BASIC** solution.

First balance the equation as if it were in ACID SOLUTION.

Step 1: Balance the major atoms.

- The Pb's are already balanced. **Note:** you will often find that the major atoms are already balanced; don't get into the habit of ignoring this step or you will have problems when the major atoms are NOT balanced.

Step 2: Balance the O's. $Pb + 2\,H_2O \rightleftharpoons HPbO_2^-$

Step 3: Balance the H's. $Pb + 2\,H_2O \rightleftharpoons 3\,H^+ + HPbO_2^-$

Step 4: Balance the charge. $Pb + 2\,H_2O \rightleftharpoons 2\,e^- + 3\,H^+ + HPbO_2^-$

Now convert this equation to BASIC conditions by adding the water equilibrium equation in such a way as to **cancel all the H^+** in the half–reaction.

$$Pb + 2\,H_2O \rightleftharpoons 2\,e^- + 3\,H^+ + HPbO_2^-$$
$$3\,H^+ + 3\,OH^- \rightleftharpoons 3\,H_2O$$

$$Pb + 3\,OH^- \rightleftharpoons 2\,e^- + H_2O + HPbO_2^-$$

Note: In order to cancel all the H^+ in the half–reaction, the equation

$$H_2O \rightleftharpoons H^+ + OH^-$$

is multiplied by 3 (that is, the number of H^+'s in the half–reaction), and then turned around so as to put the H^+ in the water equilibrium on the side ***opposite*** to the H^+ in the half–reaction. Some of the H_2O's may cancel each other, ***but*** the purpose of adding the water equilibrium is to cancel the H^+'s, ***not necessarily*** the H_2O's.

EXAMPLE: Balance the following half–reaction which occurs in acidic solution: $H_2 \longrightarrow$.

At first this may seem nonsensical but let's think a minute. Are the major atoms balanced? Yes, because there aren't any! Are the oxygens balanced? Again, yes because there aren't any. Aha! Now balance the H's by adding 2 H^+, and then add electrons.

$$H_2 \longrightarrow 2\,H^+ + 2\,e^-.$$

Comment: Any time you find an isolated species made up of only H and/or O atoms, just proceed with the rules in the usual way to get a correct balance. The only known examples of neutral species (other than H_2O) that are made up of H's and/or O's are:

H_2, O_2, O_3 and H_2O_2.

EXERCISE:

19. Balance the following half–reactions.

a) $Ce^{4+} \rightleftharpoons Ce^{2+}$

b) $I_2 \rightleftharpoons I^-$

c) $Mn^{2+} \rightleftharpoons MnO_2$ (acidic solution)

d) $O_2 \rightleftharpoons H_2O_2$ (acidic solution)

e) $S_2O_8^{2-} \rightleftharpoons HSO_4^-$ (acidic solution)

f) $H_3AsO_4 \rightleftharpoons HAsO_2$ (acidic solution)

g) $H_2SeO_3 \rightleftharpoons Se$ (acidic solution)

h) $N_2H_4 \rightleftharpoons N_2$ (basic solution)

i) $HO_2^- \rightleftharpoons O_2$ (basic solution)

j) $HXeO_4^- \rightleftharpoons HXeO_6^{3-}$ (basic solution)

k) $HC_2H_3O_2 \rightleftharpoons C_2H_5OH$ (acidic solution)

l) $Cr(OH)_3 \rightleftharpoons CrO_4^{2-}$ (basic solution)

m) $CH_3CHO \rightleftharpoons CH_2CH_2$ (acidic solution)

CHANGES IN OXIDATION NUMBERS DURING A HALF–REACTION

The following exercises investigate the relationship between changes in oxidation numbers and the numbers of electrons involved in half–reactions.

EXERCISES:

20. In the half–reaction $NO_2^- \rightleftharpoons NO_3^-$:
    a) calculate the oxidation numbers for N on both sides of the equation.
    b) calculate "ΔON" (the "change in **O**xidation **N**umber"), and decide on a sign for the value of ΔON. (Hint: the change equals the oxidation number of the nitrogen on the product side minus the oxidation number of the nitrogen on the reactant side.)
    c) balance the half–reaction in acid solution.
    d) look at the number of electrons involved and compare this to the value of ΔON. Is the half–reaction a reduction or oxidation?

21. In the half–reaction $MnO_4^- \rightleftharpoons MnO_2$:
    a) calculate the oxidation numbers for Mn on both sides of the equation.
    b) calculate ΔON and assign a sign for the value of ΔON.
    c) balance the half–reaction in acid solution.
    d) look at the number of electrons involved and compare this to the value of ΔON. Is the half–reaction a reduction or oxidation?

22. Summarize the results of the above two exercises by completing the following sentence.

    The OXIDATION NUMBER ____________ during a REDUCTION reaction and ____________ during an OXIDATION reaction.

23. For each of the half–reactions below
    i) determine the change in oxidation number of the atom in bold type.
    ii) state whether the half–reaction is an oxidation or a reduction.

    a) $\mathbf{Te} \rightleftharpoons \mathbf{Te}O_4^-$
    b) $\mathbf{Cl}O_3^- \rightleftharpoons \mathbf{Cl}^-$
    c) $\mathbf{U}^{4+} \rightleftharpoons \mathbf{U}O_2^{2+}$
    d) $\mathbf{C}_2H_5OH \rightleftharpoons \mathbf{C}H_3\mathbf{C}OOH$ (treat both carbons in CH_3COOH identically)
    e) $\mathbf{P}O_4^{3-} \rightleftharpoons H\mathbf{P}O_3^{2-}$

V.5. BALANCING REDOX EQUATIONS USING HALF–REACTIONS

NOTE: There are two common methods for balancing redox equations: using half–reactions and using oxidation numbers. You are not REQUIRED to learn both methods, but MAY FIND IT TO YOUR ADVANTAGE to be familiar with both methods. The method of oxidation numbers (next section) is quicker to use when balancing simple redox equations; the method of half–reactions is easier to use with more complicated redox equations.

The method used in this section balances a redox equation by breaking the equation into separate reduction and oxidation half–reactions.

***EXAMPLE*:** Balance $Os + IO_3^- \longrightarrow OsO_4 + I_2$ (in acidic solution).

Step 1: Break the equation into TWO half–reactions. The easiest way to do this is to assume that the species changing their oxidation numbers (Os and I) are in separate half–reactions.

$$Os \longrightarrow OsO_4$$
$$IO_3^- \longrightarrow I_2$$

Step 2: Balance the individual half–reactions.

$$Os + 4\,H_2O \longrightarrow OsO_4 + 8\,H^+ + 8\,e^-$$
$$2\,IO_3^- + 12\,H^+ + 10\,e^- \longrightarrow I_2 + 6\,H_2O$$

Step 3: Multiply the half–reactions by whole numbers so as to make:

(total electrons lost) = (total electrons gained)

- In this case multiply the osmium (Os) half–reaction by 5 and the iodine half–reaction by 4 (you could have cross–multiplied by 10 and 8, but since both 10 and 8 are divisible by 2, use the smaller values).

$$5 \times (\quad Os + 4\,H_2O \longrightarrow OsO_4 + 8\,H^+ + 8\,e^- \quad)$$
$$4 \times (\,2\,IO_3^- + 12\,H^+ + 10\,e^- \longrightarrow I_2 + 6\,H_2O \quad)$$

Step 4: Finally, add the two half–reactions, cancelling electrons and any other species common to both sides of the resulting equation.

$$5\,Os + 20\,H_2O \longrightarrow 5\,OsO_4 + 40\,H^+ + \cancel{40\,e^-}$$
$$8\,IO_3^- + 48\,H^+ + \cancel{40\,e^-} \longrightarrow 4\,I_2 + 24\,H_2O$$

$$5\,Os + 8\,IO_3^- + 8\,H^+ \longrightarrow 5\,OsO_4 + 4\,I_2 + 4\,H_2O$$

EXAMPLE: Balance $MnO_4^- + C_2O_4^{2-} \longrightarrow MnO_2 + CO_2$ in basic solution.

Rather than balancing each half–reaction and separately converting it to basic, first balance the overall redox equation in acidic solution and then apply the procedure for converting a reaction to basic conditions. In this way you don't have to "convert to basic" twice.

Step 1: Break into half–reactions.

$$MnO_4^- \longrightarrow MnO_2$$
$$C_2O_4^{2-} \longrightarrow CO_2$$

Step 2: Balance the half–reactions.

$$3\,e^- + 4\,H^+ + MnO_4^- \longrightarrow MnO_2 + 2\,H_2O$$
$$C_2O_4^{2-} \longrightarrow 2\,CO_2 + 2\,e^-$$

Step 3: Cross–multiply to make: electrons lost = electrons gained.

$$2\times\ (3\,e^- + 4\,H^+ + MnO_4^- \longrightarrow MnO_2 + 2\,H_2O\ )$$
$$3\times\ (\ C_2O_4^{2-} \longrightarrow 2\,CO_2 + 2\,e^-\ )$$

Step 4: Add the two half–reactions.

$$6\,e^- + 8\,H^+ + 2\,MnO_4^- \longrightarrow 2\,MnO_2 + 4\,H_2O$$
$$3\,C_2O_4^{2-} \longrightarrow 6\,CO_2 + 6\,e^-$$

$$8\,H^+ + 2\,MnO_4^- + 3\,C_2O_4^{2-} \longrightarrow 2\,MnO_2 + 4\,H_2O + 6\,CO_2$$

Step 5: Convert the resulting redox equation to basic conditions.

$$8\,H^+ + 2\,MnO_4^- + 3\,C_2O_4^{2-} \longrightarrow 2\,MnO_2 + 4\,H_2O + 6\,CO_2$$
$$8\,H_2O \longrightarrow 8\,H^+ + 8\,OH^-$$

$$2\,MnO_4^- + 3\,C_2O_4^{2-} + 4\,H_2O \longrightarrow 2\,MnO_2 + 6\,CO_2 + 8\,OH^-$$

EXAMPLE: Balance $ClO_2^- \longrightarrow ClO_3^- + Cl^-$ in basic solution.

This looks a little strange, but some thought resolves the problem of only having ONE reactant. Since both the products contain chlorine, and since there is only one reactant containing chlorine, then the reactant MUST be involved in both the reduction reaction AND the oxidation reaction.

Step 1: Break into two half–reactions.

$$ClO_2^- \longrightarrow ClO_3^-$$
$$ClO_2^- \longrightarrow Cl^-$$

Step 2: Balance the half–reactions.

$$H_2O + ClO_2^- \longrightarrow ClO_3^- + 2\,H^+ + 2\,e^-$$
$$4\,e^- + 4\,H^+ + ClO_2^- \longrightarrow Cl^- + 2\,H_2O$$

Step 3: Cross–multiply to make: electrons lost = electrons gained

$$2 \times (\quad H_2O + ClO_2^- \longrightarrow ClO_3^- + 2\,H^+ + 2\,e^- \quad)$$
$$1 \times (\, 4\,e^- + 4\,H^+ + ClO_2^- \longrightarrow Cl^- + 2\,H_2O \quad)$$

Step 4: Add the two half–reactions.

$$2\,H_2O + 2ClO_2^- \longrightarrow 2ClO_3^- + 4\,H^+ + 4\,e^-$$
$$4\,e^- + 4\,H^+ + ClO_2^- \longrightarrow Cl^- + 2\,H_2O$$

$$3ClO_2^- \longrightarrow 2ClO_3^- + Cl^-$$

Note: There are no H^+'s left to convert to basic conditions. The individual half–reactions may operate in basic conditions, but the overall equation doesn't reflect that fact.

Definition: A **DISPROPORTIONATION** reaction is a redox reaction in which the same species is both reduced and oxidized.

In the above example, the ClO_2^- undergoes disproportionation.

EXERCISE:

24. Balance the following redox equations.

a) $U^{4+} + MnO_4^- \longrightarrow Mn^{2+} + UO_2^{2+}$ (acidic)

b) $Zn + As_2O_3 \longrightarrow AsH_3 + Zn^{2+}$ (acidic)

c) $Fe^{2+} + Cr_2O_7^{2-} \longrightarrow Cr^{3+} + Fe^{3+}$ (acidic)

d) $Cl_2 + SO_2 \longrightarrow Cl^- + SO_4^{2-}$ (acidic)

e) $Cu + NO_3^- \longrightarrow Cu^{2+} + NO$ (acidic)

f) $S^{2} + ClO_3^- \longrightarrow Cl^- + S$ (basic)

g) $OCl^- \longrightarrow Cl^- + ClO_3^-$ (basic)

h) $CN^- + IO_3^- \longrightarrow I^- + CNO^-$ (basic)

i) $Sn^{2+} + H_2O_2 \longrightarrow Sn^{4+}$ (basic)

j) $Br_2 \longrightarrow Br^- + BrO_3^-$ (basic)

k) $HSO_3^- + IO_3^- \longrightarrow I_2 + SO_4^{2-}$ (acidic)

l) $HNO_2 \longrightarrow HNO_3 + NO$

m) $Mn^{2+} + HBiO_3 \longrightarrow Bi^{3+} + MnO_4^-$ (acidic)

n) $H_2O_2 + Cr(OH)_4^- \longrightarrow CrO_4^{2-}$ (basic)

o) $Sb_2S_3 + NO_3^- \longrightarrow NO_2 + SO_4^{2-} + Sb_2O_5$ (acidic)

p) $As_2S_3 + NO_3^- \longrightarrow NO + SO_4^{2-} + H_3AsO_4$ (acidic)

q) $FeS + NO_3^- \longrightarrow NO + SO_4^{2-} + Fe^{3+}$ (acidic)

r) $FeHPO_3 + Cr_2O_7^{2-} \longrightarrow Cr^{3+} + H_3PO_4 + Fe^{3+}$ (acidic)

s) $SnS_2O_3 + MnO_4^- \longrightarrow Mn^{2+} + SO_4^{2-} + Sn^{4+}$ (acidic)

t) $CuS + HNO_3 \longrightarrow Cu(NO_3)_2 + NO_2 + SO_2$

u) $Ca_3(PO_4)_2 + SiO_2 + C \longrightarrow P_4 + CaSiO_3 + CO$

v) $KMnO_4 + H_2S + H_2SO_4 \longrightarrow K_2SO_4 + MnSO_4 + S$

w) $CuF_2 + NH_3 \longrightarrow Cu_3N + NH_4F + N_2$

V.6. BALANCING REDOX EQUATIONS USING OXIDATION NUMBERS

Section V.4 showed that a gain or loss of electrons is directly related to a decrease or increase in oxidation number. Since the total number of electrons lost in an oxidation half–reaction must equal the total number of electrons gained in a reduction half–reaction, the following statements are true.

a) An increase in oxidation number in one species must be balanced by a corresponding decrease in oxidation number in a second species.

b) In any redox equation the **overall change in oxidation numbers must be zero.**

EXAMPLE: Balance the following equation in acidic solution

$$U^{4+} + MnO_4^- \longrightarrow Mn^{2+} + UO_2^{2+} .$$

First assign oxidation numbers to all atoms involved in a change of oxidation number. (Recall that ΔON means "change in oxidation number".)

$$U^{4+} + \overset{+7}{\mathbf{Mn}}O_4^- \longrightarrow \mathbf{Mn}^{2+} + \overset{+6}{\mathbf{U}}O_2^{2+}$$

ΔON = –5

ΔON = +2

Since the total ΔON must be ZERO, cross–multiply each half–reaction by the oxidation numbers involved.

$$2 \times (MnO_4^- \longrightarrow Mn^{2+}) \;;\quad \Delta ON = 2 \times (-5) = -10$$

$$5 \times (\;U^{4+} \longrightarrow UO_2^{2+}) \;;\quad \Delta ON = 5 \times (+2) = +10$$

total ΔON = –10 + 10 = 0

Adding the reactions: $5\,U^{4+} + 2\,MnO_4^- \longrightarrow 2\,Mn^{2+} + 5\,UO_2^{2+}$

Finally, balance the O's by adding H_2O's and then balance the H's by adding H^+ 's, similar to what was done with the method of balancing half–reactions:

$$5\,U^{4+} + 2\,MnO_4^- + 2\,H_2O \longrightarrow 2\,Mn^{2+} + 5\,UO_2^{2+} + 4\,H^+ .$$

As a check, the charge is now balanced: $+20 - 2 = +4 + 10 + 4$.

EXAMPLE: Balance the equation $Zn + As_2O_3 \longrightarrow AsH_3 + Zn^{2+}$ in basic solution.

First balance major atoms by inspection. ("Major atoms" are all atoms other than O and H.)

$$Zn + As_2O_3 \longrightarrow \mathbf{2}\ AsH_3 + Zn^{2+}.$$

Next, assign oxidation numbers to all species involved in a change of oxidation number.

$$\mathbf{Zn} + \overset{+3}{\mathbf{As}_2O_3} \longrightarrow 2\,\overset{-3}{\mathbf{As}H_3} + \mathbf{Zn}^{2+}$$

$\Delta ON = 2 \times (-6) = -12$ (As)

$\Delta ON = +2$ (Zn)

In order to find ΔON for the arsenic–containing species, the change in oxidation number is doubled since there are two arsenic atoms in As_2O_3. Since the total ΔON must be ZERO, then:

$$6 \times (\ Zn \longrightarrow Zn^{2+}\ )\ ; \quad \Delta ON = 6 \times (+2) = +12$$
$$1 \times (\ As_2O_3 \longrightarrow 2\,AsH_3\ )\ ; \quad \Delta ON = -12$$
$$\text{total } \Delta ON = +12 - 12 = 0\,.$$

Adding the reactions: $6\,Zn + As_2O_3 \longrightarrow 2\,AsH_3 + 6\,Zn^{2+}$.

At this point you would normally add H_2O to balance the O's, add H^+ to balance H's, and change to basic. However, a shortcut is to add OH^- ions to balance the charge (since you are asked for a basic solution), and then add H_2O to balance H and O together. Since the left side has a charge of zero, and the right side has a charge of $6 \times (2+) = 12+$, add 12 OH^- to the right side.

$$6\,Zn + As_2O_3 \longrightarrow 2\,AsH_3 + 6\,Zn^{2+} + 12\,OH^-$$

Now there are 18 H atoms on the right. Adding 9 H_2O to the left balances both H and O:

$$6\,Zn + As_2O_3 + 9\,H_2O \longrightarrow 2\,AsH_3 + 6\,Zn^{2+} + 12\,OH^-.$$

EXAMPLE: Balance $P_4 \longrightarrow H_2PO_2^- + PH_3$ in acidic solution.

In this DISPROPORTIONATION reaction (see section V.5) the P_4 molecules act in two ways.

$$\overset{0}{\mathbf{P}_4} + \overset{0}{\mathbf{P}_4} \longrightarrow 4\,H_2\overset{+1}{\mathbf{P}}O_2^- + 4\,\overset{-3}{\mathbf{P}}H_3$$

$\Delta ON = 4 \times (+1) = +4$

$\Delta ON = 4 \times (-3) = -12$

Note that a preliminary balance has been done for phosphorus. Next balance the changes in the oxidation numbers.

$$3 \times (P_4 \longrightarrow 4\,H_2PO_2^-\ );\quad \Delta ON = 3 \times (+4) = +12$$
$$1 \times (P_4 \longrightarrow 4\,PH_3\ );\quad \Delta ON = -12$$
$$\text{total } \Delta ON = +12 - 12 = 0$$

Overall: $3\,P_4 + P_4 \longrightarrow 12\,H_2PO_2^- + 4\,PH_3$.

Dividing by 4, balancing for H and O, and checking for charge:

$$P_4 + 6\,H_2O \longrightarrow 3\,H_2PO_2^- + PH_3 + 3\,H^+.$$

EXERCISE:

25. Balance the following using oxidation numbers.

a) $SeO_3^{2-} + I^- \longrightarrow Se + I_2$ (acidic solution)

b) $I_2 + HOCl \longrightarrow IO_3^- + Cl^-$ (acidic)

c) $Zn + NO_3^- \longrightarrow ZnO_2^{2-} + NH_3$ (basic)

d) $SO_3^{2-} + Cr_2O_7^{2-} \longrightarrow SO_4^{2-} + Cr^{3+}$ (acidic)

e) $AuCl_4^- + C_2O_4^{2-} \longrightarrow Au + Cl^- + CO_2$

f) $H_2PO_2^- + TeO_4^{2-} \longrightarrow PO_4^{3-} + Te$ (acidic)

g) $CdS + NO_3^- \longrightarrow Cd^{2+} + S + NO$ (acidic)

h) $As_4 + NaOCl + H_2O \longrightarrow AsO_4^{3-} + NaCl$ (basic)

i) $PbS + NO_3^- \longrightarrow Pb(NO_3)_2 + NO + S$ (acidic)

j) $HNO_2 + Ti^{3+} \longrightarrow NH_4^+ + Ti^{4+}$ (acidic)

k) $CrO_4^{2-} + HCHO \longrightarrow Cr(OH)_3 + HCOO^-$ (basic)

l) $Pt + NO_3^- + Cl^- \longrightarrow PtCl_6^{2-} + NO$ (acidic)

m) $MnO_4^- + Sb_2O_3 \longrightarrow MnO_2 + Sb_2O_5$ (basic)

n) $MnO_4^- + HN_3 + SO_4^{2-} \longrightarrow MnSO_4 + N_2$ (acidic)

V.7. REDOX TITRATIONS

Acid–base titrations are very useful because they allow an accurate determination of an unknown concentration of an acid or base. Similarly, there are many occasions in which you may need to know the concentration of a substance which is capable of undergoing an oxidation or reduction reaction.

OXIDIZING AGENTS:

One of the most useful oxidizing agents encountered is acidic $KMnO_4$. The half–reaction:

$$MnO_4^- + 8\,H^+ + 5\,e^- \longrightarrow Mn^{2+} + 4\,H_2O\,;\ E^0 = 1.51\ V$$

has such a strong tendency to reduce that it is able to oxidize a large number of other substances. (The K^+ in $KMnO_4$ is a spectator ion.)

For example, to find the $[Fe^{2+}]$ in a solution you can use the fact that Fe^{2+} is easily oxidized to Fe^{3+}. A solution containing an unknown $[Fe^{2+}]$ reacts with acidic MnO_4^- according to the redox equation:

$$5\times(Fe^{2+} \longrightarrow Fe^{3+} + e^-)$$
$$MnO_4^- + 8\,H^+ + 5\,e^- \longrightarrow Mn^{2+} + 4\,H_2O$$

$$MnO_4^- + 8\,H^+ + 5\,Fe^{2+} \longrightarrow Mn^{2+} + 4\,H_2O + 5\,Fe^{3+}.$$

Acid–base titrations use an indicator dye which changes colour and helps to identify the equivalence point of the titration. The redox titration between Fe^{2+} and MnO_4^- also requires some way to identify the equivalence point. Fortunately, there is another feature of the half–reaction

$$MnO_4^- + 8\,H^+ + 5\,e^- \longrightarrow Mn^{2+} + 4\,H_2O$$

which causes it to be used extensively in redox titrations:

MnO_4^- is purple in solution and Mn^{2+} is colourless.

If MnO_4^- is added from a burette to a solution containing Fe^{2+}, the purple coloration due to the added

MnO_4^- is continually destroyed. At the equivalence point, the last of the Fe^{2+} is used up, so that the next drop of MnO_4^- does **not** react and a light purple tint remains in the solution. The endpoint of this redox titration is therefore shown by a change from a clear to a light purple solution.

***EXAMPLE*:** When 25.00 mL of a solution containing an unknown concentration of Fe^{2+} is titrated to an endpoint with acidic $KMnO_4$, the titration requires 17.52 mL of acidified 0.1000 M $KMnO_4$. The equation for the reaction is:

$$MnO_4^- + 8\,H^+ + 5\,Fe^{2+} \longrightarrow Mn^{2+} + 4\,H_2O + 5\,Fe^{3+}.$$

What is the concentration of Fe^{2+} in the solution?

The calculations are very similar to those for acid–base titrations.

$$\text{moles } MnO_4^- = 0.1000\,\frac{\text{mmol}}{\text{mL}} \times 17.52\text{ mL} = 1.752\text{ mmol}$$

$$\text{moles } Fe^{2+} = 1.752\text{ mmol } MnO_4^- \times \frac{5\text{ mmol } Fe^{2+}}{1\text{ mmol } MnO_4^-} = 8.760\text{ mmol}$$

$$[Fe^{2+}] = \frac{8.760\text{ mmol}}{25.00\text{ mL}} = \mathbf{0.3504\ M}$$

REDUCING AGENTS:

An example of a substance which is commonly used as a reducing agent is NaI or KI. A large number of substances can oxidize I^- to I_2.

$$2\,I^- \longrightarrow I_2 + 2\,e^-$$

Titrations involving I^- generally involve two consecutive steps:

- first, the I^- is oxidized to I_2 by the substance being reduced, and
- second, the I_2 produced in the first step is reduced back to I^- by a second reducing agent, such as thiosulphate ion $S_2O_3^{2-}$.

An example of a reaction involving I^- is the reduction of laundry bleach, NaOCl. The reaction between I^- and OCl^- proceeds according to:

$$2\,I^- \longrightarrow I_2 + 2\,e^-$$
$$2\,e^- + 2\,H^+ + OCl^- \longrightarrow Cl^- + H_2O$$

$$2\,H^+ + OCl^- + 2\,I^- \longrightarrow Cl^- + H_2O + I_2\,.$$

No attempt is made to add exactly enough I^- to react with the OCl^-. Rather, a deliberate excess of I^- is added in order to ensure that all the OCl^- has reacted. The excess I^- does not affect the results. The only fact of interest is that every mole of OCl^- present reacts to form one mole of I_2.

The above reaction between OCl^- and I^- is the "initial" reaction because the actual redox titration involves a **second** reaction between the I_2 produced and the reducing agent sodium thiosulphate, $Na_2S_2O_3$.

$$I_2 + 2e^- \longrightarrow 2I^-$$
$$2S_2O_3^{2-} \longrightarrow S_4O_6^{2-} + 2e^-$$

$$2S_2O_3^{2-} + I_2 \longrightarrow S_4O_6^{2-} + 2I^-$$

When the addition of $S_2O_3^{2-}$ has reacted most of the I_2 present, the brown colour of the I_2 almost disappears (a pale yellow remains). Some starch solution then is added to the titration, producing a dark blue colour. (The intense blue coloration is produced by the reaction between the starch and the remaining I_2 in solution.) After adding the starch, the last of the $S_2O_3^{2-}$ is added, causing the blue colour of the starch–I_2 mixture to fade: the last of the colour just disappears at the equivalence point.

EXAMPLE: A 25.00 mL sample of bleach is reacted with excess KI according to the equation:

$$2H^+ + OCl^- + 2I^- \longrightarrow Cl^- + H_2O + I_2.$$

The I_2 produced requires exactly 46.84 mL of 0.7500 M $Na_2S_2O_3$ to bring the titration to the endpoint according to the equation:

$$2S_2O_3^{2-} + I_2 \longrightarrow S_4O_6^{2-} + 2I^-,$$

using starch solution as an indicator. What is the $[OCl^-]$ in the bleach?

Note: TWO reactions are linked together here. The I_2 produced in the first reaction

$$2H^+ + OCl^- + 2I^- \longrightarrow Cl^- + H_2O + \mathbf{I_2}$$

is used up in the second $\quad 2S_2O_3^{2-} + \mathbf{I_2} \longrightarrow S_4O_6^{2-} + 2I^-.$

Because there is sufficient data to calculate the moles of $S_2O_3^{2-}$, the calculation starts there. The number of moles of $S_2O_3^{2-}$ is related to the number of moles of I_2 used up in the 2nd reaction (and equals the number of moles of I_2 produced in the 1st reaction). The moles of I_2 in the 1st reaction is then related to the moles of OCl^- present.

$$\text{moles } S_2O_3^{2-} = 0.7500\,\frac{\text{mmol}}{\text{mL}} \times 46.84\text{ mL} = 35.13\text{ mmol}$$

$$\text{moles } I_2 = 35.13\text{ mmol } S_2O_3^{2-} \times \frac{1\text{ mmol } I_2}{2\text{ mmol } S_2O_3^{2-}} = 17.57\text{ mmol}$$

$$\text{moles } OCl^- = 17.57\text{ mmol } I_2 \times \frac{1\text{ mmol } OCl^-}{1\text{ mmol } I_2} = 17.57\text{ mmol}$$

If desired, these last two steps can be combined into one calculation.

$$\text{moles } OCl^- = 35.13\text{ mmol } S_2O_3^{2-} \times \frac{1\text{ mmol } I_2}{2\text{ mmol } S_2O_3^{2-}} \times \frac{1\text{ mmol } OCl^-}{1\text{ mmol } I_2} = 17.57\text{ mmol}$$

Finally, the $[OCl^-]$ is calculated.

$$[OCl^-] = \frac{17.57\text{ mmol}}{25.00\text{ mL}} = \mathbf{0.7026\ M}$$

***EXERCISES*:**

26. When 25.00 mL of a hot oxalic acid solution ($H_2C_2O_4$) is titrated with 0.2500 M $KMnO_4$, the titration takes 35.25 mL of the $KMnO_4$ solution to reach the endpoint according to the reaction equation

$$2\,MnO_4^- + 6\,H^+ + 5\,H_2C_2O_4 \longrightarrow 2\,Mn^{2+} + 8\,H_2O + 10\,CO_2\,.$$

What is the concentration of the oxalic acid solution?

27. A 25.0 mL solution of nitrous acid, $HNO_2(aq)$, is reacted with an excess of KI solution according to the equation

$$2\,HNO_2 + 2\,I^- + 2\,H^+ \longrightarrow 2\,NO + I_2 + 2\,H_2O\,.$$

If the I_2 produced requires 14.6 mL of 0.150 M $Na_2S_2O_3$ solution to reach a stoichiometric point according to the equation

$$2\,S_2O_3^{2-} + I_2 \longrightarrow S_4O_6^{2-} + 2\,I^-,$$

what is the concentration of the nitrous acid solution?

28. A 3.00 g sample of pure iron is dissolved in hydrochloric acid and the resulting solution treated to produce Fe^{2+}. The final volume of the solution is 500.0 mL. What volume of 0.0500 M $KMnO_4$ is required to titrate a 25.0 mL sample of the Fe^{2+} solution according to the reaction equation

$$MnO_4^- + 8\,H^+ + 5\,Fe^{2+} \longrightarrow Mn^{2+} + 4\,H_2O + 5\,Fe^{3+}\ ?$$

29. When Sn^{2+} is titrated with MnO_4^-, the Sn^{2+} is oxidized to Sn^{4+} and the MnO_4^- is reduced to Mn^{2+}. A sample of pure tin metal is dissolved in nitric acid to produce 25.0 mL of solution containing Sn^{2+}. When the tin solution is titrated, a total of 41.7 mL of 0.135 M $KMnO_4$ is required to reach the equivalence point.

   a) Complete and balance the overall redox reaction equation.
   b) What is the concentration of the Sn^{2+} solution?
   c) What mass of tin was used to make the tin solution?

30. A 25.0 mL sample of 0.500 M bleach solution, NaOCl, is reacted with an excess of KI solution according to the following reaction equation

$$2\,H^+ + OCl^- + 2\,I^- \longrightarrow Cl^- + H_2O + I_2.$$

The I_2 produced is subsequently reacted according to the equation

$$2\,S_2O_3^{2-} + I_2 \longrightarrow S_4O_6^{2-} + 2\,I^-.$$

What volume of 0.750 M $Na_2S_2O_3$ is required to titrate the I_2?

31. A 25.00 mL portion of a solution containing an unknown concentration of $CuSO_4$ is reacted with excess KI solution. The unbalanced reaction equation is

$$Cu^{2+} + I^- \longrightarrow CuI(s) + I_2.$$

The titration requires 15.69 mL of 0.1650 M $Na_2S_2O_3$ to react the I_2 present, using starch as an indicator. The reaction equation for the titration is:

$$2\,S_2O_3^{2-} + I_2 \longrightarrow S_4O_6^{2-} + 2\,I^-.$$

   a) What is the balanced redox equation for the reaction between Cu^{2+} and I^-?
   b) What is the $[CuSO_4]$ in the original solution?

32. A 5.00 g sample contains a mixture of solid KIO_3 and some unreactive impurities. When the sample is dissolved and diluted to 1.00 L, a 25.0 mL sample of the resulting solution is reacted with excess KI and H_2SO_4 (to provide H^+). The IO_3^- present is reduced to I_2, while the I^- is oxidized to I_2. The I_2 produced requires 13.1 mL of 0.248 M $Na_2S_2O_3$ solution to reach the equivalence point in the reaction:

$$2\,S_2O_3^{2-} + I_2 \longrightarrow S_4O_6^{2-} + 2\,I^-$$

when starch is used as an indicator.

   a) What is the balanced redox equation for the reaction between IO_3^- and I^-?
   b) What is the concentration of the KIO_3 in the original solution?
   c) What is the percentage purity of the KIO_3 in the original sample?

33. You have the task of determining the concentration of a sample of hydrogen peroxide, H_2O_2, by titration with acidic potassium permanganate, $KMnO_4$. Explain briefly how to perform the titration, how you will know when the titration is at the stoichiometric point, what data you will need and what calculation steps will be needed.

V.8. THE ELECTROCHEMICAL CELL

***Definitions*:** **ELECTRODE** = a conductor at which a half–reaction occurs (this is a general term)

ANODE = the electrode at which **oxidation** occurs
= the electrode receiving the electrons from a substance being oxidized
= the electrode toward which **anions** travel

CATHODE = the electrode at which **reduction** occurs
= the electrode supplying electrons to a substance being reduced
= the electrode toward which **cations** travel

MEMORY AID:	**O**xidation at the **A**node (both vowels) **R**eduction at the **C**athode (both consonants)
or:	**AN OX CARED**
	(**AN**ode is where **OX**idation occurs and **CA**thode is where **RED**uction occurs)

The functioning of an electrochemical cell:

Examine the electrochemical cell shown below while reading what follows.

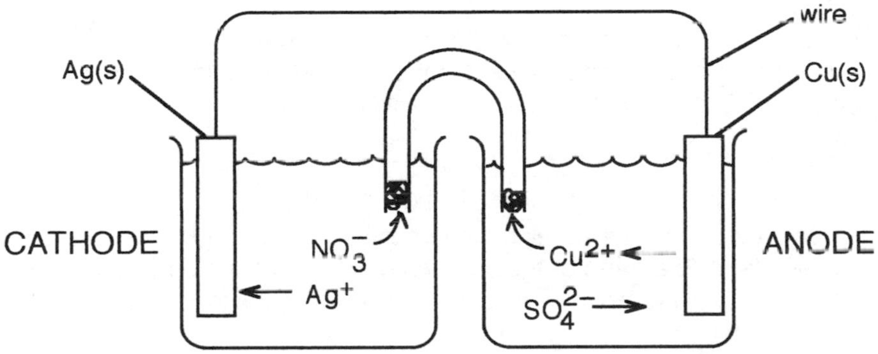

1. The half–reactions are: $Ag \rightleftharpoons Ag^+ + e^-$
   $Cu \rightleftharpoons Cu^{2+} + 2\,e^-$.

   Before connecting each half–cell there is a small tendency for the metals to oxidize and produce positive ions, such that any electrons given off remain behind on the metal. Experimentally it is found that Cu has a greater tendency to oxidize than does Ag.

2. After the half–cells are connected, the Cu has a greater tendency to oxidize than Ag, causing an excess of electrons to accumulate on the Cu electrode. This excess of electrons at the Cu electrode causes electrons to flow from the Cu to the Ag electrode. As a result, the Cu loses electrons (oxidizes) and Cu becomes the ANODE.

3. As electrons are supplied to the Ag electrode (via the wire), the equilibrium $Ag \rightleftharpoons Ag^+ + e^-$ is upset and according to Le Chatelier's Principle the Ag^+ is forced to reduce: $Ag^+ + e^- \longrightarrow Ag$. Therefore, a reduction reaction occurs at the Ag electrode and it is the CATHODE.

4. Overall, the electron flow is from Cu to Ag so that:

   ELECTRONS FLOW FROM THE ANODE TO THE CATHODE.

5. Water and certain ions (Cu^{2+} and NO_3^-, in the above diagram) are able to pass through the salt bridge without too much difficulty, but totally–free mixing of the solutions is prevented. In this way the Ag^+ ions are reduced to Ag(s) in the left half–cell while being unable to contact the Cu and transfer electrons directly from Cu to Ag^+. (The discussion below will show you why the Ag^+ and SO_4^{2-} do not enter the salt bridge.) By separating the reactants, the electrons are forced to travel through the wire in order to get from Cu to Ag^+. A measurement device such as a voltmeter can be inserted along the wire to measure such things as the direction of electron flow.

6. As Cu^{2+} ions are formed, they accumulate around the anode. This excess of positive charge is depleted by simultaneous migration of:

   a) Cu^{2+} ions away from the anode by random movement. There is a greater probability that Cu^{2+} will leave the region of high $[Cu^{2+}]$ around the anode than enter the region.

   b) negative ions, such as SO_4^{2-}, toward the anode. The presence of more positive charges at the anode end of the cell will attract the negative ions toward the anode.

7. As the $[Ag^+]$ is depleted around the cathode, by reduction to Ag(s), the net amount of positive charge is decreased around the cathode. The resulting deficiency of positive charge is corrected by simultaneous migration of:

   a) Ag^+ ions toward the cathode by random movement. There is a greater probability that Ag^+ will move into the region of low $[Ag^+]$ around the cathode than away from the region.

   b) negative ions, such as NO_3^-, away from the cathode. The greater amount of positive charge at the anode end of the cell will attract the negative ions toward the anode.

Important Note:

i) No electrons flow in the solution, only ions. The electrons only flow in the external wire.
ii) The number of electrons involved in the oxidation reaction must equal the number of electrons involved in the reduction reaction.

EXAMPLE: Assume two half–cells consisting of Pb(s) in a $Pb(NO_3)_2$ solution and Zn(s) in a $ZnCl_2$ solution are connected to make an electrochemical cell. During the reaction, more Pb(s) is formed. Draw and label the parts of the cell, write the equations for the individual half–reactions and overall reaction, and indicate the directions in which the ions and electrons move.

The electrochemical cell below has been completely labelled, but in order to show you how to go about working through this example, the logic behind the work is given below the diagram.

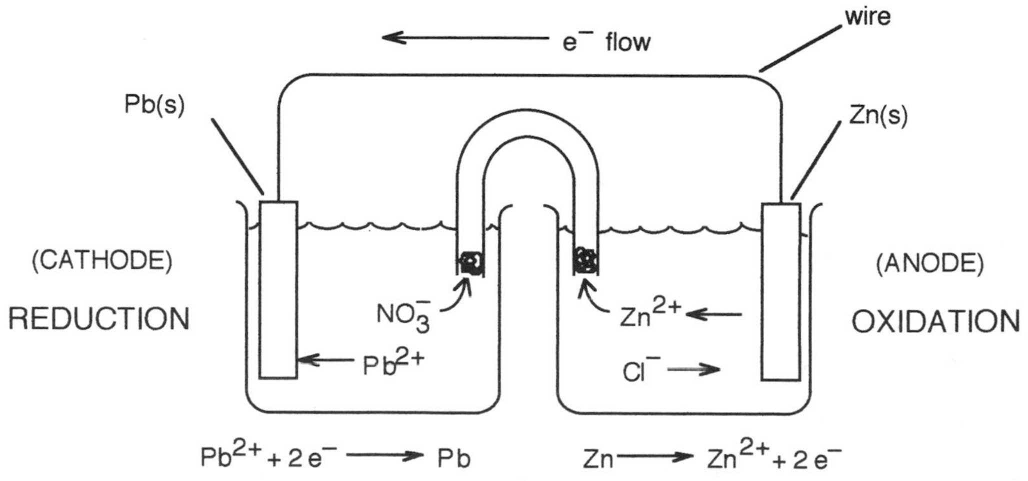

- Since Pb(s) is formed then Pb^{2+} must be undergoing reduction. The Zn therefore must be oxidizing and the half–reactions are:

$$Pb^{2+} + 2\,e^- \longrightarrow Pb \qquad \text{(reduction)}$$
$$Zn \longrightarrow Zn^{2+} + 2\,e^- \qquad \text{(oxidation)}\,.$$

- The net ionic equation is obtained by adding together the reduction and oxidation half–reactions and cancelling out the electrons:

$$Pb^{2+} + Zn \longrightarrow Pb + Zn^{2+}\,.$$

- Since oxidation occurs at the anode, then the Zn electrode is the anode. The Pb must be the cathode.
- Since electron flow is from anode to cathode, draw the electron flow ***from*** Zn ***to*** Pb. (Note that the electrons given off by Zn in the oxidation must flow through the wire to the Pb^{2+} side in order to be available for the reduction.)
- Since positive ions are cations, the positive ions migrate toward the cathode. The negative ions migrate toward the anode.

EXERCISES:

34. A cell is made up as follows. A piece of Ni foil is immersed in a beaker of $NiCl_2$ solution, and a strip of Cu foil is immersed in a beaker of $CuSO_4$ solution. The metal electrodes are connected by a wire and the beakers connected by a salt bridge. The net ionic equation for the reaction is:

$$Ni + Cu^{2+} \longrightarrow Ni^{2+} + Cu\,.$$

a) Which electrode is the anode?
b) Toward which electrode do the SO_4^{2-} ions migrate?
c) Which way do the electrons flow in the wire?
d) If 0.025 mol of Cu(s) is produced in the reaction, how many moles of electrons flow through the wire?
e) Toward which electrode do the Ni^{2+} ions migrate after being formed?

35. An electrochemical cell is made by placing a weighed strip of Sn in a beaker containing 1 M $SnSO_4$ and a weighed strip of Ag in a beaker containing 1 M $AgNO_3$. The metal strips are connected by a wire and the beakers are connected by a salt bridge. After several hours the Sn electrode decreases in mass.

a) What is the net ionic equation for the reaction?
b) Which electrode is the cathode?
c) Toward which electrode do the Ag^+ ions migrate?
d) Which way do the electrons flow in the wire?
e) Does the Ag electrode gain or lose mass?
f) If 0.010 mol of Sn(s) goes into solution, how many moles of electrons flow through the wire?
g) If 0.020 mol of Sn goes into solution, how many moles of Ag are involved in the reaction?
h) How many moles of electrons flow through the salt bridge in part (g)?

V.9. STANDARD REDUCTION POTENTIALS

The tendency of electrons to flow in an electrochemical cell is called the **VOLTAGE**, or **ELECTRICAL POTENTIAL** to do work.

The VOLTAGE is the WORK DONE PER ELECTRON TRANSFERRED.

Since electrons cannot flow in an isolated half–cell, an individual half–cell voltage cannot be determined. However the ***difference*** in electrical potentials between two half–cells CAN be measured. (By analogy, you may not know your net worth, but if you are given $10, you DO know that the difference between your new and previous net worth is exactly $10.)

A ZERO–POINT is **ARBITRARILY** defined on the voltage scale. Specifically, the voltage for the **HYDROGEN HALF–CELL** is defined to be

$$2H^+(aq) + 2\,e^- \longrightarrow H_2(g) \;;\; E^o = 0.000\ V$$

where: E^o = the **STANDARD REDUCTION POTENTIAL,** in volts and the "o" in E^o implies this is a **STANDARD STATE.**

An electrochemical cell is said to be at STANDARD STATE if

- it is at 25°C, and
- all gases are at 101.3 kPa (1 atm), and
- all elements are in their standard states (that is, their normal phase at 25°C), and
- there exists a 1 M concentration for **ALL** solutions involved in the half–cell (both on the reactants and products side).

The diagram below shows how to make a standard hydrogen half–cell.

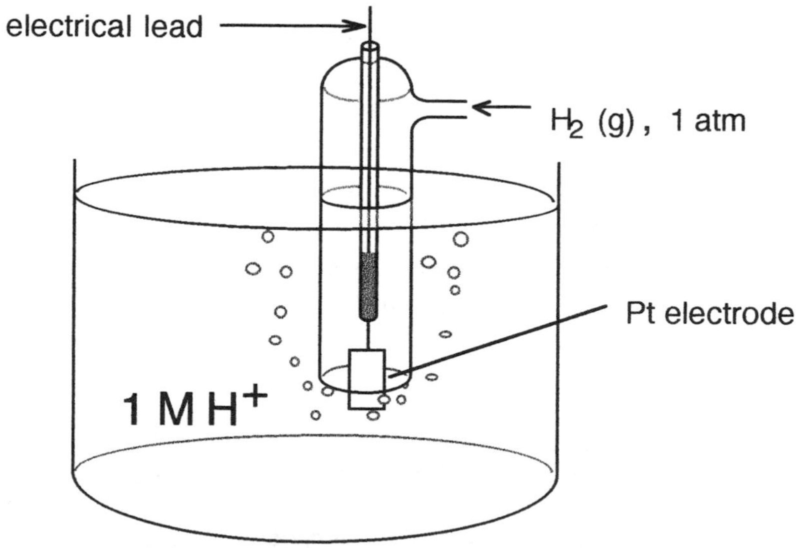

- The $H_2(g)$ passes over a platinum metal electrode which accepts electrons from, or supplies electrons to, the half–cell as required. (Platinum is used because it is an **inert electrode** — it doesn't react but conducts electrons and allows the reaction to occur at its surface.)
- Platinum (or less expensively, carbon) is often used as an inert electrode when all the materials in the half–reaction are ions, liquids or gases. For example, inert electrodes would be suitable for use with half–reactions such as

$$NO(g) + 2\,H_2O(l) \longrightarrow NO_3^-(aq) + 4\,H^+(aq) + 3\,e^- .$$

EXAMPLES: The half–reaction $ClO_4^- + 8\,H^+ + 8\,e^- \rightleftharpoons Cl^- + 4\,H_2O$ has a standard reduction potential of 1.39 V. Each of the species ClO_4^-, H^+ and Cl^- **must** have a 1 M concentration. If any of these species have concentrations which differ from 1 M, the new reduction potential will not be 1.39 V and cannot be referred to as a "standard reduction potential".

The half–reaction $Cu^{2+} + 2\,e^- \rightleftharpoons Cu(s)$ has a measured standard reduction potential of 0.34 V. The $[Cu^{2+}]$ is 1 M and some copper metal is present. If the $[Cu^{2+}]$ is not 1 M and/or Cu(s) is not present, the reduction potential will be changed.

Reminder: The fact that the hydrogen half–reaction is written as $\mathbf{2}\,H^+(aq) + 2\,e^- \rightleftharpoons H_2(g)$ indicates that 2 H^+ are used up for every H_2 produced; the "2" does NOT mean that $[H^+]$ is 2 M. By definition, the $[H^+]$ is **1 M** for a half–cell at STANDARD CONDITIONS.

The voltages associated with each of the half–reactions are relative to the voltage for the hydrogen half–cell.

EXAMPLES: Placing a piece of copper metal in a 1 M Cu^{2+} solution, sets up the half–cell:

$$Cu^{2+} + 2\,e^- \rightleftharpoons Cu \;;\quad E^o = 0.34\ V$$

This half–cell has a voltage which is 0.34 V more than that of the hydrogen half–cell.

Similarly, placing a strip of metallic zinc in a 1 M Zn^{2+} solution, creates the half–cell:

$$Zn^{2+} + 2\,e^- \rightleftharpoons Zn \;;\quad E^o = -0.76\ V,$$

which has a voltage 0.76 V less than that of the hydrogen half–cell.

Since the voltage is a measure of the work done, reversing a reduction reaction such as

$$Zn^{2+} + 2\,e^- \longrightarrow Zn \;;\quad E^o = \mathbf{-0.76\ V}$$

produces an oxidation reaction with a changed sign for E^o:

$$Zn \longrightarrow Zn^{2+} + 2\,e^- \;;\quad E^o = \mathbf{+0.76\ V}\ .$$

This is seen to be reasonable by noting that, like energy, work will have a different sign depending on whether work is DONE **ON** THE SYSTEM or DONE **BY** THE SYSTEM. Generalizing this sign behaviour:

IF A HALF–REACTION IS REVERSED, THE SIGN OF ITS E° VALUE IS REVERSED.

Next, let's see what happens when the following two half–cells are joined.

$$\boxed{Hg^{2+}} + 2\,e^- \rightleftharpoons Hg \;;\quad E^o = 0.85\ V$$

$$Cu^{2+} + 2\,e^- \rightleftharpoons \boxed{Cu} \;;\quad E^o = 0.34\ V$$

The experimentally observed voltage for the overall reaction is found to be the difference between the voltages of the individual half–cells. That is:

$$\begin{array}{lcl} Hg^{2+} + 2\,e^- \longrightarrow Hg & ; & E^o = 0.85\ V \\ Cu \longrightarrow Cu^{2+} + 2\,e^- & ; & E^o = -0.34\ V \\ \hline Hg^{2+} + Cu \longrightarrow Hg + Cu^{2+} & ; & \mathbf{E^o_{CELL} = 0.51\ V}\ . \end{array}$$

Conclusion: **IF TWO HALF–REACTIONS CAN BE ADDED TOGETHER TO GIVE A REDOX EQUATION, THE VOLTAGES ASSOCIATED WITH THE HALF–REACTIONS CAN ALSO BE ADDED.**

The cell potential can also be calculated in the following manner.

If: E^o_{RED} = the reduction potential of the reduction reaction, and
E^o_{OX} = the reduction potential of the oxidation reaction

then: $$E^o_{CELL} = E^o_{RED} - E^o_{OX}$$

Conclusion: **THE POTENTIAL OF AN ELECTROCHEMICAL CELL IS JUST THE DIFFERENCE BETWEEN THE HALF–CELL VOLTAGES FOR THE REDUCTION REACTION AND THE OXIDATION REACTION.**

No matter which method you use to calculate the value of E^o_{CELL}, keep in mind that you are simply finding the voltage gap between the two half–reactions involved.

EXAMPLES:

a) **Calculate the potential of the cell: $Ni^{2+} + Fe \longrightarrow Ni + Fe^{2+}$.**

The half–reactions involved are

$$\boxed{Ni^{2+}} + 2e^- \rightleftharpoons Ni \quad ; E^o = -0.26\ V$$
$$Fe^{2+} + 2e^- \rightleftharpoons \boxed{Fe} \quad ; E^o = -0.45\ V.$$

Re–writing the Fe^{2+}/Fe half–reaction as an oxidation, reversing the voltage and adding the two half–reactions:

$$Ni^{2+} + 2e^- \longrightarrow Ni \quad ; \quad E^o = -0.26\ V$$
$$Fe \longrightarrow Fe^{2+} + 2e^- \quad ; \quad E^o = +0.45\ V$$

$$Ni^{2+} + Fe \longrightarrow Ni + Fe^{2+} \quad ; \mathbf{E^o_{CELL} = 0.19\ V}$$

Alternately, the cell potential is calculated from:

$$E^o_{CELL} = E^o_{RED} - E^o_{OX} = (-0.26) - (-0.45) = \mathbf{+0.19\ V}.$$

Note: This reaction is **SPONTANEOUS** (since the reduction of Ni^{2+} is higher on the Table than the oxidation of Fe) **AND** it has a POSITIVE value for E^o_{CELL} (that is, a **POSITIVE** POTENTIAL TO DO WORK).

b) Calculate the potential of the cell: $Ni + Fe^{2+} \longrightarrow Ni^{2+} + Fe$.

The half–reactions involved are

$$\boxed{Fe^{2+}} + 2e^- \rightleftharpoons Fe \quad ; E^o = -0.45\ V$$

$$Ni^{2+} + 2e^- \rightleftharpoons \boxed{Ni} \quad ; E^o = -0.26\ V .$$

Re–writing the Ni^{2+}/Ni half–reaction as an oxidation, and adding the two half–reactions:

$$Fe^{2+} + 2e^- \longrightarrow Fe \quad ; \quad E^o = -0.45\ V$$

$$Ni \longrightarrow Ni^{2+} + 2e^- \quad ; \quad E^o = +0.26\ V$$

$$Fe^{2+} + Ni \longrightarrow Fe + Ni^{2+} \quad ; \mathbf{E^o_{CELL} = -0.19\ V} .$$

Alternately, calculating the cell potential from the difference in half–cell potentials gives:

$$E^o_{CELL} = E^o_{RED} - E^o_{OX} = (-0.45) - (-0.26) = \mathbf{-0.19\ V} .$$

Note: This reaction is **NOT SPONTANEOUS** (since the reduction of Fe^{2+} is lower on the Table than the oxidation of Ni) **AND** it has a NEGATIVE value for E^o_{CELL} (work must be added to the system to get the cell to operate).

Conclusion:

IF E^o_{CELL} IS POSITIVE FOR A REDOX REACTION, THE REACTION IS EXPECTED TO BE SPONTANEOUS.

IF E^o_{CELL} IS NEGATIVE FOR A REDOX REACTION, THE REACTION IS NON–SPONTANEOUS.

c) Calculate the cell potential of: $3\ Ag^+ + Al \longrightarrow 3\ Ag + Al^{3+}$.

After the half–reactions are written,

$$\boxed{Ag^+} + e^- \rightleftharpoons Ag \quad ; E^o = 0.80\ V$$

$$Al^{3+} + 3e^- \rightleftharpoons \boxed{Al} \quad ; E^o = -1.66\ V$$

an immediate question arises: "When the Ag^+/Ag half–reaction is multiplied by 3 (to make the electrons gained equal the electrons lost), is the half–reaction voltage also multiplied by 3?"

Since "voltage" is the WORK DONE **PER ELECTRON, do not** multiply the E^o value for the reduction of Ag^+ by 3. The reason is as follows. If the voltage has a value of "0.80 V", defined as a certain amount of work required to transfer 1 electron, then 3 times as much work is required to transfer 3 times as many electrons. Overall, the ratio remains unchanged, as shown below.

For $Ag^+ + e^- \rightleftharpoons Ag$: $\quad \text{voltage} = \dfrac{\text{work}}{1\ \text{electron}} = 0.80\ V$

For $3\ Ag^+ + 3e^- \rightleftharpoons 3\ Ag$: $\quad \text{voltage} = \dfrac{3 \times \text{work}}{3\ \text{electrons}} = 0.80\ V$

Therefore, the reaction is simply:

$$\begin{array}{rcll} 3\,Ag^+ + 3\,e^- & \longrightarrow & 3\,Ag & ; \quad E^o = \ \ 0.80\ V \\ Al & \longrightarrow & Al^{3+} + 3\,e^- & ; \quad E^o = +1.66\ V \\ \hline 3\,Ag^+ + Al & \longrightarrow & 3\,Ag + Al^{3+} & ; \quad \mathbf{E^o_{CELL} = \ \ 2.46\ V.} \end{array}$$

Alternately: $E^o_{CELL} = E^o_{RED} - E^o_{OX} = (0.80) - (-1.66) = \mathbf{2.46\ V.}$

NOTE: The fact that E^o_{CELL} is large and positive **does not** tell you anything about the **RATE** of the reaction. For example, the reduction of Ag^+ by Al does not occur at an appreciable rate, except as noted below.

A COMMENT ON ACTIVATION ENERGIES

The reason Al(s) does not react with Ag^+ is that aluminum quickly reacts with oxygen to form a protective oxide coating of $Al_2O_3(s)$. The oxide adheres strongly to the metal surface and prevents the underlying metal from oxidizing. In order to allow Al(s) to react with Ag^+, sufficient energy (the activation energy) must be supplied to remove the oxide.

In the following procedure, the addition of heat and baking soda allows the addition of the required activation energy for removal of Al_2O_3. As an added bonus, you can also clean tarnished silverware. Silver "tarnish" is the result of silver being oxidized to Ag^+, in the form of Ag_2O and Ag_2S.

> Dissolve several spoonfuls of baking soda ($NaHCO_3$) in a metal pan full of water. Put a sheet of aluminum foil in the bottom of the pan and place tarnished silverware on top of the foil. Heat the pan on top of a stove. The silverware should slowly regain its shine as the tarnish is reduced to Ag(s) and the Al(s) oxidizes to Al^{3+}. (The $NaHCO_3$ provides a weakly basic solution which removes the oxide layer from the aluminum when heat is applied.) This procedure is similar to that used with commercially–advertised tarnish removers made of aluminum alloy bars.

SOME COMMENTS ON WATER

In some texts, the reduction of neutral water is given as:

$$2\,H^+\,(10^{-7}\,M) + 2\,e^- \rightleftharpoons H_2(g)\ ;\ E = -0.41\ V.$$

Other texts show this same reaction as:

$$2\,H_2O + 2\,e^- \rightleftharpoons H_2(g) + 2\,OH^-\,(10^{-7}\,M)\ ;\ E = -0.41\ V.$$

The first equation starts with neutral conditions and uses H^+, while the second equation starts with neutral conditions and produces OH^-. These are equivalent statements. The second equation is produced by simply adding the water equilibrium, $2\,H_2O \rightleftharpoons 2\,H^+\,(10^{-7}\,M) + 2\,OH^-\,(10^{-7}\,M)$, to the first equation.

$$\begin{array}{rcl} \cancel{2\,H^+\,(10^{-7}\,M)} + 2\,e^- & \rightleftharpoons & H_2(g) \\ 2\,H_2O & \rightleftharpoons & \cancel{2\,H^+\,(10^{-7}\,M)} + 2\,OH^-\,(10^{-7}\,M) \\ \hline 2\,H_2O + 2\,e^- & \rightleftharpoons & H_2(g) + 2\,OH^-\,(10^{-7}\,M) \end{array}$$

IMPORTANT: If a reaction occurs in an acidic solution, the reduction of H^+ (at 0.00 V) may be a possible reaction and must be considered along with any other reductions possible. (See Section V.10 for further comments)

$$2\,H^+ + 2\,e^- \rightleftharpoons H_2(g) \;\ldots\ldots\ldots\ldots\ldots\ldots\; 0.00\ V$$

If a reaction occurs in a neutral solution, the reduction of neutral water (at –0.41 V) may be a possible reaction and must be considered along with any other reductions possible. (See Section V.10 for further comments)

$$2\,H_2O + 2\,e^- \rightleftharpoons H_2(g) + 2\,OH^-(10^{-7}\ M) \;\ldots\; -0.41\ V$$

You will not be required to deal with basic solutions.

THE EFFECT OF SURFACE AREA ON THE HALF–CELL POTENTIAL

Experimentally, the following behaviour is observed.

> An electrochemical cell is set up such that the anode is a strip of Cu(s) immersed in 1.0 M $Cu(NO_3)_2$ and the cathode is a strip of Ag(s) immersed in 1.0 M $AgNO_3$. A salt bridge containing $NaNO_3$ joins the two half–cells and a voltmeter connects the metal strips. The voltage is 0.46 V. As the strip of Cu(s) is slowly withdrawn from the $Cu(NO_3)_2$ solution, the voltage does not change at all (unless the metal strip leaves the liquid, which causes the voltage to immediately drop to zero). A similar effect is observed when the Ag(s) is withdrawn from the solution.

This NON–EFFECT of surface area on the cell voltage is explained as follows. Recall that the concentration of a SOLID has a CONSTANT VALUE. Therefore, increasing the surface area of a solid electrode has no effect on the concentration of the solid. As a result, there is no equilibrium–related shift of the half–reaction involving the electrode, and no change in the half–cell potential.

CONCLUSION: THE SURFACE AREA OF AN ELECTRODE HAS NO EFFECT ON THE CELL POTENTIAL.

When the surface area of an electrode is increased, the reaction rate at the electrode increases. That is, the number of electrons per second being transferred increases. This increased reaction rate does not increase the cell voltage. (The **amperage** which the cell can deliver increases when the number of electrons per second increases, but this is of no concern to us in Chemistry 12.)

Increasing the amount of electrode material also increases the length of time that the cell can operate — big batteries operate longer than smaller batteries made of identical materials. This increase in the amount of reactant does not increase the cell voltage.

A COMMENT ON HALF–CELLS WHICH ARE *NOT* AT STANDARD CONDITIONS

What happens to the half–cell voltage if non–standard conditions exist? If the $[H^+]$ is **decreased** in a hydrogen half–cell, then according to Le Chatelier's Principle:

$$2\,H^+(aq) + 2\,e^- \leftarrow H_2(g).$$

The half–cell now has **less** tendency to undergo reduction. For example, when $[H^+] = 1.0 \times 10^{-7}$ M the resulting half–cell will be found **lower** on the chart:

$$2\,H^+(10^{-7}\ M) + 2\,e^- \rightleftharpoons H_2(g) \qquad ;\ E = -0.41\ V$$

or its equivalent:

$$2\,H_2O + 2\,e^- \rightleftharpoons H_2(g) + 2\,OH^-(10^{-7}\ M) \quad ;\ E = -0.41\ V.$$

Since this is no longer at "standard conditions", the " o " is omitted from the E^o symbol.

Similarly, if $[Cu^{2+}]$ is increased from 1 M to 2 M, then the half–cell

$$Cu^{2+} + 2\,e^- \rightleftharpoons Cu$$

has an increased tendency to reduce (go forward) and the reduction potential increases (becomes greater than 0.34 V).

A SPECIAL NOTE ON CELLS WHICH REACH EQUILIBRIUM

Operating electrochemical cells are NOT in equilibrium, but many of the principles applied to equilibrium situations can be used to study electrochemistry.

Consider the cell $2\,Ag^+ + Cu \longrightarrow 2\,Ag + Cu^{2+}$. Initially, this reaction has a great tendency to form products. As the cell operates, using up reactants and making more products, two effects are found.

THE REDUCTION REACTION: $\boxed{2\,Ag^+} + 2\,e^- \longrightarrow 2\,Ag$

As the $[Ag^+]$ decreases, the reduction potential decreases and the half–reaction goes lower on the chart. As a result, the tendency to form products decreases as the cell operates.

THE OXIDATION REACTION: $Cu^{2+} + 2\,e^- \longleftarrow \boxed{Cu}$

As the $[Cu^{2+}]$ increases the tendency for this reaction to undergo reduction increases (the reduction potential of $Cu^{2+} + 2\,e^- \longrightarrow Cu$ increases). Therefore, the tendency to be oxidized is increasingly opposed by a greater tendency to be reduced as the cell operates.

Overall, the following occurs as the cell goes to equilibrium.

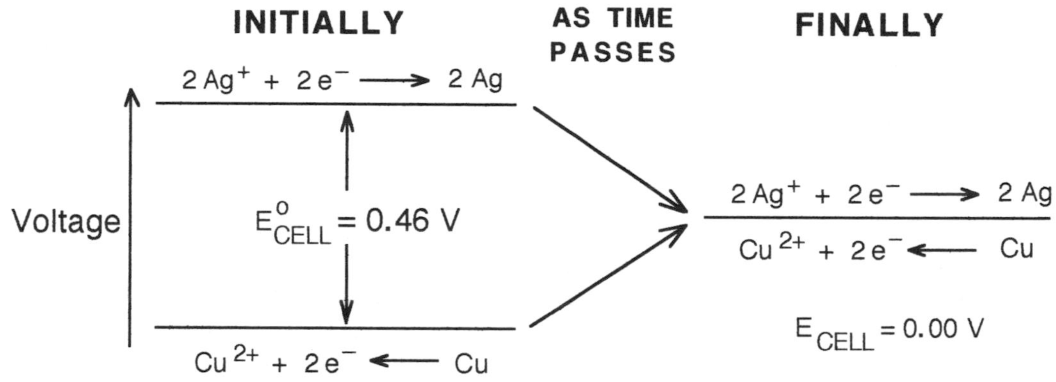

The reduction potential of the Ag^+/Ag reaction decreases and the reduction potential of the Cu/Cu^{2+} reaction increases until both reactions have the same reduction potential. The **DIFFERENCE** in reduction potentials is now zero ($E_{CELL} = 0$): the reaction is at equilibrium.

EXERCISES:

36. Calculate E^{o}_{CELL} for each reaction and state whether the reaction is expected to be spontaneous.
   a) $Cr + 3\,Ag^+ \longrightarrow Cr^{3+} + 3\,Ag$
   b) $Cu^+ + Fe^{3+} \longrightarrow Cu^{2+} + Fe^{2+}$
   c) $Mn^{2+} + 2\,H_2O + I_2 \longrightarrow MnO_2 + 4\,H^+ + 2\,I^-$
   d) $3\,Cu + 2\,NO_3^- + 8\,H^+ \longrightarrow 3\,Cu^{2+} + 4\,H_2O + 2\,NO$
   e) $2\,Cr^{3+} + 7\,H_2O + 3\,Pb^{2+} \longrightarrow Cr_2O_7^{2-} + 14\,H^+ + 3\,Pb$
   f) $2\,H_2O_2 \longrightarrow 2\,H_2O + O_2$
   g) $3\,Fe^{2+} \longrightarrow 2\,Fe^{3+} + Fe$
   h) $Hg^{2+} + Hg \longrightarrow Hg_2^{2+}$

37. You have six half–cells available (all solutions are 1 M).

    i) $CuSO_4$ solution containing an electrode of Cu
    ii) $Cr_2(SO_4)_3$ solution containing an electrode of Cr
    iii) $MgSO_4$ solution containing an electrode of Mg
    iv) $ZnSO_4$ solution containing an electrode of Zn
    v) $AgNO_3$ solution containing an electrode of Ag
    vi) $FeSO_4$ solution containing an electrode of Fe

    a) Which pair of half–cells will form the cell with the highest voltage?
    b) Which pair of half–cells will form the cell with the lowest voltage?

38. Given: $Te^{4+} + 4\,Ru^{3+} \longrightarrow Te + 4\,Ru^{4+}$; $E^o_{CELL} = -0.23$ V

    $2\,Ru^{4+} + Nb^{3+} \longrightarrow 2\,Ru^{3+} + Nb^{5+}$; $E^o_{CELL} = +0.52$ V

    Explain why Nb^{5+} will or will not react spontaneously with Te.

39. For a hypothetical metal, A: $A^{2+} + 2\,e^- \rightleftharpoons A$; $E^o = 0.31$ V

    and $A^+ + e^- \rightleftharpoons A$; $E^o = -0.29$ V.

    a) Can metal A react with pure water ($[H^+] = [OH^-] = 10^{-7}$ M) to produce $H_2(g)$? If so, is the A^+ or A^{2+} ion produced? (**Hint:** see "Some Comments on Water", previously)
    b) Can metal A dissolve in 1 M H^+ to produce $H_2(g)$? If so, is the A^+ or A^{2+} ion produced?

40. You have four metals A, B, C and D in 1.00 M solutions of A^{2+}, B^{2+}, C^{2+} and D^{2+} respectively. The following results are found when some of the half–cells are connected together.

Cathode	Anode	Cell voltage
C	A	0.75 V
D	A	0.49 V
D	B	0.61 V

Arrange the metal ions in order of DECREASING strength as oxidizing agents.

41. You have five metals A, B, C, D and E in 1.00 M solutions of A^{3+}, B^{3+}, C^{3+}, D^{3+} and E^{3+} respectively. When some of the half–cells are connected, the following results are found.

Cathode	Anode	Cell voltage
C	E	0.10 V
D	B	0.08 V
A	C	1.41 V
D	C	0.55 V

Arrange the ions in DECREASING strength as oxidizing agents.

42. Half–cell A consists of a zinc electrode in a solution of Zn^{2+} having a concentration less than 1 M. Half–cell B consists of a copper electrode in a solution of Cu^{2+} having a concentration greater than 1 M. Would the potential of the cell formed by joining half–cells A and B be greater than, equal to, or less than 1.10 V?

43. The voltage of the cell $Pb^{2+} + Zn(s) \longrightarrow Pb(s) + Zn^{2+}$ changes depending on the conditions used. Arrange the following three sets of conditions in order of the voltages they produce, from highest to lowest. Each pair of half–cells is connected to form an electrochemical cell using a salt bridge.
   a) A thin zinc wire is immersed in 0.5 M Zn^{2+} and a thick lead strip is immersed in 1 M Pb^{2+}.
   b) A thick zinc strip is immersed in 1 M Zn^{2+} and a thin lead wire is immersed in 0.5 M Pb^{2+}.
   c) A thick zinc strip is immersed in 1 M Zn^{2+} and a thick lead wire is immersed in 1 M Pb^{2+}.

44. a) Which is the stronger oxidizing agent: 1 M Pb^{2+} or 2 M Pb^{2+} ?
   b) Which is the stronger reducing agent: 1 M I^- or 2 M I^- ?

45. Given the half–cell $Sn^{4+} + 2\,e^- \rightleftharpoons Sn^{2+}$, which of the following cases has the highest reduction potential?

   CASE 1: $[Sn^{4+}] = 1$ M and $[Sn^{2+}] = 2$ M
   CASE 2: $[Sn^{4+}] = 1$ M and $[Sn^{2+}] = 1$ M
   CASE 3: $[Sn^{4+}] = 2$ M and $[Sn^{2+}] = 1$ M

46. A battery is simply an electrochemical cell. If a battery is used continuously in a flashlight, why does the light from the flashlight grow dimmer and dimmer, rather than staying at the same intensity until the battery "dies"?

V.10. SELECTING PREFERRED REACTIONS

When a cell contains a mixture of substances, several different reactions may appear to be possible. For example, assume the following cell exists.

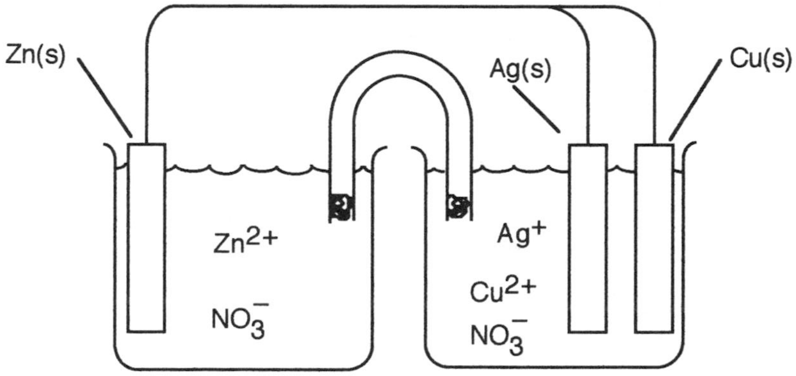

The possible half–reactions are:

$$Ag^+ + e^- \rightleftharpoons Ag(s)\ ;\ E^o = 0.80\ V$$
$$Cu^{2+} + 2\,e^- \rightleftharpoons Cu(s)\ ;\ E^o = 0.34\ V$$
$$Zn^{2+} + 2\,e^- \rightleftharpoons Zn(s)\ ;\ E^o = -0.76\ V.$$

When several different reduction half–reactions can occur, the half–reaction having the highest tendency to accept electrons (highest reduction potential) will occur preferentially.

Therefore, the Ag^+ will reduce preferentially and form Ag(s).

When several different oxidation half–reactions can occur, the half–reaction having the highest tendency to lose electrons (lowest reduction potential) will occur preferentially.

Therefore, the Zn(s) will oxidize preferentially and form Zn^{2+}.

The following method works well for determining the preferred half–reactions.

- First, list the species present, making sure that all ionic compounds are broken up into ions.
- Next, start at the **upper left** hand side (reduction side) of the Table and look down the Table until you find the first match with a species on the list. (Obviously, the first species which matches MUST have the greatest tendency to reduce of any of the species on the list.)
- Then, start at the **lower right** hand side (oxidation side) of the Table and look up the Table until you find the first match with a species on the list. (Again, the first species which matches MUST have the greatest tendency to oxidize of any of the species on the list.)

EXAMPLE: An iron strip is placed in a mixture of $Br_2(aq)$ and $I_2(aq)$. What is the preferred reaction which occurs?

The species present and the possible reactions are:

$$\boxed{Br_2} + 2\,e^- \rightleftharpoons 2\,Br^- \;;\; E^o = 1.09\ V$$

$$\boxed{I_2} + 2\,e^- \rightleftharpoons 2\,I^- \;;\; E^o = 0.54\ V$$

$$Fe^{2+} + 2\,e^- \rightleftharpoons \boxed{Fe} \;;\; E^o = -0.45\ V$$

The preferred reduction involves Br_2 (greater tendency to reduce than I_2) and the only oxidation possible involves Fe. Adding the preferred reactions gives the overall reaction.

$$Br_2 + 2\,e^- \longrightarrow 2\,Br^-$$
$$Fe \longrightarrow Fe^{2+} + 2\,e^-$$
$$\overline{\qquad\qquad\qquad\qquad}$$
$$Fe + Br_2 \longrightarrow Fe^{2+} + 2\,Br^-$$

EXAMPLE: A beaker contains an iron nail wrapped with both a piece of copper wire and a piece of magnesium ribbon, immersed in an aqueous solution containing $CuSO_4$ and some dissolved $Cl_2(g)$. What is the overall preferred reaction?

The species present are: Fe, Cu, Mg, Cu^{2+}, SO_4^{2-}, Cl_2, H_2O.

Looking down the left side of the Table, the highest reduction reaction is:

$$\boxed{Cl_2} + 2\,e^- \longrightarrow 2\,Cl^- \;;\; E^o = 1.36\ V$$

Looking up the right side of the Table, the lowest oxidation reaction is:

$$Mg^{2+} + 2\,e^- \longleftarrow \boxed{Mg} \;;\; E^o = -2.37\ V$$

Adding the preferred reactions gives the overall reaction.

$$Cl_2 + 2\,e^- \longrightarrow 2\,Cl^-$$
$$Mg(s) \longrightarrow Mg^{2+} + 2\,e^-$$
$$\overline{\qquad\qquad\qquad\qquad}$$
$$Mg + Cl_2 \longrightarrow Mg^{2+} + 2\,Cl^-$$

A COMMENT ON SPECTATOR IONS

Any ion capable of being REDUCED will be a SPECTATOR if there is another ion in the same solution which has a greater tendency to be reduced. Similarly, any ion capable of being OXIDIZED will be a SPECTATOR if there is another ion in the same solution which has a greater tendency to be oxidized. Some ions are used extensively in making up electrochemical solutions because they have such low tendencies either to oxidize or reduce that they are spectator ions under most circumstances.

In particular, the following ions are generally considered to be spectators:

Na^+, K^+, Ca^{2+}, Mg^{2+}, SO_4^{2-} (in **neutral** solution) and Cl^-.

EXERCISES:

47. Predict the overall reaction which will be favoured in the following mixtures.
    a) A mixture of $Br_2(aq)$ and $Cl_2(aq)$ is added to a beaker containing $CuSO_4(aq)$ and a copper rod.
    b) A mixture of powdered aluminum and iron is added to a beaker of Cr^{3+} solution.
    c) A tin strip is immersed in $HNO_3(aq)$.
    d) A copper strip is immersed in $HNO_3(aq)$.
    e) A copper rod is immersed in $HCl(aq)$, through which is bubbled $O_2(g)$.
    f) $Hg(l)$ is dropped into a solution which contains $H_2SO_4(aq)$ and $KMnO_4(aq)$.
    g) H_2O_2 is mixed with $HCl(aq)$.

48. **(Nasty!)** Gold (Au) will not react with any **pure** acid known. More specifically, gold will not react with concentrated nitric acid or hydrochloric acid. In addition, gold will not react with a dilute solution containing a mixture of 1 M HNO_3 and 1 M HCl. However, gold WILL react with "aqua regia", which is a mixture of 1 part concentrated HNO_3 (15 M) and 3 or 4 parts concentrated HCl (12 M). Explain, using appropriate half–reactions, why gold is able to react with "aqua regia".

V.11. APPLIED ELECTROCHEMISTRY

Electrochemistry has numerous applications, some extremely common and some more exotic. A few applications are examined in this section.

A. THE BREATHALYSER

The oxidation of ethanol (C_2H_5OH; also known as "beverage alcohol") by an acidic solution of dichromate ions is represented by the unbalanced reaction equation:

$$C_2H_5OH + K_2Cr_2O_7 + H_2SO_4 \longrightarrow CH_3COOH + Cr_2(SO_4)_3 + K_2SO_4 + H_2O\ .$$

This reaction is simple to carry out and forms the basis of the "breathalyser" test. The test determines the amount of alcohol which has been consumed based on the colours produced by the reaction: the dichromate ion ($Cr_2O_7^{2-}$) is orange–yellow; the chromium (III) ion (Cr^{3+}) is dark green.

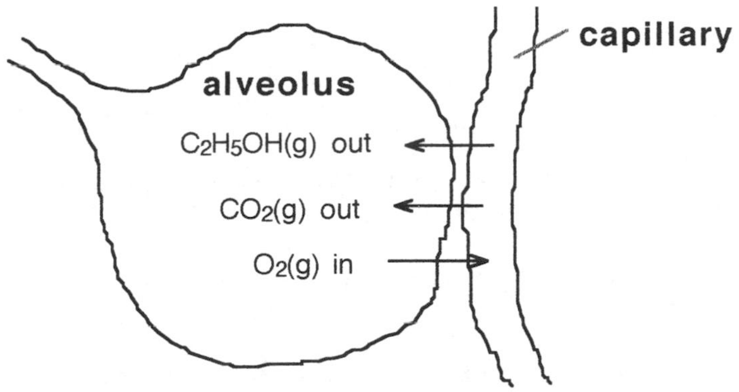

When alcohol is consumed, it is absorbed into the blood stream from the stomach. Tiny blood capillaries are close to the inner surface of the "alveoli" or air sacs which make up the lungs. When alcohol is in the bloodstream, some of it passes through the cell walls of blood capillaries into the air sacs ("alveoli") which make up the lungs, in the same way that $CO_2(g)$ and $O_2(g)$ pass freely into and out of the blood stream.

The passage of alcohol back and forth between the blood stream and the alveoli is an equilibrium process, so that the concentration of alcohol in exhaled air is a very good measure of the alcohol concentration in the blood stream. The greater the concentration of alcohol in the blood, the greater the concentration of alcohol in the exhaled air. The amount of alcohol in the exhaled air is called the **breath alcohol content (BAC)**.

The exhaled air is mixed with a standardized solution containing $K_2Cr_2O_7$, H_2SO_4 and a little Ag^+ to stabilize the mixture. The solution is placed inside a spectrophotometer which is set to record the amount of green coloration produced by the Cr^{3+} ion, and the reaction mixture is kept at about 50°C to decrease the reaction time. The more alcohol in the air sample, the more green coloration produced. Before each session, a technician calibrates the apparatus to make sure that a sample having a known alcohol concentration gives the correct reading.

Very simple; very effective ... but is it foolproof? This question is equivalent to asking: "Can you 'beat' the breathalyser test?" The answer involves knowing which substances can also react with the acidic $Cr_2O_7^{2-}$. There are many substances which DO react with acidic $Cr_2O_7^{2-}$ which ARE NOT "beverage alcohol". The substances which give similar reactions are other alcohols: methanol ("methyl hydrate"; blindness and death follow the consumption of a mouthful or so), isopropyl alcohol (used for cleaning tape deck recording heads; lethal in small quantities), butanol (very toxic), etc. There are many other substances which might be present in exhaled air, but they either don't react with the breathalyser solution or react too slowly to be considered. Perhaps you see a trend; the breathalyser is made to be specific for alcohols, but the only alcohol which you can have in your blood stream and still be alive is ethanol (beverage alcohol). Hence, the answer to the question "Can you 'beat' the breathalyser?" is "Not if you want to live".

EXERCISES:

49. Balance the redox equation for the oxidation of ethanol by acidic potassium dichromate:

$$C_2H_5OH + K_2Cr_2O_7 + H_2SO_4 \longrightarrow CH_3COOH + Cr_2(SO_4)_3 + K_2SO_4 + H_2O.$$

50. The blood in the capillaries is low in $[O_2]$ and high in $[CO_2]$ as it approaches the lungs from the rest of the body, whereas air freshly inhaled into the lungs is high in $[O_2]$ and low in $[CO_2]$. Both O_2 and CO_2 can pass freely back and forth between an alveolus and the capillaries surrounding it. Based on the probability that a given O_2 or CO_2 molecule will move from alveolus to capillary or vice versa, and the relative number of molecules involved, why does the $[O_2]$ decrease and the $[CO_2]$ increase in an alveolus between the time we inhale and the time we exhale?

51. Formaldehyde (HCHO) is a highly toxic substance produced when methanol (CH_3OH) is consumed and oxidized by the liver. Write and balance the redox equation for the oxidation of methanol to formaldehyde using $K_2Cr_2O_7$ and H_2SO_4.

B. BATTERIES AND FUEL CELLS

a) The Lead–Acid Storage Battery

The lead–acid storage battery, or common automobile battery, consists of alternating pairs of plates made of Pb(s) and PbO_2(s), immersed in dilute H_2SO_4 (sulphuric acid or "battery acid").

The anode reaction is $Pb(s) + HSO_4^-(aq) \longrightarrow PbSO_4(s) + H^+(aq) + 2\,e^-$

or simply $Pb \longrightarrow Pb^{2+} + 2\,e^-$

(Notice that the simplified reaction, and those that follow on the next few pages, are written to allow you to see how a metal atom or ion changes its oxidation number. The actual reaction is the one originally given.)

The cathode reaction is $PbO_2(s) + HSO_4^-(aq) + 3\,H^+(aq) + 2\,e^- \longrightarrow PbSO_4(s) + 2\,H_2O(l)$

or simply $Pb^{4+} + 2\,e^- \longrightarrow Pb^{2+}$

The overall reaction is $Pb(s) + PbO_2(s) + 2\,H^+(aq) + 2HSO_4^-(aq) \longrightarrow 2\,PbSO_4(s) + 2\,H_2O(l)$

or $Pb + Pb^{4+} \longrightarrow Pb^{2+} + Pb^{2+}$.

The above reaction occurs when the battery is DISCHARGING; that is, spontaneously reacting to produce electrical energy. As the discharging reaction continues, the insoluble $PbSO_4$(s) forms a layer around the Pb(s) and PbO_2(s) "plates" of the battery.

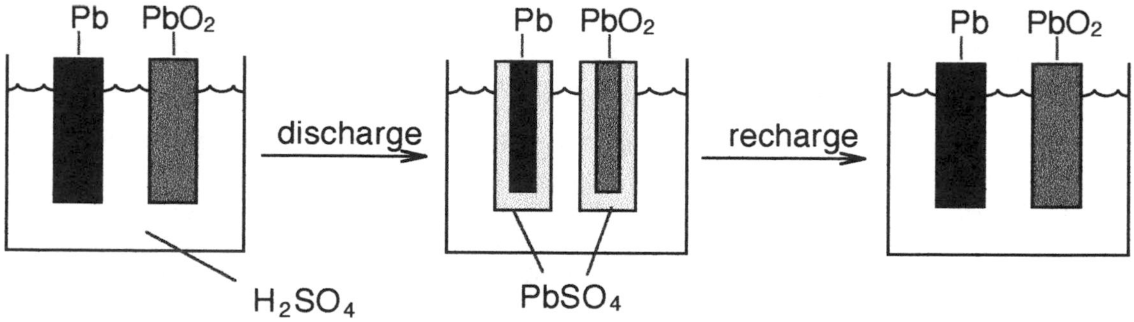

When an external source of electrical energy is applied to the battery to "recharge" it, the spontaneous "discharging" reaction is driven backward.

$$2\,PbSO_4(s) + 2\,H_2O(l) \longrightarrow Pb(s) + PbO_2(s) + 2\,H^+(aq) + 2\,HSO_4^-(aq)$$

During a series of charge–discharge cycles some of the $PbSO_4$(s) flakes off because it does not adhere strongly to the underlying Pb or PbO_2. As a result, less Pb and PbO_2 can be re–formed in subsequent cycles, leading to deterioration of the cell.

As the cell discharges, H_2O is formed and H_2SO_4 is used up. The smaller [H_2SO_4] in the discharged cell lowers the density of the solution in the cell.

FULLY CHARGED ⟶	DISCHARGED ⟶	FULLY CHARGED
d = 1.30 g/mL	d = 1.10 g/mL	d = 1.30 g/mL

Checking the "condition" of a lead–acid battery only requires finding the density of the "electrolyte" (H_2SO_4). Batteries can be checked with a "hydrometer", which allows acid from the battery to enter a glass tube with a squeeze bulb on top. Inside the tube is a calibrated "float" which sinks more or less in the battery acid depending on whether the density of the acid is relatively low or high.

EXERCISES:

52. Why is it correct to classify the recharging reaction as a disproportionation?
53. What happens if one of the Pb plates is bent and touches a PbO_2 plate?

b) The Zinc–Carbon Battery

The zinc–carbon battery is just the common dry cell used in flashlights, etc. The construction of the battery is shown below.

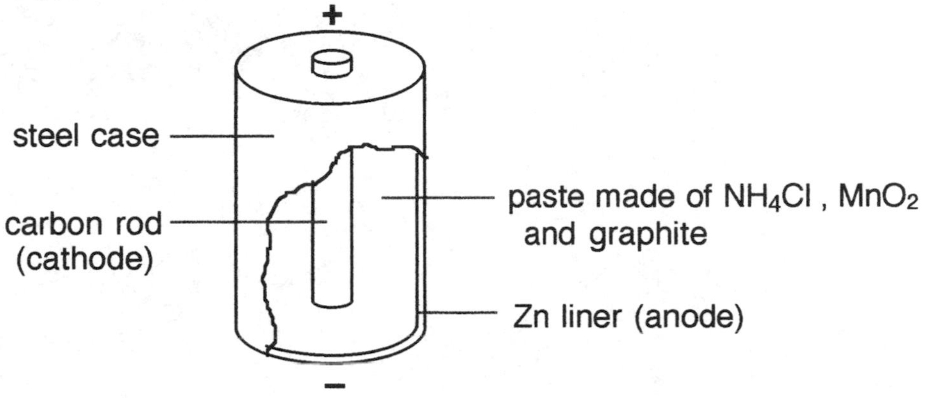

The cathode reaction is $2\ MnO_2(s) + 2NH_4^+(aq) + 2\ e^- \longrightarrow 2\ MnO(OH)(s) + 2\ NH_3(aq)$

or simply $Mn^{4+} + e^- \longrightarrow Mn^{3+}$

The anode reaction is $Zn(s) + 4\ NH_3(aq) \longrightarrow Zn(NH_3)_4^{2+}(aq) + 2\ e^-$

or simply $Zn \longrightarrow Zn^{2+} + 2\ e^-$

As the Zn is used up and $Zn(NH_3)_4^{2+}$ accumulates around the anode, the battery "wears out" and the voltage decreases.

The advantage of the zinc–carbon battery is that it is cheap to make. There are three main disadvantages of the battery: it cannot be recharged, it has a relatively short shelf life (because it continually reacts at a slow rate), and it quickly ceases to function if required to produce large currents (large amounts of electricity in a short time). The voltage also decreases relatively quickly under normal operating conditions.

EXERCISE:

54. Oxidation potential is the opposite of reduction potential. The standard oxidation potential of Zn(s) is 0.76 V. Is the standard oxidation potential of the anode reaction in the zinc–carbon battery greater than, equal to, or less than 0.76 V? Why?

Little Known Fact! One year after Alessandro Volta invented the battery in 1800, his son Giuseppe made the first 'getto blaster'. Although it had both a 'tweeter' and 'woofer', its lack of portability made it unpopular.

c) The Alkaline Dry Cell

The alkaline dry cell gets its name from the fact that the electrolyte (KOH) is "alkaline", or basic. This battery is very similar to the zinc–carbon battery and also uses MnO_2 and Zn. The reaction differs mainly in that the battery operates under basic conditions.

The cathode reaction is $2\,MnO_2(s) + H_2O(l) + 2\,e^- \longrightarrow Mn_2O_3(s) + 2\,OH^-(aq)$.

The anode reaction is $Zn(s) + 2\,OH^-(aq) \longrightarrow ZnO(s) + H_2O(l) + 2\,e^-$

The advantages of the alkaline cell are that it delivers a much greater current and more constant voltage than a carbon battery.

EXERCISE:

55. a) What happens to the total amount of OH^- present when the alkaline cell operates?
    b) What is the effect on the oxidation potential when the $[OH^-]$ decreases around the anode?

d) Fuel Cells

A fuel cell is a device into which a fuel is continuously fed and from which electricity is continuously obtained. (In contrast, batteries contain all the chemical reactants within themselves.)

Unlike a gasoline or diesel powered electrical generator, a fuel cell is pollution free and operates silently, and often more cheaply. Fuel cells operate at about 70–80% efficiency, compared to a coal–burning steam power plant at 35%. The disadvantage of fuel cells is that the electrodes corrode relatively quickly and the cells require constant maintenance. Also, the cells are rather expensive to make and need to be quite large in order to produce significant amounts of electrical energy.

The most common type of fuel cell is the hydrogen–oxygen fuel cell shown below.

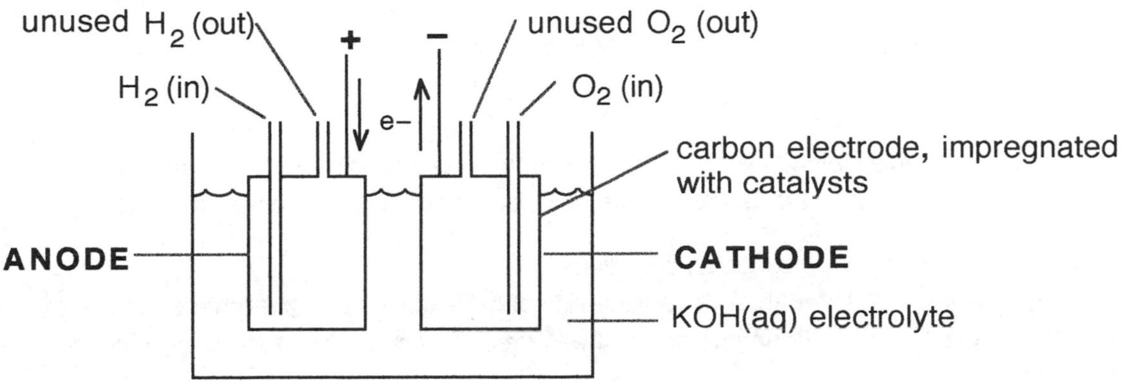

The anode reaction is	$2\,H_2(g) + 4\,OH^-(aq) \longrightarrow 4\,H_2O(l) + 4\,e^-$
The cathode reaction is	$O_2(g) + 2\,H_2O(l) + 4\,e^- \longrightarrow 4\,OH^-(aq)$
The overall reaction is	$2\,H_2(g) + O_2(g) \longrightarrow 2\,H_2O(l)$

One of the most successful uses for this fuel cell has been in space capsules. The fuel gases are easily stored in high pressure tanks, and the water produced can be used for drinking, etc.

EXERCISE:

56. Why is it true to say that the above fuel cell is "pollution free"?

V.12. CORROSION OF METALS : CAUSE AND PREVENTION

The most widely known form of metal corrosion is the "rusting" of iron. (The term "rusting" only applies to the oxidation of iron; oxidation of other metals is described by the general term "corrosion".) Under ordinary circumstances, the two major agents responsible for corrosion are very plentiful: water and oxygen. When a drop of water rests on an iron surface a spontaneous reaction occurs.

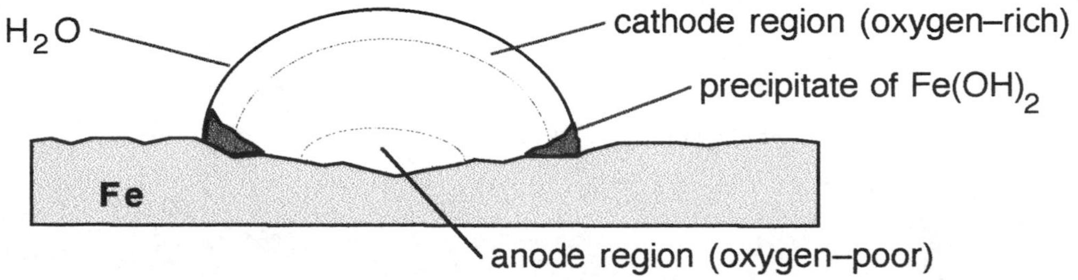

At the oxygen–poor region in the centre of the drop, the iron oxidizes.

$$Fe(s) \longrightarrow Fe^{2+} + 2\,e^-$$

After being formed, the Fe^{2+} ions migrate away from the anodic region to the cathodic region as a result of random movement. As the Fe^{2+} ions move away, they expose fresh Fe(s) for further oxidation. In the meantime, the reaction

$$\tfrac{1}{2}\,O_2 + H_2O + 2\,e^- \longrightarrow 2\,OH^-$$

is proceeding at the oxygen–rich outer surface of the drop. Upon reaching the outer region of the drop, the Fe^{2+} meets the OH^- and precipitates out as insoluble $Fe(OH)_2(s)$. Since the precipitate forms at the outer edge of the drop, a characteristic "ring" of rust is formed when the water drop evaporates.

The anode area is oxygen–poor simply because the reaction

$$\tfrac{1}{2}\,O_2 + H_2O + 2\,e^- \longrightarrow 2\,OH^-$$

uses up most of the available O_2 at the OUTSIDE of the drop, so that little O_2 makes its way into the drop's INTERIOR. Hence the Fe^{2+} must migrate some distance before being deposited as "rust".

The $Fe(OH)_2$ is eventually oxidized to a complex mixture of Fe_2O_3 and H_2O by the O_2 in the air. "RUST" is just $Fe_2O_3 \cdot XH_2O$, where "X" is variable. The variability of "X" explains the different colours rust can have (red, brown, yellow, black) since differing numbers of water molecules attached to the Fe_2O_3 will change the colour of the compound.

A metal may corrode if it touches a different type of metal in the presence of an electrolyte solution exposed to oxygen. For example, if iron touches some copper wire and the place where they touch gets wet, then:

$$Fe \longrightarrow Fe^{2+} + 2\,e^- \text{ (Fe has greater tendency to oxidize than Cu)}.$$

The copper conducts the electrons away from the Fe and makes the electrons available to the oxygen/water touching the wire.

$$\tfrac{1}{2}\,O_2 + H_2O + 2\,e^- \longrightarrow 2\,OH^-$$

EXERCISES:

57. "Native copper" is the term used by geologists for copper which is found in elemental form; that is, as natural deposits of copper metal. Suggest why native gold is found in nature, but native iron is extremely rare, compared to native gold.

58. If a planet has an atmosphere containing large amounts of hydrogen gas, but no oxygen gas, would you expect that native iron might be found on the surface of the planet? Why?

59. In a region of India there exists a pillar of iron which was once a boundary marker for the territory of a Moghul prince. The pillar is upright and partly buried in the soil, but remains largely rust–free even though the pillar has been standing for many centuries. Suggest a reason why the pillar has remained largely without rust.

PREVENTING CORROSION

There are several methods which can stop or slow down the corrosion of metals. All the methods fall into one of two basic categories: those which stop corrosion by preventing the corrosive environment from getting at the metal and those which use electrochemical principles to prevent corrosion even when the metal is exposed to an otherwise–corrosive environment.

A. *Methods which depend on isolating a metal from its environment*

a) Apply a protective layer such as paint or plastic to the surface. If oxygen and water can't get at the metal, it won't corrode.

b) Apply a metal which is corrosion–resistant to the surface of the original metal. Steel, an alloy of iron, contains small amounts of carbon and various metals. Because unprotected steel cans are unsuitable for use with foods, the steel is plated with a thin layer of tin. The outermost layers of tin atoms oxidize quickly, producing a very thin tin oxide layer. This "protective oxide" coating adheres strongly to the underlying tin metal so as to prevent further corrosion. In this way the tin and underlying iron are protected.

B. *Methods which depend on electrochemical principles*

a) Cathodic Protection

In section V.10, "Selecting Preferred Reactions", magnesium was seen to have a higher tendency to oxidize than does iron. This implies that when magnesium is in contact with iron and an oxidizing agent is present, the magnesium will corrode but the iron will not. In other words, the presence of the magnesium will prevent the iron from oxidizing.

> The term **CATHODIC PROTECTION** is applied to the process of protecting a substance from unwanted oxidation by connecting it to a substance having a higher tendency to oxidize.

Since the substance with the greater tendency to oxidize, Mg, acts as the ANODE, then the Fe is forced to act as a CATHODE relative to the Mg and therefore the Fe remains in its REDUCED FORM.

***EXAMPLES*:** Strips of zinc metal are bolted below the water line of iron–hulled ships. By allowing the zinc to be preferentially "sacrificed", the iron in the hulls is kept from oxidizing and corroding. (Some modern ships accomplish the same thing by putting a low voltage electric current into the hull from an electrical generator. By constantly forcing electrons onto the metal, the metal is unable to give off electrons and oxidize.)

Galvanized iron consists of a zinc coating on iron sheets. When galvanized iron is exposed to air and water, the zinc oxidizes preferentially, forming zinc oxide, and protects the iron. The zinc oxide adheres strongly to the surface of the zinc metal and prevents further oxidation of the underlying metal.

Some buried gas and oil tanks made from steel have a thick braided wire connected to them. The wire comes to the surface and is attached to a post driven into the ground and made of an easily oxidized metal such as magnesium or zinc. Because the post oxidizes, the buried (and expensive) metal tank is protected from corrosion.

b) Change the conditions in the chemical surroundings so as to lower the tendency of the surroundings to reduce

When iron is placed in contact with water containing oxygen, the half–reaction

$$\tfrac{1}{2}\,O_2 + 2\,H^+\,(10^{-7}\,M) + 2\,e^- \longrightarrow H_2O\,;\ E = 0.82\ V$$

oxidizes the iron. If oxygen is removed from the solution, the reduction tendency drops drastically. The only reduction reaction which can now occur is much lower on the Table:

$$2\,H^+\,(10^{-7}\,M) + 2\,e^- \longrightarrow H_2(g)\,;\ E = -0.41\ V$$

which is just above the iron half–cell:

$$Fe^{2+} + 2\,e^- \longrightarrow Fe(s)\,;\ E^o = -0.45\ V\,.$$

In addition to removing the oxygen, another method of preventing the oxidation of iron is to lower the $[H^+]$ by adding OH^- ions. The resulting half–cell is much lower on the Table than the iron half–cell:

$$2\,H_2O + 2\,e^- \longrightarrow H_2(g) + 2\,OH^-\,;\ E^o = -0.83\ V\,.$$

As a result, a piece of iron placed in a solution of NaOH solution will not rust. (If some oxygen ***is*** present in the water, a small amount of rust forms on the iron until the oxygen present has been removed from solution by being reacted.)

EXERCISES:

60. Aluminum corrodes quickly in salt water. Suggest three ways in which you could slow down or stop the corrosion of an aluminum boat in the ocean.

61. Chromium metal oxidizes to form a "protective oxide" layer which prevents any further oxidation of the underlying chromium metal. Plating an iron bumper directly with chromium metal can cause problems if the chromium layer is scratched deeply enough to expose the underlying iron. The iron is left unprotected and oxidizes. Suggest a procedure which will protect the iron in the bumper from rusting, even if the bumper is scratched, and yet allow a shiny coating of chromium metal to be used on the bumper.

62. An iron can has a coating of tin. When tin oxidizes, it forms SnO, which adheres strongly to the surface of the tin and prevents further oxidation of the underlying metals. If the tin coating is scratched and the underlying iron is exposed, will the tin provide cathodic protection for the iron? If so, why? If not, what will happen?

63. A small strip of magnesium is attached below the water line of a steel outboard motor casing. What is the purpose of the strip?

V.13. ELECTROLYSIS

Definitions: **ELECTROLYSIS** is the process of supplying electrical energy to a molten ionic compound or a solution containing ions so as to produce a chemical change.

An **ELECTROLYTIC CELL** or **ELECTROLYSIS CELL** is an apparatus in which electrolysis can occur.

Electrolysis supplies energy to non–spontaneous electrochemical reactions ($E^o_{CELL} < 0$), allowing them to occur.

A Simple Electrolytic Cell : Electrolysis of a Molten Binary Salt

Consider what happens when a molten binary salt such as NaCl is electrolyzed. (A "binary salt" is made of only two different elements, eg. NaCl, KBr, MgI_2, AlF_3, etc.) NaCl is an ionic solid; when melted, the ions are mobile. Note that there is no need for a salt bridge or porous barrier to keep the reactants separated — no spontaneous reaction occurs between the reactants.

direct current (DC) power supply or battery

(the symbol ⊣⊢ is sometimes used)

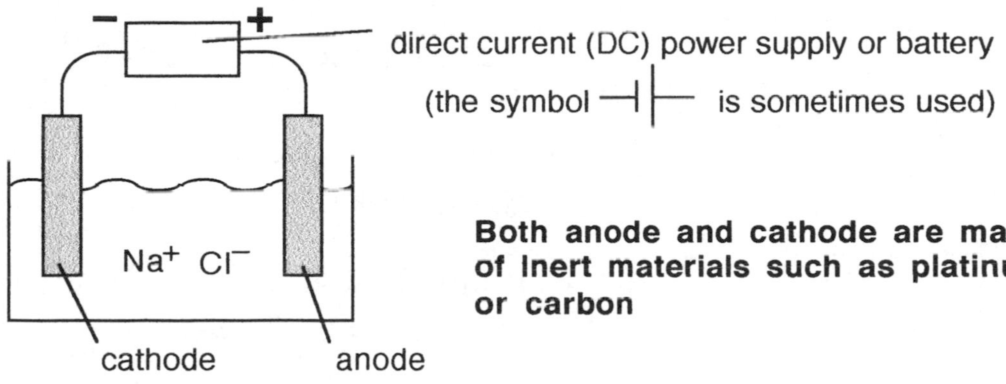

Both anode and cathode are made of Inert materials such as platinum or carbon

The only reactants present are Na^+ and Cl^-:

$$Cl_2 + 2e^- \longleftarrow \boxed{2Cl^-}$$
$$\boxed{Na^+} + e^- \longrightarrow Na$$

The anode reaction is $\qquad 2Cl^- \longrightarrow Cl_2 + 2e^- \; ; \quad E^o = -1.36 \text{ V}$

The cathode reaction is $\qquad Na^+ + e^- \longrightarrow Na \qquad ; \quad E^o = -2.71 \text{ V}$

The overall reaction is $\qquad 2Na^+ + 2Cl^- \longrightarrow 2Na + Cl_2 \; ; \; E^o_{CELL} = -4.07 \text{ V}$

Note: It may take you some time to adjust to the fact that the REDUCTION half–reaction is now **below** the OXIDATION half–reaction on the Table. This is why the reaction is **not** spontaneous and requires electrical energy to be added before any reaction will occur.

To make this cell operate **AT LEAST +4.07 V** must be added. Since the half–cells are not at standard state (no products exist at the start of the reaction), the reduction potentials of the half–cells involved will be different from those listed on the Table. In actual practice, the cell may require as much as 10 V to be applied in order to overcome such things as the internal resistance of the cell.

(In practice, the cell is more elaborate than shown. At the temperatures required to keep the salt molten (850°C), the sodium metal melts and sinks to the bottom of the cell. Since sodium metal and chlorine gas react violently when mixed, the cell allows the chlorine gas to be vented off and the liquid sodium to be drained from the bottom of the cell.)

EXERCISE:

64. For each of the following molten ionic compounds show the half–cell reactions which occur at the cathode and the anode, the overall reaction and the minimum voltage which must be applied to make the electrolysis reaction occur.

    (a) $KBr(l)$ (b) $CaI_2(l)$ (c) $SnCl_2(l)$

Electrolysis of Aqueous NaI

This electrolysis cell introduces a new complication: **water.** Again, the experimental setup is relatively simple, as shown below. Inert electrodes are used to prevent the complication of having to consider additional reactions.

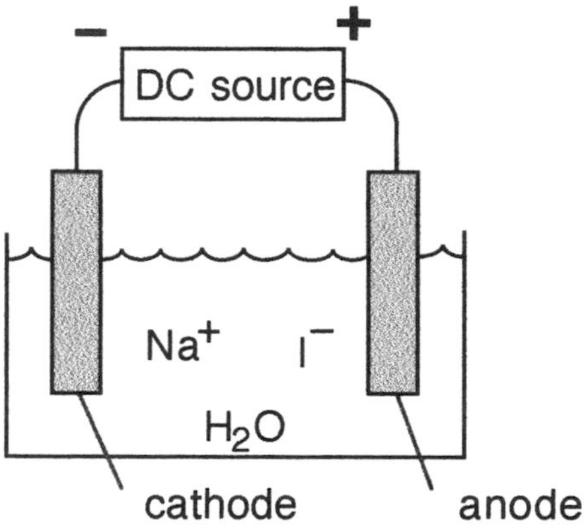

The electrodes are made of an inert material such as Pt or C

Species in solution: Na^+, I^-, H_2O

Note: The solution is NEUTRAL because no acid (H^+) was shown.

IMPORTANT: **DURING THE ELECTROLYSIS OF AQUEOUS SOLUTIONS, YOU MUST ALWAYS CONSIDER THE POSSIBILITY THAT H_2O MAY OXIDIZE AND/OR REDUCE.**

There are two possible reductions:

$$\boxed{2\,H_2O} + 2\,e^- \longrightarrow H_2(g) + 2\,OH^-(10^{-7}\,M)$$

$$\boxed{Na^+} + e^- \longrightarrow Na\,.$$

There are also two possible oxidations:

$$\tfrac{1}{2}\,O_2(g) + 2\,H^+(10^{-7}\,M) + 2\,e^- \longleftarrow \boxed{H_2O}$$

$$I_2 + 2\,e^- \longleftarrow \boxed{2\,I^-}\,.$$

Now a problem occurs: what criterion should be used to select the preferred half–reactions when dealing with electrolysis reactions? Consider the diagram below.

$\frac{1}{2}O_2(g) + 2H^+(10^{-7}M) + 2e^- \longleftarrow \boxed{H_2O}$

$I_2 + 2e^- \longleftarrow \boxed{2I^-}$

$\boxed{2H_2O} + 2e^- \longrightarrow H_2(g) + 2OH^-(10^{-7}M)$

$\boxed{Na^+} + e^- \longrightarrow Na$

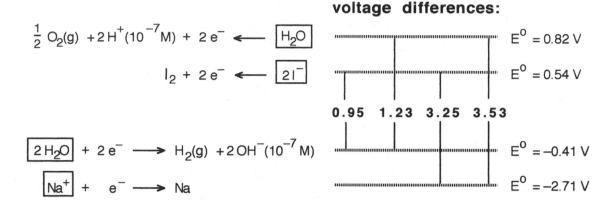

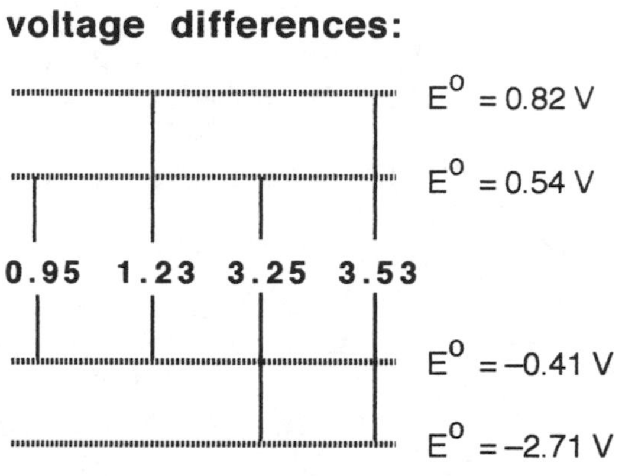

According to the above voltage differences, a reaction occurs if at least +0.95 V is added. It makes sense that the reaction will not "wait for a better deal involving a larger voltage", and therefore:

the preferred reaction will be the one requiring the least voltage input.

Based on the above four half–reactions, the preferred reaction (the one requiring the least voltage input) involves the higher of the two possible reductions and the lower of the two possible oxidations. Therefore, the same situation exists for electrolysis reactions as was found for spontaneous reactions.

THE HALF–REACTIONS HAVING THE GREATEST TENDENCY TO REDUCE AND GREATEST TENDENCY TO OXIDIZE ARE PREFERRED.

Completing the example, the half–reactions and overall reaction involved in the electrolysis of NaI(aq) are:

$$2H_2O + 2e^- \longrightarrow H_2(g) + 2OH^-(10^{-7}M) \quad ; \quad E^o = -0.41\ V\ \text{(cathode)}$$
$$2I^- \longrightarrow I_2 + 2e^- \quad ; \quad E^o = -0.54\ V\ \text{(anode)}$$

$$2H_2O + 2I^- \longrightarrow H_2(g) + I_2 + 2OH^-(10^{-7}M) \ ; \ E^o_{CELL} = -0.95\ V$$

so that at least +0.95 V must be applied to the cell to make it operate.

Notes: The concentrations of the materials in cells will not be of concern; as long as there is sufficient material in the cell you can assume the reactions proceed as predicted.

Most of the examples and problems you will encounter will exist in NEUTRAL SOLUTION. The few cases of ACIDIC SOLUTIONS you encounter will simply involve the substitution of H^+ for any metal ions in solution, so as to keep the problems simple.

Assuming a **NEUTRAL *aqueous*** solution is present, there are two "water equations" which must be considered.

OXIDATION $\frac{1}{2}O_2(g) + 2H^+(10^{-7}M) + 2e^- \leftarrow$ $\boxed{H_2O}$; $E^o = 0.82$ V

REDUCTION $\boxed{2H_2O}$ $+ 2e^- \rightarrow H_2(g) + 2OH^-(10^{-7}M)$; $E^o = -0.41$ V

In **ACIDIC** solutions there are also two "water equations" which must be considered.

OXIDATION $\frac{1}{2}O_2(g) + 2H^+ + 2e^- \leftarrow$ $\boxed{H_2O}$; $E^o = 1.23$ V

REDUCTION $\boxed{2H^+}$ $+ 2e^- \rightarrow H_2(g)$; $E^o = 0.00$ V

You will **NOT** be required to work with cells operating in basic conditions. (This is just as well because the OH^- precipitates many metal ions out of solution.)

Beautiful theories often have to face the cold light of awkward facts. When dilute neutral aqueous solutions (about 1 M or less) containing Cl^- or Br^- are electrolyzed, we expect that the water will oxidize before either Cl^- or Br^- since water is lower on the Table.

$$Cl_2 + 2e^- \leftarrow 2Cl^- \quad ; E^o = 1.36 \text{ V}$$
$$\tfrac{1}{2}O_2 + 2H^+(10^{-7}\text{ M}) + 2e^- \leftarrow H_2O \quad ; E^o = 0.82 \text{ V}$$

Contrary to our expectation, O_2 is **not** produced; Cl_2 (or Br_2) is! Rather than going into the messy details of "why" (you can look up "overpotentials" if you truly thirst for knowledge), simply memorize the following "exceptions to the rule".

Electrolysis of aqueous solutions containing Cl^- or Br^- will produce Cl_2 or Br_2 at the anode.

***EXAMPLES*:**

a) What products are formed at the anode and cathode and what is the overall reaction when a solution containing $NiSO_4(aq)$ is electrolyzed using inert electrodes? Determine the minimum voltage which must be applied before the reaction will occur.

***First*:** Establish all the species present.

Ni^{2+}, SO_4^{2-}, H_2O (ALWAYS consider the presence of water)

***Second*:** Determine whether the conditions are **acidic** or **neutral.**

Since no acid is present, the conditions are **neutral.** (ALWAYS assume conditions are neutral unless one of the chemicals used is an acid.)

***Third*:** Find the **highest reduction** reaction which can occur with the species in the list.

The highest reduction is $Ni^{2+} + 2e^- \rightarrow Ni$; $E^o = -0.26$ V.

Note: $SO_4^{2-} + 4H^+ + 2e^- \rightarrow H_2SO_3 + H_2O$; $E^o = 0.17$ V is NOT acceptable. (SO_4^{2-} is present **but** NOT H^+; this half–reaction requires acidic conditions but the problem involves neutral conditions.)

Fourth: Find the **lowest oxidation** reaction which can occur with the species in the list. If Cl^- or Br^- is present, Cl_2 or Br_2 will be produced instead of O_2. (In this case, no exceptions are present.)

The only species in the solution which can oxidize is H_2O. Write the reaction as an oxidation and reverse the voltage.

$$H_2O \longrightarrow \frac{1}{2} O_2 + 2\,H^+(10^{-7}\,M) + 2\,e^- \ ; \ E^o = -0.82\ V$$

Fifth: Determine the overall reaction equation and finish the problem.

$$\begin{array}{lrl} \text{Anode:} & H_2O \longrightarrow \frac{1}{2} O_2 + 2\,H^+(10^{-7}\,M) + 2\,e^- & ; \quad E^o = -0.82\ V \\ \text{Cathode:} & Ni^{2+} + 2\,e^- \longrightarrow Ni & ; \quad E^o = -0.26\ V \\ \hline & H_2O + Ni^{2+} \longrightarrow \frac{1}{2} O_2 + 2\,H^+(10^{-7}\,M) + Ni & ; \quad E^o_{CELL} = -1.08\ V \end{array}$$

Therefore at least +1.08 V must be applied to make the reaction occur.

b) What is the overall reaction which occurs when a 1 M solution of HCl(aq) is electrolyzed using carbon electrodes?

First: Establish all the species present.

H^+, Cl^-, H_2O (note that the "inert" carbon electrodes are omitted)

Second: Determine whether the conditions are **acidic** or **neutral.**

An acid is present and therefore the conditions are ACIDIC.

Third: Find the **highest** possible **reduction** reaction which can occur with the species in the list.

The highest reduction is $2\,H^+ + 2\,e^- \longrightarrow H_2$; $E^o = 0.00\ V$.

Fourth: Find the **lowest** possible **oxidation** reaction which can occur with the species in the list. Check for the presence of oxidation exceptions: Cl^- and Br^-.

Cl^- is present and will oxidize before the water. Write the reaction as an oxidation and reverse the voltage.

$$2\,Cl^- \longrightarrow Cl_2 + 2\,e^- \ ; \ E^o = -1.36\ V$$

Fifth: Determine the overall reaction equation and finish the problem.

$$\begin{array}{lrl} \text{Anode:} & 2\,Cl^- \longrightarrow Cl_2 + 2\,e^- & ; \quad E^o = -1.36\ V \\ \text{Cathode:} & 2\,H^+ + 2\,e^- \longrightarrow H_2 & ; \quad E^o = \ \ 0.00\ V \\ \hline & 2\,H^+ + 2\,Cl^- \longrightarrow H_2 + Cl_2 & ; \quad E^o_{CELL} = -1.36\ V \end{array}$$

Therefore at least +1.36 V must be applied to make the reaction occur.

For those of you who can't get your reactions to work try adding another battery
AMPS
A budding Tim Taylor
-ZimBOBwe

EXERCISES:

65. What products are formed when the following solutions are electrolyzed? What is the minimum voltage which would have to be applied in each case?

    a) 1 M $NiI_2(aq)$ b) 1 M $MnI_2(aq)$ c) 1 M $MnF_2(aq)$ d) 1 M $HI(aq)$

66. If pure, molten $CuCl_2$ is electrolyzed using inert electrodes, what substances will be produced at the anode and cathode? What is the minimum voltage which must be applied to the cell?

67. A solution of $CuSO_4(aq)$ is electrolyzed using inert electrodes. What substance is produced at each of the electrodes? What is the minimum voltage which must be applied to the cell?

68. Predict the overall reactions expected when the following solutions are electrolyzed.

    a) 1 M $KI(aq)$ c) 1 M $CuBr_2(aq)$ e) 1 M $K_2SO_4(aq)$ g) 1 M $FeCl_3(aq)$
    b) 1 M $SnCl_2(aq)$ d) 1 M $HBr(aq)$ f) 1 M $CoI_2(aq)$ h) 1 M $H_2SO_4(aq)$

69. An aqueous solution of Na_2SO_4 is electrolyzed. If litmus paper is dipped into the solution around the anode during the reaction, what colour will the litmus turn? What colour will the litmus turn when dipped into the solution around the cathode? If the electric current is turned off and the anode and cathode solutions are stirred together, what is the pH of the resulting solution?

70. Why can't aluminum metal be produced by electrolysis of $AlCl_3(aq)$?

71. Examine the following cell setup.

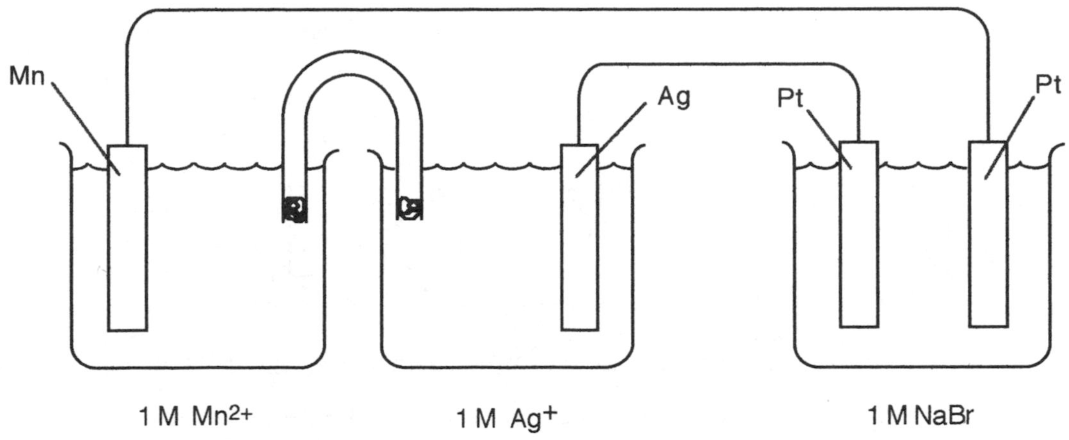

a) What is the voltage of the cell formed by joining the Mn^{2+}/Mn and Ag^+/Ag half–cells?
b) Describe completely what happens when the cell in part a is connected to the cell containing NaBr.

72. A half–cell consisting of 0.1 M $CoSO_4$ and a cobalt electrode was connected to a half–cell consisting of 0.1 M $SnSO_4$ and a tin electrode. As time passed it was observed that the concentration of sulphate ions was increasing in the tin half–cell. Was the reaction occurring in an electrochemical cell or an electrolytic cell? Explain your answer.

Electroplating

Electroplating is an electrolytic process in which a metal is reduced or "plated out" at a cathode.

- The **CATHODE** is made out of the material which will receive the metal plating.
- The **ELECTROPLATING SOLUTION** contains ions of the metal which is to be "plated" onto the cathode.
- The **ANODE** may be made of the same metal which is to be "plated out" onto the cathode. (This is normal, but an inert electrode can also be used.)

Note: For the sake of simplicity, you will only be asked about electroplating in NEUTRAL solutions.

EXAMPLE: Design a cell to electroplate a copper medallion with nickel metal. Include in the design: the ions present in solution, the direction of ion flow, the substances used for the anode and cathode, and the direction of electron flow when the cell is connected to a DC power source.

Since nickel metal must be produced, the reduction reaction is:

$$Ni^{2+} + 2\,e^- \longrightarrow Ni(s)\ ;\ E^o = -0.26\ V\,.$$

The experimental setup shown below will work well.

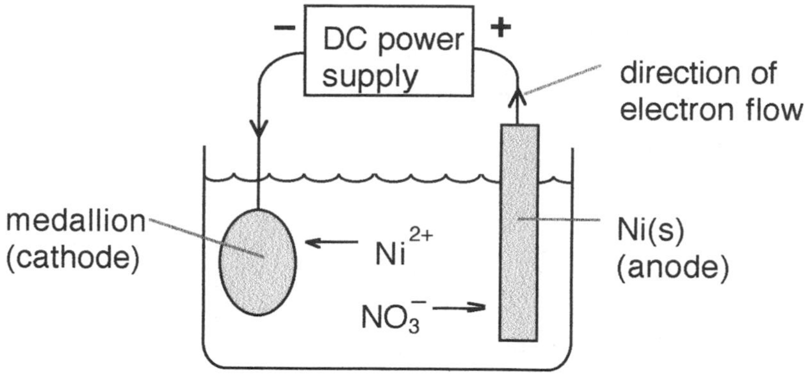

- The medallion must have the Ni(s) plated onto it, so it must be the cathode.
- Make the anode out of Ni(s) so that the oxidation reaction $Ni(s) \longrightarrow Ni^{2+} + 2\,e^-$ will ensure a continuous supply of Ni^{2+} ions in the solution.
- Since electron flow is always "ANODE TO CATHODE", connect the DC power supply up in such a way as to supply electrons to the cathode.
- The ions needed in solution will be Ni^{2+} (obviously) and some anion which does not form a precipitate with Ni^{2+}. The NO_3^- ion is a good choice since nitrates are always soluble.
- As with spontaneous reactions, CATIONS (Ni^{2+}) still migrate toward the CATHODE and ANIONS (NO_3^-) migrate toward the ANODE.

EXERCISES:

73. You have a piece of iron which you wish to electroplate with chromium metal. Should the iron be the anode or cathode?

74. These questions refer to the nickel–plating of the copper medallion which was used in the example above.
    a) Is it important that the medallion be made of copper? Why? What is the most important requirement to be considered when choosing a material for the cathode?
    b) If OH^- is used instead of NO_3^-, the nickel ions present will form a precipitate of $Ni(OH)_2(s)$. What problem(s) will this cause in the cell?
    c) If Na^+ is used instead of Ni^{2+}, but the rest of the cell is left the same, what might occur during the electrolysis reaction? (Hint: What happens at first? What happens after some of the anode has oxidized and the resulting ions have migrated toward the cathode?)

75. Design a cell to silver plate an iron spoon. Include in your design: the ions in solution, the direction of ion flow, the substances used for the anode and cathode, and the direction of electron flow when the cell is connected to a DC power source.

76. Design a cell which can be used to electroplate copper onto a strip of tin. Include in your design: the ions in solution, the direction of ion flow, the substances used for the anode and cathode, and the direction of electron flow when the cell is connected to a DC power source.

Electrorefining

Electrorefining is the process of purifying a metal by electrolysis. Examine the following cell.

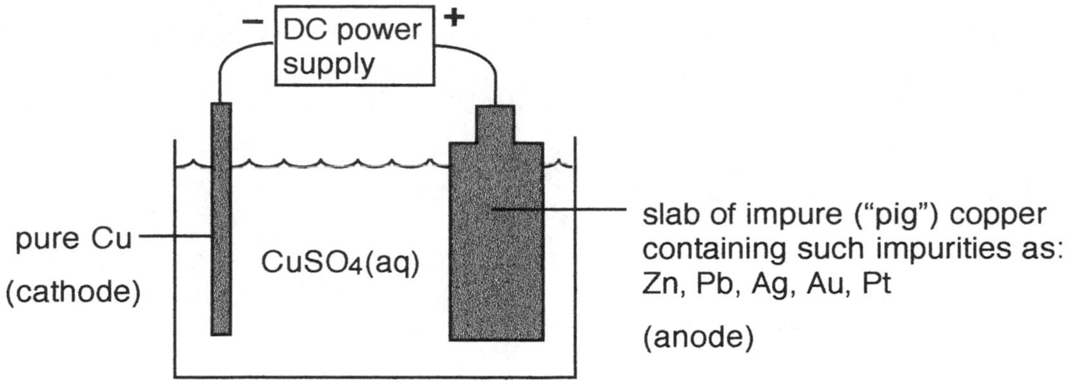

***The anode reaction*:**

Apart from the small amounts of Pb and Zn, the Cu has the greatest tendency to oxidize.

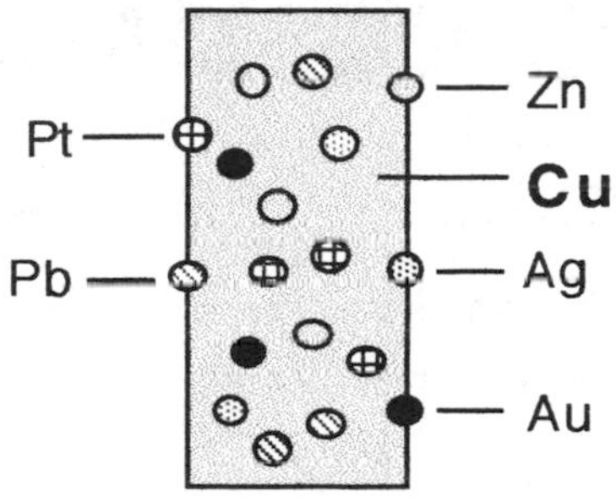

The small amount of Zn or Pb present is preferentially oxidized as it is exposed at the surface. When any exposed Pb/Zn atoms have oxidized and gone into solution as ions, only the Cu atoms are available to be oxidized. Any Au, Ag or Pt atoms present can't be oxidized because the anode is mostly copper, which is oxidized in preference to Au, etc. Therefore the particles of Au, etc. simply drop off the anode and accumulate on the bottom of the electrolytic cell, forming a valuable "anode sludge". Companies which electrorefine copper sell or process this sludge for a substantial profit.

***The cathode reaction*:**

The Cu^{2+} in solution is preferentially reduced at the cathode but none of the Pb^{2+} or Zn^{2+} can be reduced. (Cu^{2+} exists in larger amounts and has a higher reduction potential than Zn^{2+} and Pb^{2+}.)

***In summary*:**

No metals above Cu on the Table can oxidize and go into solution, and no metal below Cu on the chart can reduce and come back out of solution. As a result, only Cu is involved in both the oxidation and reduction.

Anode	$Cu(impure) \longrightarrow Cu^{2+} + 2\,e^-$	;	$E^o = -0.34$ V
cathode	$Cu^{2+} + 2\,e^- \longrightarrow Cu(pure)$	;	$E^o = 0.34$ V
overall	$Cu(impure) + Cu^{2+} \longrightarrow Cu(pure) + Cu^{2+}$	;	$E^o_{CELL} = 0.00$ V

Although this predicts that 0.00 V is required to make the cell operate, in practice several volts must be applied to supply the energy required for the reaction.

Various other metals, such as Pb, Sn and Ni can also be purified in cells which are virtually identical to the above situation (except that the anode/cathode is made of the new metal to be refined).

(Another process which is used to purify metals is called "ELECTROWINNING". In this process, the metal to be purified is introduced in the form of a solution of the metal ion, and the desired pure form of the metal is produced by causing it to reduce at the cathode.)

EXERCISE:

77. An aqueous solution of $SnSO_4$ was electrolyzed using tin electrodes. The anode contained a few percent of silver, copper and zinc as impurities. Which substance(s) will be oxidized at the anode? Which substance(s) will be reduced at the cathode?

Applied Electrolysis: Electrolytic Production of Aluminum

The process of making aluminum metal starts with a raw material called "bauxite", an impure form of aluminum oxide. Bauxite is about 50% aluminum oxide, mixed with oxides of iron, silicon and titanium. After initial purification of the ore, $Al_2O_3 \cdot 3H_2O(s)$ is produced. The water of hydration attached to the aluminum oxide is driven off by heating.

$$Al_2O_3 \cdot 3H_2O \longrightarrow Al_2O_3 + 3\ H_2O$$

In order to lower the 2045°C melting temperature of the "alumina" (Al_2O_3), a "flux" made of AlF_3 and the mineral "cryolite" (Na_3AlF_6) is added, lowering the melting temperature to a manageable 1000°C. (A "flux" is a substance added in order to reduce the melting temperature of another substance. The melting temperature of a mixture is always less than the individual melting temperatures of the substances in the mixture.) The molten alumina is then electrolyzed using carbon electrodes.

anode reaction $C(s) + 2\ O^{2-} \longrightarrow CO_2(g) + 4\ e^-$

cathode reaction $2\ Al^{3+} + 6\ e^- \longrightarrow 2\ Al(l)$

Note that the anode is continually being corroded as it reacts with the oxide ion (O^{2-}) to form $CO_2(g)$.

A voltage of 4.1 to 6 volts is used during the electrolysis process. It is of interest to note that the electrolytic production of aluminum by Alcan at Kitimat, B.C., uses about 10 million amperes of electrical energy. (By comparison, an electric kettle uses about 15 amperes.) As a result, aluminum is quite costly to produce due to the enormous consumption of electrical energy which occurs during the process.

EXERCISES:

78. Why must the water of hydration be driven off from the $Al_2O_3 \cdot 3H_2O$?

79. During the electrolysis reaction, some of the AlF_3 and Na_3AlF_6 added as flux also react. Suggest a reason why these substances might have been chosen to make a flux, rather than some other substance such as $SnCl_2$ or $FeBr_3$.

80. What is the overall reaction for the electrolysis of Al_2O_3 using carbon electrodes?

Well, I hope you enjoyed your year in Chem 12. You've learned lots of Chemistry so go out and make a better world. Your journey has just started.
-ZimBOBwe

ANSWERS TO UNIT I : REACTION KINETICS

1. Rate of consumption = $\frac{5.0\text{ g}}{150\text{ s}} \times \frac{60\text{ s}}{1\text{ min}} = \frac{2.0\text{ g}}{\text{min}}$

2. Time = $45.0\text{ g} \times \frac{1\text{ min}}{2.35\text{ g}} = 19.1\text{ min}$

3. Volume of $O_2 = 7.50\text{ min} \times \frac{32.5\text{ mL}}{\text{min}} = 244\text{ mL}$

4. (a) OK; moles/second = amount/time
   (b) Not acceptable; this is a "rate" but not "amount/time"
   (c) OK; moles/litre is an amount and (moles/litre)/second = amount/time
   (d) Not acceptable; this is a density or concentration
   (e) OK; millilitres/hour = amount/time
   (f) OK; grams/minute = amount/time

5. Rate of consumption of $O_2 = \frac{1.34\text{ mol }H_2O}{\text{min}} \times \frac{1\text{ mol }O_2}{2\text{ mol }H_2O} = \frac{0.67\text{ mol }O_2}{\text{min}}$

6. (a) The mass is decreasing because $CO_2(g)$ is being lost from the solution.
   (b) Slope = –0.006
   (c) i) unit of rise = g ii) unit of run = s iii) units of slope = g/s
   (d) Expected units for rate = g/s
   (e) The rate of the reaction = the slope of the line = –0.006 g/s (a loss of 0.006 g every second)

7. If the reaction occurred in a closed container, no mass would be lost (conservation of mass). If the $NO_2(g)$ was allowed to escape, the mass decrease would be due to the loss of $NO_2(g)$, NOT the loss of Cu(s). [Incidentally, $NO_2(g)$ is quite soluble in water and not all of the NO_2 produced would escape.]

8. (a) Measure the rate at which the intensity of the blue colour in the solution increases.
   (b) Measure the change in mass of Cu(s) and calculate the rate as the mass of Cu used divided by the time required for the reaction; or measure the change in mass of Ag(s) and calculate the rate as the mass of Ag produced divided by the reaction time; or measure the increase in temperature (the reaction is exothermic) and calculate the rate as the temperature change divided by reaction time.

9. (a) The reaction produces two moles of gas for every two moles of gas used up. Hence the number of moles of gas in the container doesn't change, and the gas pressure doesn't change as the reaction proceeds. (Recall "Avogadro's Hypothesis" from Chem 11: equal volumes of gases at the same temperature and pressure contain the same number of molecules or moles.)

   (b) Rate = $\frac{1.2\text{ g HCl}}{120\text{ s}} \times \frac{1\text{ mol HCl}}{36.5\text{ g HCl}} = 2.7 \times 10^{-4}\text{ mol HCl/s}$

   (c) Rate (of HCl) = $\frac{0.200\text{ L }H_2}{1\text{ min}} \times \frac{2\text{ L HCl}}{1\text{ L }H_2} = 0.400\text{ L HCl/min}$

10. Reaction (b) is fastest: a single H^+ is removed from NH_4^+ and added to CO_3^{2-}.

    Reaction (a) is moderately slow: 6 bonds have to be broken and made. An O–O bond and 2 O–H bonds have to be broken; 2 O–H bonds and a second bond in O=O must be made.

    Reaction (c) is very slow: many bonds have to be broken and made. Incidentally ... gasoline does not undergo combustion at ROOM TEMPERATURE; a mixture of gasoline and oxygen can exist indefinitely at room temperature. Of course, if you add HEAT (in the form of a spark or match) then BOOM!

11. Since nothing was changed, other than exchanging one reactant (Li) for another (K), the reaction rate change was due to "the nature of the reactants".

12. Surface area has ***no effect*** on a reaction between two gases because gases will completely intermix when combined. The intermolecular forces are too weak to make gas molecules clump together. As a result, there is no "surface" inside which one kind of gas is found and outside which the other kind of gas is found. In general, surface area will not be an important factor in **any** homogeneous reaction because of the complete mixing which must exist in a homogeneous mixture. In fact, the concept of a "surface" cannot even be defined for a homogeneous mixture.

13. (a) $Ag^+(aq) + I^-(aq) \longrightarrow AgI(s)$ Aqueous ions react faster than gases.
    (b) $CH_3COOH(aq) + H_2O(l) \longrightarrow CH_3COO^-(aq) + H_3O^+(aq)$ The two liquids form a fast–reacting homogeneous mixture, whereas Fe(s) and water can only react at the surface of the iron.
    (c) $CaO(s) + H_2O(l) \longrightarrow Ca(OH)_2(s)$ A liquid and solid are expected to react faster than two solid reactants.
    (d) C(s, powder) $+ O_2(g) \longrightarrow CO_2(g)$ A powder has a greater surface area than a solid chunk.
    (e) $H^+(aq) + OH^-(aq) \longrightarrow H_2O(l)$ Two aqueous ions react faster than a neutral aqueous molecule and an aqueous ion.

14. Both reactions in (a) are homogeneous (the solid AgI is irrelevant since the REACTANTS are in the same phase in each case).

    The second reaction in (b) is homogeneous because $H_2O(l)$ is liquid water and $CH_3COOH(aq)$ refers to acetic acid dissolved in water.

    Both reactions in (e) are homogeneous.

    Note: In (c) the reaction between Cu(s) and S(s) is NOT homogeneous because Cu and S are different solid "phases" (have different properties depending on where one takes a sample).

15. All factors EXCEPT surface area are important in homogeneous reactions. All factors are important in heterogeneous reactions.

16. (a) Powder the Al(s)
    (b) Increase the temperature
    (c) Reduce the volume of the container, so as to increase the pressure
    (d) Add a catalyst
    (e) Add more $F_2(g)$, keeping the volume constant

17. (a) The concentration of the reactants decreases (reactants are used up)
    (b) The rate decreases
    (c) i) graph B. Initially the [reactants] is high and the [products] is zero. Reactants are used up quickly and products are produced quickly, but toward the end the [reactants] is small so that [reactants] decreases very slowly and [products] increases very slowly (levels off).
        ii) graph C. See the explanation for part i)
    (d) i) graph C. Initially there is a large [reactants] and the rate is high. As the reactants get used up, the rate at which the remaining reactants get used slows down and the rate starts to level off.
        ii) graph C. The rate at which the reactants are used up equals the rate at which the products are made.

18. Using the tangent line drawn to the curve at time = 20 s:

$$\text{Rate} = \text{slope} = \frac{\text{rise}}{\text{run}} = \frac{-0.21\ \text{mol/L}}{42\ \text{s}} = -0.0050\ \text{mol/L·s}.$$

19. (a) −0.11 g/s
    (b) −0.047 g/s
    (c) In (b) there are less reactants, including HCl(aq), which decreases the rate of reaction.

20. If the surface area of reactant A is increased, a given molecule of reactant B has a greater chance of striking a molecule of A so that more collisions can occur between A and B in a specified time. As a result, the reaction rate increases. Molecules of A which are INSIDE a chunk of solid A cannot react; only molecules at the surface can react.

21. (a) Decreases rate. The collisions are less energetic and there are fewer collisions at the lower temperature.
(b) Increases rate. Greater frequency of collisions between O_2 and S.
(c) No effect. Changing the amount of product will not affect the rate of collisions between reactants.
(d) Increases rate. Greater surface area of S exposes more S atoms to collisions with O_2 molecules.
(e) Decreases rate. Increasing the volume decreases the pressure and decreases the $[O_2]$, which decreases the frequency of collisions.

22. Kindling has a larger surface area and therefore a greater frequency of collision between oxygen molecules and the wood.

23. PE must increase (electrons must have sufficient energy to separate from one another and break the bond).

24. $A \longrightarrow B + 25\ kJ$

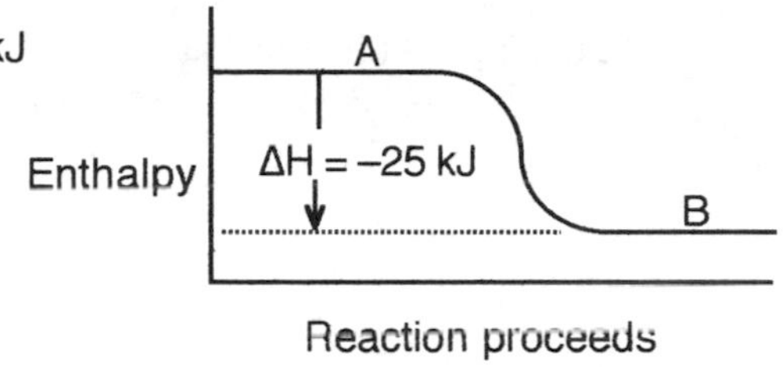

Since the system of reactants gives off energy to the surroundings, the surroundings feel warmer.

25. $\Delta H = +40\ kJ$

26. $\Delta H = +30\ kJ$. The products have more energy than the reactants.

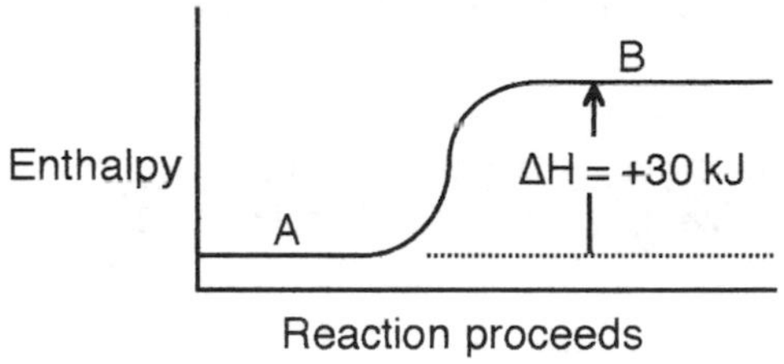

Since the system of reactants absorbs energy from the surroundings, the surroundings feel cooler.

27.

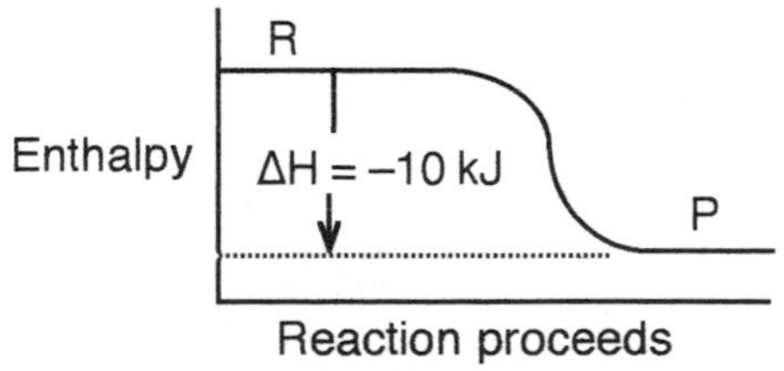

The surroundings will feel warmer.

28.

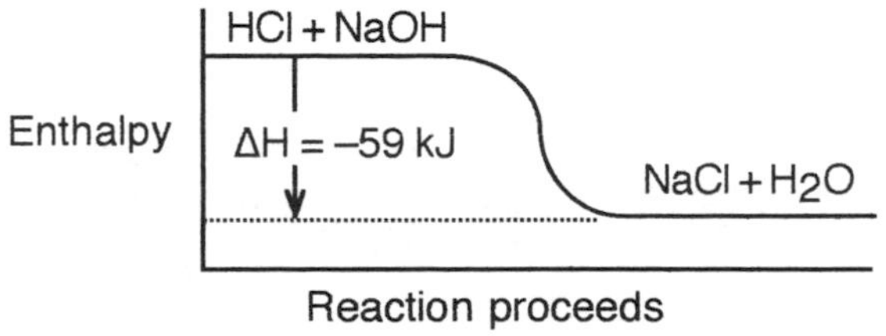

Since heat is absorbed by the surroundings, the system gave off heat.

29. (a) ii
(b) No, there would be little effect on the rate; the "doubling of rate with a 10°C increase in temperature" rule of thumb ONLY applies to SLOW reactions – this is a fast reaction.

30. (a) The curve is proportionally smaller along the vertical axis, but the peak is still at the same KE value.

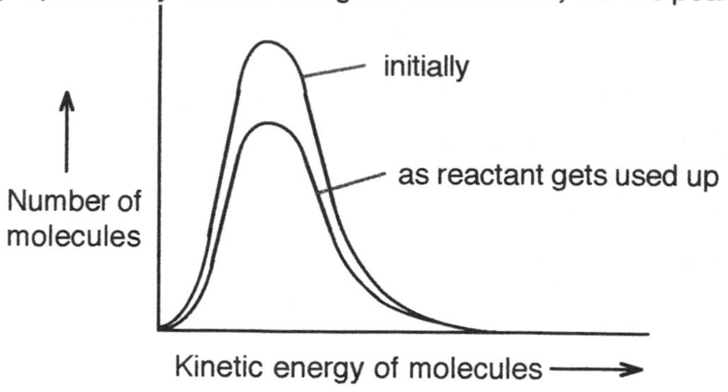

(b) The peak is at lower KE values, and a bit higher on the vertical axis.

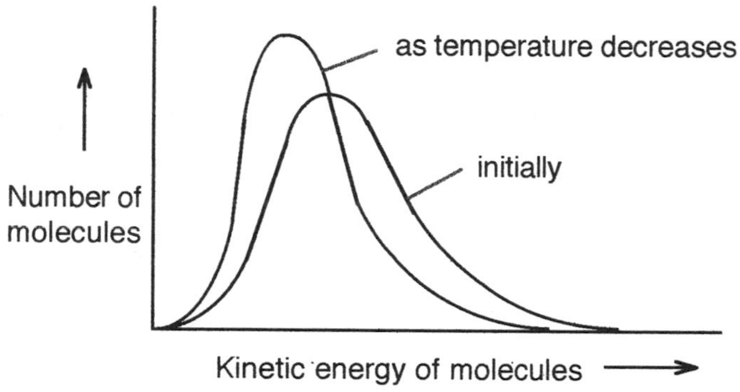

(c) No effect. Increasing the surface area has no effect on the energies of the molecules; it just makes more molecules available for reaction.

(d) The overall height of the curve is proportionally larger (a greater concentration of reactants means there will be more molecules at all energies), but the peak is still at the same KE value.

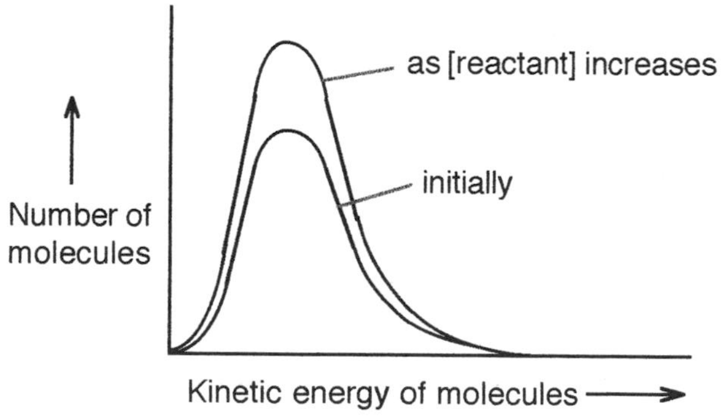

31. Since the rate doubles for every 10°C temperature increase, and since the final temperature is 20°C higher than the original temperature, there are TWO doublings of the rate and the new rate will be:

$$2 \times 2 \times 1.0 \times 10^{-7}\ \text{mol/s} = 4.0 \times 10^{-7}\ \text{mol/s}.$$

32. Since the temperature has been raised by 30°C, the new rate will be:
$2 \times 2 \times 2 \times 2.0 \times 10^{-4}$ mol/s = 1.6×10^{-3} mol/s.

33. The activation energy for the reaction is very large, so that the rate is impossibly slow (luckily).

34. (a)

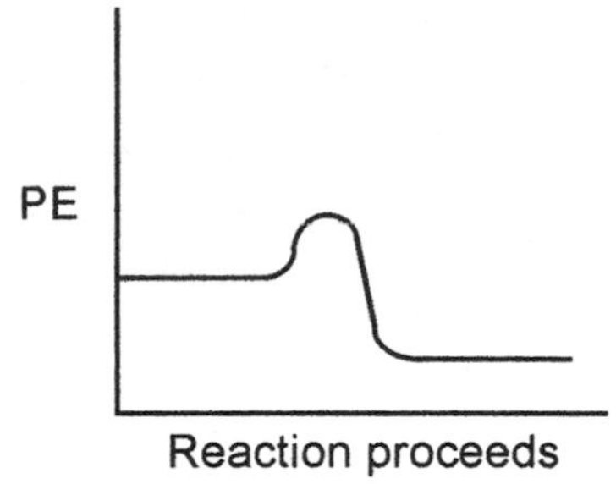

(b)

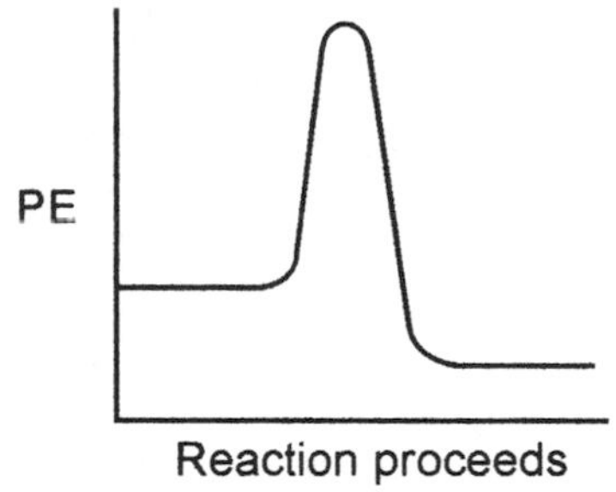

(c)

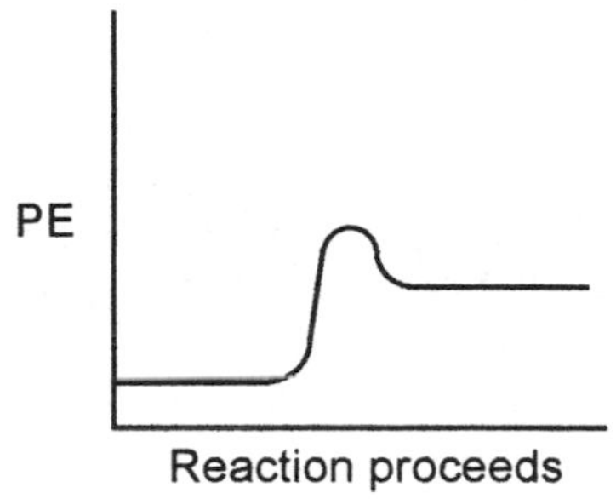

(d)

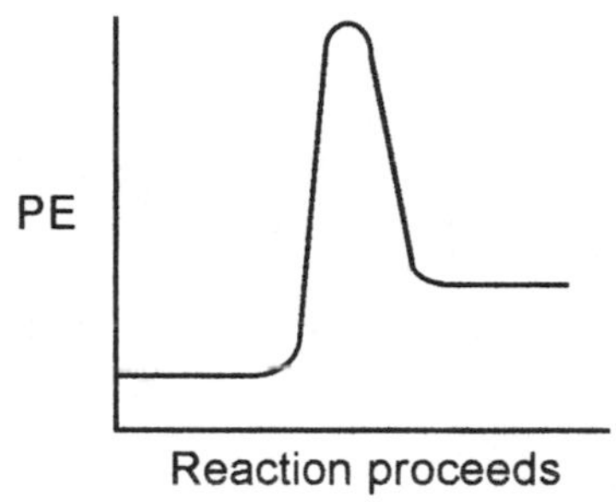

(e) The smaller the hill, the more molecules will have sufficient energy to get over the hill.

35. Not necessarily. Although sufficient KE is available, a favourable geometry is also required.

36. (a) (i) KE decreases: the repulsion of their outer electrons slows down their approach to each other.
(ii) PE increases: the KE lost is gained as PE.
(b) $(KE + PE)_{BEFORE} = (KE + PE)_{AFTER}$; that is, the total energy before equals the total energy after

37. (a) The activation energy would be increased.
(b) The formation of a bond results in the decrease of PE.
(c) exothermic
(d) $A_2 + B_2 \longrightarrow 2\,AB + 70$ kJ
(e) 120 – 80 = 40 kJ

38. The activation energy for the reaction involving F_2 will be less than that for the reaction involving I_2. Because I_2 has more electrons than F_2, it experiences more repulsion from the electrons on the approaching H_2. Overcoming this greater repulsion requires a greater input of energy.

39. The reaction has a very large activation energy.

40. The kinetic energy decreases when the potential energy increases, and vice versa. Therefore, since the products have less KE then they must also possess more PE and this reaction is endothermic.

41. 55 kJ

42. endothermic (ΔH = +25 kJ)

43.

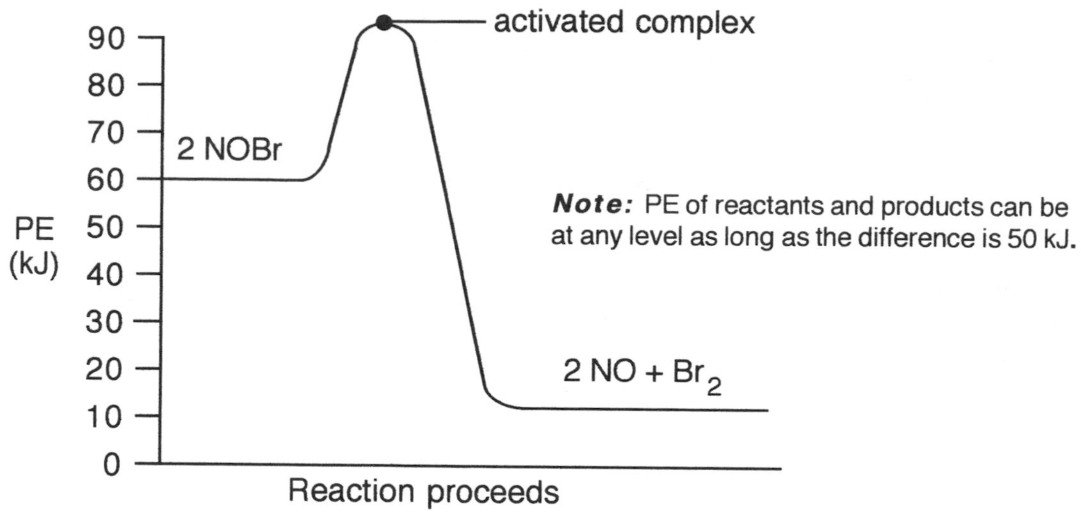

44.

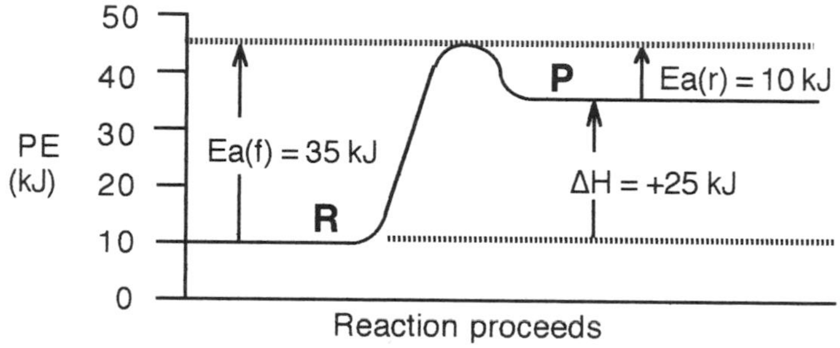

45.

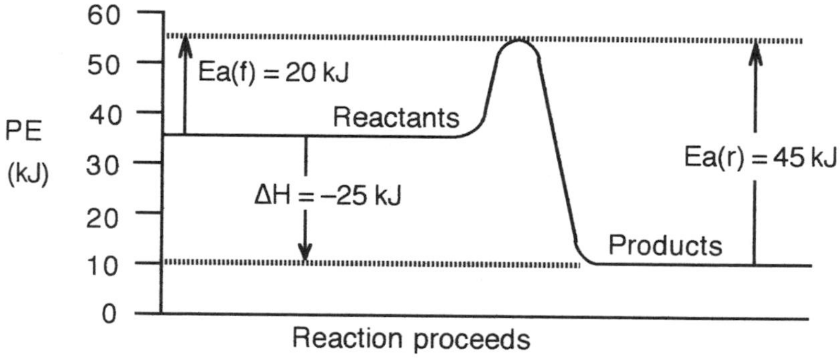

46. (a) $2\,NO + 2\,H_2 \longrightarrow N_2 + 2\,H_2O$
 (b) $[H_2O_2]$ will remain small (H_2O_2 is used up as fast as it is made)
 (c) Step 1 is rate–determining
 (d) NO is used in the rate–determining step and therefore the overall rate would increase.
 (e) Little or no effect: speeding up a step which is not rate–determining will have little effect on the rate of the overall reaction.
 (f) First step = $H_2N_2O_2$; Second step = H_4O_2 (The formulae are found by simply adding up every atom and charge found in the reactants for the step.)
 (g) 2 (there are 2 steps in the mechanism)

47. An ***activated complex*** is a short–lived, unstable species which only exists after the reactants have received an energy equal to the activation energy.

A ***reaction intermediate*** is an ordinary chemical species which is produced during one step of a reaction and used up in a subsequent step of the reaction.

48. The concentration of B would increase very quickly, and then slowly decrease as the slow second reaction steadily uses the B.

49. A reaction mechanism is the detailed sequence of actual steps in a reaction. If this reaction is a reaction mechanism, then it is a one–step reaction involving 18 molecules colliding simultaneously. Such a mechanism step is virtually impossible.

50. (a) $3\,ClO^- \longrightarrow ClO_3^- + 2\,Cl^-$ (b) reaction intermediate (c) $Cl_2O_3^{2-}$

51. (a) There are several ways to think of the process used to find the answer. Essentially, you have to see that:

FIRST EQUATION + SECOND EQUATION = OVERALL EQUATION

which rearranges to:

FIRST EQUATION = OVERALL EQUATION – SECOND EQUATION .

But, subtracting a chemical reaction equation is equivalent to interchanging the chemicals on the reactant and product sides, adding the resulting reversed equation and cancelling species which appear on opposite sides of the equations being added.

Therefore:

$2\,(CH_3)_2CO \longrightarrow \cancel{C_2H_4} + \cancel{2\,CO} + 2\,CH_4$ (overall equation)

$\cancel{C_2H_4} + \cancel{2\,CO} \longrightarrow 2\,CH_2CO$ (add the reverse of 2nd equation)

$2\,(CH_3)_2CO \longrightarrow 2\,CH_4 + 2\,CH_2CO$ (equals the 1st equation)

(b) First step = $C_6H_{12}O_2$; second step = $C_4H_4O_2$

52. (a) $\cancel{2\,NO} + O_2 \longrightarrow \cancel{2\,NO_2}$ (overall equation)

$N_2O_2 \longrightarrow \cancel{2\,NO}$ (add the reverse of 1st equation)

$\cancel{2\,NO_2} \longrightarrow N_2O_4$ (add the reverse of 3rd equation)

$O_2 + N_2O_2 \longrightarrow N_2O_4$ (equals the 2nd equation)

(b) N_2O_4

53. (a) The Cl produced in step 3 can be used to react with another H_2 so that step 2 can occur again after step 3.
(b) The light supplies the required activation energy to break the Cl–Cl bond in Cl_2.
(c) Since the sequence of steps is: 1, 2, 3, 2, 3, 2, 3, 2, . . . it appears that there is an almost endless "chain" of steps 2 & 3 linked ("chained") together.

54. Step 1 has the greatest activation energy; step 2 has the least.

55. (a) 3 steps (b) endothermic (c) endothermic

56. (a) (i) catalyst = H^+ (ii) reaction intermediate = $CH_3{-}CH_2^+$
(iii) overall reaction: $CH_2{=}CH_2 + H_2O \longrightarrow CH_3{-}CH_2{-}OH$
(b) (i) catalyst is D (ii) reaction intermediates = C and E
(iii) overall reaction: $A + 2\,B \longrightarrow 2\,F$
(c) (i) catalyst = CH_3COO^- (ii) reaction intermediates = CH_3COOH, $NHNO_2^-$ and OH^-
(iii) overall reaction: $NH_2NO_2 \longrightarrow N_2O + H_2O$

(d) (i) catalyst = Pt (ii) reaction intermediates = PtC_2H_2 and PtC_2H_4
(iii) overall reaction: $C_2H_2 + 2\,H_2 \longrightarrow C_2H_6$
(e) (i) catalyst = C (ii) reaction intermediates = B, D and G
(iii) overall reaction: $A + F \longrightarrow E + H$

57. If a catalyst is used up in one step and regenerated in a subsequent step, then obviously there is more than one step.

58. The reaction will not stop completely, but the rate of the reaction will be much less. Catalysts speed up reactions; they do not necessarily make impossible reactions occur.

59. A catalyst only decreases the activation energy; the energies of the reactants and products are not changed. Hence, ΔH can't be changed and exothermic reactions remain exothermic while endothermic reactions remain endothermic.

60. Step 1 is already very fast, so that adding a catalyst to speed it up has little or no effect on the overall reaction rate. The overall rate is controlled by the rate–determining step 3; a catalyst for this step would have a significant effect on the overall rate.

61. No change in rate. Since the original reaction mechanism has a lower activation energy, the vast majority of reacting particle will continue to take the previous, lower–energy route.

62. (a) Overall reaction: $O_3 + O \longrightarrow 2\,O_2$
(b) reaction intermediate = ClO, catalyst = Cl
(c) The chlorine atoms act as catalysts, are regenerated in the second step of the mechanism, and are available to react again. A single chlorine atom can therefore destroy large numbers of ozone molecules and only a small number of chlorine atoms need to be present in order to destroy a substantial amount of ozone.
(d) Ozone molecules absorb ultraviolet light ($h\nu$), as shown in reaction (3) of the problem statement. Since Cl atoms destroy ozone, the lowered concentration of ozone allows more ultraviolet light to reach the Earth's surface.

63. (a) Overall reaction: $CH_3OH + CH_3COOH \longrightarrow CH_3COOCH_3 + H_2O$
(b) The H^+ is consumed in the first step and regenerated in the last step.
(c) The H^+ used in the first step eventually ends up as part of a water molecule in the second step so that the water would be radioactive but the CH_3COOCH_3 would not.

ANSWERS TO UNIT II : EQUILIBRIUM

1. (a) Wrap the container in insulation.
   (b) Wrap the container in aluminum foil or paint it with black paint.
   (c) Put the system in an airtight container.

2. (a) The colour does not change, so $NO_2(g)$ is being made at the same rate that it is destroyed.
   (b) Temperature CAN affect an equilibrium – the colour became lighter or darker when the temperature was changed, meaning more or less $NO_2(g)$ was present.
   (c) The colour does not change while the tube full of gas remains at a constant 100°C. The colour would become very dark red–brown if the temperature were raised above 100°C.
   (d) The reaction is endothermic as written: $N_2O_4(g) + \text{energy} \rightleftharpoons 2\ NO_2(g)$. As heat is added the forward reaction should occur to a greater extent and produce more of the red–brown $NO_2(g)$, which is exactly what occurred.
   (e) $N_2O_4(g)$ predominated at low temperatures (colourless).
   $NO_2(g)$ predominated at high temperatures (dark red–brown).
   At room temperature the content of the tube was a mixture of $N_2O_4(g)$ and $NO_2(g)$.
   (f) The tubes should become the same colour. A tube containing mostly $N_2O_4(g)$ at low temperatures and another tube containing mostly $NO_2(g)$ at high temperatures eventually became the same colour at room temperature.

3. The system is NOT at equilibrium because the system is OPEN. Gas is steadily escaping from the liquid but no gas is going back into the liquid.

4. Water is evaporating inside the flask, but water vapour is re–entering the liquid phase at the same rate so that the system is at equilibrium.

5. The reaction will not make pure $COCl_2(g)$ because there will always be some $CO(g)$ and $Cl_2(g)$ in equilibrium with the $COCl_2(g)$. If some pure $COCl_2(g)$ could be obtained, it would partly decompose into $CO(g)$ and $Cl_2(g)$ as equilibrium occurred.

6. (a), and 7(f)

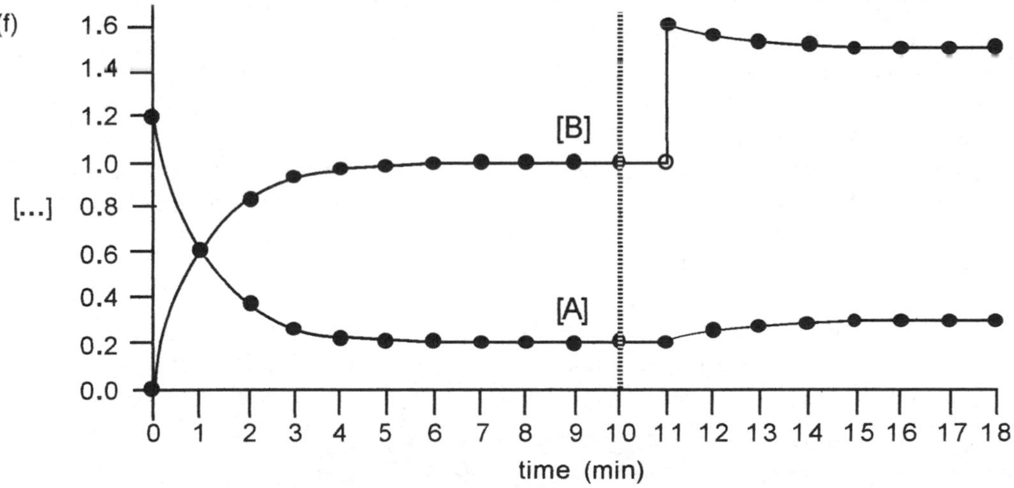

   (b) Equilibrium occurs by 9 min. At equilibrium the concentrations of both A and B remain constant. The forward and reverse rates remain constant and the forward rate equals the reverse rate.
   (c) After 1 minute, [A] = [B]; that is, [REACTANT] = [PRODUCT]. However, even though the reaction equation shows that one molecule of A produces one molecule of B, it is not required (and it is not true) that [REACTANT] = [PRODUCT] at equilibrium (although it is remotely possible).
   (d) Forward rate is greatest when [A] is greatest. As [A] decreases, so does forward rate.
   (e) $\text{Ratio} = \dfrac{1.000}{0.200} = 5.00$

7. (a) see 6(a), above
   (b) Equilibrium is re–established by 17 min.
   (c) Ratio = $\frac{1.500}{0.300}$ = 5.00
   (d) The concentrations of A and B have changed. The forward and reverse rates have changed. The forward rate still equals the reverse rate. The concentrations and rates become constant, as before. The ratio of [PRODUCTS]/[REACTANTS] is constant. (Incidentally, notice that the ratio of $k_{forward}/k_{reverse}$ = 0.50/0.10 = 5.0 ... interesting, but not testable in Chem 12.)

8. The ratio will not necessarily be 3:1. (Recall Exercise 6(c).)

9. The forward and reverse rates must be constant.
   The concentrations of reactants and products must be constant.
   The forward and reverse rates must be equal (that is, the rate at which reactants are used must equal the rate at which reactants are produced).

10. Equilibrium does not exist. The ratio of moles oxygen **reacting** to moles ozone **reacting** is 1:1, but should be 3:2 according to the coefficients of the equilibrium equation.

11. The mixture IS at equilibrium. At equilibrium 2 mol of NOCl must be involved in the forward reaction for every 2 mol of NO ***and*** 1 mol of Cl_2 which are involved in the reverse reaction. That is, 2 mol of NOCl must react for every 3 mol of products which react.

12.

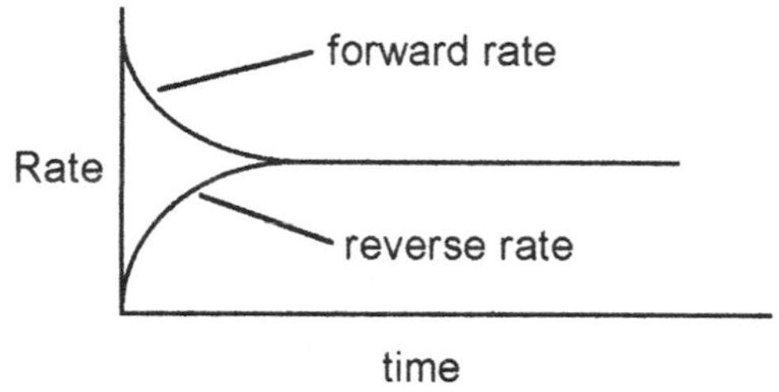

13. The forward and reverse reactions occur at the same rate, using up the N_2 as fast as it is made.

14. (a) $H_2O(g)$ (b) $Cl_2(g)$ (c) $NH_3(aq)$ (d) $CH_3COO^-(aq) + H^+(aq)$

15. (a) minimum enthalpy favours PRODUCTS
   maximum entropy favours PRODUCTS
   reaction GOES 100%
   (b) minimum enthalpy favours REACTANTS
   maximum entropy favours REACTANTS
   reaction WON'T OCCUR
   (c) minimum enthalpy favours PRODUCTS
   maximum entropy favours REACTANTS
   reaction is an EQUILIBRIUM
   (d) minimum enthalpy favours REACTANTS
   maximum entropy favours PRODUCTS
   reaction is an EQUILIBRIUM
   (e) minimum enthalpy favours PRODUCTS
   maximum entropy favours PRODUCTS
   reaction GOES 100%
   (f) minimum enthalpy favours REACTANTS
   maximum entropy favours PRODUCTS
   reaction is an EQUILIBRIUM
   (g) minimum enthalpy favours REACTANTS
   maximum entropy favours REACTANTS
   reaction WON'T OCCUR
   (h) minimum enthalpy favours PRODUCTS
   maximum entropy favours PRODUCTS
   reaction GOES 100%

16. (a) Maximum entropy favours PRODUCTS (liquid $\longrightarrow$ gases).
   Minimum enthalpy favours PRODUCTS (exothermic, explosion).
   (b) Maximum entropy must favour PRODUCTS: $AgBr(s) \longrightarrow Ag^+(aq) + Br^-(aq)$. Since the reaction has VERY LITTLE tendency to form products ("almost insoluble") a strong tendency to form REACTANTS must prevent AgBr from forming products. Hence, tendency to minimum enthalpy must strongly favour REACTANTS (ΔH must be large and positive).
   (c) Maximum entropy favours PRODUCTS: liquid + liquid $\longrightarrow$ mixture. Since the reaction GOES 100% ("mix completely in all proportions") the tendency to minimum enthalpy favours PRODUCTS ($\Delta H < 0$).

(d) Maximum entropy favours REACTANTS (gas is the most random phase). Since the reaction DOES NOT OCCUR, then the tendency to minimum enthalpy must also favour REACTANTS ($\Delta H > 0$).

(e) Maximum entropy favours PRODUCTS: <u>1</u> $N_2O_4(g) \longrightarrow$ <u>**2**</u> $NO_2(g)$. Since equilibrium occurs ("**some** of it decomposes") one tendency must oppose the tendency to products by maximum entropy, so that minimum enthalpy favours REACTANTS ($\Delta H > 0$).

(f) Maximum entropy favours REACTANTS: smoke + $CO_2(g)$ + $H_2O(g) \longrightarrow$ solid wood + $O_2(g)$. Since the reaction WON'T GO, the tendency to minimum enthalpy favours REACTANTS ($\Delta H > 0$).

17. (a) shift to reactant side (b) shift to product side (c) shift to reactant side (d) no shift

18. (a) shift to product side (b) shift to reactant side (c) shift to reactant side

19. (a) shift to reactant side (b) shift to product side (c) no shift

20. (a) shift to reactant side (c) no shift (same numbers of gas particles on both sides)
(b) shift to reactant side

21. (a) DEC (b) INC (c) INC (d) NC

22. (a) DEC (b) INC (c) NC, after the initial increase in all concentrations

23. (a) INC (b) NC (c) INC

24. (a)

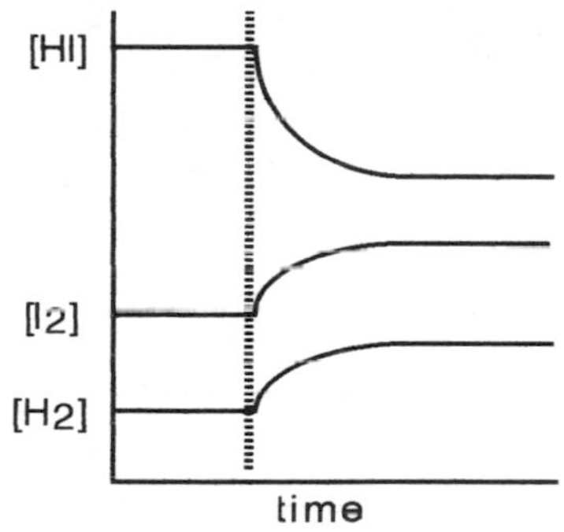

(b)

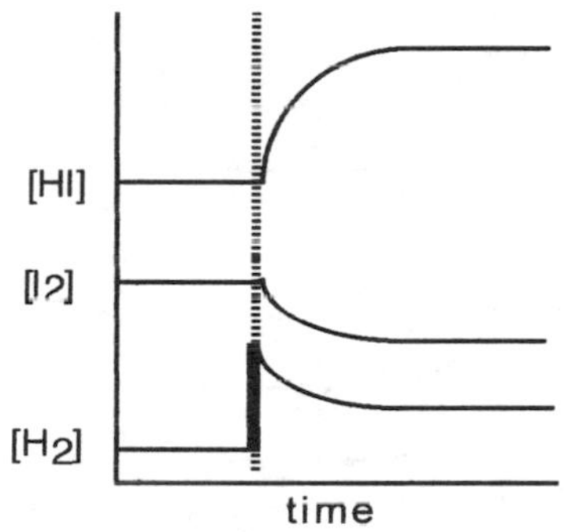

(c)

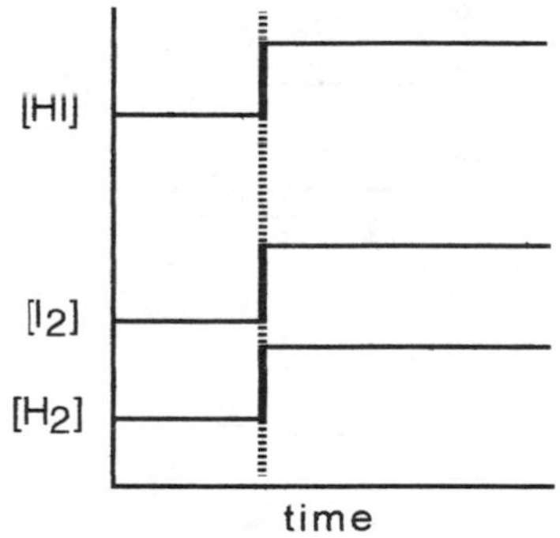

(d)

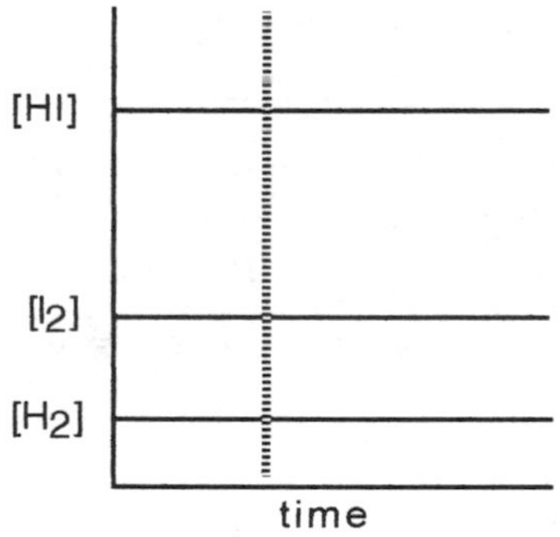

25. (a)

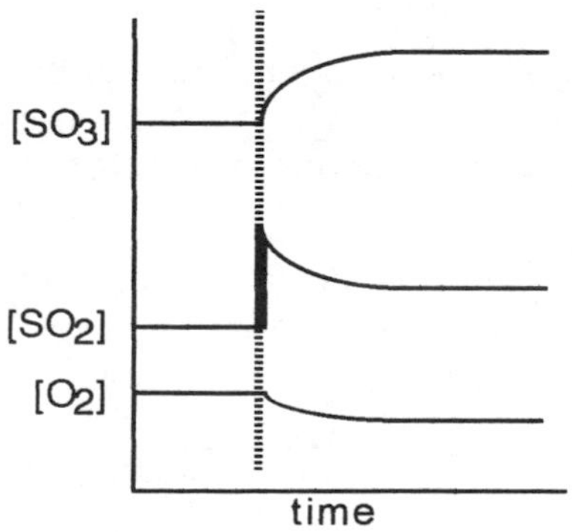

(b)

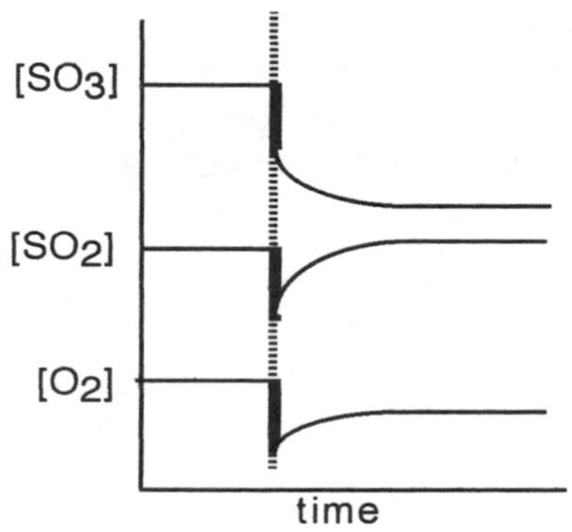

(c)

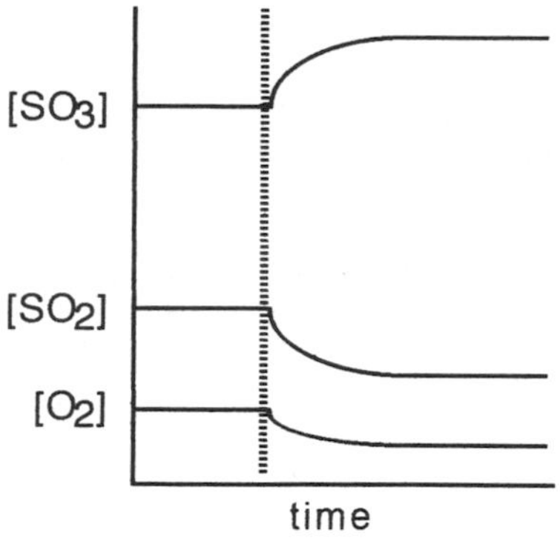

(d)

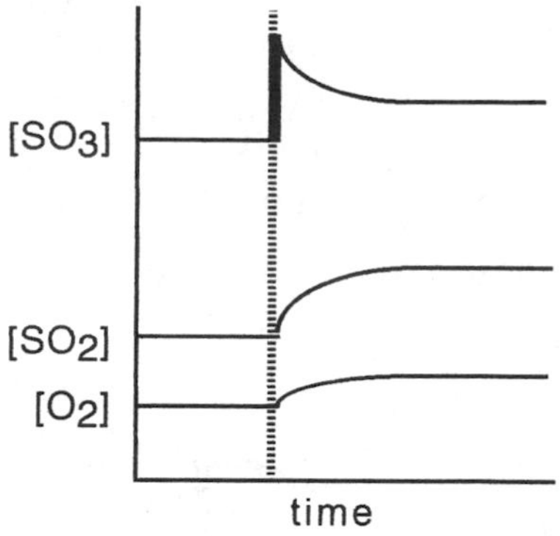

26. (a)

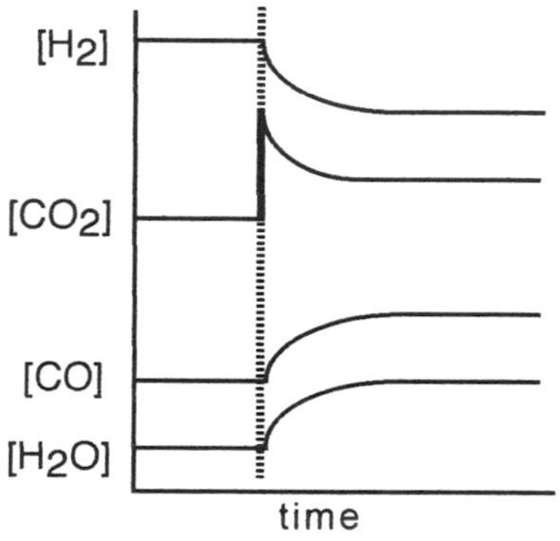

(b)

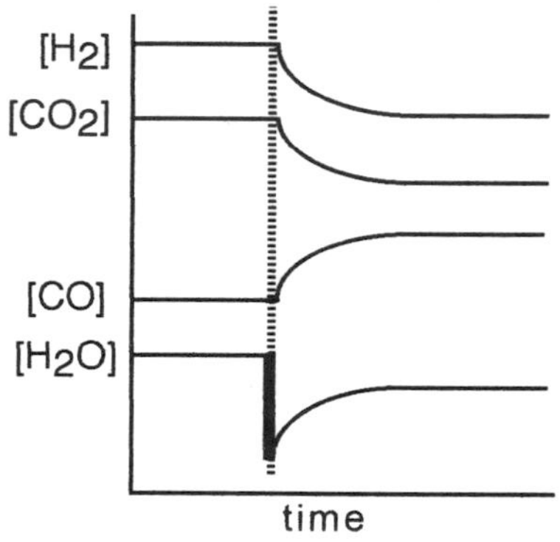

(c)

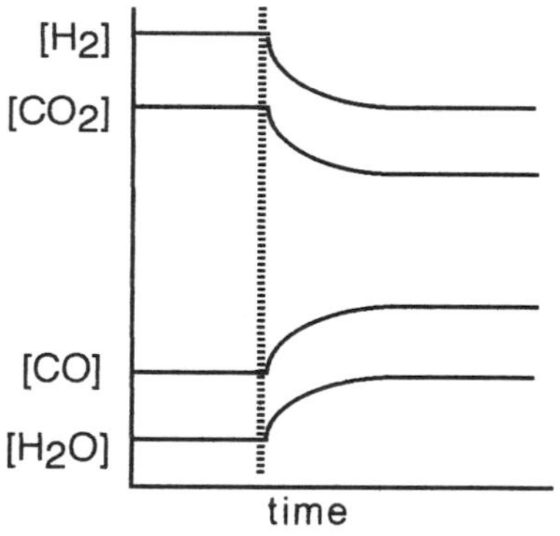

(d)

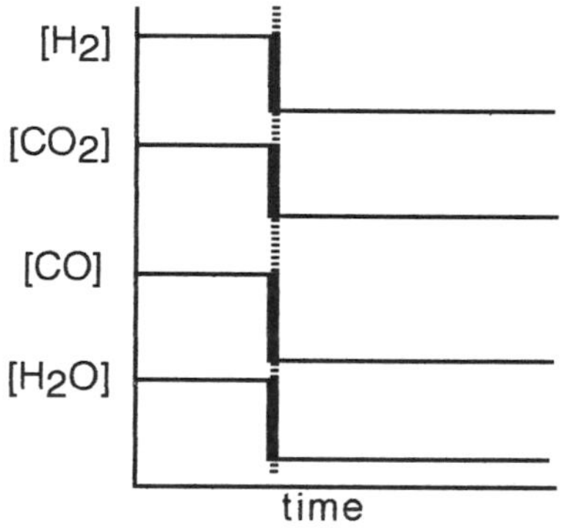

27. (a) temperature is decreased (b) some PCl_5 is injected

28. (a) pressure is decreased by increasing the volume (b) temperature is increased

29. (a) high pressure
(b) low temperature
(c) high temperature
(d) High temperature is needed to get a fast reaction (get to equilibrium quickly) but at high temperature the reaction gives little products at equilibrium. Choose an intermediate temperature: a somewhat slower reaction occurs but it gives an acceptable amount of product in return.
(e) add a catalyst

30. (a) high temperature
(b) low pressure. Let the $CO_2(g)$ produced escape to the atmosphere.
(c) high temperature (which agrees with the requirements for a large yield of CaO)

31. (a) $K_{eq} = \frac{[I_2(g)]\,[Cl_2(g)]}{[ICl(g)]^2}$

(b) $K_{eq} = \frac{[NO(g)]^2}{[N_2(g)]\,[O_2(g)]}$

(c) $K_{eq} = \frac{[O_3(g)]^2}{[O_2(g)]^3}$

(d) $K_{eq} = \frac{[H^+(aq)]^6}{[Bi^{3+}(aq)]^2\,[H_2S(g)]^3}$

(e) $K_{eq} = [CO_2(g)] = \text{constant}$

(f) $K_{eq} = [C_2H_2(g)] = \text{constant}$

(g) $K_{eq} = \frac{[C_6H_5Br(l)]\,[HBr(g)]}{[C_6H_6(l)]\,[Br_2(l)]}$

(h) $K_{eq} = \frac{[Cu^{2+}(aq)]}{[Ag^+(aq)]^2}$

(i) $K_{eq} = \frac{[H_2O(g)]^6\,[NO(g)]^4}{[NH_3(g)]^4\,[O_2(g)]^5}$

(j) $K_{eq} = \frac{1}{[H_2(g)]\,[O_2(g)]^{1/2}}$

32. (a) $K_{eq} = \frac{[NO_2]^2}{[N_2O_4]}$ (b) $K_{eq} = \frac{[N_2O_4]}{[NO_2]^2}$

The K_{eq} expression in (a) is the inverse of the K_{eq} expression in (b).

If $K_{eq} = 10.0$ for equation (a), then $K_{eq} = 1/10.0 = 0.100$ for equation (b).

CONCLUSION: Reversing a reaction means the value of K_{eq} for the new reaction is the inverse of K_{eq} for the old reaction.

33. (a) $K_{eq} = \frac{[SO_3]}{[SO_2]\,[O_2]^{1/2}}$ (b) $K_{eq} = \frac{[SO_3]^2}{[SO_2]^2\,[O_2]}$

When equation (a) is doubled to get equation (b), the coefficients are doubled in front of each species in reaction (a). But when the equilibrium expression is written the coefficients become powers. Therefore, doubling the powers in the equilibrium expression means the equilibrium expression is SQUARED.

If $K_{eq} = 3$ for equation (a), then $K_{eq} = (3)^2 = 9$ for equation (b).

CONCLUSION: Doubling a reaction means the value of K_{eq} for the new reaction is the square of K_{eq} for the old reaction.

34. (a) to products (b) no shift; a solid was added (c) to products (d) to reactants

35. (a) $[H_3O^+] = \frac{K_{eq}\,[HF]}{[F^-]}$

(b) $[HF] = \frac{[H_3O^+][F^-]}{K_{eq}}$

(c) $[NO_2] = (K_{eq})^{1/2}[NO]\,[O_2]^{1/2}$

(d) $[NO] = \frac{[NO_2]}{(K_{eq})^{1/2}\,[O_2]^{1/2}}$

(e) $[H_2] = \frac{[NH_3]^{2/3}}{(K_{eq})^{1/3}\,[N_2]^{1/3}}$

(f) $[NO_2] = \frac{[N_2O_4]^{1/2}}{(K_{eq})^{1/2}}$

(g) $[NH_3] = (K_{eq})^{1/2}\,[N_2]^{1/2}[H_2]^{3/2}$

(h) $[Cl_2] = \frac{[PCl_3]^{2/3}}{(K_{eq})^{1/6}\,[P_4]^{1/6}}$

36. (a) iii (b) ii

37. decreases

38. endothermic

39. decreases

40. no change; K_{eq} is only affected by temperature changes

41. exothermic

42.

	(a)	(b)	(c)	(d)
21	NC	DEC	NC	NC
22	DEC	NC	NC	
23	INC	NC	NC	NC

43. (a) NC (but more **solid** Sn is formed) ; K_{eq} = INC
(b) NC ; K_{eq} = NC
(c) NC (but more **solid** Sn) ; K_{eq} = NC
(d) NC ; K_{eq} = NC

44. (i) equilibrium shifts to reactants; K_{eq} is not changed
(ii) equilibrium shifts to reactants; K_{eq} is decreased
(iii) equilibrium is unaffected by adding a solid; K_{eq} is not changed

45. Exothermic. Increasing temperature decreases K_{eq}, and since K_{eq} = [Products]/[Reactants] then the concentration of products decreases as the temperature increases. This means heat is on the product side: increasing the temperature shifts the reaction to the reactant side by Le Chatelier's principle.

46. As the temperature is increased, the $[O_2]$ (the reactant) decreases. Hence, heat is on the reactant side and the reaction must be ENDOTHERMIC.

47.

	CO	+	H_2O	$\rightleftharpoons$	CO_2	+	H_2
START	0.750		0.275		0		0
+Δ	−0.250		−0.250		+0.250		+0.250
= EQUIL	0.500		0.025		0.250		0.250

$$K_{eq} = \frac{[CO_2][H_2]}{[CO][H_2O]} = \frac{(0.250)(0.250)}{(0.500)(0.025)} = \mathbf{5.0}$$

48.

	SO_2	+	NO_2	$\rightleftharpoons$	SO_3	+	NO
START	1.2		0.50		0.20		0
+Δ	−0.40		−0.40		+0.40		+0.40
= EQUIL	0.80		0.10		0.60		0.40

$$K_{eq} = \frac{[SO_3][NO]}{[SO_2][NO_2]} = \frac{(0.60)(0.40)}{(0.80)(0.10)} = \mathbf{3.0}$$

49. (a)

	N_2	+	$3\,H_2$	$\rightleftharpoons$	$2\,NH_3$
START	0.60		0.40		0
+Δ	−0.010		−0.030		+0.020
= EQUIL	0.59		0.37		0.020

$$K_{eq} = \frac{[NH_3]^2}{[N_2][H_2]^3} = \frac{(0.020)^2}{(0.59)(0.37)^3} = \mathbf{0.013}$$

(b)

	N_2	+	$3\,H_2$	$\rightleftharpoons$	$2\,NH_3$
START	0		0		0.60
+Δ	+0.20		+0.60		−0.40
= EQUIL	0.20		0.60		0.20

$$K_{eq} = \frac{[NH_3]^2}{[N_2][H_2]^3} = \frac{(0.20)^2}{(0.20)(0.60)^3} = \mathbf{0.93}$$

50. (a) $Q = \frac{[H_2][F_2]}{[HF]^2} = \frac{(0.40)(0.80)}{(0.60)^2} = 0.89 = \frac{[\text{PRODUCTS}]\uparrow}{[\text{REACTANTS}]} < K_{eq} = 4$

The reaction shifts to the PRODUCT side to bring the value of Q up to that of K_{eq}.

(b) $Q = \dfrac{(0.10)(0.12)}{(0.040)^2} = 7.5 = \dfrac{[\text{PRODUCTS}]}{[\text{REACTANTS}]} \downarrow > K_{eq} = 4$

The reaction shifts to the REACTANT side to bring the value of Q down to that of K_{eq}.

(c) $Q = \dfrac{(0.36)(0.040)}{(0.060)^2} = 4 = K_{eq}$ There will be no shift since the reaction is at equilibrium.

51. (a) $Q = \dfrac{[O_2]^3}{[O_3]^2} = \dfrac{(0.30)^3}{(0.060)^2} = 7.5 = \dfrac{[\text{PRODUCTS}]}{[\text{REACTANTS}]} \uparrow < K_{eq} = 75$

The reaction shifts to the PRODUCT side to bring the value of Q up to that of K_{eq}.

(b) $Q = \dfrac{(0.70)^3}{(0.0050)^2} = 1.4 \times 10^4 = \dfrac{[\text{PRODUCTS}]}{[\text{REACTANTS}]} \downarrow > K_{eq} = 75$

The reaction shifts to the REACTANT side to bring the value of Q down to that of K_{eq}.

(c) The reaction will have to shift to PRODUCTS side in order to have some of both reactants and products at equilibrium.

52.

	$2\,SO_2$ +	O_2 $\rightleftharpoons$	$2\,SO_3$
START	0	0	X
+Δ	+0.30	+0.15	−0.30
= EQUIL	0.30	0.15	X − 0.30

$K_{eq} = 5.0 = \dfrac{[SO_3]^2}{[SO_2]^2[O_2]} = \dfrac{(X-0.30)^2}{(0.30)^2(0.15)}$ which solves to give: $X = [SO_3] =$ **0.56 M.**

53. There is no sense of time passing, so the available values are put directly into the equilibrium expression.

$K_{eq} = 35.0 = \dfrac{[PCl_3][Cl_2]}{[PCl_5]} = \dfrac{(0.205)[Cl_2]}{1.34 \times 10^{-3}}$, which solves to give: $[Cl_2] =$ **0.229 M.**

54. $Q = \dfrac{[HI]^2}{[H_2][I_2]} = \dfrac{(0.015)^2}{(0.0034)(0.0096)} = 6.9 = \dfrac{[\text{PRODUCTS}]}{[\text{REACTANTS}]} \uparrow < K_{eq} = 125$

The reaction shifts to the PRODUCT side to bring the value of Q up to that of K_{eq}.

55. First calculate the value of K_{eq} from the initial equilibrium conditions.

$K_{eq} = \dfrac{[CO_2][H_2]}{[CO][H_2O]} = \dfrac{(1.00)(0.500)}{(1.00)(1.00)} = 0.500$

Starting with the given equilibrium concentrations, alter the initial set of conditions by adding an extra 1.00 mol of H_2. The change in concentrations is the unknown, and since the equilibrium is upset by adding extra H_2, the products side will lose a concentration "X" and the reactants side will gain the same amount.

	CO +	H_2O $\rightleftharpoons$	CO_2 +	H_2
START	1.00	1.00	1.00	0.500 + 0.500
+ Δ	+X	+X	−X	−X
= EQUIL	1.00 + X	1.00 + X	1.00 − X	1.000 − X

$K_{eq} = 0.500 = \dfrac{(1.00-X)^2}{(1.00+X)^2}$. Take the square root of both sides.

$0.7071 = \dfrac{1.00 - X}{1.00 + X}$, and solving: $X = 0.172$, so that $[CO] = 1.00 + X =$ **1.17 M.**

56. $K_{eq} = \frac{[Cd^{2+}]}{[Tl^{+}]^2} = \frac{0.414}{(0.316)^2} = 4.15$ (from the first data set)

The $[Cd^{2+}]$ is found using the second data set: $[Cd^{2+}] = 0.339$ mol/5.00 L = 0.0678 M.

Now: $K_{eq} = 4.15 = \frac{[Cd^{2+}]}{[Tl^{+}]^2} = \frac{0.0678}{[Tl^{+}]^2}$

Solving: $[Tl^{+}] = 0.128$ M and # of moles = $0.128 \frac{mol}{L} \times 5.00\ L =$ **0.639 mol.**

57.

	$2\ NOCl$	$\rightleftharpoons$	$2\ NO$	+	Cl_2
START	0.50		0		0
+ Δ	−0.20		+0.20		+0.10
= EQUIL	0.30		0.20		0.10

$K_{eq} = \frac{[NO]^2[Cl_2]}{[NOCl]^2} = \frac{(0.20)^2(0.10)}{(0.30)^2} = \mathbf{0.044}$

58.

	$2\ H_2$	+	S_2	$\rightleftharpoons$	$2\ H_2S$
START	0		0		X
+ Δ	+0.036		+0.018		−0.036
= EQUIL	0.036		0.018		X − 0.036

$K_{eq} = 7.5 = \frac{[H_2S]^2}{[H_2]^2[S_2]} = \frac{(X - 0.036)^2}{(0.036)^2(0.018)}$. Solving: $X = 0.049\ M = [H_2S]$

and moles $H_2S = 0.049 \frac{mol}{L} \times 2.0\ L =$ **0.098 mol.**

59. First find K_{eq} from the initial equilibrium conditions:

$K_{eq} = \frac{[CO][H_2O]}{[CO_2][H_2]} = \frac{(0.60)(0.50)}{(0.80)(0.30)} = 1.25$

Next alter the initial conditions by removing CO_2. The equilibrium [CO] will be 2.50 mol/5.0 L = 0.50 M.

	CO_2	+	H_2	$\rightleftharpoons$	CO	+	H_2O
START	0.80 − X		0.30		0.60		0.50
+ Δ	+0.10		+0.10		−0.10		−0.10
= EQUIL	0.90 − X		0.40		0.50		0.40

Now $K_{eq} = 1.25 = \frac{(0.50)(0.40)}{(0.90 - X)(0.40)}$; Solving: X = 0.50 M = concentration of CO_2 removed

moles of CO_2 removed $= 0.50 \frac{mol}{L} \times 5.0\ L =$ **2.5 mol.**

60.

	H_2	+	I_2	$\rightleftharpoons$	2 HI
START	0.0250		0.0250		0
+ Δ	–X		–X		+2X
= EQUIL	0.0250 – X		0.0250 – X		2X

$K_{eq} = 49.5 = \frac{[HI]^2}{[H_2][I_2]} = \frac{(2X)^2}{(0.0250 - X)^2}$ and taking the square root: $7.036 = \frac{2X}{0.0250 - X}$

which gives X = 0.0195 M and [HI] = 2X = **0.0389 M**, $[H_2] = [I_2] = 0.0250 - X =$ **0.0055 M.**

61.

	N_2	+	$3\ H_2$	$\rightleftharpoons$	$2\ NH_3$
START	0		0		X
+ Δ	+0.50		+1.50		–1.0
= EQUIL	0.50		1.50		X – 1.0

$K_{eq} = 3.0 = \frac{[NH_3]^2}{[N_2][H_2]^3} = \frac{(X - 1.0)^2}{(0.50)(1.5)^3}$, which gives: $X = 3.25\ M = [NH_3]_{START}$

and moles NH_3 added $= 3.25\ \frac{mol}{L} \times 5.0\ L =$ **16 mol.**

62.

	N_2O_2	+	H_2	$\rightleftharpoons$	N_2O	+	H_2O
START	0		0		0.150		0.250
+ Δ	+X		+X		–X		–X
= EQUIL	X		X		0.150 – X		0.250 – X

$K_{eq} = 1.00 = \frac{[N_2O][H_2O]}{[N_2O_2][H_2]} = \frac{(0.150 - X)(0.250 - X)}{X^2}$

Expanding: $X^2 = 0.0375 - 0.400\ X + X^2$, and: $X = [N_2O_2] =$ **0.0938 M.**

63. First find the value of K_{eq} for the initial equilibrium conditions: $K_{eq} = \frac{[HI]^2}{[H_2][I_2]} = \frac{(0.0870)^2}{(0.0150)^2} = 33.64$

Now let the initial set of conditions be altered by the added HI. According to Le Chatelier's Principle, the addition of HI will cause the equilibrium to shift so as to use up some of the added HI.

	H_2	+	I_2	$\rightleftharpoons$	2 HI
START	0.0150		0.0150		0.0870 + 0.0400
+ Δ	+X		+X		–2X
= EQUIL	0.0150 + X		0.0150 + X		0.1270 – 2X

Now $K_{eq} = 33.64 = \frac{(0.1270 - 2X)^2}{(0.0150 + X)^2}$, and taking the square root:

$5.80 = \frac{0.1270 - 2X}{0.0150 + X}$. Solving: X = 0.005128

and $[H_2] = [I_2] = 0.0150 + X =$ **0.0201 M**, $[HI] = 0.1270 - 2X =$ **0.1167 M** .

64. First find the value of K_{eq} from the initial equilibrium conditions.

$$K_{eq} = \frac{[NO_2]^2}{[NO]^2[O_2]} = \frac{(0.600)^2}{(0.120)^2(0.0430)} = 581.4$$

Now let the initial set of conditions be altered by adding O_2.
The $[NO_2]$ at equilibrium will be 1.28 mol/2.0 L = 0.64 M.

	2 NO	+	O_2	⇌	2 NO_2
START	0.120		0.0430 + X		0.600
+ Δ	−0.040		−0.020		+0.040
= EQUIL	0.080		0.023 + X		0.640

And: $K_{eq} = 581.4 = \frac{(0.640)^2}{(0.080)^2(0.023 + X)}$

Solving: X = 0.0871 M , and moles O_2 added = 0.0871 $\frac{mol}{L}$ x 2.00 L = **0.174 mol.**

65. First calculate the value of K_{eq} from the initial equilibrium conditions.

$$K_{eq} = \frac{[I_2][HCl]^2}{[ICl]^2[H_2]} = \frac{(1.36)(0.800)^2}{(0.500)^2(0.0560)} = 62.17$$

Now let the initial set of conditions be altered by removing ICl. The [HCl] at equilibrium is 0.680 M.

	2 ICl	+	H_2	⇌	I_2	+	2 HCl
START	0.500 − X		0.0560		1.36		0.800
+ Δ	+0.120		+0.060		−0.060		−0.120
= EQUIL	0.620 − X		0.116		1.30		0.680

And $K_{eq} = 62.17 = \frac{(1.300)(0.680)^2}{(0.620 - X)^2(0.116)}$, which rearranges to:

$(0.620 - X)^2 = \frac{(1.300)(0.680)^2}{(62.17)(0.116)} = 0.08335$. Taking the square root & solving: X = 0.331 M

and: moles ICl removed = 0.331 $\frac{mol}{L}$ x 1.00 L = **0.331 mol.**

66.

	CH_4 +	2 H_2S	⇌	CS_2 +	4 H_2
START	NOT NEEDED			0	0
+ Δ				+X	+4X
= EQUIL	0.10	0.30		X	4X

$$K_{eq} = 100 = \frac{[CS_2][H_2]^4}{[CH_4][H_2S]^2} = \frac{(X)(4X)^4}{(0.10)(0.30)^2} = \frac{256X^5}{0.0090}$$

rearranging: $X^5 = 0.00352$, and taking the fifth root: X = $[CS_2]$ = **0.32 M.**

ANSWERS TO UNIT III : SOLUBILITY EQUILIBRIUM

1. (a) ionic (b) molecular (c) ionic (d) ionic (e) molecular (f) ionic (g) ionic (h) molecular (i) ionic (j) molecular

2. (a) $(NH_4)_2SO_4(s) \longrightarrow 2\,NH_4^+(aq) + SO_4^{2-}(aq)$
   (b) $CH_3CH_2OH(l) \longrightarrow CH_3CH_2OH(aq)$
   (c) $K_2CO_3(s) \longrightarrow 2\,K^+(aq) + CO_3^{2-}(aq)$
   (d) $CaCl_2(s) \longrightarrow Ca^{2+}(aq) + 2\,Cl^-(aq)$

3. (a) $K_3PO_4(s) \rightleftharpoons 3\,K^+(aq) + PO_4^{3-}(aq)$
   (b) $NH_4Cl(s) \rightleftharpoons NH_4^+(aq) + Cl^-(aq)$
   (c) $Al(NO_3)_3(s) \rightleftharpoons Al^{3+}(aq) + 3\,NO_3^-(aq)$

4. $Mg^{2+}(aq) + 2\,Br^-(aq) \longrightarrow MgBr_2(s)$

5. $C_6H_{12}O_6(s) \longrightarrow C_6H_{12}O_6(aq)$

6. The solution is **not** saturated because no solid is present to establish equilibrium with the ions.

7. The student was incorrect; the time required to saturate a solution varies from a few minutes to a day or so, but is never immediate.

8. $\text{solubility} = 5.59\,\frac{\text{g}}{\text{L}} \times \frac{1\text{ mol}}{84.0\text{ g}} = \mathbf{6.65 \times 10^{-2}\ M}$

9. $\text{solubility} = \frac{0.99\text{ g}}{0.100\text{ L}} \times \frac{1\text{ mol}}{278.2\text{ g}} = \mathbf{3.6 \times 10^{-2}\ M}$

10. $\text{solubility} = 1.26 \times 10^{-3}\,\frac{\text{mol}}{\text{L}} \times \frac{84.3\text{ g}}{1\text{ mol}} = \mathbf{0.106\ g/L}$

11. $\text{solubility} = 1.2 \times 10^{-4}\,\frac{\text{mol}}{\text{L}} \times \frac{275.8\text{ g}}{1\text{ mol}} \times 0.100\text{ L} = \mathbf{3.3 \times 10^{-3}\ g}$ (in 100 mL)

12. $\text{solubility} = \frac{92.6\text{ g}}{0.150\text{ L}} \times \frac{1\text{ mol}}{100.0\text{ g}} = \mathbf{6.17\ M}$

13. $\text{mass } AgClO_2 = 0.014\,\frac{\text{mol}}{\text{L}} \times 0.0500\text{ L} \times \frac{175.4\text{ g}}{\text{mol}} = \mathbf{0.12\ g}$

14. $\text{mass } MnCl_2 = 5.75\,\frac{\text{mol}}{\text{L}} \times 0.125\text{ L} \times \frac{125.9\text{ g}}{1\text{ mol}} = \mathbf{90.5\ g}$

15. (a) 84.84 g − 54.87 g = 29.97 g
    (b) 62.59 g − 54.87 g = 7.72 g
    (c) Since "solution" = water + solid, then water = solution − solid
    mass of water = 29.97 g − 7.72 g = 22.25 g
    (d) $\frac{7.72\text{ g KCl}}{22.25\text{ g water}} = \frac{X\text{ g KCl}}{100.0\text{ g water}}$, and $X = \mathbf{34.7\ g}$
    (e) $\text{solubility} = \frac{7.72\text{ g}}{0.02500\text{ L}} \times \frac{1\text{ mol}}{74.6\text{ g}} = \mathbf{4.14\ M}$

16. (a) 147.42 g − 87.23 g = 60.19 g of solution
    (b) 104.08 g − 87.23 g = 16.85 g of $(NH_4)_2SO_4$
    (c) 60.19 g − 16.85 g = 43.34 g of water
    (d) $\frac{16.85\text{ g }(NH_4)_2SO_4}{43.34\text{ g water}} = \frac{X\text{ g }(NH_4)_2SO_4}{100.0\text{ g water}}$, and $X = \mathbf{38.88\ g}$
    (e) $[(NH_4)_2SO_4] = \frac{16.85\text{ g}}{0.0700\text{ L}} \times \frac{1\text{ mol}}{132.1\text{ g}} = \mathbf{1.82\ M}$

17. (a) LiCl
(b) The solution won't be saturated because at 90°C about 50 g of KCl dissolves in 100 g of water.
(c) As you heat the $Ca(CH_3COO)_2$ solution, more precipitate forms because the solubility decreases as temperature increases.
(d) Initially some of the $MgCl_2(s)$ dissolves. Then, as the temperature increases, more of the solid dissolves; by about 70°C the last of the solid dissolves.
(e) Initially all the solid is dissolved but as the temperature decreases to 10°C the KBr forms crystals first. As the temperature decreases, KBr's solubility starts at about 97 g at 90°C (unsaturated solution) but by about 75°C the solubility drops to about 90 g (saturated solution) and at temperatures lower than 75°C the solution deposits the excess KBr in the form of crystals.
(f) Since KCl has a lower solubility (about 30 g/100 g H_2O) than does KBr (about 60 g/100 g H_2O), the KCl solution becomes saturated first when the water evaporates and KCl forms crystals first.
(g) The solubility of LiCl increases with an increase in temperature. This implies the equation

$$LiCl(s) + heat \rightleftharpoons Li^+(aq) + Cl^-(aq)$$

shifts to the product side when temperature is increased and is ENDOTHERMIC.
(h) The dissolving of $Ca(CH_3COO)_2(s)$ is exothermic. As temperature is increased the solubility decreases, which implies that heat is on the product side of the dissolving reaction.

$$Ca(CH_3COO)_2(s) \rightleftharpoons Ca^{2+}(aq) + 2\,CH_3COO^-(aq) + heat$$

18. (a) $[Fe^{3+}] = 0.25\ M$, $[Cl^-] = 0.75\ M$
(b) $[Al^{3+}] = 3.0 \times 10^{-3}\ M$, $[SO_4^{2-}] = 4.5 \times 10^{-3}\ M$
(c) $[(NH_4)_2CO_3] = \frac{12.0\ g}{2.50\ L} \times \frac{1\ mol}{96.0\ g} = 0.0500\ M$, so $[NH_4^+] = 0.100\ M$ and $[CO_3^{2-}] = 0.0500\ M$
(d) $[Ca(OH)_2] = \frac{0.41\ g}{0.500\ L} \times \frac{1\ mol}{74.1\ g} = 0.011\ M$, so $[Ca^{2+}] = 0.011\ M$ and $[OH^-] = 0.022\ M$
(e) $[KBr] = \frac{2.50\ g}{0.150\ L} \times \frac{1\ mol}{119.0\ g} = 0.140\ M$, so $[K^+] = [Br^-] = 0.140\ M$

19. (a) $PbBr_2(s) \rightleftharpoons Pb^{2+}(aq) + 2\,Br^-(aq)$
(b) $[PbBr_2] = \frac{0.844\ g}{0.100\ L} \times \frac{1\ mol}{367.0\ g} = 2.30 \times 10^{-2}\ M$
(c) $[Pb^{2+}] = 2.30 \times 10^{-2}\ M$, $[Br^-] = 4.60 \times 10^{-2}\ M$

20. (a) $[Fe^{3+}] = 0.35\ M \times \frac{20.0\ mL}{45.0\ mL} = 0.16\ M$

(b) $[Ag^+] = 0.25\ M \times \frac{50.0\ mL}{150.0\ mL} = 0.083\ M$, $[NO_3^-] = 0.10\ M \times \frac{100.0\ mL}{150.0\ mL} = 0.067\ M$

(c) $[Cu^{2+}] = 6.5 \times 10^{-5}\ M \times \frac{15.0\ mL}{55.0\ mL} = 1.8 \times 10^{-5}\ M$

$[Cl^-] = 3.2 \times 10^{-3}\ M \times \frac{40.0\ mL}{55.0\ mL} = 2.3 \times 10^{-3}\ M$

(d) $[MgCl_2] = 0.185\ M \times \frac{55.0\ mL}{80.0\ mL} = 0.127\ M$, so $[Mg^{2+}] = 0.127\ M$, $[Cl^-] = 0.254\ M$

$[CaBr_2] = 4.8 \times 10^{-2}\ M \times \frac{25.0\ mL}{80.0\ mL} = 1.5 \times 10^{-2}\ M$, so $[Ca^{2+}] = 1.5 \times 10^{-2}\ M$

$[Br^-] = 3.0 \times 10^{-2}\ M$

(e) $[Al(NO_3)_3] = 8.65 \times 10^{-4}\ M \times \frac{95.0\ mL}{110.0\ mL} = 7.47 \times 10^{-4}\ M$

so: $[Al^{3+}] = 7.47 \times 10^{-4}\ M$, $[NO_3^-] = 2.24 \times 10^{-3}\ M$

$[Ag_2SO_4] = 7.50 \times 10^{-6}\ M \times \frac{15.0\ mL}{110.0\ mL} = 1.02 \times 10^{-6}\ M$

so: $[Ag^+] = 2.05 \times 10^{-6}\ M$, $[SO_4^{2-}] = 1.02 \times 10^{-6}\ M$

(f) $[CaCl_2] = 0.200\ M \times \frac{50.0\ mL}{100.0\ mL} = 0.100\ M$; $[Ca^{2+}] = 0.100\ M$ and $[Cl^-]_{\#1} = 0.200\ M$

$[NaCl] = 0.200\ M \times \frac{50.0\ mL}{100.0\ mL} = 0.100\ M$; $[Na^+] = 0.100\ M$ and $[Cl^-]_{\#2} = 0.100\ M$

$[Cl^-]_{total} = 0.200\ M + 0.100\ M = 0.300\ M$

(g) $[NH_4Br] = 0.360\ M \times \frac{25.0\ mL}{100.0\ mL} = 0.0900\ M$; $[NH_4^+]_{\#1} = 0.0900\ M$ and $[Br^-] = 0.0900\ M$

$[(NH_4)_2SO_4] = 0.160\ M \times \frac{75.0\ mL}{100.0\ mL} = 0.120\ M$; $[NH_4^+]_{\#2} = 0.240\ M$ and $[SO_4^{2-}] = 0.120\ M$

$[NH_4^+]_{total} = 0.0900\ M + 0.240\ M = 0.330\ M$

(h) $[Ba(NO_3)_2] = 0.100\ M \times \frac{10.0\ mL}{50.0\ mL} = 0.0200\ M$; $[Ba^{2+}] = 0.0200\ M$ and $[NO_3^-]_{\#1} = 0.0400\ M$

$[AgNO_3] = 0.300\ M \times \frac{40.0\ mL}{50.0\ mL} = 0.240\ M$; $[Ag^+] = 0.240\ M$ and $[NO_3^-]_{\#2} = 0.240\ M$

$[NO_3^-]_{total} = 0.0400\ M + 0.240\ M - 0.280\ M$

21. (a) low solubility (b) soluble (c) low solubility (d) soluble (e) low solubility (f) soluble (g) soluble (h) low solubility (i) soluble (j) low solubility

22. (a) AgBr is a precipitate (b) no precipitate (c) $Al(OH)_3$ is a precipitate (d) PbI_2 is a precipitate (e) $BaSO_4$ is a precipitate (f) no precipitate

23. (a) $BaSO_4$ has a very low solubility, so that the $[Ba^{2+}]$ is very low and hence there is little toxicity. (What can't dissolve, can't poison you.)
(b) AgBr also has a very low solubility: a saturated solution at 18°C has a silver ion concentration of 69 parts per billion (69 g per 10^6 L of water). Ag^+ ion is toxic to micro–organisms at concentrations as low as 10 parts per billion, yet is harmless to humans at such low concentrations.

24. (a) $Pb(NO_3)_2$ and NaCl (b) $AgNO_3$ and NaBr (c) $Cr(NO_3)_3$ and Na_2S (d) $Sr(NO_3)_2$ and Na_2SO_4

25. (a) $MgS(aq) + Sr(OH)_2(aq) \longrightarrow Mg(OH)_2(s) + SrS(aq)$; $Mg(OH)_2(s)$ has a low solubility

$Mg^{2+}(aq) + S^{2-}(aq) + Sr^{2+}(aq) + 2\ OH^-(aq) \longrightarrow Mg(OH)_2(s) + Sr^{2+}(aq) + S^{2-}(aq)$

$Mg^{2+}(aq) + 2\ OH^-(aq) \longrightarrow Mg(OH)_2(s)$

(b) $CuBr_2(aq) + Pb(NO_3)_2(aq) \longrightarrow PbBr_2(s) + Cu(NO_3)_2(aq)$; $PbBr_2(s)$ has a low solubility

$Cu^{2+}(aq) + 2\ Br^-(aq) + Pb^{2+}(aq) + 2\ NO_3^-(aq) \longrightarrow PbBr_2(s) + Cu^{2+}(aq) + 2\ NO_3^-(aq)$

$Pb^{2+}(aq) + 2\ Br^-(aq) \longrightarrow PbBr_2(s)$

(c) all products soluble

(d) $Ba(NO_3)_2(aq) + Li_2SO_4(aq) \longrightarrow BaSO_4(s) + 2\ LiNO_3(aq)$; $BaSO_4(s)$ has a low solubility

$Ba^{2+}(aq) + 2\ NO_3^-(aq) + 2\ Li^+(aq) + SO_4^{2-}(aq) \longrightarrow BaSO_4(s) + 2\ Li^+(aq) + 2\ NO_3^-(aq)$

$Ba^{2+}(aq) + SO_4^{2-}(aq) \longrightarrow BaSO_4(s)$

(e) $2\ K_3PO_4(aq) + 3\ CuCl_2(aq) \longrightarrow Cu_3(PO_4)_2(s) + 6\ KCl(aq)$; $Cu_3(PO_4)_2(s)$ has a low solubility

$6\ K^+(aq) + 2\ PO_4^{3-}(aq) + 3\ Cu^{2+}(aq) + 6\ Cl^-(aq) \longrightarrow Cu_3(PO_4)_2(s) + 6\ K^+(aq) + 6\ Cl^-(aq)$

$3\ Cu^{2+}(aq) + 2\ PO_4^{3-}(aq) \longrightarrow Cu_3(PO_4)_2(s)$

(f) $3\ (NH_4)_2SO_3(aq) + Al_2(SO_4)_3(aq) \longrightarrow Al_2(SO_3)_3(s) + 3\ (NH_4)_2SO_4(aq)$;

$Al_2(SO_3)_3(s)$ has a low solubility.

$6\ NH_4^+(aq) + 3\ SO_3^{2-}(aq) + 2\ Al^{3+}(aq) + 3\ SO_4^{2-}(aq) \longrightarrow Al_2(SO_3)_3(s) + 6\ NH_4^+(aq) + 3\ SO_4^{2-}(aq)$

$2\ Al^{3+}(aq) + 3\ SO_3^{2-}(aq) \longrightarrow Al_2(SO_3)_3(s)$

(g) $3\ AgNO_3(aq) + Na_3PO_4(aq) \longrightarrow Ag_3PO_4(s) + 3\ NaNO_3(aq)$; $Ag_3PO_4(s)$ has a low solubility.

$3\ Ag^+(aq) + 3\ NO_3^-(aq) + 3\ Na^+(aq) + PO_4^{3-}(aq) \longrightarrow Ag_3PO_4(s) + 3\ Na^+(aq) + 3\ NO_3^-(aq)$

$3\ Ag^+(aq) + PO_4^{3-}(aq) \longrightarrow Ag_3PO_4(s)$

(h) all products soluble

(i) $CoSO_4(aq) + Li_2CO_3(aq) \longrightarrow CoCO_3(s) + Li_2SO_4(aq)$; $CoCO_3(s)$ has a low solubility.

$Co^{2+}(aq) + SO_4^{2-}(aq) + 2\ Li^+(aq) + CO_3^{2-}(aq) \longrightarrow CoCO_3(s) + 2\ Li^+(aq) + SO_4^{2-}(aq)$

$Co^{2+}(aq) + CO_3^{2-}(aq) \longrightarrow CoCO_3(s)$

(j) $2\ Fe(NO_3)_3(aq) + 3\ MgS(aq) \longrightarrow Fe_2S_3(s) + 3\ Mg(NO_3)_2(aq)$; $Fe_2S_3(s)$ has a low solubility.

$2\ Fe^{3+}(aq) + 6\ NO_3^-(aq) + 3\ Mg^{2+}(aq) + 3\ S^{2-}(aq) \longrightarrow Fe_2S_3(s) + 3\ Mg^{2+}(aq) + 6\ NO_3^-(aq)$

$2\ Fe^{3+}(aq) + 3\ S^{2-}(aq) \longrightarrow Fe_2S_3(s)$

(k) $BeSO_4(aq) + (NH_4)_2CO_3(aq) \longrightarrow BeCO_3(s) + (NH_4)_2SO_4(aq)$; $BeCO_3(s)$ has a low solubility

$Be^{2+}(aq) + SO_4^{2-}(aq) + 2\ NH_4^+(aq) + CO_3^{2-}(aq) \longrightarrow BeCO_3(s) + 2\ NH_4^+(aq) + SO_4^{2-}(aq)$

$Be^{2+}(aq) + CO_3^{2-}(aq) \longrightarrow BeCO_3(s)$

(l) $MgSO_4(aq) + Sr(OH)_2(aq) \longrightarrow Mg(OH)_2(s) + SrSO_4(s)$; both products have low solubility.

$Mg^{2+}(aq) + SO_4^{2-}(aq) + Sr^{2+}(aq) + 2\ OH^-(aq) \longrightarrow Mg(OH)_2(s) + SrSO_4(s)$; (net and complete)

26. The salt must be **soluble** so as to obtain a sufficiently high concentration of the anion to be added.

27. (a) Ag^+, Ba^{2+}, Pb^{2+} or Ca^{2+} (b) Sr^{2+}

28. You cannot differentiate between Ag^+ and Pb^{2+}. Any anion which will precipitate Ag^+ will also precipitate Pb^{2+}, and vice versa. (However, other information such as colour of the precipitate can eventually lead to differentiation.)

29. Analyze for solubility.

	Cl^-	SO_4^{2-}	S^{2-}	OH^-	PO_4^{3-}
Al^{3+}	—	—	ppt	ppt	ppt
Ag^+	ppt	ppt	ppt	ppt	ppt

Precipitate the Ag^+ with NaCl or Na_2SO_4. Then precipitate the Al^{3+} with Na_2S, NaOH or Na_3PO_4.

30. Analyze for solubility.

	Cl^-	SO_4^{2-}	S^{2-}	OH^-	PO_4^{3-}
Sr^{2+}	—	ppt	—	—	ppt
Ca^{2+}	—	ppt	—	ppt	ppt
Ag^+	ppt	ppt	ppt	ppt	ppt

First precipitate the Ag^+ by adding NaCl or Na_2S.
Then precipitate the Ca^{2+} by adding NaOH.
Finally precipitate the Sr^{2+} by adding Na_2SO_4 or Na_3PO_4.

31. Analyze for solubility.

	Cl^-	SO_4^{2-}	S^{2-}	OH^-	PO_4^{3-}
Mg^{2+}	—	—	—	ppt	ppt
Pb^{2+}	ppt	ppt	ppt	ppt	ppt
Zn^{2+}	—	—	ppt	ppt	ppt

First precipitate the Pb^{2+} by adding Na_2SO_4 or NaCl.
Then precipitate the Zn^{2+} by adding Na_2S.
Finally precipitate the Mg^{2+} by adding NaOH or Na_3PO_4.

32. Analyze for solubility.

	Cl^-	SO_4^{2-}	S^{2-}	OH^-	PO_4^{3-}
Fe^{3+}	—	—	ppt	ppt	ppt
Ca^{2+}	—	ppt	—	ppt	ppt
Ag^+	ppt	ppt	ppt	ppt	ppt
Be^{2+}	—	—	—	ppt	ppt

First precipitate the Ag^+ by adding NaCl.
Next, **either** precipitate Ca^{2+} by adding Na_2SO_4, followed by the addition of Na_2S to precipitate Fe^{3+} and finally either NaOH or Na_3PO_4 to precipitate Be^{2+}.

or precipitate Fe^{3+} by adding Na_2S, followed by the addition of Na_2SO_4 to precipitate Ca^{2+} and finally either NaOH or Na_3PO_4 to precipitate Be^{2+}.

33. **Step 1:** Take 1 mL of the solution which might contain Ag^+ and/or Al^{3+}. Add a few drops of 1 M NaCl solution.

If there is NO PRECIPITATE then **Ag^+ is absent.** Proceed to Step 2.

If a PRECIPITATE FORMS then **Ag^+ is present.** Filter off and discard the precipitate and proceed to Step 2 to test the rest of the solution.

Step 2: To the solution from Step 1, add a few drops of 1 M Na_3PO_4 solution.

If there is NO PRECIPITATE then **Al^{3+} is absent.**

If a PRECIPITATE FORMS then **Al^{3+} is present.**

34. **Step 1:** Take 1 mL of the solution which might contain Ag^+, Ca^{2+} and/or Sr^{2+}. Add a few drops of 1 M NaCl solution.

If there is NO PRECIPITATE then **Ag^+ is absent.** Proceed to Step 2.

If a PRECIPITATE FORMS then **Ag^+ is present.** Filter off and discard the precipitate and proceed to Step 2 to test the rest of the solution.

Step 2: To the solution from Step 1, add a few drops of 1 M NaOH solution.

If there is NO PRECIPITATE then **Ca^{2+} is absent.** Proceed to Step 3.

If a PRECIPITATE FORMS then **Ca^{2+} is present.** Filter off and discard the precipitate and proceed to Step 3 to test the rest of the solution.

Step 3: To the solution from Step 2, add a few drops of 1 M Na_2SO_4.

If there is NO PRECIPITATE then **Sr^{2+} is absent.**

If a PRECIPITATE FORMS then **Sr^{2+} is present.**

35. (a) Qualitative analysis
(b) Analyze for solubility.

	Ag^+	Ca^{2+}	Mg^{2+}
I^-	ppt	—	—
SO_4^{2-}	ppt	ppt	—
OH^-	ppt	ppt	ppt

Add $Mg(NO_3)_2$ first to precipitate any OH^-; any other cation would precipitate more than one anion. If a precipitate occurs then OH^- is present, otherwise OH^- is absent.

(c) After filtering off any precipitate, add $Ca(NO_3)_2$. If a precipitate occurs then SO_4^{2-} is present; if not, SO_4^{2-} is absent. Filter off and discard any precipitate and add $AgNO_3$. If a precipitate occurs then I^- is present; if not, I^- is absent.

36. Analyze for solubility.

	Ag^+	Cu^{2+}	Ba^{2+}	Sr^{2+}
S^{2-}	ppt	ppt	—	—
OH^-	ppt	ppt	ppt	—
Cl^-	ppt	—	—	—
CO_3^{2-}	ppt	ppt	ppt	ppt

Step 1: Add $Sr(NO_3)_2$ to the test solution. If a precipitate forms, CO_3^{2-} is present. Filter off and discard any precipitate and proceed to Step 2.

Step 2: Add $Ba(NO_3)_2$ to the test solution. If a precipitate forms, OH^- is present. Filter off and discard any precipitate and proceed to Step 3.

Step 3: Add $Cu(NO_3)_2$ to the test solution. If a precipitate forms, S^{2-} is present. Filter off and discard any precipitate and proceed to Step 4.

Step 4: Add $AgNO_3$ to the test solution. If a precipitate forms, Cl^- is present.

37. (a) mass $BaSO_4 = 3.75\text{ g} - 1.21\text{ g} = 2.54\text{ g}$; moles $BaSO_4 = 2.54\text{ g} \times \frac{1\text{ mol}}{233.4\text{ g}} =$ **0.0109 mol**

(b) moles Ba^{2+} in solution = moles $BaSO_4$ precipitated ; $[Ba^{2+}] = \frac{0.0109\text{ mol}}{0.0250\text{ L}} =$ **0.435 M**

38. moles Pb^{2+} = moles $PbSO_4 = 4.28\text{ g} \times \frac{1\text{ mol}}{303.3\text{ g}} = 0.0141\text{ mol}$; $[Pb^{2+}] = \frac{0.0141\text{ mol}}{0.1000\text{ L}} =$ **0.141 M**

39. moles $Ag^+ = 1.57\text{ g } Ag_3PO_4 \times \frac{1\text{ mol } Ag_3PO_4}{418.7\text{ g } Ag_3PO_4} \times \frac{3\text{ mol } Ag^+}{1\text{ mol } Ag_3PO_4} = 0.0112\text{ mol}$

$[Ag^+] = \frac{0.0112\text{ mol}}{0.02500\text{ L}} =$ **0.450 M**

40. (a) $BaSO_4(s) \rightleftharpoons Ba^{2+}(aq) + SO_4^{2-}(aq)$; $K_{sp} = [Ba^{2+}][SO_4^{2-}]$

(b) $MgF_2(s) \rightleftharpoons Mg^{2+}(aq) + 2\,F^-(aq)$; $K_{sp} = [Mg^{2+}][F^-]^2$

(c) $Ag_2S(s) \rightleftharpoons 2\,Ag^+(aq) + S^{2-}(aq)$; $K_{sp} = [Ag^+]^2[S^{2-}]$

(d) $Cu(IO_3)_2(s) \rightleftharpoons Cu^{2+}(aq) + 2\,IO_3^-(aq)$; $K_{sp} = [Cu^{2+}][IO_3^-]^2$

41. AgCl is the most soluble because its K_{sp} value is the largest.
AgI is the least soluble because its K_{sp} value is the smallest.

42. $FeCO_3 \rightleftharpoons Fe^{2+} + CO_3^{2-}$; $K_{sp} = [Fe^{2+}][CO_3^{2-}] = (5.0 \times 10^{-6})(6.0 \times 10^{-6}) =$ **3.0×10^{-11}**

43. $ZnS \rightleftharpoons Zn^{2+} + S^{2-}$; $K_{sp} = [Zn^{2+}][S^{2-}] = 2.0 \times 10^{-25} = X^2$, so: $X = [Zn^{2+}] =$ **4.5×10^{-13}**

44. $PbSO_4 \rightleftharpoons Pb^{2+} + SO_4^{2-}$; $K_{sp} = [Pb^{2+}][SO_4^{2-}] = 1.8 \times 10^{-8} = X^2$

so $X = [PbSO_4]_{DISSOLVED} = 1.34 \times 10^{-4}\text{ M}$

mass $PbSO_4 = 1.34 \times 10^{-4}\,\frac{\text{mol}}{\text{L}} \times 5.0\text{ L} \times \frac{303.3\text{ g}}{1\text{ mol}} =$ **0.20 g**

45. $BaCrO_4 \rightleftharpoons Ba^{2+} + CrO_4^{2-}$; $K_{sp} = [Ba^{2+}][CrO_4^{2-}] = 1.2 \times 10^{-10} = X^2$

so $X = [BaCrO_4]_{DISSOLVED} = 1.10 \times 10^{-5}\text{ M}$

mass $BaCrO_4 = 1.10 \times 10^{-5}\,\frac{\text{mol}}{\text{L}} \times 10\text{ L} \times \frac{253.3\text{ g}}{1\text{ mol}} =$ **0.028 g**

46. $AgCH_3COO \rightleftharpoons Ag^+ + CH_3COO^-$

$[AgCH_3COO]_{DISSOLVED} = \frac{7.35\text{ g}}{1.00\text{ L}} \times \frac{1\text{ mol}}{166.9\text{ g}} = 4.404 \times 10^{-2}\text{ M} = [Ag^+] = [CH_3COO^-]$

$K_{sp} = [Ag^+][CH_3COO^-] = (4.404 \times 10^{-2})^2 =$ **1.94×10^{-3}**

47. $Ag_2CrO_4 \rightleftharpoons 2\,Ag^+ + CrO_4^{2-}$; $K_{sp} = [Ag^+]^2[CrO_4^{2-}] = 1.1 \times 10^{-12} = (X)(2X)^2 = 4X^3$

so: $X = [Ag_2CrO_4]_{DISSOLVED}$ = molar solubility of $Ag_2CrO_4 =$ **6.5×10^{-5} M**

48. $CaSO_4 \rightleftharpoons Ca^{2+} + SO_4^{2-}$; $K_{sp} = [Ca^{2+}][SO_4^{2-}] = 7.1 \times 10^{-5} = X^2$

so: $X = [CaSO_4]_{DISSOLVED} = 8.43 \times 10^{-3}\text{ M}$, solubility (g/L) $= 8.43 \times 10^{-3}\,\frac{\text{mol}}{\text{L}} \times \frac{136.2\text{ g}}{1\text{ mol}} =$ **1.1 g/L**

49. $Fe(OH)_2 \rightleftharpoons Fe^{2+} + 2\,OH^-$; $K_{sp} = [Fe^{2+}][OH^-]^2 = 4.9 \times 10^{-17} = (X)(2X)^2 = 4X^3$

so: $X = [Fe(OH)_2]_{DISSOLVED} = 2.31 \times 10^{-6}\text{ M}$

solubility (g/L) $= 2.31 \times 10^{-6}\,\frac{\text{mol}}{\text{L}} \times \frac{89.8\text{ g}}{1\text{ mol}} =$ **2.1×10^{-4} g/L**

50. $Ag_2S \rightleftharpoons 2\,Ag^+ + S^{2-}$; $K_{sp} = [Ag^+]^2[S^{2-}] = (2.6 \times 10^{-17})^2(1.6 \times 10^{-16}) = \mathbf{1.1 \times 10^{-49}}$

51. $ZnCO_3 \rightleftharpoons Zn^{2+} + CO_3^{2-}$

$$[ZnCO_3]_{DISSOLVED} = \frac{1.4 \times 10^{-4}\ g}{0.1000\ L} \times \frac{1\ mol}{125.4\ g} = 1.12 \times 10^{-5}\ M = [Zn^{2+}] = [CO_3^{2-}]$$

$K_{sp} = [Zn^{2+}][CO_3^{2-}] = (1.12 \times 10^{-5})^2 = \mathbf{1.2 \times 10^{-10}}$

52. $Zn(OH)_2 \rightleftharpoons Zn^{2+} + 2\,OH^-$; $K_{sp} = [Zn^{2+}][OH^-]^2 = 4.1 \times 10^{-17} = (X)(2X)^2 = 4X^3$
so $X = [Zn^{2+}] = 2.17 \times 10^{-6}\ M$ and $[OH^-] = 2 \times [Zn^{2+}] = \mathbf{4.3 \times 10^{-6}\ M}$

53. $Cd(OH)_2 \rightleftharpoons Cd^{2+} + 2\,OH^-$; $K_{sp} = [Cd^{2+}][OH^-]^2 = 5.3 \times 10^{-15} = (X)(2X)^2 = 4X^3$
so $X = [Cd^{2+}] = \mathbf{1.1 \times 10^{-5}\ M}$

54. $Pb(IO_3)_2 \rightleftharpoons Pb^{2+} + 2\,IO_3^-$; $K_{sp} = [Pb^{2+}][IO_3^-]^2 = 3.7 \times 10^{-13} = (X)(2X)^2 = 4X^3$
so $X = [Pb^{2+}] = 4.52 \times 10^{-5}\ M$

$$\text{mass } Pb^{2+} = 4.52 \times 10^{-5}\ \frac{mol}{L} \times 5.0\ L \times \frac{207.2\ g}{1\ mol} = \mathbf{4.7 \times 10^{-2}\ g}$$

55. First, use the data from Trial #1 to calculate the K_{sp} for $Mn(OH)_2$.
$Mn(OH)_2 \rightleftharpoons Mn^{2+} + 2\,OH^-$; $K_{sp} = [Mn^{2+}][OH^-]^2 = (2.1 \times 10^{-5})(1.0 \times 10^{-4})^2 = 2.1 \times 10^{-13}$
Now use Trial 2: $[Mn^{2+}][OH^-]^2 = 2.1 \times 10^{-13} = (7.8 \times 10^{-4})[OH^-]^2$
solving $[OH^-] = \mathbf{1.6 \times 10^{-5}\ M}$

56. $FeS \rightleftharpoons Fe^{2+} + S^{2-}$; $K_{sp} = [Fe^{2+}][S^{2-}] = 6.0 \times 10^{-19}$

$$[Fe^{2+}] = 3.0 \times 10^{-10}\ M \times \frac{1.0\ L}{2.0\ L} = 1.5 \times 10^{-10}\ M; \quad [S^{2-}] = 1.2 \times 10^{-8}\ M \times \frac{1.0\ L}{2.0\ L} = 6.0 \times 10^{-9}\ M$$

$Q = [Fe^{2+}][S^{2-}] = (1.5 \times 10^{-10})(6.0 \times 10^{-9}) = 9.0 \times 10^{-19} > K_{sp} = 6.0 \times 10^{-19}$
and a precipitate forms (just barely)

57. $CuS \rightleftharpoons Cu^{2+} + S^{2-}$; $K_{sp} = [Cu^{2+}][S^{2-}] = 6.0 \times 10^{-37}$

$$[S^{2-}] = \frac{K_{sp}}{[Cu^{2+}]} = \frac{6.0 \times 10^{-37}}{0.20} = \mathbf{3.0 \times 10^{-36}\ M}$$

58. $CaF_2 \rightleftharpoons Ca^{2+} + 2\,F^-$; $K_{sp} = [Ca^{2+}][F^-]^2 = 1.5 \times 10^{-10}$

$$[F^-]^2 = \frac{K_{sp}}{[Ca^{2+}]} = \frac{1.5 \times 10^{-10}}{3.0 \times 10^{-3}} = 5.00 \times 10^{-8} \qquad \text{so: } [F^-] = \mathbf{2.2 \times 10^{-4}\ M}$$

59. $PbSO_4 \rightleftharpoons Pb^{2+} + SO_4^{2-}$; $K_{sp} = [Pb^{2+}][SO_4^{2-}] = 1.8 \times 10^{-8}$

$$[SO_4^{2-}] = 1.5 \times 10^{-4}\ M \times \frac{40.0\ mL}{50.0\ mL} = 1.2 \times 10^{-4}\ M; \quad [Pb^{2+}] = 1.0 \times 10^{-3}\ M \times \frac{10.0\ mL}{50.0\ mL} = 2.0 \times 10^{-4}\ M$$

$Q = [Pb^{2+}][SO_4^{2-}] = (2.0 \times 10^{-4})(1.2 \times 10^{-4}) = 2.4 \times 10^{-8} > K_{sp} = 1.8 \times 10^{-8}$ and a precipitate forms

60. $NiCO_3 \rightleftharpoons Ni^{2+} + CO_3^{2-}$; $K_{sp} = [Ni^{2+}][CO_3^{2-}]$

$$[Ni^{2+}] = 3.00 \times 10^{-3}\ M \times \frac{20.0\ mL}{80.0\ mL} = 7.50 \times 10^{-4}\ M$$

$$[CO_3^{2-}] = 2.52 \times 10^{-4}\ M \times \frac{60.0\ mL}{80.0\ mL} = 1.89 \times 10^{-4}\ M$$

$K_{sp} = Q = [Ni^{2+}][CO_3^{2-}] = (7.50 \times 10^{-4})(1.89 \times 10^{-4}) = \mathbf{1.42 \times 10^{-7}}$

61. $Zn(OH)_2 \rightleftharpoons Zn^{2+} + 2\,OH^-$; $K_{sp} = [Zn^{2+}][OH^-]^2 = 4.1 \times 10^{-17}$

$[Zn^{2+}] = 1.0 \times 10^{-4}\ M \times \dfrac{25.0\ mL}{70.0\ mL} = 3.57 \times 10^{-5}\ M$

$[Ca(OH)_2] = 2.4 \times 10^{-5}\ M \times \dfrac{45.0\ mL}{70.0\ mL} = 1.54 \times 10^{-5}\ M$; $[OH^-] = 2 \times [Ca(OH)_2] = 3.09 \times 10^{-5}\ M$

$Q = [Zn^{2+}][OH^-]^2 = (3.57 \times 10^{-5})(3.09 \times 10^{-5})^2 = 3.4 \times 10^{-14} > K_{sp} = 4.1 \times 10^{-17}$
and a precipitate forms

62. $Ca(OH)_2 \rightleftharpoons Ca^{2+} + 2\,OH^-$; $K_{sp} = [Ca^{2+}][OH^-]^2$

$[Ca^{2+}] = 4.0 \times 10^{-2}\ M \times \dfrac{100.0\ mL}{250.0\ mL} = 1.60 \times 10^{-2}\ M$

$[OH^-] = 2.9 \times 10^{-2}\ M \times \dfrac{150.0\ mL}{250.0\ mL} = 1.74 \times 10^{-2}\ M$

$K_{sp} = Q = [Ca^{2+}][OH^-]^2 = (1.60 \times 10^{-2})(1.74 \times 10^{-2})^2 = \mathbf{4.8 \times 10^{-6}}$

63. $PbI_2 \rightleftharpoons Pb^{2+} + 2\,I^-$; $K_{sp} = [Pb^{2+}][I^-]^2 = 8.5 \times 10^{-9}$

$[Pb^{2+}] = 5.0\ M \times \dfrac{0.050\ mL}{100.05\ mL} = 2.50 \times 10^{-3}\ M$; $[I^-] = 3.0 \times 10^{-5}\ M \times \dfrac{100.00\ mL}{100.05\ mL} = 3.00 \times 10^{-5}\ M$

$Q = [Pb^{2+}][I^-]^2 = (2.50 \times 10^{-3})(3.00 \times 10^{-5})^2 = 2.2 \times 10^{-12} < K_{sp} = 8.5 \times 10^{-9}$
and no precipitate forms

64. $CaC_2O_4 \rightleftharpoons Ca^{2+} + C_2O_4^{2-}$; $K_{sp} = [Ca^{2+}][C_2O_4^{2-}] = 2.3 \times 10^{-9}$

$[Ca^{2+}] = 5.0 \times 10^{-5}\ M \times \dfrac{20.0\ mL}{25.0\ mL} = 4.0 \times 10^{-5}\ M$

$[C_2O_4^{2-}] = 2.5 \times 10^{-4}\ M \times \dfrac{35.0\ mL}{25.0\ mL} = 3.5 \times 10^{-4}\ M$

$Q = [Ca^{2+}][C_2O_4^{2-}] = (4.0 \times 10^{-5})(3.5 \times 10^{-4}) = 1.4 \times 10^{-8} > K_{sp} = 2.3 \times 10^{-9}$ and a precipitate forms

65. $Ag_2CO_3 \rightleftharpoons 2\,Ag^+ + CO_3^{2-}$; $K_{sp} = [Ag^+]^2[CO_3^{2-}] = 8.5 \times 10^{-12}$

$[CO_3^{2-}] = \dfrac{K_{sp}}{[Ag^+]^2} = \dfrac{8.5 \times 10^{-12}}{(0.050)^2} = \mathbf{3.4 \times 10^{-9}\ M}$

66. $PbS \rightleftharpoons Pb^{2+} + S^{2-}$; $K_{sp} = [Pb^{2+}][S^{2-}]$

$[S^{2-}] = 1.0 \times 10^{-9}\ M \times \dfrac{0.0050\ L}{1.0\ L} \times \dfrac{10.0\ mL}{100.0\ mL} = 5.0 \times 10^{-13}\ M$

$[Pb^{2+}] = 2.0 \times 10^{-16}\ M \times \dfrac{90.0\ mL}{100.0\ mL} = 1.8 \times 10^{-16}\ M$

$K_{sp} = Q = [Pb^{2+}][S^{2-}] = (1.8 \times 10^{-16})(5.0 \times 10^{-13}) = \mathbf{9.0 \times 10^{-29}}$

67. You are given thè "solubility", **NOT** the solubility product (K_{sp}), so first you have to calculate K_{sp}.

$[Mn^{2+}] = [Mn(IO_3)_2] = 4.78 \times 10^{-3}\ M$; $[IO_3^-] = 2 \times [Mn^{2+}] = 9.56 \times 10^{-3}\ M$

$Mn(IO_3)_2 \rightleftharpoons Mn^{2+} + 2\,IO_3^-$; $K_{sp} = [Mn^{2+}][IO_3^-]^2 = (4.78 \times 10^{-3})(9.56 \times 10^{-3})^2 = 4.37 \times 10^{-7}$

$[Mn^{2+}] = \dfrac{K_{sp}}{[IO_3^-]^2} = \dfrac{4.37 \times 10^{-7}}{(0.0200)^2} = \mathbf{1.09 \times 10^{-3}\ M}$

68. Calculate $[Pb^{2+}]$ required to form a precipitate with each ion; the smallest $[Pb^{2+}]$ will form the first precipitate as $[Pb^{2+}]$ increases. (The initial $[Pb^{2+}]$ given is not relevent, provided it is not too small.)

for $PbCl_2$: $PbCl_2 \rightleftharpoons Pb^{2+} + 2\,Cl^-$; $K_{sp} = [Pb^{2+}][Cl^-]^2 = 1.2 \times 10^{-5}$

$$[Pb^{2+}] = \frac{K_{sp}}{[Cl^-]^2} = \frac{1.2 \times 10^{-5}}{(0.10)^2} = 1.2 \times 10^{-3}\text{ M}$$

for PbI_2: $PbI_2 \rightleftharpoons Pb^{2+} + 2\,I^-$; $K_{sp} = [Pb^{2+}][I^-]^2 = 8.5 \times 10^{-9}$

$$[Pb^{2+}] = \frac{K_{sp}}{[I^-]^2} = \frac{8.5 \times 10^{-9}}{(0.10)^2} = 8.5 \times 10^{-7}\text{ M}$$

for $PbSO_4$: $PbSO_4 \rightleftharpoons Pb^{2+} + SO_4^{2-}$; $K_{sp} = [Pb^{2+}][SO_4^{2-}] = 1.8 \times 10^{-8}$

$$[Pb^{2+}] = \frac{K_{sp}}{[SO_4^{2-}]} = \frac{1.8 \times 10^{-8}}{0.10} = 1.8 \times 10^{-7}\text{ M}$$

Therefore $PbSO_4$ will be the first precipitate because it requires the smallest $[Pb^{2+}]$.

69. Calculate the $[Ag^+]$ required to form a precipitate with each ion; the smallest $[Ag^+]$ will correspond to the first precipitate as the $[Ag^+]$ increases.

for Ag_2CO_3: $Ag_2CO_3 \rightleftharpoons 2\,Ag^+ + CO_3^{2-}$; $K_{sp} = [Ag^+]^2[CO_3^{2-}] = 8.5 \times 10^{-12}$

$$[Ag^+] = \sqrt{\frac{K_{sp}}{[CO_3^{2-}]}} = \sqrt{\frac{8.5 \times 10^{-12}}{1.0}} = 2.9 \times 10^{-6}\text{ M}$$

for $AgIO_3$: $AgIO_3 \rightleftharpoons Ag^+ + IO_3^-$; $K_{sp} = [Ag^+][IO_3^-] = 3.2 \times 10^{-8}$

$$[Ag^+] = \frac{K_{sp}}{[IO_3^-]} = \frac{3.2 \times 10^{-8}}{1.0} = 3.2 \times 10^{-8}\text{ M}$$

for Ag_2CrO_4: $Ag_2CrO_4 \rightleftharpoons 2\,Ag^+ + CrO_4^{2-}$; $K_{sp} = [Ag^+]^2[CrO_4^{2-}] = 1.1 \times 10^{-12}$

$$[Ag^+] = \sqrt{\frac{K_{sp}}{[CrO_4^{2-}]}} = \sqrt{\frac{1.1 \times 10^{-12}}{1.0}} = 1.0 \times 10^{-6}\text{ M}$$

Therefore $AgIO_3$ will be the first precipitate because it requires the smallest $[Ag^+]$.

70. $Ag^+ + Cl^- \longrightarrow AgCl$

moles $Ag^+ = 0.100\,\frac{\text{mol}}{\text{L}} \times 0.0368\text{ L} = 0.00368\text{ mol}$ = moles Cl^-; $[Cl^-] = \frac{0.00368\text{ mol}}{0.0250\text{ L}} = \mathbf{0.147\ M}$

71. $Ag^+ + Cl^- \longrightarrow AgCl$

moles $Ag^+ = 0.0750\,\frac{\text{mol}}{\text{L}} \times 0.0250\text{ L} = 1.875 \times 10^{-3}\text{ mol}$ = moles Cl^-

volume Cl^- solution $= \frac{1.875 \times 10^{-3}\text{ mol}}{0.0988\text{ mol/L}} = 0.0190\text{ L} = \mathbf{19.0\ mL}$

72. $[Cl^-] = [KCl] = \frac{3.25\text{ g}}{0.5000\text{ L}} \times \frac{1\text{ mol}}{74.6\text{ g}} = 0.08713\text{ M}$

moles $Cl^- = 0.08713\,\frac{\text{mol}}{\text{L}} \times 0.02500\text{ L} = 0.002178\text{ mol}$ = moles Ag^+

$[Ag^+] = \frac{0.002178\text{ mol}}{0.00948\text{ L}} = \mathbf{0.230\ M}$

73. Moles Cl^- = moles NaCl = $0.100\ \frac{mol}{L} \times 0.0306\ L = 0.00306$ mol

= moles Ag^+ = moles $AgCH_3COO$ (dissolved)

$[AgCH_3COO] = [Ag^+] = \frac{0.00306\ mol}{0.0500\ L} = 0.0612\ M$

$AgCH_3COO(s) \rightleftharpoons Ag^+ + CH_3COO^-$; $K_{sp} = [Ag^+][CH_3COO^-]$

Since $AgCH_3COO$ is used to produce the saturated solution then $[CH_3COO^-] = [Ag^+] = 0.0612\ M$

and $K_{sp} = (0.0612)^2 = \mathbf{3.75 \times 10^{-3}}$

74. $Ag^+ + Cl^- \longrightarrow AgCl$

moles $Cl^- = 0.200\ \frac{mol}{L} \times 0.0250\ L = 5.00 \times 10^{-3}$ mol = moles Ag^+

actual $[Ag^+] = \frac{5.00 \times 10^{-3}\ mol}{0.0288\ L} = 0.1736\ M$; expected $[Ag^+] = \frac{4.75\ g}{0.250\ L} \times \frac{1\ mol}{107.9\ g} = 0.1761\ M$

percentage purity = $\frac{\text{actual } [Ag^+]}{\text{expected } [Ag^+]} \times 100\ \% = \frac{0.1736\ M}{0.1761\ M} \times 100\ \% = \mathbf{98.6\ \%}$

75. (a) moles $Ag^+ = 0.0200\ \frac{mol}{L} \times 0.0153\ L = 3.06 \times 10^{-4}\ M$ = moles Cl^-

$[Cl^-] = \frac{3.06 \times 10^{-4}\ mol}{0.0250\ L} = 1.22 \times 10^{-2}\ M$

(b) mass NaCl = $1.22 \times 10^{-2}\ \frac{mol}{L} \times 1.00\ L \times \frac{58.5\ g}{1\ mol} = 0.716\ g$

(c) percentage = $\frac{\text{mass NaCl}}{\text{mass meat}} \times 100\ \% = \frac{0.716\ g}{95.6\ g} \times 100\ \% = \mathbf{0.749\ \%}$

76. $CaCO_3(s)$ and/or $MgCO_3(s)$

77. Both temporarily hard and permanently hard water look the same as pure distilled water. However, heating a sample of temporarily hard water will produce a milky precipitate whereas a sample of permanently hard water is unaffected by heating.

78. Since both permanently and temporarily hard water contain Ca^{2+} and/or Mg^{2+} ions, the addition of CO_3^{2-} (from washing soda) forms a precipitate in both cases and won't distinguish between the two types of hardness.

79. Acid rain would "eat away" the surface of the marble, according to the reaction:

$2\ H^+(aq) + CaCO_3(s) \longrightarrow Ca^{2+}(aq) + CO_2(g) + H_2O(l)$.

80. The pipes would eventually become clogged with deposits of $CaCO_3(s)$ and/or $MgCO_3(s)$.

81. $Sr(OH)_2(s) \rightleftharpoons Sr^{2+}(aq) + 2\ OH^-(aq)$

Increase the solubility: a) add Na_3PO_4, say, to precipitate Sr^{2+} ,
b) add $Ca(NO_3)_2$, say, to precipitate OH^- .

Decrease the solubility: a) add NaOH to precipitate more $Sr(OH)_2$,
b) add $Sr(NO_3)_2$ to precipitate more $Sr(OH)_2$.

82. A saturated solution of $BaCO_3$ has dissolved all the $BaCO_3$ that it can ; any more of the solid salt which is added will simply pile up on the bottom of the solution's container.

83. To make the $CaCO_3(s)$ dissolve, the solubility of the $CaCO_3(s)$ must be increased. Hence:

a) add Na_3PO_4, say, to precipitate Ca^{2+}, or b) add $Fe(NO_3)_3$, say, to precipitate CO_3^{2-} .

84. $PbCl_2(s) \rightleftharpoons Pb^{2+}(aq) + 2\,Cl^-(aq)$

Increase the solubility: a) add $AgNO_3$, say, to precipitate Cl^-,
b) add Na_2S, say, to precipitate Pb^{2+}.

Decrease the solubility: a) add $Pb(NO_3)_2$, say to precipitate more $PbCl_2$,
b) add NaCl, say, to precipitate more $PbCl_2$.

85. The equilibrium equation governing the solubility of $SrCl_2$ is: $SrCl_2(s) \rightleftharpoons Sr^{2+} + 2\,Cl^-$.

The solution in which $SrCl_2$ is most soluble is 1 M Na_2SO_4. (The SO_4^{2-} precipitates the Sr^{2+} entering solution as $SrCl_2$ dissolves, shifting the $SrCl_2$ equilibrium to the ions side.)

The solution in which $SrCl_2$ is least soluble is 1 M $MgCl_2$. (Both 1 M $Sr(NO_3)_2$ and 1 M $MgCl_2$ force the $SrCl_2$ equilibrium to the solid side, due to the common ion effect, but $MgCl_2$ forms a higher concentration of its common ion, Cl^-, than $Sr(NO_3)_2$ does of its common ion, Sr^{2+}.)

86. NaBr most soluble ⟶ NaBr least soluble

2 M $AgNO_3$ 1 M $AgNO_3$ 1 M KNO_3 1 M NaCl   1 M Na_2SO_4

Both 1 M $AgNO_3$ and 2 M $AgNO_3$ increase the solubility of NaBr by precipitating Br^- ions from a saturated NaBr solution. Since 2 M $AgNO_3$ has a higher $[Ag^+]$, it precipitates more Br^- ions and increases the solubility of the NaBr more than the 1 M $AgNO_3$ does.

KNO_3 doesn't affect either of the Na^+ or Br^- ions and doesn't change the solubility of NaBr.

Both 1 M Na_2SO_4 and 1 M NaCl decrease the solubility of the NaBr by the common ion effect. But, 1 M Na_2SO_4 dissociates into more Na^+ ions and produces a higher $[Na^+]$ so as to shift the solubility equilibrium for NaBr to the solid side more and decrease the solubility of NaBr to a greater extent.

ANSWERS TO UNIT IV : ACIDS AND BASES

1. (a) Salt
   (b) Acid; this is "acetic acid" and is also written as "CH_3COOH".
   (c) None; this is an organic covalent compound made from two non–metallic elements.
   (d) Base
   (e) Acid
   (f) Salt
   (g) Base
   (h) None; this is a covalent compound made from two non–metallic elements.

2. (a) $H_2SO_4 + 2\,NaOH \longrightarrow Na_2SO_4 + 2\,H_2O$
   (b) $3\,H_2SO_4 + 2\,Fe(OH)_3 \longrightarrow Fe_2(SO_4)_3 + 6\,H_2O$
   (c) $H_3PO_4 + 3\,KOH \longrightarrow K_3PO_4 + 3\,H_2O$
   (d) $4\,HCl + Sn(OH)_4 \longrightarrow SnCl_4 + 4\,H_2O$
   (e) $H_2S + Ca(OH)_2 \longrightarrow CaS + 2\,H_2O$
   (f) $H_4P_2O_7 + 4\,NaOH \longrightarrow Na_4P_2O_7 + 4\,H_2O$

3. (a) both acids and bases
   (b) neither acids nor bases
   (c) bases only
   (d) acids only
   (e) acids only
   (f) neither acids nor bases

4. Use litmus paper: if the litmus is red, you have an acid; if blue, you have a base. If litmus indicates acid is present, add a piece of Mg to some of the solution; bubbles of $H_2(g)$ should be produced.

5. Both NaOH and KOH will absorb H_2O and CO_2 from the atmosphere, reducing the purity of the bases.

6. Fertilizers – H_2SO_4, HNO_3, NH_3 Plastics – H_2SO_4, CH_3COOH, NaOH

7. (a) H_2SO_4 (b) CH_3COOH (c) NH_3 (d) KOH (e) HCl

8. H_2SO_4, NaOH, KOH

9. HNO_3

10. (a) $HNO_3(aq) + H_2O(l) \longrightarrow H_3O^+(aq) + NO_3^-(aq)$
    (b) $HClO_4(aq) + H_2O(l) \longrightarrow H_3O^+(aq) + ClO_4^-(aq)$

11. (a) acid = HNO_3, base = H_2O
    (b) acid = HCO_3^-, base = SO_3^{2-}
    (c) acid = $H_2PO_4^-$, base = HS^-
    (d) acid = H_3PO_4, base = CH_3COO^-
    (e) acid = HF, base = CO_3^{2-}

12. (a) monoprotic = HF, HCN
    (b) diprotic = H_2S, H_2CO_3
    (c) triprotic = H_3PO_4
    (d) polyprotic = H_2S, H_2CO_3, H_3PO_4, $H_4P_2O_7$

13. (a) ACID, BASE, BASE, ACID
    (b) BASE, ACID, ACID, BASE
    (c) BASE, ACID, BASE, ACID
    (d) ACID, BASE, ACID, BASE
    (e) ACID, BASE, BASE, ACID

14. HSe^-, HPO_4^{2-}, HSO_3^-

15. (a) conjugate acid = CH_3COOH, conjugate base = CH_3COO^-
    (b) conjugate acid = HSO_4^-, conjugate base = SO_4^{2-}
    (c) conjugate acid = PH_4^+, conjugate base = PH_3

16. (a) SO_4^{2-} (b) H_2SO_4 (c) O^{2-} (d) H_2O

17. (a) HF
    (b) H_2Te
    (c) HTe^-
    (d) $CH_3NH_3^+$
    (e) $H_2C_2O_4$
    (f) H_3PO_3
    (g) H_2
    (h) $N_2H_5^+$

18. (a) HCO_3^-
    (b) C_5H_5N
    (c) PO_4^{3-}
    (d) HO_2^-
    (e) N_3^-
    (f) NO_2^-
    (g) S^{2-}
    (h) $C_6H_5COO^-$

19. (a) $HCN + F^- \rightleftharpoons CN^- + HF$
(b) $S^{2-} + HCOOH \rightleftharpoons HS^- + HCOO^-$
(c) $HPO_4^{2-} + SO_4^{2-} \rightleftharpoons PO_4^{3-} + HSO_4^-$
(d) $HIO_3 + C_2O_4^{2-} \rightleftharpoons IO_3^- + HC_2O_4^-$
(e) $NO_2^- + HSO_3^- \rightleftharpoons HNO_2 + SO_3^{2-}$
(f) $HPO_4^{2-} + CH_3COO^- \rightleftharpoons PO_4^{3-} + CH_3COOH$

20. Measure the conductivity with a "light bulb conductivity tester". If the conductivity is high (that is, the light bulb burns brightly) then the substance has a STRONG ionization (many ions). If the conductivity is low (the light bulb glows, but not very brightly) then the substance has a WEAK ionization (few ions).

21. (a) HIO_3 (b) HSO_3^- (c) $H_2PO_4^-$

22. (a) PO_4^{3-} (b) HPO_4^{2-} (c) OH^- (d) $HCOO^-$

23. (a) HTe^- and HS^- (b) HS^- (since its conjugate acid is weaker)

24. (a) $F^- + H_2O \rightleftharpoons HF + OH^-$
(b) $HNO_2 + H_2O \rightleftharpoons NO_2^- + H_3O^+$
(c) $Fe(H_2O)_6^{3+} + H_2O \rightleftharpoons Fe(H_2O)_5(OH)^{2+} + H_3O^+$
(d) $HCO_3^- + H_2O \rightleftharpoons H_2CO_3 + OH^-$
(e) $HCO_3^- + H_2O \rightleftharpoons CO_3^{2-} + H_3O^+$
(f) $Al(H_2O)_5(OH)^{2+} + H_2O \rightleftharpoons Al(H_2O)_6^{3+} + OH^-$

25. (a) I^- is the conjugate of a strong acid and NEVER acts as a base in aqueous solution. (HI dissociates 100% to form H^+ and I^-, so that I^- has ZERO tendency to reform HI.)
(b) OH^- CAN act as a base (3rd position from bottom, on right–hand side), BUT the equation directly below this equation refers to O^{2-} having a 100% tendency to attract H^+ and form OH^-, so that OH^- has ZERO tendency to form H^+ and O^{2-} (notice that the reaction arrow points ***backwards***). Hence, OH^- NEVER acts as an acid in aqueous solution.
(c) $HClO_4$ and HBr are both strong acids, both are 100% dissociated in aqueous solution and both form 1 M solutions of $H_3O^+(aq)$. Hence, both $HClO_4$ and HBr are the same strength in aqueous solution. ("The levelling effect")

26. HI is a stronger acid than HCl **only when water is absent.** Both HI(aq) and HCl(aq) are 100% dissociated in water, and have the same strength (the "levelling effect"). Since both 0.10 M HI and 0.10 M HCl are dissociated to the same extent, they will produce the same $[H_3O^+]$: 0.10 M.

27. A low conductivity simply implies that a low concentration of ions is present. Hence, a relatively high concentration of a weak acid (slightly dissociated) can have the same concentration of ions as a dilute solution of a strong acid (100% dissociated).

28. $[H_3O^+] = [OH^-] = 1.0 \times 10^{-7}$ M

29. (a) $[H_3O^+]$ increases
(b) neutral; the $[OH^-]$ increases as the $[H_3O^+]$ increases, so as to keep $[H_3O^+] = [OH^-]$
(c) K_w increases

30. (a) $[H_3O^+] = 10.0$ M, $[OH^-] = 1.0 \times 10^{-15}$ M
(b) $[H_3O^+] = 2.5 \times 10^{-15}$ M, $[OH^-] = 4.0$ M
(c) $[H_3O^+] = 2.5 \times 10^{-4}$ M, $[OH^-] = 4.0 \times 10^{-11}$ M
(d) $[H_3O^+] = 8.33 \times 10^{-13}$ M, $[OH^-] = 1.20 \times 10^{-2}$ M

31. (a) $K_a = \dfrac{[H_3O^+][CN^-]}{[HCN]}$ (b) $K_a = \dfrac{[H_3O^+][PO_4^{3-}]}{[HPO_4^{2-}]}$ (c) $K_a = \dfrac{[H_3O^+][NO_2^-]}{[HNO_2]}$

32. (a) $K_b = \dfrac{[H_2S][OH^-]}{[HS^-]}$ (b) $K_b = \dfrac{[CH_3NH_3^+][OH^-]}{[CH_3NH_2]}$ (c) $K_b = \dfrac{[HF][OH^-]}{[F^-]}$

33. the acid having $K_a = 1 \times 10^{-5}$

34. the base having $K_b = 7 \times 10^{-6}$

35. (a) 8.3×10^{-13} (b) 7.1×10^{-10} (c) 2.3×10^{-8} (d) 1.6×10^{-7} (e) 6.7×10^{-13} (f) 1.1×10^{-7}

36. 5.9×10^{-9}

37. Since the problem gives a K_b value, the substance must be a weak base (even if the substance is amphiprotic it still acts as a weak base rather than a strong base).

38. (a) $HNO_2 + NH_3 \rightleftharpoons NO_2^- + NH_4^+$; conjugate pairs = ($HNO_2$, NO_2^-) and (NH_3, NH_4^+)
(b) $CO_3^{2-} + HF \rightleftharpoons HCO_3^- + F^-$; conjugate pairs = ($CO_3^{2-}$, HCO_3^-) and (HF, F^-)
(c) $HS^- + H_3PO_4 \rightleftharpoons H_2S + H_2PO_4^-$; conjugate pairs = ($HS^-$, H_2S) and (H_3PO_4, $H_2PO_4^-$)
(d) $HCO_3^- + S^{2-} \rightleftharpoons CO_3^{2-} + HS^-$; conjugate pairs = ($HCO_3^-$, CO_3^{2-}) and (S^{2-}, HS^-)
(e) $HCOOH + CN^- \rightleftharpoons HCOO^- + HCN$; conjugate pairs = (HCOOH, $HCOO^-$) and (CN^-, HCN)
(f) $H_3BO_3 + HO_2^- \rightleftharpoons H_2BO_3^- + H_2O_2$; conjugate pairs = ($H_3BO_3$, $H_2BO_3^-$) and (HO_2^-, H_2O_2)
(g) $HSO_3^- + OH^- \rightleftharpoons SO_3^{2-} + H_2O$; conjugate pairs = ($HSO_3^-$, SO_3^{2-}) and (OH^-, H_2O)
(h) $H_2O + H_2SO_3 \rightleftharpoons H_3O^+ + HSO_3^-$; conjugate pairs = ($H_2O$, H_3O^+) and (H_2SO_3, HSO_3^-)

39. (a) products (H_2S is a stronger acid than NH_4^+)

or: $$K_{eq} = \frac{K_a(H_2S)}{K_a(NH_4^+)} = \frac{9.1 \times 10^{-8}}{5.6 \times 10^{-10}} = 1.6 \times 10^{2} = \frac{[\text{products}]}{[\text{reactants}]}$$

and since $K_{eq} > 1$ then products are favoured.

(b) reactants (H_2S is a stronger acid than $H_2PO_4^-$)

or: $$K_{eq} = \frac{K_a(H_2PO_4^-)}{K_a(H_2S)} = \frac{6.2 \times 10^{-8}}{9.1 \times 10^{-8}} = 0.68 = \frac{[\text{products}]}{[\text{reactants}]}$$

and since $K_{eq} < 1$ then reactants are favoured (barely).

(c) products (NH_4^+ is a stronger acid than H_2O)

or: $$K_{eq} = \frac{K_a(NH_4^+)}{K_a(H_2O)} = \frac{5.6 \times 10^{-10}}{1.0 \times 10^{-14}} = 5.6 \times 10^{4} = \frac{[\text{products}]}{[\text{reactants}]}$$

and since $K_{eq} > 1$ then products are favoured.

(d) reactants (HSO_3^- is a stronger acid than H_2O_2)

or: $$K_{eq} = \frac{K_a(H_2O_2)}{K_a(HSO_3^-)} = \frac{2.4 \times 10^{-12}}{1.0 \times 10^{-7}} = 2.4 \times 10^{-5} = \frac{[\text{products}]}{[\text{reactants}]}$$

and since $K_{eq} < 1$ then reactants are favoured.

(e) products (CH_3COOH is a stronger acid than HPO_4^{2-})

or: $$K_{eq} = \frac{K_a(CH_3COOH)}{K_a(HPO_4^{2-})} = \frac{1.8 \times 10^{-5}}{2.2 \times 10^{-13}} = 8.2 \times 10^{7} = \frac{[\text{products}]}{[\text{reactants}]}$$

and since $K_{eq} > 1$ then products are favoured.

40. (a) $HSO_4^- + NO_2^- \rightleftharpoons SO_4^{2-} + HNO_2$

and: $K_a(HSO_4^-) > K_a(HNO_2)$, so that HSO_4^- has a greater tendency to dissociate and products are favoured.

or: $$K_{eq} = \frac{K_a(HSO_4^-)}{K_a(HNO_2)} = \frac{1.2 \times 10^{-2}}{4.6 \times 10^{-4}} = 26 = \frac{[\text{products}]}{[\text{reactants}]}$$

and since $K_{eq} > 1$ then products are favoured.

(b) $H_3PO_4 + HPO_4^{2-} \rightleftharpoons H_2PO_4^- + H_2PO_4^-$

and: $K_a(H_3PO_4) > K_a(H_2PO_4^-)$, so that H_3PO_4 has a greater tendency to dissociate and products are favoured.

or: $$K_{eq} = \frac{K_a(H_3PO_4)}{K_a(H_2PO_4^-)} = \frac{7.5 \times 10^{-3}}{6.2 \times 10^{-8}} = 1.2 \times 10^5 = \frac{[\text{products}]}{[\text{reactants}]}$$

and since $K_{eq} > 1$ then products are favoured.

(c) $HCO_3^- + HSO_3^- \rightleftharpoons H_2CO_3 + SO_3^{2-}$

and: $K_a(HSO_3^-) < K_a(H_2CO_3)$, so that H_2CO_3 has a greater tendency to dissociate and reactants are favoured.

or: $$K_{eq} = \frac{K_a(HSO_3^-)}{K_a(H_2CO_3)} = \frac{1.0 \times 10^{-7}}{4.3 \times 10^{-7}} = 0.23 = \frac{[\text{products}]}{[\text{reactants}]}$$

and since $K_{eq} < 1$ then reactants are favoured.

(d) $NH_4F \longrightarrow NH_4^+ + F^-$ (salts are 100% dissociated)

$NH_4^+ + F^- \rightleftharpoons NH_3 + HF$

and: $K_a(NH_4^+) < K_a(HF)$, so that HF has a greater tendency to dissociate and reactants are favoured.

or: $$K_{eq} = \frac{K_a(NH_4^+)}{K_a(HF)} = \frac{5.6 \times 10^{-10}}{3.5 \times 10^{-4}} = 1.6 \times 10^{-6} = \frac{[\text{products}]}{[\text{reactants}]}$$

and since $K_{eq} < 1$ then reactants are favoured.

(e) $HSO_3^- + HC_2O_4^- \rightleftharpoons H_2SO_3 + C_2O_4^{2-}$ ($HC_2O_4^-$ is a stronger acid than HSO_3^-)

and: $K_a(HC_2O_4^-) < K_a(H_2SO_3)$, so that H_2SO_3 has a greater tendency to dissociate and reactants are favoured.

or: $$K_{eq} = \frac{K_a(HC_2O_4^-)}{K_a(H_2SO_3)} = \frac{6.4 \times 10^{-5}}{1.5 \times 10^{-2}} = 4.3 \times 10^{-3} = \frac{[\text{products}]}{[\text{reactants}]}$$

and since $K_{eq} < 1$ then reactants are favoured.

(f) $H_2O_2 + HS^- \rightleftharpoons HO_2^- + H_2S$

and: $K_a(H_2O_2) < K_a(H_2S)$, so that H_2S has a greater tendency to dissociate (reactants are favoured).

or: $$K_{eq} = \frac{K_a(H_2O_2)}{K_a(H_2S)} = \frac{2.4 \times 10^{-12}}{9.1 \times 10^{-8}} = 2.6 \times 10^{-5} = \frac{[\text{products}]}{[\text{reactants}]}$$

and since $K_{eq} < 1$ then reactants are favoured.

(g) $(NH_4)_2CO_3 \longrightarrow 2\,NH_4^+ + CO_3^{2-}$ (salts are 100% dissociated)

$NH_4^+ + CO_3^{2-} \rightleftharpoons NH_3 + HCO_3^-$

and: $K_a(NH_4^+) > K_a(HCO_3^-)$, so that NH_4^+ has a greater tendency to dissociate and products are favoured.

(Note that only one proton is transferred; the fact that $[NH_4^+]$ is twice $[CO_3^{2-}]$ when $(NH_4)_2CO_3$ dissociates will only push the equilibrium farther to the products side than might otherwise occur if all reactant concentrations were 1 M.)

or: $$K_{eq} = \frac{K_a(NH_4^+)}{K_a(HCO_3^-)} = \frac{5.6 \times 10^{-10}}{5.6 \times 10^{-11}} = 1.0 \times 10^1 = \frac{[\text{products}]}{[\text{reactants}]}$$

and since $K_{eq} > 1$ then products are favoured.

(h) $H_2S + NO_2^- \rightleftharpoons HS^- + HNO_2$

and: $K_a(H_2S) < K_a(HNO_2)$, so that HNO_2 has a greater tendency to dissociate and reactants are favoured.

or: $$K_{eq} = \frac{K_a(H_2S)}{K_a(HNO_2)} = \frac{9.1 \times 10^{-8}}{4.6 \times 10^{-4}} = 2.0 \times 10^{-4} = \frac{[\text{products}]}{[\text{reactants}]}$$

and since $K_{eq} < 1$ then reactants are favoured.

(i) $Cr(H_2O)_6^{3+} + H_2PO_4^- \rightleftharpoons Cr(H_2O)_5(OH)^{2+} + H_3PO_4$

and: $K_a(H_3PO_4) > K_a(Cr(H_2O)_6^{3+})$, so that H_3PO_4 has a greater tendency to dissociate and reactants are favoured.

or: $$K_{eq} = \frac{K_a(Cr(H_2O)_6^{3+})}{K_a(H_3PO_4)} = \frac{1.5 \times 10^{-4}}{7.5 \times 10^{-3}} = 0.020 = \frac{[\text{products}]}{[\text{reactants}]}$$

and since $K_{eq} < 1$ then reactants are favoured.

(j) $H_2C_6H_5O_7^- + HSO_3^- \rightleftharpoons HC_6H_5O_7^{2-} + H_2SO_3$

and: $K_a(H_2C_6H_5O_7^-) < K_a(H_2SO_3)$, so that H_2SO_3 has a greater tendency to dissociate and reactants are favoured.

or: $$K_{eq} = \frac{K_a(H_2C_6H_5O_7^-)}{K_a(H_2SO_3)} = \frac{1.7 \times 10^{-5}}{1.5 \times 10^{-2}} = 1.1 \times 10^{-3} = \frac{[\text{products}]}{[\text{reactants}]}$$

and since $K_{eq} < 1$ then reactants are favoured.

41. (a) H_2Te (b) HSe^- c) STRONGER ACID + STRONGER BASE $\rightleftharpoons$ weaker base + weaker acid

42. greater than 1 since HSO_4^- is a stronger acid than NH_4^+ and forces the equilibrium to the products side.

or: $$K_{eq} = \frac{K_a(HSO_4^-)}{K_a(NH_4^+)} = \frac{1.2 \times 10^{-2}}{5.6 \times 10^{-10}} = 2.1 \times 10^7 > 1.$$

43. (a) X^- and A^- (b) X^- is weaker; if reactants are favoured, then HX is stronger than HA. Since the stronger the acid, the weaker its conjugate base, then X^- is weaker.

44. (a) HSO_4^- is stronger than HSe^-

(b) $NaHSe \longrightarrow Na^+ + HSe^-$; the added HSe^- shifts the equilibrium more to the reactants side.

45. $HOCl > HOBr > H_3GeO_4 > HOI$

46. In the equilibrium: $HX + F^- \rightleftharpoons X^- + HF$ the reactants are favoured if $K_a(HX) < K_a(HF)$. Only HCOOH has a K_a value less than the K_a value for HF, and therefore only HCOOH forms an equilibrium where reactants are favoured.

47. (a) 2 (b) −7 (c) −3 (d) −5.253 (e) 0.00 (f) −10.435

48. (a) 100 (b) 10^{-3} (c) 10 (d) 234 (e) 7.00×10^{-7} (f) 1.24×10^{-9}

49. (a) pH = 5.00 , pOH = 9.00
(b) pH = 11.877 , pOH = 2.123
(c) pH = 8.69 , pOH = 5.31
(d) pH = −1.097 , pOH = 15.097
(e) pH = 12.097 , pOH = 1.903
(f) pH = 0.00 , pOH = 14.00
(g) pH = 8.28 , pOH = 5.72
(h) pH = −0.070 , pOH = 14.070

50. (a) $[H_3O^+] = 1 \times 10^{-3}$ M , $[OH^-] = 1 \times 10^{-11}$ M
(b) $[H_3O^+] = 4.30 \times 10^{-9}$ M , $[OH^-] = 2.33 \times 10^{-6}$ M
(c) $[H_3O^+] = 3.86 \times 10^{-7}$ M , $[OH^-] = 2.59 \times 10^{-8}$ M
(d) $[H_3O^+] = 3.2 \times 10^{-9}$ M , $[OH^-] = 3.2 \times 10^{-6}$ M
(e) $[H_3O^+] = 3.5$ M , $[OH^-] = 2.8 \times 10^{-15}$ M
(f) $[H_3O^+] = 3.48 \times 10^{-3}$ M , $[OH^-] = 2.87 \times 10^{-12}$ M
(g) $[H_3O^+] = 3.64 \times 10^{-5}$ M , $[OH^-] = 2.75 \times 10^{-10}$ M
(h) $[H_3O^+] = 2.2 \times 10^{-3}$ M , $[OH^-] = 4.5 \times 10^{-12}$ M

51. (a) the pH decreases (b) the pOH decreases (c) pK_w decreases

52. Since the water is still neutral, then pH = pOH. Also, pH + pOH = pK_w = 2(pH). Then pH = pOH = 1/2 pK_w = 6.509 , and $[H_3O^+] = [OH^-]$ = antilog(−6.509) = 3.10×10^{-7} M.

53. HA will have the greater conductivity: it has a lower pH and is a stronger acid (greater dissociation into ions).

54. Reject the argument. The calculated $[OH^-]$ of 1.82×10^{-32} M represents the $[OH^-]$ **added to** the $[OH^-]$ which already exists in the oceans. Since the pre–existing $[OH^-]$ is 1.0×10^{-7} M, the new $[OH^-]$ will be: 1.0×10^{-7} M + 1.82×10^{-32} M, and the added OH^- has no effect on the oceans.

55. (a) acidic (b) acidic (c) basic (d) basic (e) neutral (f) acidic (g) basic (h) basic (i) neutral (j) acidic

56. (a) $[H_3O^+]$ decreases by a factor of 100
(b) $[H_3O^+]$ increases by a factor of 1000
(c) $[H_3O^+]$ increases by a factor of 10
(d) $[OH^-]$ decreases by a factor of 100

57. Since $Zn(OH)_2(s)$ has a low solubility in water, the addition of Zn^{2+} removes OH^- ions from solution and decreases the pH: $Zn^{2+} + 2\,OH^- \rightleftharpoons Zn(OH)_2(s)$.

58. $[H_3O^+] = 0.200\text{ M} \times \frac{50.0\text{ mL}}{100.0\text{ mL}} = 0.100\text{ M}$, $[OH^-] = 0.150\text{ M} \times \frac{50.0\text{ mL}}{100.0\text{ mL}} = 0.0750\text{ M}$
$[H_3O^+]_{XS} = 0.100 - 0.075 = 0.025$ M , and **pH = 1.60**

59. $[H_3O^+] = 0.200\text{ M} \times \frac{75.0\text{ mL}}{300.0\text{ mL}} = 0.0500\text{ M}$, $[OH^-] = 0.150\text{ M} \times \frac{225.0\text{ mL}}{300.0\text{ mL}} = 0.1125\text{ M}$
$[OH^-]_{XS} = 0.1125 - 0.0500 = 0.0625$ M , and **pOH = 1.204**

60. $[H_3O^+] = 0.0120\text{ M} \times \frac{125.0\text{ mL}}{150.0\text{ mL}} = 0.0100\text{ M}$, $[OH^-] = 0.0420\text{ M} \times 2 \times \frac{25.0\text{ mL}}{150.0\text{ mL}} = 0.0140\text{ M}$
$[OH^-]_{XS} = 0.0140 - 0.0100 = 0.0040$ M , so that pOH = 2.40 and **pH = 11.60**

61. $[OH^-] = 0.0185\text{ M} \times 2 \times \frac{50.0\text{ mL}}{85.0\text{ mL}} = 0.02176\text{ M}$, $[H_3O^+] = \frac{0.130\text{ g}}{0.0850\text{ L}} \times \frac{1\text{ mol}}{36.5\text{ g}} = 0.04190\text{ M}$
$[H_3O^+]_{XS} = 0.04190 - 0.02176 = 0.02014$ M, so that pH = 1.696 and **pOH = 12.304**

62. $[H_3O^+] = \frac{6.00\text{ g}}{0.2000\text{ L}} \times \frac{1\text{ mol}}{36.5\text{ g}} = 0.8219\text{ M}$, $[OH^-] = \frac{5.00\text{ g}}{0.2000\text{ L}} \times \frac{1\text{ mol}}{56.1\text{ g}} = 0.4456\text{ M}$
$[H_3O^+]_{XS} = 0.8219 - 0.4456 = 0.3763$, and **pH = 0.424**

63. $[H_3O^+] = \frac{8.09\text{ g}}{0.350\text{ L}} \times \frac{1\text{ mol}}{80.9\text{ g}} = 0.2857\text{ M}$, $[OH^-] = \frac{6.08\text{ g}}{0.350\text{ L}} \times \frac{1\text{ mol}}{121.6\text{ g}} \times 2 = 0.2857\text{ M}$
Since $[H_3O^+] = [OH^-]$, the solution is neutral and **pOH = 7**

64. $[H_3O^+] = \frac{9.50\text{ g}}{0.2000\text{ L}} \times \frac{1\text{ mol}}{127.9\text{ g}} = 0.3714\text{ M}$, $[OH^-] = \frac{0.450\text{ g}}{0.2000\text{ L}} \times \frac{1\text{ mol}}{23.9\text{ g}} = 0.09414\text{ M}$
$[H_3O^+]_{XS} = 0.3714 - 0.09414 = 0.2772\text{ M}$, and **pH = 0.557**

65. pH = 10.875 means pOH = 3.125, and $[OH^-]_{XS} = 7.499 \times 10^{-4}\text{ M}$
$7.499 \times 10^{-4} = 0.00120 - [H_3O^+]_{ST}$, and $[H_3O^+]_{ST} = 4.501 \times 10^{-4}\text{ M}$
mass HCl $= 4.501 \times 10^{-4} \frac{\text{mol}}{\text{L}} \times 2.000\text{ L} \times \frac{36.5\text{ g}}{1\text{ mol}} = \mathbf{0.033\text{ g}}$

66. pH = 2.500 gives $[H_3O^+]_{XS} = 0.003162\text{ M}$
$0.003162 = 0.0550 - [OH^-]_{ST}$, and $[OH^-]_{ST} = 0.05184\text{ M}$
mass LiOH $= 0.05184 \frac{\text{mol}}{\text{L}} \times 0.7500\text{ L} \times \frac{23.9\text{ g}}{1\text{ mol}} = \mathbf{0.929\text{ g}}$

67. pH = 2.750 gives $[H_3O^+] = 1.778 \times 10^{-3}\text{ M}$
$1.778 \times 10^{-3} = 0.0150 - [OH^-]_{ST}$, and $[OH^-]_{ST} = 0.01322\text{ M}$
mass $Ca(OH)_2 = 0.01322 \frac{\text{mol OH}^-}{\text{L}} \times \frac{1\text{ mol Ca(OH)}_2}{2\text{ mol OH}^-} \times 0.5000\text{ L} \times \frac{74.1\text{ g}}{1\text{ mol Ca(OH)}_2} = \mathbf{0.245\text{ g}}$

68. (a) $Ca(OH)_2 \rightleftharpoons Ca^{2+} + 2\,OH^-$; $K_{sp} = [Ca^{2+}][OH^-]^2 = 3.88 \times 10^{-5}$
X 2X $= (X)(2X)^2 = 4X^3 = 3.88 \times 10^{-5}$
Solving: X = 0.0213 M and $[OH^-] = 2X = 0.0426\text{ M}$, so pOH = 1.370 and **pH = 12.630**

(b) The equilibrium which exists in the solution is: $Ca(OH)_{2(s)} \rightleftharpoons Ca^{2+} + 2\,OH^-$. If HCl is added, the $[OH^-]$ will be decreased as a result of being neutralized by the added HCl. Therefore, the equilibrium shifts to the product side to make up for the decreased $[OH^-]$ and the solid $Ca(OH)_2$ will dissolve.

69. (a) $Na_2SO_3 \longrightarrow 2\,Na^+ + SO_3^{2-}$; $SO_3^{2-} + H_2O \rightleftharpoons HSO_3^- + OH^-$ (basic solution)

(b) $Na_2HPO_4 \longrightarrow 2\,Na^+ + HPO_4^{2-}$

Since $K_b(HPO_4^{2-}) = \frac{K_w}{K_a(H_2PO_4^-)} = \frac{1.0 \times 10^{-14}}{6.2 \times 10^{-8}} = 1.6 \times 10^{-7} > K_a(HPO_4^{2-}) = 2.2 \times 10^{-13}$

then HPO_4^{2-} acts preferentially as a base: $HPO_4^{2-} + H_2O \rightleftharpoons H_2PO_4^- + OH^-$ (basic solution)

(c) $LiBr \longrightarrow Li^+ + Br^-$; no hydrolysis occurs (neutral solution)

(d) $K_2CO_3 \longrightarrow 2\,K^+ + CO_3^{2-}$; $CO_3^{2-} + H_2O \rightleftharpoons HCO_3^- + OH^-$ (basic solution)

(e) $NH_4CH_3COO \longrightarrow NH_4^+ + CH_3COO^-$ and: $NH_4^+ + H_2O \rightleftharpoons NH_3 + H_3O^+$; $K_a(NH_4^+) = 5.6 \times 10^{-10}$

$CH_3COO^- + H_2O \rightleftharpoons CH_3COOH + OH^-$; $K_b(CH_3COO^-) = \frac{K_w}{K_a(CH_3COOH)} = \frac{1.0 \times 10^{-14}}{1.8 \times 10^{-5}}$
$= 5.6 \times 10^{-10}$

Since $K_a(NH_4^+) = K_b(CH_3COO^-)$ then the solution is neutral.

(f) $Na_2HC_6H_5O_7 \longrightarrow 2\,Na^+ + HC_6H_5O_7^{2-}$

Since: $K_a(HC_6H_5O_7^{2-}) = 4.1 \times 10^{-7} > K_b(HC_6H_5O_7^{2-}) = \dfrac{K_w}{K_a(H_2C_6H_5O_7^-)} = \dfrac{1.0 \times 10^{-14}}{1.7 \times 10^{-5}}$

$= 5.9 \times 10^{-10}$

then $HC_6H_5O_7^{2-}$ produces an acidic solution: $HC_6H_5O_7^{2-} + H_2O \rightleftharpoons H_3O^+ + C_6H_5O_7^{3-}$.

(g) $K_2C_2O_4 \longrightarrow 2\,K^+ + C_2O_4^{2-}$; $C_2O_4^{2-} + H_2O \rightleftharpoons HC_2O_4^- + OH^-$ (basic solution)

(h) $Ca(NO_3)_2 \longrightarrow Ca^{2+} + 2\,NO_3^-$; no hydrolysis occurs (neutral solution)

(i) $Al(H_2O)_6Cl_3 \longrightarrow Al(H_2O)_6^{3+} + 3\,Cl^-$; $Al(H_2O)_6^{3+} + H_2O \rightleftharpoons Al(H_2O)_5(OH)^{2+} + H_3O^+$ (acidic solution)

(j) $NH_4F \longrightarrow NH_4^+ + F^-$

$NH_4^+ + H_2O \rightleftharpoons NH_3 + H_3O^+$; $K_a(NH_4^+) = 5.6 \times 10^{-10}$

$F^- + H_2O \rightleftharpoons HF + OH^-$; $K_b(F^-) = \dfrac{K_w}{K_a(HF)} = \dfrac{1.00 \times 10^{-14}}{3.5 \times 10^{-4}} = 2.9 \times 10^{-11}$

Since $K_a(NH_4^+) > K_b(F^-)$ the solution is acidic.

70. (a) basic
(b) neutral
(c) acidic
(d) neutral
(e) basic
(f) basic
(g) acidic; $K_a(HSO_3^-) = 1.0 \times 10^{-7} > K_b(HSO_3^-) = 6.7 \times 10^{-13}$
(h) basic; $K_b(HPO_4^{2-}) = 1.6 \times 10^{-7} > K_a(HPO_4^{2-}) = 2.2 \times 10^{-13}$
(i) basic
(j) basic; $K_b(C_6H_5O_7^{3-}) = 2.4 \times 10^{-8} > K_a(NH_4^+) = 5.6 \times 10^{-10}$

71. The $NaNO_2$ dissociates to form Na^+ and NO_2^-. Na^+ is a spectator but NO_2^- is a weak base:

$NO_2^- + H_2O \rightleftharpoons HNO_2 + OH^-$ (produces a low $[OH^-]$)

The $Fe(OH)_3$ is a strong base (it is a metal hydroxide) BUT $Fe(OH)_3$ has a very low solubility:

$Fe(OH)_3(s) \rightleftharpoons Fe^{3+} + 3\,OH^-$ (produces a low $[OH^-]$)

72. Since the reaction of each substance with water occurs as follows:

$KF \longrightarrow K^+ + F^-$ (100% dissociated into ions)

$HF \rightleftharpoons H^+ + F^-$ (slightly dissociated into ions)

then 1 M KF contains more ions and has the greater conductivity.

73. Highest: **NaOH** is a strong base

$NaCH_3COO$ contains CH_3COO^- (a weak base)

NH_4CH_3COO is neutral (NH_4^+ has $K_a = 5.6 \times 10^{-10}$, CH_3COO^- has $K_b = 5.6 \times 10^{-10}$)

NH_4Cl contains NH_4^+ (a weak acid)

Lowest: **HCl** is a strong acid

74.

	H_2S + H_2O ⇌	HS^- +	H_3O^+
ST	0.050	0	0
+Δ	−X	+X	+X
= EQ	0.050 − X	X	X

; Assume: $0.050 - X \cong 0.050$

$K_a = \dfrac{[H_3O^+][HS^-]}{[H_2S]} = 9.1 \times 10^{-8} = \dfrac{X^2}{0.050}$

Solving: $X = [H_3O^+] = \mathbf{6.7 \times 10^{-5}\ M}$

75. $H_2O_2 + H_2O \rightleftharpoons HO_2^- + H_3O^+$

	H_2O_2	HO_2^-	H_3O^+
ST	0.20	0	0
+Δ	−X	X	X
= EQ	0.20 − X	X	X

; Assume: $0.20 - X \cong 0.20$

$$K_a = \frac{[H_3O^+][HO_2^-]}{[H_2O_2]} = 2.4 \times 10^{-12} = \frac{X^2}{0.20}$$

Solving $X = [H_3O^+] = 6.9 \times 10^{-7}$ M, and pH = **6.16**

76. $[H_3O^+]$ = antilog(−1.93) = 1.17×10^{-2} M

$HCOOH + H_2O \rightleftharpoons HCOO^- + H_3O^+$

	$HCOOH$	$HCOO^-$	H_3O^+
ST	X	0	0
+Δ	-1.17×10^{-2}	$+1.17 \times 10^{-2}$	$+1.17 \times 10^{-2}$
= EQ	$X - 1.17 \times 10^{-2}$	1.17×10^{-2}	1.17×10^{-2}

$$K_a = \frac{[H_3O^+][HCOO^-]}{[HCOOH]} = 1.8 \times 10^{-4} = \frac{(1.17 \times 10^{-2})^2}{X - 1.17 \times 10^{-2}}$$

Solving X = [HCOOH] = **0.78 M**

77. $[H_3O^+]$ = antilog(−1.357) = 0.04395 M

$HX + H_2O \rightleftharpoons H_3O^+ + X^-$

	HX	H_3O^+	X^-
ST	0.250	0	0
+Δ	−0.04395	+0.04395	+0.04395
= EQ	0.2060	0.04395	0.04395

; The amount of ionization is not negligible.

$$K_a = \frac{[H_3O^+][X^-]}{[HX]} = \frac{(0.04395)^2}{0.2060} = \mathbf{9.38 \times 10^{-3}}$$

78. $[H_3O^+]$ = antilog(−4.18) = 6.61×10^{-5} M

$H_2CO_3 + H_2O \rightleftharpoons HCO_3^- + H_3O^+$

	H_2CO_3	HCO_3^-	H_3O^+
ST	X	0	0
+Δ	-6.61×10^{-5}	$+6.61 \times 10^{-5}$	$+6.61 \times 10^{-5}$
= EQ	$X - 6.61 \times 10^{-5}$	6.61×10^{-5}	6.61×10^{-5}

$$K_a = \frac{[H_3O^+][HCO_3^-]}{[H_2CO_3]} = 4.3 \times 10^{-7} = \frac{(6.61 \times 10^{-5})^2}{X - 6.61 \times 10^{-5}}$$

Solving $X = [H_2CO_3] = [CO_2(aq)]$ = **0.010 M**

79. $NH_4NO_3 \longrightarrow NH_4^+ + NO_3^-$ (NO_3^- = spectator)

$NH_4^+ + H_2O \rightleftharpoons NH_3 + H_3O^+$

	NH_4^+	NH_3	H_3O^+
ST	0.30	0	0
+Δ	−X	+X	+X
= EQ	0.30 − X	X	X

; Assume: $0.30 - X \cong 0.30$

$$K_a = \frac{[H_3O^+][NH_3]}{[NH_4^+]} = 5.6 \times 10^{-10} = \frac{X^2}{0.30}$$

Solving $X = [H_3O^+] = 1.3 \times 10^{-5}$ M, and pH = **4.89**

80. $[H_3O^+]$ = antilog(–5.343) = 4.539×10^{-6} M

	$HOBr + H_2O \rightleftharpoons$	H_3O^+ +	OBr^-
ST	0.100	0	0
+Δ	-4.539×10^{-6}	$+4.539 \times 10^{-6}$	$+4.539 \times 10^{-6}$
= EQ	$0.100 - 4.539 \times 10^{-6}$	4.539×10^{-6}	4.539×10^{-6}

Assume: $0.100 - 4.539 \times 10^{-6} \cong 0.100$

$$K_a = \frac{[H_3O^+][OBr^-]}{[HOBr]} = \frac{(4.539 \times 10^{-6})^2}{0.100} = \mathbf{2.06 \times 10^{-10}}$$

81. $Fe(H_2O)_6Cl_3 \longrightarrow Fe(H_2O)_6^{3+} + 3\,Cl^-$ (Cl^- is a spectator)

	$Fe(H_2O)_6^{3+} + H_2O \rightleftharpoons$	$Fe(H_2O)_5(OH)^{2+}$ +	H_3O^+
ST	3.0	0	0
+Δ	–X	+X	+X
= EQ	3.0 – X	X	X

; Assume: 3.0 – X ≅ 3.0

$$K_a = \frac{[H_3O^+][Fe(H_2O)_5(OH)^{2+}]}{[Fe(H_2O)_6^{3+}]} = 6.0 \times 10^{-3} = \frac{X^2}{3.0}$$

Solving X = $[H_3O^+]$ = 0.134 M, and pH = **0.87**

82. $[H_3O^+]$ = antilog(–2.00) = 0.010 M

	$HBr + H_2O \rightleftharpoons$	H_3O^+ +	Br^-
ST	0.010	0	0
+Δ	–0.010	+0.010	+0.010
= EQ	0	0.010	0.010

$$K_a = \frac{[H_3O^+][Br^-]}{[HBr]} = \frac{(0.010)^2}{0}$$, and the value is undefined (HBr is a strong acid)

83. $[H_3O^+]$ = antilog(–3.00) = 0.0010 M

	$CH_3COOH + H_2O \rightleftharpoons$	CH_3COO^- +	H_3O^+
ST	X	0	0
+Δ	–0.0010	+0.0010	+0.0010
= EQ	X – 0.0010	0.0010	0.0010

; Assume: X – 0.0010 ≅ X

$$K_a = \frac{[H_3O^+][CH_3COO^-]}{[CH_3COOH]} = 1.8 \times 10^{-5} = \frac{(0.0010)^2}{X}.$$ Solving: X = $[CH_3COOH]$ = 0.0556 M

$$\text{mass } CH_3COOH = 0.0556\ \frac{mol}{L} \times 0.100\ L \times \frac{60.0\ g}{1\ mol} = \mathbf{0.33\ g}$$

84. pOH = 14.000 – 9.69 = 4.31 , $[OH^-]$ = antilog(–4.31) = 4.90 x 10^{-5} M

	$SO_3^{2-} + H_2O \rightleftharpoons$	HSO_3^-	+ OH^-
ST	X	0	0
+Δ	-4.90×10^{-5}	$+4.90 \times 10^{-5}$	$+4.90 \times 10^{-5}$
= EQ	$X - 4.90 \times 10^{-5}$	4.90×10^{-5}	4.90×10^{-5}

; Assume: $X - 4.90 \times 10^{-5} \cong X$

$$K_b = \frac{[HSO_3^-][OH^-]}{[SO_3^{2-}]} = \frac{K_w}{K_a(HSO_3^-)} = \frac{1.0 \times 10^{-14}}{1.0 \times 10^{-7}} = 1.0 \times 10^{-7} = \frac{(4.909 \times 10^{-5})^2}{X}$$

Solving $X = [SO_3^{2-}] = $ **0.024 M**

85.

	$NH_3 + H_2O \rightleftharpoons$	NH_4^+	+ OH^-
ST	0.20	0	0
+Δ	–X	+X	+X
= EQ	0.20 – X	X	X

; Assume: $0.20 - X \cong 0.20$

$$K_b = \frac{[NH_4^+][OH^-]}{[NH_3]} = \frac{K_w}{K_a(NH_4^+)} = \frac{1.0 \times 10^{-14}}{5.6 \times 10^{-10}} = 1.79 \times 10^{-5} = \frac{X^2}{0.20}$$

Solving $X = [OH^-] =$ **1.9×10^{-3} M**, $[H_3O^+] =$ **5.3×10^{-12} M**, pOH = **2.72**, pH = **11.28**

86. pOH = 14.00 – 10.50 = 3.5 , $[OH^-]$ = antilog(–3.50) = 3.16 x 10^{-4} M

	$N_2H_4 + H_2O \rightleftharpoons$	$N_2H_5^+$	+ OH^-
ST	X	0	0
+Δ	-3.16×10^{-4}	$+3.16 \times 10^{-4}$	$+3.16 \times 10^{-4}$
= EQ	$X - 3.16 \times 10^{-4}$	3.16×10^{-4}	3.16×10^{-4}

; Assume: $X - 3.16 \times 10^{-4} \cong X$

$$K_b = \frac{[N_2H_5^+][OH^-]}{[N_2H_4]} = 1.7 \times 10^{-6} = \frac{(3.16 \times 10^{-4})^2}{X}$$

Solving $X = [N_2H_4] = $ **0.059 M**

87. pOH = 14.000 – 12.438 = 1.562 , $[OH^-]$ = 0.02742 M

	$Te^{2-} + H_2O \rightleftharpoons$	HTe^-	+ OH^-
ST	0.75	0	0
+Δ	–0.02742	+0.02742	+0.02742
= EQ	0.723	0.02742	0.02742

$$K_b = \frac{[HTe^-][OH^-]}{[Te^{2-}]} = \frac{(0.02742)^2}{0.723} = \mathbf{1.04 \times 10^{-3}}$$

88. $NaCN \longrightarrow Na^+ + CN^-$

	$CN^- + H_2O \rightleftharpoons$	HCN	+ OH^-
ST	0.50	0	0
+Δ	–X	+X	+X
= EQ	0.50 – X	X	X

; Assume: $0.50 - X \cong 0.50$

$$K_b = \frac{[HCN][OH^-]}{[CN^-]} = \frac{K_w}{K_a(HCN)} = \frac{1.0 \times 10^{-14}}{4.9 \times 10^{-10}} = 2.04 \times 10^{-5} = \frac{X^2}{0.50}$$

Solving $X = [OH^-] = 3.19 \times 10^{-3}$ M, and pOH = 2.496 , and pH = **11.50**

89. pOH = 14.000 – 9.904 = 4.096 , $[OH^-] = 8.017 \times 10^{-5}$ M

	$NH_2OH + H_2O \rightleftharpoons$	NH_3OH^+	+ OH^-
ST	0.600	0	0
+Δ	-8.017×10^{-5}	$+8.017 \times 10^{-5}$	$+8.017 \times 10^{-5}$
= EQ	$0.600 - 8.017 \times 10^{-5}$	8.017×10^{-5}	8.017×10^{-5}

Assume: $0.600 - 8.017 \times 10^{-5} \cong 0.600$

$$K_b = \frac{[NH_3OH^+][OH^-]}{[NH_2OH]} = \frac{(8.017 \times 10^{-5})^2}{0.600} = 1.07 \times 10^{-8}$$

and: $K_a(NH_3OH^+) = \frac{K_w}{K_b(NH_2OH)} = \frac{1.0 \times 10^{-14}}{1.07 \times 10^{-8}} = \mathbf{9.34 \times 10^{-7}}$

90. $NaC_6H_5O \longrightarrow Na^+ + C_6H_5O^-$

	$C_6H_5O^- + H_2O \rightleftharpoons$	C_6H_5OH	+ OH^-
ST	0.80	0	0
+Δ	–X	+X	+X
= EQ	0.80 – X	X	X

; Assume: $0.80 - X \cong 0.80$

$$K_b = \frac{[C_6H_5OH][OH^-]}{[C_6H_5O^-]} = \frac{K_w}{K_a(C_6H_5OH)} = \frac{1.0 \times 10^{-14}}{1.3 \times 10^{-10}} = 7.69 \times 10^{-5} = \frac{X^2}{0.80}$$

Solving $X = [OH^-] = 7.84 \times 10^{-3}$ M, and pOH = 2.105 , and pH = **11.89**

91.

	$NH_3 + H_2O \rightleftharpoons$	NH_4^+	+ OH^-
ST	X	0	0
+Δ	–0.0130 X	+0.0130 X	+0.0130 X
= EQ	0.987 X	0.0130 X	0.0130 X

$$K_b = \frac{[NH_4^+][OH^-]}{[NH_3]} = \frac{K_w}{K_a(NH_4^+)} = \frac{1.0 \times 10^{-14}}{5.6 \times 10^{-10}} = 1.79 \times 10^{-5} = \frac{(0.0130\ X)^2}{0.987\ X} = \frac{(0.0130)^2\ X}{0.987}$$

Solving $X = [NH_3] =$ **0.10 M**, $[OH^-] = 0.0130\ X =$ **0.0014 M**

92. $CaF_2(s) \rightleftharpoons Ca^{2+} + 2F^-$; $K_{sp} = [Ca^{2+}][F^-]^2 = 1.46 \times 10^{-10}$

–X X 2X $= (X)(2X)^2 = 4X^3 = 1.46 \times 10^{-10}$

Solving $X = 3.317 \times 10^{-4}$ M = $[CaF_2]$ and $[F^-] = 2X = 6.634 \times 10^{-4}$ M

The F^- undergoes base dissociation in water.

	F^- + $H_2O \rightleftharpoons$	HF	+ OH^-
ST	6.634×10^{-4}	0	0
+Δ	–Y	+Y	+Y
= EQ	$6.634 \times 10^{-4} - Y$	Y	Y

; Assume that $6.634 \times 10^{-4} - Y \cong 6.634 \times 10^{-4}$

$$K_b(F^-) = \frac{[HF][OH^-]}{[F^-]} = \frac{K_w}{K_a(HF)} = \frac{1.00 \times 10^{-14}}{3.5 \times 10^{-4}} = 2.86 \times 10^{-11} = \frac{Y^2}{6.634 \times 10^{-4}}$$

Solving $Y = [OH^-] = 1.38 \times 10^{-7}$ M, and pOH = 6.86 and pH = **7.14**

93. $pOH = 14.00 - 8.82 = 5.18$, $[OH^-] = 6.61 \times 10^{-6}$ M

	$C_2O_4^{2-}$ + $H_2O \rightleftharpoons$	$HC_2O_4^-$ +	OH^-
ST	X	0	0
$+\Delta$	-6.61×10^{-6}	$+6.61 \times 10^{-6}$	$+6.61 \times 10^{-6}$
= EQ	$X - 6.61 \times 10^{-6}$	6.61×10^{-6}	6.61×10^{-6}

; Assume $X - 6.61 \times 10^{-6} \cong X$

$$K_b(C_2O_4^{2-}) = \frac{[HC_2O_4^-][OH^-]}{[C_2O_4^{2-}]} = \frac{K_w}{K_a(HC_2O_4^-)} = \frac{1.00 \times 10^{-14}}{6.4 \times 10^{-5}} = 1.56 \times 10^{-10} = \frac{(6.61 \times 10^{-6})^2}{X}$$

Solving $X = 0.279\ M = [C_2O_4^{2-}]$ (when saturated)

Since the $Na_2C_2O_4$ forms a saturated solution, we write the equilibrium equation and K_{sp} expression.

$Na_2C_2O_4(s) \rightleftharpoons 2\,Na^+ + C_2O_4^{2-}$; $K_{sp} = [Na^+]^2[C_2O_4^{2-}] = (0.559)^2(0.279) =$ **8.7×10^{-2}**

-0.279 $\quad$ 0.559 $\quad$ 0.279

94. $HCl + NaOH \longrightarrow NaCl + H_2O$

moles HCl $= 0.125 \frac{mmol}{mL} \times 15.3\ mL = 1.913$ mmol = moles NaOH

$[NaOH] = \frac{1.913\ mmol}{25.0\ mL} =$ **0.0765 M**

95. moles KOH $= 0.0635 \frac{mmol}{mL} \times 28.2\ mL = 1.791$ mmol

moles $H_2SO_4 = 1.791$ mmol KOH $\times \frac{1\ mmol\ H_2SO_4}{2\ mmol\ KOH} = 0.8954$ mmol

$[H_2SO_4] = \frac{0.8954\ mmol}{25.0\ mL} =$ **0.0358 M**

96. $NH_3 + HCl \longrightarrow NH_4Cl$

moles HCl $= 0.0275 \frac{mmol}{mL} \times 50.0\ mL = 1.375$ mmol = moles NH_3

volume $NH_3 = \frac{1.375\ mmol}{0.0350\ mmol/mL} =$ **39.3 mL**

97. moles $H_2SO_4 = 0.175 \frac{mmol}{mL} \times 25.0\ mL = 4.375$ mmol

moles NaOH $= 4.375$ mmol $H_2SO_4 \times \frac{2\ mmol\ NaOH}{1\ mmol\ H_2SO_4} = 8.75$ mmol

volume NaOH $= \frac{8.75\ mmol}{0.230\ mmol/mL} =$ **38.0 mL**

98. moles $H_3Cit = 0.0475 \frac{mmol}{mL} \times 35.0\ mL = 1.663$ mmol

moles NaOH $= 0.120 \frac{mmol}{mL} \times 27.8\ mL = 3.336$ mmol

$\frac{moles\ NaOH}{moles\ H_3Cit} = \frac{3.336\ mmol}{1.663\ mmol} = \frac{2.01\ mmol\ NaOH}{1\ mmol\ H_3Cit}$ so that **2** protons on each H_3Cit are removed.

Therefore 2 protons on each H_3Cit are removed.

$2\,NaOH + H_3Cit \longrightarrow Na_2HCit + 2\,H_2O$; the salt is **Na_2HCit**

99. moles $H_4P_2O_7 = 0.0136 \frac{mmol}{mL} \times 28.7\ mL = 0.3903\ mmol$

moles KOH $= 0.0387 \frac{mmol}{mL} \times 40.3\ mL = 1.560\ mmol$

$\frac{\text{moles KOH}}{\text{moles } H_4P_2O_7} = \frac{1.560\ mmol}{0.3903\ mmol} = \frac{4.00\ mmol\ KOH}{1\ mmol\ H_4P_2O_7}$ so that **4** protons are removed per $H_4P_2O_7$.

$4\ KOH + H_4P_2O_7 \longrightarrow K_4P_2O_7 + 4\ H_2O$; the salt is $\mathbf{K_4P_2O_7}$

100. $C_6H_5COOH + NaOH \longrightarrow NaC_6H_5COO + H_2O$

moles NaOH $= 0.1236 \frac{mmol}{mL} \times 31.84\ mL = 3.9354\ mmol$ = moles C_6H_5COOH

$[C_6H_5COOH] = \frac{3.9354\ mmol}{25.00\ mL} = 0.15742\ M$ (this is the ACTUAL concentration)

$[C_6H_5COOH] = \frac{5.000\ g}{0.2500\ L} \times \frac{1\ mol}{122.0\ g} = 0.16393\ M$

(this is the EXPECTED concentration if the benzoic acid were 100% pure)

% purity $= \frac{[C_6H_5COOH]\ (actual)}{[C_6H_5COOH]\ (expected)} \times 100\% = \frac{0.15742\ M}{0.16393\ M} \times 100\% = \mathbf{96.02\%}$

101. $HA + KOH \longrightarrow KA + H_2O$

moles KOH $= 0.2000 \frac{mmol}{mL} \times 23.61\ mL = 4.722\ mmol$ = moles HA

$[HA] = \frac{4.722\ mmol}{25.00\ mL} = 0.18888\ M$

moles of HA in 100.0 mL $= 0.18888 \frac{mol}{L} \times 0.1000\ L = 0.018888\ mol$

molar mass $= \frac{3.857\ g}{0.018888\ mol} = \mathbf{204.2\ g/mol}$

102. $HCl + NaOH \longrightarrow NaCl + H_2O$

moles HCl $= 0.288 \frac{mmol}{mL} \times 37.5\ mL = 10.8\ mmol$ = moles NaOH

$[NaOH] = \frac{10.8\ mmol}{50.0\ mL} = 0.216\ M$ (this is the ACTUAL concentration)

$[NaOH] = \frac{0.470\ g}{0.0500\ L} \times \frac{1\ mol}{40.0\ g} = 0.235\ M$

(this is the EXPECTED concentration if the NaOH were 100% pure)

% purity $= \frac{[NaOH]\ (actual)}{[NaOH]\ (expected)} \times 100\% = \frac{0.216\ M}{0.235\ M} \times 100\% = \mathbf{91.9\ \%}$

103. Discarding titration #1, the average of the other two volumes is 17.81 mL.

moles HCl $= 0.05023 \frac{mmol}{mL} \times 17.81\ mL = 0.89460\ mmol$ = moles unknown base

$[base] = \frac{0.89460\ mmol}{25.00\ mL} = 0.035784\ M$

moles of base in 100.0 mL $= 0.035784 \frac{mol}{L} \times 0.1000\ L = 0.0035784\ mol$

molar mass $= \frac{1.021\ g}{0.0035784\ mol} = \mathbf{285.3\ g/mol}$

104. $Ca(OH)_2 + 2\,HCl \longrightarrow CaCl_2 + 2\,H_2O$

$$\text{moles HCl} = 0.0500\ \frac{\text{mmol}}{\text{mL}} \times 19.1\ \text{mL} = 0.9550\ \text{mmol}$$

$$\text{moles } Ca(OH)_2 = 0.9550\ \text{mmol HCl} \times \frac{1\ \text{mmol } Ca(OH)_2}{2\ \text{mmol HCl}} = 0.4775\ \text{mmol}$$

$$[Ca(OH)_2]\ (\text{pure}) = \frac{0.4775\ \text{mmol}}{25.0\ \text{mL}} = 0.01910\ \text{M}$$

$$[Ca(OH)_2]\ (\text{based on impure material}) = \frac{1.50\ \text{g}}{1.00\ \text{L}} \times \frac{1\ \text{mol}}{74.1\ \text{g}} = 0.02024\ \text{M}$$

$$\%\ \text{purity} = \frac{[Ca(OH)_2]\ (\text{pure})}{[Ca(OH)_2]\ (\text{impure})} \times 100\% = \frac{0.01910\ \text{M}}{0.02024\ \text{M}} \times 100\% = \mathbf{94.4\%}$$

105. Disregarding titration #2, the average of the NaOH volumes is 39.66 mL.

$H_2X + 2\,NaOH \longrightarrow Na_2X + 2\,H_2O$

$$\text{moles NaOH} = 0.1328\ \frac{\text{mmol}}{\text{mL}} \times 39.66\ \text{mL} = 5.2668\ \text{mmol}$$

$$\text{moles } H_2X = 5.2668\ \text{mmol NaOH} \times \frac{1\ \text{mmol } H_2X}{2\ \text{mmol NaOH}} = 2.6334\ \text{mmol}$$

$$[H_2X] = \frac{2.6334\ \text{mmol}}{25.00\ \text{mL}} = 0.10534\ \text{M}$$

$$\text{moles of } H_2X \text{ in } 250.0\ \text{mL} = 0.10534\ \frac{\text{mol}}{\text{L}} \times 0.2500\ \text{L} = 0.026334\ \text{mol}$$

$$\text{molar mass} = \frac{2.500\ \text{g}}{0.026334\ \text{mol}} = \mathbf{94.93\ g/mol}$$

106. Both acids require the same volume of NaOH. Since the volume and concentration of the acids are the same, the number of moles of acid present is the same and the same number of moles of NaOH is required. The fact that CH_3COOH is weak is irrelevant because the equilibrium

$$CH_3COOH \rightleftharpoons CH_3COO^- + H^+$$

will continue to shift to the product side as the H^+ is removed by neutralization, supplying the solution with more H^+ until the supply of CH_3COOH is eventually exhausted.

107. (a) $Ba(OH)_2(aq) + H_2SO_4(aq) \rightleftharpoons BaSO_4(s) + 2\,H_2O(l)$

(b) Both $Ba(OH)_2$ and H_2SO_4 are ionic in solution, but the products of the reaction are water and insoluble $BaSO_4(s)$. Therefore, the addition of $H_2SO_4(aq)$ reduces the concentrations of the Ba^{2+} and OH^- ions and decreases the conductivity.

(c) $\text{moles } Ba(OH)_2 \text{ present} = 0.100\ \frac{\text{mmol}}{\text{mL}} \times 25.0\ \text{mL} = 2.50\ \text{mmol} = \text{moles } H_2SO_4 \text{ required}$

$$\text{volume } H_2SO_4 = \frac{2.50\ \text{mmol}}{0.100\ \text{mmol/mL}} = \mathbf{25.0\ mL}$$

At the equivalence point there is no excess of either $Ba(OH)_2$ or H_2SO_4, so that a saturated solution of $BaSO_4$ will be present. Therefore the conductivity of the solution will be very small (very few ions will be present in the solution since $BaSO_4$ has a low solubility).

(d) After the equivalence point, the addition of H_2SO_4, a strong acid, adds extra ions to the solution and the conductivity increases.

(e)

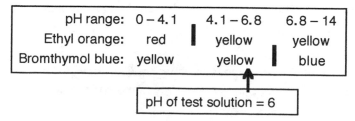

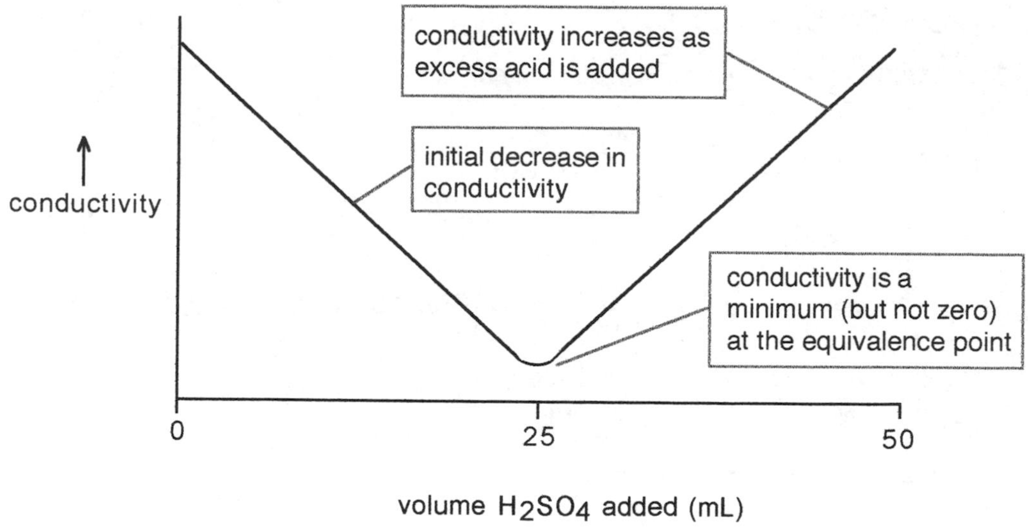

108. Blue (indicators will be in their conjugate base form in basic solutions)

109. The pH of 0.01 M HCl is 2, which is on the acidic side of the indicator's transition range. Since bromcresol purple is yellow in its acidic form, then the indicator will be yellow.

110. $pK_a = pH = 12.7$, and $K_a = \text{antilog}(-12.7) = 2 \times 10^{-13}$

111. $pK_a = pH = 3.4$, and $K_a = \text{antilog}(-3.4) = 4 \times 10^{-4}$

112. The indicator changes colour at pH = 5. Below pH = 5 the indicator will find an excess of H^+ present and the indicator will be predominantly in its conjugate acid form. Above pH = 5 the indicator will find an excess of OH^- present and the indicator will be predominantly in its conjugate base form. Hence, at pH = 8 the solution will have $[HIn] < [In^-]$.

113. There are 2 acidic groups since there are two colour changes:

$K_a(\#1) = \text{antilog}(-6.4) = 4 \times 10^{-7}$

$K_a(\#2) = \text{antilog}(-11.7) = 2 \times 10^{-12}$

The stronger acid group, $K_a = 4 \times 10^{-7}$, ionizes at a lower pH, whereas it requires a more basic solution to ionize the weaker acid group, $K_a = 2 \times 10^{-12}$.

114. The indicator changes colour at $pH = pK_a = -\log(1 \times 10^{-5}) = 5$. Since the conjugate base, Eth^-, is red, the indicator is red on the basic side and colourless on the acidic side of its transition point. Pure water's pH is 7, which is on the basic side of the indicator's transition point. Hence, the indicator is red in pure water.

115. The diagram which summarizes the available information is shown below.

pH range:	0 – 4.1	4.1 – 6.8	6.8 – 14
Ethyl orange:	red	yellow	yellow
Bromthymol blue:	yellow	yellow	blue

pH of test solution = 6

Since pH = 6 is on the basic side of the ethyl orange transition (indicator is yellow at pH = 6) and the acidic side of the bromthymol blue transition (indicator is yellow at pH = 6), the resulting mixture is yellow.

116. If $[OH^-] = 1.0 \times 10^{-4}$ M, then pOH = 4.0 and pH = 10.0.
The diagram which summarizes the available information is shown below.

pH range:	0 – 8.8	8.8 – 11.1	11.1 – 14
Thymol blue:	yellow	blue	blue
Alizarin yellow:	yellow	yellow	red

pH of test solution = 10

Since a pH of 10 is on the basic side of the thymol blue transition (this indicator is blue) and the acidic side of the Alizarin transition (this indicator is yellow), the resulting mixture will be green.

117. Since methyl orange is yellow, the pH is 4.4 or above.
Since bromthymol blue is yellow, the pH is 6.0 or below.
(The fact that the thymol blue is yellow gives no new information.)
Therefore, the pH is in the range 4.4 to 6.0.

118. Since methyl red is yellow, the pH is 6.0 or above.
Since phenol red is red, the pH must be 8.0 or above.
Since phenolphthalein is colourless, the pH must be 8.2 or below.
Therefore, the pH must be in the range 8.0 to 8.2.

119. Use a pH meter or a suitable indicator such as litmus or bromthymol blue to determine whether an acid or base is present. If pH < 7, or litmus is red or bromthymol blue is yellow then you have an acid. If pH > 7 or litmus is blue or bromthymol blue is blue then you have a base. Since a 0.10 M solution of a strong base has $[OH^-] = 0.10$ M and hence a pH of 13.0, check for a pH in this range. If you have a base but pH < 13 then the base is weak. A 0.10 M solution of a strong acid will have a pH of 1.0. If you have an acid but pH > 1, then the acid is weak. **ALTERNATELY**: You can check for an acid or base with litmus and then check the conductivity. If the conductivity is high you have a strong acid or base; if the conductivity is low you have a weak acid or base. You cannot use a titration to determine whether the acid (or base) is weak versus strong.

120. H_3PO_4 is quite acidic ($K_a = 7.5 \times 10^{-3}$)
NaH_2PO_4 is mildly acidic ($K_a = 6.2 \times 10^{-8} > K_b = 1.3 \times 10^{-12}$)
Na_2HPO_4 is mildly basic ($K_a = 2.2 \times 10^{-13} < K_b = 1.6 \times 10^{-7}$)
Na_3PO_4 is quite basic ($K_b = 4.5 \times 10^{-2}$)

Bottle 1: Litmus shows basic; Alizarin yellow shows pH > 12;
Methyl orange shows pH > 4.4
Conclusion: highly basic and hence Na_3PO_4

Bottle 2: Litmus shows acidic; Alizarin yellow shows pH < 10.1 ;
Methyl orange shows pH > 4.4
Conclusion: mildly acidic and hence NaH_2PO_4

Bottle 3: Litmus shows acidic; Alizarin yellow shows pH < 10.1 ;
Methyl orange shows pH < 3.2
Conclusion: strongly acidic and hence H_3PO_4

Bottle 4: Litmus shows basic; Alizarin yellow shows pH < 10.1 ;
Methyl orange shows pH > 4.4
Conclusion: mildly basic and hence Na_2HPO_4

121. No. The fact that barium hydroxide reacts with the CO_2 in the air means it cannot be trusted to be pure enough for use as a primary standard. In addition, $Ba(OH)_2$ has a low solubility in water.

122. (a) $Na_4B_4O_7$ and HCl were "standards" (b) $Na_4B_4O_7$ was a "primary standard"

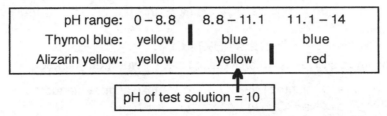

123. Use pure sodium carbonate as a primary standard to prepare a solution having an accurately known [Na_2CO_3]. Pipette a known volume of the unknown HCl into a flask and fill a burette with Na_2CO_3 solution. (Alternately, pipette the Na_2CO_3 solution and put the HCl in the burette.) Titrate to the stoichiometric point:

$$2\,HCl + Na_2CO_3 \longrightarrow 2\,NaCl + H_2O + CO_2.$$

The indicator which was suggested when titrating Na_2CO_3 was methyl orange.

Data needed: mass and volume of Na_2CO_3 used to make primary standard
volume of Na_2CO_3 used in titration
volume of HCl pipetted

Calculations: $[Na_2CO_3] = \dfrac{\text{mass sodium carbonate}}{\text{volume}} \times \dfrac{1\text{ mol}}{\text{molecular mass of } Na_2CO_3}$

moles Na_2CO_3 = [Na_2CO_3] x volume Na_2CO_3
moles HCl = 2 x moles Na_2CO_3

$[HCl] = \dfrac{\text{moles HCl}}{\text{volume HCl}}$

124. (a) The graph resembles:

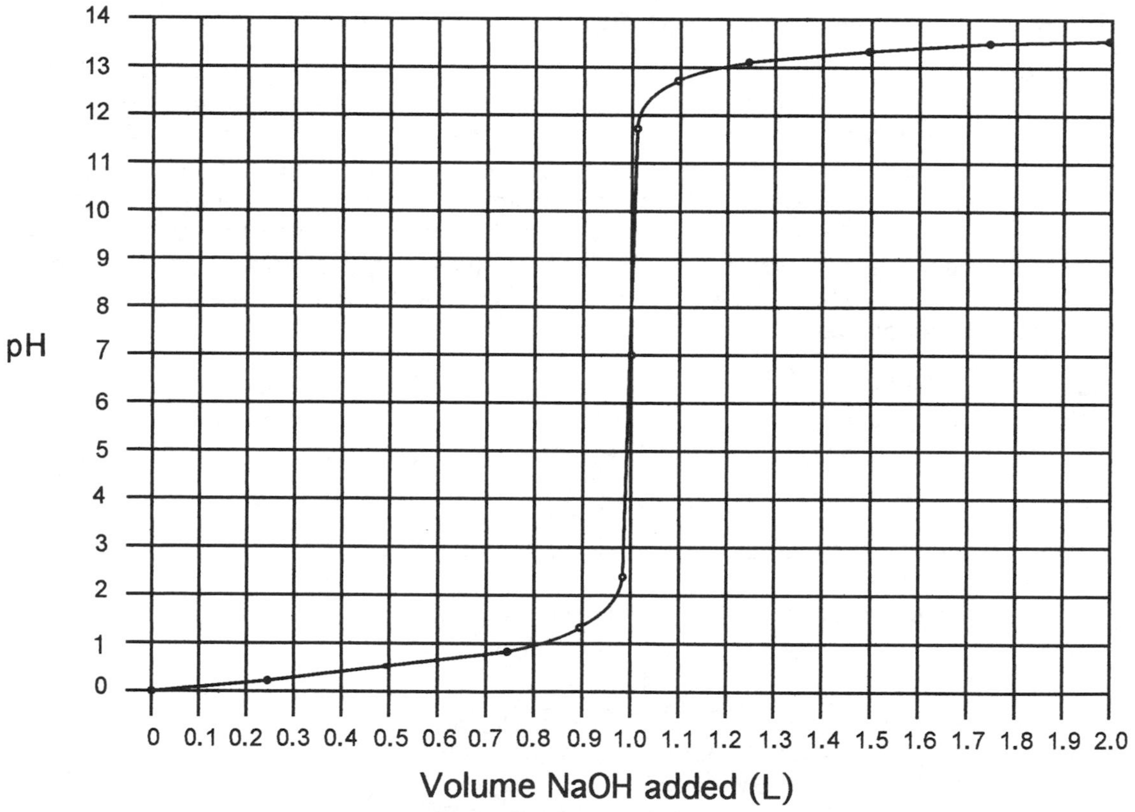

(b) 1.00 L
(c) between pH 3 and 11
(d) $HCl + NaOH \longrightarrow NaCl + H_2O$, and the NaCl solution is **neutral.**
(e) The "ideal" indicator would have a pH of 7 at its equivalence point (neutral pH). However, the pH changes so rapidly around the equivalence point that a very small change in volume of NaOH added produces a large change in the pH. The volume difference required to produce a pH of 7 and a pH of 9.1 is so small as to be negligible.

125. (a) $HF + NaOH \longrightarrow NaF + H_2O$, and the NaF(aq) formed at the equivalence point is **basic.** Choose phenolphthalein.
(b) $NH_3 + HI \longrightarrow NH_4I$, and the NH_4I(aq) formed at the equivalence point is **acidic.** Choose methyl red.
(c) $LiOH + HBr \longrightarrow LiBr + H_2O$, and the LiBr(aq) formed at the equivalence point is **neutral.** Choose bromthymol blue to get a transition point pH of about 7.
(d) $2\,C_6H_5COOH + Ca(OH)_2 \longrightarrow Ca(C_6H_5COO)_2 + 2\,H_2O$, and the $Ca(C_6H_5COO)_2$(aq) formed at the equivalence point is **basic.** Therefore, choose phenolphthalein.
(e) $NH_3 + CH_3COOH \longrightarrow NH_4CH_3COO$, and the NH_4CH_3COO formed at the equivalence point is **neutral:** $K_a(NH_4^+) = K_b(CH_3COO^-)$. Therefore, choose Bromthymol Blue.
(f) $HNO_3 + KOH \longrightarrow KNO_3 + H_2O$, and the KNO_3(aq) formed at the equivalence point is **neutral.** Use Bromthymol Blue to get a transition point pH of about 7.

126. (a) pK_a = pH at the half–volume point in the titration, so that K_a = antilog(–4.873) = **1.34 x 10⁻⁵** .

(b) $\text{moles NaOH} = 0.100\,\frac{\text{mmol}}{\text{mL}} \times 23.8\text{ mL} = 2.38\text{ mmol} = \text{moles } C_2H_5COOH$

$$[C_2H_5COOH] = \frac{2.38\text{ mmol}}{25.0\text{ mL}} = \mathbf{0.0952\ M}$$

(c) $[H_3O^+]$ = antilog(–2.950) = 1.122×10^{-3} M

$$K_a = \frac{[H_3O^+]^2}{[C_2H_5COOH]_{EQ}}, \quad \text{and} \quad [C_2H_5COOH]_{EQ} = \frac{[H_3O^+]^2}{K_a} = \frac{(1.122 \times 10^{-3})^2}{1.34 \times 10^{-5}} = 0.0940\text{ M}$$

Therefore, initial $[C_2H_5COOH]$ = 0.0940 + 0.001122 = **0.0951 M.**

127. (a) pK_b = pOH at the half–volume point in the titration.
pOH = 14.00 – 4.63 = 9.37, and: K_b = antilog(–9.37) = 4.27×10^{-10} (which rounds off to 4.3×10^{-10} for this part of the exercise).

(b) The reaction equation: $C_6H_5NH_2 + HCl \longrightarrow C_6H_5NH_3^+ + Cl^-$.

Since the volume of aniline is not given, the following equation is used $K_b = \frac{[OH^-]^2}{[C_6H_5NH_2]_{EQ}}$.

So: pOH = 14.00 – 8.72 = 5.28 , $[OH^-]$ = antilog(–5.28) = 5.25×10^{-6} M.

$$[C_6H_5NH_2]_{EQ} = \frac{[OH^-]^2}{K_b} = \frac{(5.25 \times 10^{-6})^2}{4.27 \times 10^{-10}} = \mathbf{0.065\ M}$$

Adding 5.25×10^{-6} M to this last value (to get the initial concentration) has a negligible effect.

128. No effect. The pOH at the "half–volume point" is given by the equation: pOH = pK_b, and this equation does not involve the concentration of the solutions used.

129. (a) pK_a = pH at the half–volume point in the titration, and K_a = antilog(–4.191) = 6.44×10^{-5}.
(b) Since the volume of C_6H_5COOH is not given, the initial pH of the benzoic acid must be used in order to find the required concentration. $[H_3O^+]$ = antilog(–2.628) = 2.36×10^{-3} M

$$K_a = \frac{[H_3O^+]^2}{[C_6H_5COOH]_{EQ}}, \quad \text{and} \quad [C_6H_5COOH]_{EQ} = \frac{[H_3O^+]^2}{K_a} = \frac{(2.36 \times 10^{-3})^2}{6.44 \times 10^{-5}} = 0.0861\text{ M}$$

and the initial $[C_6H_5COOH]$ = 0.0861 + 2.36×10^{-3} = **0.0885 M**

130. (a) pK_b = pOH at the half–volume point in the titration.
pOH = 14.00 – 7.047 = 6.953, and: K_b = antilog(–6.953) = 1.11×10^{-7}

(b) moles HCl = $0.0986 \frac{\text{mmol}}{\text{mL}} \times 36.8\text{ mL} = 3.63\text{ mmol}$ = moles $C_3H_4N_2$

$[C_3H_4N_2] = \frac{3.63\text{ mmol}}{25.0\text{ mL}} = \mathbf{0.145\ M}$

(c) pOH = 14.000 − 10.104 = 3.896 , $[OH^-]$ = antilog(−3.896) = 1.27×10^{-4} M

$K_b = \frac{[OH^-]^2}{[C_3H_4N_2]_{EQ}}$, and $[C_3H_4N_2]_{EQ} = \frac{[OH^-]^2}{K_b} = \frac{(1.27 \times 10^{-4})^2}{1.11 \times 10^{-7}} = 0.145\text{ M}$

And since the amount of imidazole which dissociates is very small (1.27×10^{-4} M) compared to the initial $[C_3H_4N_2]$, then the initial $[C_3H_4N_2]$ is **0.145 M** .

131. The pH's will be the same. Both solutions have the same $[NH_4^+]/[NH_3]$ ratio but the 0.1 M solution is ten–fold diluted relative to the 1.0 M solution and diluting a buffer has no effect on its pH.

132. (a) This is a buffer because it contains substantial amounts of **both** a weak acid (HCN) and its conjugate base (CN^-).
(b) This is not a buffer because it contains two unrelated weak acids.
(c) This is not a buffer — it contains a strong base (NaOH) and a salt made of spectator ions (NaCl).
(d) This is a buffer because it contains substantial amounts of **both** a weak base (CO_3^{2-}) and its conjugate acid (HCO_3^-).

133. If NaOH is added, there is little effect on the pH, other than a slight increase. If too much NaOH is added, the buffering capacity will be exceeded and a large increase in pH will occur.

If HCl is added, there is little effect on the pH, other than a slight decrease. If too much HCl is added, the buffering capacity will be exceeded and a large decrease in pH will occur.

134. The solution in the bottle is used to wash yourself when an acid or base is spilled on your hands or other part of your body. In this way you don't need a basic solution to treat acid spills and a separate acidic solution to treat base spills. Also, if the nature of the material spilled is not certain, the solution will neutralize either an acid or base. Adding an acid such as CH_3COOH to an acidic spill would only worsen matters.

135. Add a few drops of 0.1 M HCl to a small amount of the solution and check the pH before and after the addition with some universal indicator paper. Repeat the procedure, using a few drops of 0.1 M NaOH. If there is no apparent change with either the acid or base, the substance is a buffer.
Alternatively, ***if the solution is not neutral,*** simply dilute the solution ten–fold with distilled water. If the pH is unchanged, the solution is a buffer.

136. No. A buffer requires substantial amounts of **both** a weak acid and its conjugate weak base to be present; HNO_3 is a strong acid and NO_3^- is a spectator ion.

137. No. There is only 0.10 mol of acid (NH_4^+) present, so that the addition of 0.15 mol of OH^- will exceed the capacity of the buffer to neutralize OH^-.

138. (a) $[NH_4^+]$ increases ; $[NH_3]$ decreases (b) $[NH_4^+]$ decreases ; $[NH_3]$ increases

139. Ideally, a buffer will have its pH equal to the pK_a of the weak acid present. Therefore, pK_a = pH = 7.2 implies $K_a = 6 \times 10^{-8}$. This is close to the K_a value for $H_2PO_4^-$. A suitable buffer could be made, for example, by mixing 1 mol of NaH_2PO_4 and 1 mol of Na_2HPO_4 and diluting to 1L .

140. Similar to the previous example, pK_a = pH = 2.1, which requires $K_a = 8 \times 10^{-3}$. This is close to the K_a value for H_3PO_4. A suitable buffer could be made, for example, by mixing 1 mol of H_3PO_4 and 1 mol of NaH_2PO_4 and diluting to 1 L .

141. The addition of HCO_3^- shifts the equilibrium $CO_2(aq) + 2\,H_2O \rightleftharpoons H_3O^+ + HCO_3^-$, lowering the $[H_3O^+]$ slightly and increasing the pH. (It also increases the $[CO_2]$ in the blood, which in turn triggers the breathing reflex.)

142. $H_2PO_4^- + OH^- \rightleftharpoons HPO_4^{2-} + H_2O$, $HPO_4^{2-} + H_3O^+ \rightleftharpoons H_2PO_4^- + H_2O$

143. (a) The following shifts will occur: $CO_2(g) \rightleftharpoons CO_2(aq)$ ...(1)

and the loss of $CO_2(aq)$ causes $CO_2(aq) + 2\,H_2O(l) \rightleftharpoons H_3O^+(aq) + HCO_3^-(aq)$ ...(2)

and the loss of HCO_3^- causes $HCO_3^-(aq) + H_2O(l) \rightleftharpoons H_3O^+(aq) + CO_3^{2-}(aq)$ ...(3)

and the loss of CO_3^{2-} causes $CaCO_3(s) \rightleftharpoons Ca^{2+}(aq) + CO_3^{2-}(aq)$. ...(4)

(b) The dissolving of the $CaCO_3$ causes the egg shells to become very thin.

(c) The addition of $CO_2(aq)$ causes the equilibrium shifts in part (a) to be reversed:

$$CO_2(aq) + 2\,H_2O(l) \rightleftharpoons H_3O^+(aq) + HCO_3^-(aq) \quad ...(2)$$

$$HCO_3^-(aq) + H_2O(l) \rightleftharpoons H_3O^+(aq) + CO_3^{2-}(aq) \quad ...(3)$$

$$CaCO_3(s) \rightleftharpoons Ca^{2+}(aq) + CO_3^{2-}(aq) \quad ...(4)$$

The shifting of equilibrium (4) to the $CaCO_3(s)$ side causes more $CaCO_3(s)$ to be available and therefore thicker eggshells are produced.

144. (a) $Li_2O + H_2O \longrightarrow 2\,LiOH$ (c) $CO_2 + H_2O \longrightarrow H_2CO_3$ (e) $SO_2 + H_2O \longrightarrow H_2SO_3$

(b) $MgO + H_2O \longrightarrow Mg(OH)_2$ (d) $BaO + H_2O \longrightarrow Ba(OH)_2$ (f) $K_2O + H_2O \longrightarrow 2\,KOH$

145. a, b, d and f

146. A pH of 2.2 implies $[H_3O^+] = \text{antilog}(-2.2) = 6.3 \times 10^{-3}$ M.

volume of water $= 2.5 \times 10^5\,m^2 \times 2.5 \times 10^{-2}\,m = 6.25 \times 10^3\,m^3 = 6.25 \times 10^3\,m^3 \times \dfrac{10^3\ L}{1\ m^3} = 6.25 \times 10^6$ L

moles H_3O^+ $= 6.3 \times 10^{-3}\,\dfrac{mol}{L} \times 6.25 \times 10^6\,L = 3.94 \times 10^4$ mol

mass $CaCO_3$ $= 3.94 \times 10^4\,mol\ H_3O^+ \times \dfrac{1\ mol\ CaCO_3}{2\ mol\ H_3O^+} \times \dfrac{100.1\ g}{1\ mol\ CaCO_3} \times \dfrac{1\ kg}{10^3\ g} = \mathbf{2 \times 10^3\ kg}$

147. $Al(H_2O)_6^{3+}$ is a weak acid having $K_a = 1.4 \times 10^{-5}$; that is, a fairly "strong" weak acid.

ANSWERS TO UNIT V : ELECTROCHEMISTRY

1. (a) $Mn \longrightarrow Mn^{2+} + 2\,e^-$; Mn is oxidized and is the reducing agent.
   $Hg^{2+} + 2\,e^- \longrightarrow Hg$; Hg^{2+} is reduced and is the oxidizing agent.

   (b) $H_2 \longrightarrow 2\,H^+ + 2\,e^-$; H_2 is oxidized and is the reducing agent.
   $Sn^{4+} + 2\,e^- \longrightarrow Sn^{2+}$; Sn^{4+} is reduced and is the oxidizing agent.

   (c) $Li \longrightarrow Li^+ + e^-$; Li is oxidized and is the reducing agent.
   $F_2 + 2\,e^- \longrightarrow 2\,F^-$; F_2 is reduced and is the oxidizing agent.

   (d) $Cr^{2+} \longrightarrow Cr^{3+} + e^-$; Cr^{2+} is oxidized and is the reducing agent.
   $Br_2 + 2\,e^- \longrightarrow 2\,Br^-$; Br_2 is reduced and is the oxidizing agent.

   (e) $Fe^{2+} \longrightarrow Fe^{3+} + e^-$; Fe^{2+} is oxidized and is the reducing agent.
   $Sn^{4+} + 2\,e^- \longrightarrow Sn^{2+}$; Sn^{4+} is reduced and is the oxidizing agent.

2. (a) $2\,Cs + Cl_2 \longrightarrow 2\,CsCl$
   (b) $Cs \longrightarrow Cs^+ + e^-$ (oxidation) $Cl_2 + 2\,e^- \longrightarrow 2\,Cl^-$ (reduction)
   (c) Cs is the reducing agent; Cl_2 is the oxidizing agent.

3.

(a) +5	(d) +6	(g) −3	(j) +5	(m) +5	(o) −1	(q) +6	(s) 0
(b) +3	(e) −3	(h) −8/3	(k) +3	(n) −2	(p) +3	(r) −4/3	(t) −3/2
(c) +6	(f) −1/3	(i) +3	(l) +7				

4. a) $\mathbf{ClO_2} + \mathbf{C} \longrightarrow \mathbf{ClO_2^-} + \mathbf{CO_3^{2-}}$; C is oxidized
   +4 0 +3 +4

   b) $\mathbf{Sn^{2+}} + Cl^- + \mathbf{BrO_3^-} \longrightarrow \mathbf{SnCl_6^{2-}} + \mathbf{Br^-}$; Sn is oxidized
   +2 +5 +4 −1

   c) $\mathbf{MnO_4^-} + \mathbf{C_2O_4^{2-}} \longrightarrow \mathbf{MnO_2} + \mathbf{CO_2}$; C is oxidized
   +7 +3 +4 +4

   d) $\mathbf{NO_3^-} + H_2\mathbf{Te} \longrightarrow NO + \mathbf{TeO_4^{2-}}$; Te is oxidized
   +5 −2 +2 +6

5. Equations a, d and f

6. (a) Cl_2, Cl^-, Cl_2O (b) NO_3^-, NO_2^-, N_2O_3

7. (a) Na^+ can only be reduced
   (b) I^- can only be oxidized
   (c) Cu^+ can be either reduced or oxidized
   (d) Sn^{4+} can only be reduced
   (e) NO_3^- cannot react at all (needs H^+ to react)
   (f) Hg(l) can only be oxidized
   (g) Fe^{2+} can be either reduced or oxidized
   (h) Co^{2+} can only be reduced
   (i) Se(s) cannot react at all (needs H^+ to react)
   (j) Sn^{2+} can be either reduced or oxidized
   (k) Al(s) can only be oxidized
   (l) acidic $Cr_2O_7^{2-}$ can only be reduced

8. (a) no reaction; the species to be reduced (Ni^{2+}) is below the species to be oxidized (Ag) on the Table.
   (b) spontaneous: $2\,Li + Zn^{2+} \longrightarrow 2\,Li^+ + Zn$.
   (c) no reaction; both species can only be oxidized.
   (d) no reaction; the species to be reduced (H^+) is below the species to be oxidized (Cu) on the Table.
   (e) spontaneous: $2\,H^+ + Fe \longrightarrow H_2 + Fe^{2+}$.

(f) no reaction; the species to be reduced (Sn^{4+}) is below the species to be oxidized (Au) on the Table.
(g) spontaneous: $Sn^{2+} + Co \longrightarrow Sn + Co^{2+}$ (Note that there is another half–reaction involving Sn^{2+} at 0.15 V, but it cannot be combined with our Co half–reaction.)
(h) spontaneous: $2\,Cu^{+} + Sn \longrightarrow 2\,Cu + Sn^{2+}$ (Note that there is another half–reaction involving Cu^{+} at 0.15 V, but it cannot be combined with our Sn half–reaction.)
(i) no reaction; the species to be reduced (Al^{3+}) is below the species to be oxidized (Ni) on the Table.
(j) spontaneous: $Hg^{2+} + H_2 \longrightarrow Hg + 2\,H^{+}$

9. This question asks for the species with the greater tendency to reduce; that is, the species which is higher on the left side of the Table.
(a) Zn^{2+} (b) Cu^{2+} (c) Br_2

10. This question asks for the species with the greater tendency to oxidize; that is, the species which is lower on the right side of the Table.
(a) Mn (b) Sn^{2+} (c) Cr^{2+}

11. (a) no reaction
(b) spontaneous: $Sn + Sn^{4+} \longrightarrow 2\,Sn^{2+}$
(c) spontaneous: $2\,H^{+} + Mn \longrightarrow H_2 + Mn^{2+}$
(d) no reaction (requires H^{+} with the $Cr_2O_7^{2-}$)
(e) spontaneous: $6\,Fe^{2+} + Cr_2O_7^{2-} + 14\,H^{+} \longrightarrow 6\,Fe^{3+} + 2\,Cr^{3+} + 7\,H_2O$
(f) no reaction. Recall that the Introduction to this unit asked why Cu(s) wouldn't react with HCl. Well, now you know: the reduction of H^{+} is not above the oxidation of Cu(s) on the Table.
(g) spontaneous: $MnO_2 + 4\,H^{+} + 2\,I^{-} \longrightarrow Mn^{2+} + 2\,H_2O + I_2$
(h) no reaction. Sulphate requires acid to be present in order to react with tin.

12. (a) I_2 and Fe^{3+}
(b) H_2 and H_2O_2 (There are two half–reactions involving H_2O_2; one at 1.78 V and one at 0.70 V.)
(c) Pb
(d) Cu^{2+} and acidic NO_3^{-}
(e) Cu, S and H_2SO_3. The question asks you to find species which are BELOW the I_2 half–reaction (0.54 V) but not BELOW the acidic SO_4^{2-} half–cell (0.17 V).
(f) Fe^{3+}, acidic O_2, MnO_4^{-}
(g) H^{+}, Sn^{4+} and acidic S
(h) none

13. Since the reaction is $Pb^{2+} + Zn \longrightarrow Pb + Zn^{2+}$, the [$Pb^{2+}$] decreases and the [$Zn^{2+}$] increases.

14. In order for A^{2+} to reduce and allow C to oxidize, the half reaction involving A^{2+} must be ABOVE the half reaction involving C. Since A^{2+} DOES NOT react with B, then the half reaction involving A^{2+} must be BELOW the half reaction involving B. Overall:

$$B^{2+} + 2\,e^{-} \rightleftharpoons B$$
$$A^{2+} + 2\,e^{-} \rightleftharpoons A$$
$$C^{2+} + 2\,e^{-} \rightleftharpoons C.$$

15. Putting the strongest oxidizing agent first means putting the ion with the greatest tendency to reduce first.
Since "F^{2+} reacts with D(s), E(s) and G(s)", then F^{2+} is above the other ions.

greatest tendency to reduce	F^{2+}
least tendency to reduce	D^{2+}, E^{2+}, G^{2+} (equal, so far)

Since "no reaction was observed between D^{2+} and any of the metals", then D^{2+} is below all other ions.

greatest tendency to reduce	F^{2+}
	E^{2+}, G^{2+} (still equal, so far)
least tendency to reduce	D^{2+}

Since "G^{2+} was only observed to react with D(s)", then G^{2+} is only above D^{2+}.

greatest tendency to reduce:	F^{2+}
	E^{2+}
	G^{2+}
least tendency to reduce:	D^{2+}

16. Since "K^{2+} only reacted with I(s) and H(s)", then K^{2+} is only above I^{2+} and H^{2+}. Hence, K^{2+} must also be below J^{2+} and L^{2+}.

greatest tendency to reduce:	J^{2+}, L^{2+} (equal, so far)
	K^{2+}
least tendency to reduce:	I^{2+}, H^{2+} (equal, so far)

Since "L^{2+} did not react with J(s)", then L^{2+} is below J^{2+}.

greatest tendency to reduce:	J^{2+}
	L^{2+}
	K^{2+}
least tendency to reduce:	I^{2+}, H^{2+} (equal, so far)

Since "I^{2+} reacted with H(s)", then I^{2+} is above H^{2+}.

greatest tendency to reduce:	J^{2+}
	L^{2+}
	K^{2+}
	I^{2+}
least tendency to reduce:	H^{2+}

17.

	Fe^{2+}	Au^{3+}	Ni^{2+}	Pb^{2+}
Fe		RX	RX	RX
Au	—		—	—
Ni	—	RX		RX
Pb	—	RX	—	

18. $Cd^{2+} > Ga^{3+} > V^{2+} > Ti^{2+}$

19. (a) $Ce^{4+} + 2e^- \rightleftharpoons Ce^{2+}$
(b) $I_2 + 2e^- \rightleftharpoons 2I^-$
(c) $Mn^{2+} + 2H_2O \rightleftharpoons MnO_2 + 4H^+ + 2e^-$
(d) $O_2 + 2H^+ + 2e^- \rightleftharpoons H_2O_2$
(e) $S_2O_8^{2-} + 2H^+ + 2e^- \rightleftharpoons 2HSO_4^-$
(f) $H_3AsO_4 + 2H^+ + 2e^- \rightleftharpoons HAsO_2 + 2H_2O$
(g) $H_2SeO_3 + 4H^+ + 4e^- \rightleftharpoons Se + 3H_2O$
(h) $N_2H_4 + 4OH^- \rightleftharpoons N_2 + 4H_2O + 4e^-$
(i) $HO_2^- + OH^- \rightleftharpoons O_2 + H_2O + 2e^-$
(j) $HXeO_4^- + 4OH^- \rightleftharpoons HXeO_6^{3-} + 2H_2O + 2e^-$
(k) $HC_2H_3O_2 + 4H^+ + 4e^- \rightleftharpoons C_2H_5OH + H_2O$
(l) $Cr(OH)_3 + 5OH^- \rightleftharpoons CrO_4^{2-} + 4H_2O + 3e^-$
(m) $CH_3CHO + 2H^+ + 2e^- \rightleftharpoons CH_2CH_2 + H_2O$

20. (a) $NO_2^- \rightleftharpoons NO_3^-$
+3 +5
(b) $\Delta ON = (+5) - (+3) = +2$
(c) $H_2O + NO_2^- \rightleftharpoons NO_3^- + 2H^+ + 2e^-$
(d) $2e^-$ produced; oxidation number increases by 2; an oxidation

21. (a) $MnO_4^- \rightleftharpoons MnO_2$
+7 +4
(b) $\Delta ON = (+4) - (+7) = -3$
(c) $3e^- + 4H^+ + MnO_4^- \rightleftharpoons MnO_2 + 2H_2O$
(d) $3e^-$ used up; oxidation number decreases by 3; a reduction

22. The OXIDATION NUMBER DECREASES during a REDUCTION reaction and INCREASES during an OXIDATION reaction.

23. (a) $\Delta ON = (+7) - (0) = +7$. Oxidation
(b) $\Delta ON = (-1) - (+5) = -6$. Reduction
(c) $\Delta ON = (+6) - (+4) = +2$. Oxidation
(d) $\Delta ON = (0) - (-2) = +2$. Oxidation
(e) $\Delta ON = (+3) - (+5) = -2$. Reduction

24. (a)
$$\mathbf{5}\,(U^{4+} + 2H_2O \longrightarrow UO_2^{2+} + 4H^+ + 2e^-)$$
$$\mathbf{2}\,(MnO_4^- + 8H^+ + 5e^- \longrightarrow Mn^{2+} + 4H_2O)$$
$$2H_2O + 5U^{4+} + 2MnO_4^- \longrightarrow 2Mn^{2+} + 5UO_2^{2+} + 4H^+$$

(b)
$$\mathbf{6}\,(Zn \longrightarrow Zn^{2+} + 2e^-)$$
$$\mathbf{1}\,(As_2O_3 + 12H^+ + 12e^- \longrightarrow 2AsH_3 + 3H_2O)$$
$$6Zn + As_2O_3 + 12H^+ \longrightarrow 2AsH_3 + 6Zn^{2+} + 3H_2O$$

(c)
$$\mathbf{6}\,(Fe^{2+} \longrightarrow Fe^{3+} + e^-)$$
$$\mathbf{1}\,(Cr_2O_7^{2-} + 14H^+ + 6e^- \longrightarrow 2Cr^{3+} + 7H_2O)$$
$$6Fe^{2+} + Cr_2O_7^{2-} + 14H^+ \longrightarrow 2Cr^{3+} + 6Fe^{3+} + 7H_2O$$

(d)
$$\mathbf{1}\,(Cl_2 + 2e^- \longrightarrow 2Cl^-)$$
$$\mathbf{1}\,(SO_2 + 2H_2O \longrightarrow SO_4^{2-} + 4H^+ + 2e^-)$$
$$Cl_2 + SO_2 + 2H_2O \longrightarrow 2Cl^- + SO_4^{2-} + 4H^+$$

(e)
$$3\ (\mathrm{Cu} \longrightarrow \mathrm{Cu^{2+}} + 2\,e^-)$$
$$2\ (\mathrm{NO_3^-} + 4\,H^+ + 3\,e^- \longrightarrow \mathrm{NO} + 2\,H_2O)$$

$$3\,\mathrm{Cu} + 2\,\mathrm{NO_3^-} + 8\,H^+ \longrightarrow 3\,\mathrm{Cu^{2+}} + 2\,\mathrm{NO} + 4\,H_2O$$

(f)
$$3\ (S^{2-} \longrightarrow S + 2\,e^-)$$
$$1\ (\mathrm{ClO_3^-} + 6\,H^+ + 6\,e^- \longrightarrow \mathrm{Cl^-} + 3\,H_2O)$$

$$3\,S^{2-} + \mathrm{ClO_3^-} + 6\,H^+ \longrightarrow 3\,S + \mathrm{Cl^-} + 3\,H_2O$$
$$6\,H_2O \longrightarrow 6\,H^+ + 6\,OH^-$$ (convert to basic)

$$3\,S^{2-} + \mathrm{ClO_3^-} + 3\,H_2O \longrightarrow 3\,S + \mathrm{Cl^-} + 6\,OH^-$$

(g)
$$2\ (\mathrm{OCl^-} + 2\,H^+ + 2\,e^- \longrightarrow \mathrm{Cl^-} + H_2O)$$
$$1\ (\mathrm{OCl^-} + 2\,H_2O \longrightarrow \mathrm{ClO_3^-} + 4\,H^+ + 4\,e^-)$$

$$3\,\mathrm{OCl^-} \longrightarrow 2\,\mathrm{Cl^-} + \mathrm{ClO_3^-}$$ (Note: no H^+ is left to "convert to basic".)

(h)
$$3\ (\mathrm{CN^-} + H_2O \longrightarrow \mathrm{CNO^-} + 2\,H^+ + 2\,e^-)$$
$$1\ (\mathrm{IO_3^-} + 6\,H^+ + 6\,e^- \longrightarrow \mathrm{I^-} + 3\,H_2O)$$

$$3\,\mathrm{CN^-} + \mathrm{IO_3^-} \longrightarrow \mathrm{I^-} + 3\,\mathrm{CNO^-}$$ (Note: no H^+ is left to "convert to basic".)

(i)
$$1\ (\mathrm{Sn^{2+}} \longrightarrow \mathrm{Sn^{4+}} + 2\,e^-)$$
$$1\ (H_2O_2 + 2\,H^+ + 2\,e^- \longrightarrow 2\,H_2O)$$

$$H_2O_2 + 2\,H^+ + \mathrm{Sn^{2+}} \longrightarrow \mathrm{Sn^{4+}} + 2\,H_2O$$
$$2\,H_2O \longrightarrow 2\,H^+ + 2\,OH^-$$

$$\mathrm{Sn^{2+}} + H_2O_2 \longrightarrow \mathrm{Sn^{4+}} + 2\,OH^-$$

(j)
$$1\ (\mathrm{Br_2} + 6\,H_2O \longrightarrow 2\,\mathrm{BrO_3^-} + 12\,H^+ + 10\,e^-)$$
$$5\ (\mathrm{Br_2} + 2\,e^- \longrightarrow 2\,\mathrm{Br^-})$$

$$3\,\mathrm{Br_2} + 3\,H_2O \longrightarrow \mathrm{BrO_3^-} + 5\,\mathrm{Br^-} + 6\,H^+$$ (after dividing by 2)
$$6\,H^+ + 6\,OH^- \longrightarrow 6\,H_2O$$

$$3\,\mathrm{Br_2} + 6\,OH^- \longrightarrow 5\,\mathrm{Br^-} + \mathrm{BrO_3^-} + 3\,H_2O$$

k)
$$5\ (\mathrm{HSO_3^-} + H_2O \longrightarrow \mathrm{SO_4^{2-}} + 3\,H^+ + 2\,e^-)$$
$$1\ (2\,\mathrm{IO_3^-} + 12\,H^+ + 10\,e^- \longrightarrow \mathrm{I_2} + 6\,H_2O)$$

$$5\,\mathrm{HSO_3^-} + 2\,\mathrm{IO_3^-} \longrightarrow \mathrm{I_2} + 5\,\mathrm{SO_4^{2-}} + 3\,H^+ + H_2O$$

(l)
$$2\,(HNO_2 + H^+ + e^- \longrightarrow NO + H_2O)$$
$$1\,(HNO_2 + H_2O \longrightarrow HNO_3 + 2\,H^+ + 2\,e^-)$$
$$3\,HNO_2 \longrightarrow HNO_3 + 2\,NO + H_2O$$

(m)
$$2\,(Mn^{2+} + 4\,H_2O \longrightarrow MnO_4^- + 8\,H^+ + 5\,e^-)$$
$$5\,(HBiO_3 + 5\,H^+ + 2\,e^- \longrightarrow Bi^{3+} + 3\,H_2O)$$
$$2\,Mn^{2+} + 5\,HBiO_3 + 9\,H^+ \longrightarrow 5\,Bi^{3+} + 2\,MnO_4^- + 7\,H_2O$$

(n)
$$3\,(H_2O_2 + 2\,H^+ + 2\,e^- \longrightarrow 2\,H_2O)$$
$$2\,(Cr(OH)_4^- \longrightarrow CrO_4^{2-} + 4\,H^+ + 3\,e^-)$$
$$3\,H_2O_2 + 2\,Cr(OH)_4^- \longrightarrow 2\,CrO_4^{2-} + 6\,H_2O + 2\,H^+$$
$$2\,H^+ + 2\,OH^- \longrightarrow 2\,H_2O$$
$$3\,H_2O_2 + 2\,Cr(OH)_4^- + 2\,OH^- \longrightarrow 2\,CrO_4^{2-} + 8\,H_2O$$

(o)
$$1\,(Sb_2S_3 + 17\,H_2O \longrightarrow Sb_2O_5 + 3\,SO_4^{2-} + 34\,H^+ + 28\,e^-)$$
$$28\,(e^- + 2\,H^+ + NO_3^- \longrightarrow NO_2 + H_2O)$$
$$Sb_2S_3 + 28\,NO_3^- + 22\,H^+ \longrightarrow Sb_2O_5 + 3\,SO_4^{2-} + 28\,NO_2 + 11\,H_2O$$

(p)
$$28\,(3\,e^- + 4\,H^+ + NO_3^- \longrightarrow NO + 2\,H_2O)$$
$$3\,(20\,H_2O + As_2S_3 \longrightarrow 2\,H_3AsO_4 + 3\,SO_4^{2-} + 34\,H^+ + 28\,e^-)$$
$$4\,H_2O + 28\,NO_3^- + 3\,As_2S_3 + 10\,H^+ \longrightarrow 6\,H_3AsO_4 + 9\,SO_4^{2-} + 28\,NO$$

(q)
$$1\,(4\,H_2O + FeS \longrightarrow Fe^{3+} + SO_4^{2-} + 8\,H^+ + 9\,e^-)$$
$$3\,(3\,e^- + 4\,H^+ + NO_3^- \longrightarrow NO + 2\,H_2O)$$
$$4\,H^+ + 3\,NO_3^- + FeS \longrightarrow Fe^{3+} + SO_4^{2-} + 3\,NO + 2\,H_2O$$

(r)
$$2\,(H_2O + FeHPO_3 \longrightarrow H_3PO_4 + Fe^{3+} + 3\,e^-)$$
$$1\,(6\,e^- + 14\,H^+ + Cr_2O_7^{2-} \longrightarrow 2\,Cr^{3+} + 7\,H_2O)$$
$$14\,H^+ + Cr_2O_7^{2-} + 2\,FeHPO_3 \longrightarrow 2\,H_3PO_4 + 2\,Fe^{3+} + 2\,Cr^{3+} + 5\,H_2O$$

(s)
$$1\,(5\,H_2O + SnS_2O_3 \longrightarrow Sn^{4+} + 2\,SO_4^{2-} + 10\,H^+ + 10\,e^-)$$
$$2\,(5\,e^- + 8\,H^+ + MnO_4^- \longrightarrow Mn^{2+} + 4\,H_2O)$$
$$6\,H^+ + 2\,MnO_4^- + SnS_2O_3 \longrightarrow Sn^{4+} + 2\,SO_4^{2-} + 2\,Mn^{2+} + 3\,H_2O$$

(t) $\mathbf{1}\ (2\,H_2O + 2\,HNO_3 + CuS \longrightarrow Cu(NO_3)_2 + SO_2 + 6\,H^+ + 6\,e^-)$

$\mathbf{6}\ (e^- + H^+ + HNO_3 \longrightarrow NO_2 + H_2O)$

$CuS + 8\,HNO_3 \longrightarrow Cu(NO_3)_2 + SO_2 + 6\,NO_2 + 4\,H_2O$

(u) $\mathbf{1}\ (20\,e^- + 20\,H^+ + 6\,SiO_2 + 2\,Ca_3(PO_4)_2 \longrightarrow 6\,CaSiO_3 + P_4 + 10\,H_2O)$

$\mathbf{10}\ (H_2O + C \longrightarrow CO + 2\,H^+ + 2\,e^-)$

$2\,Ca_3(PO_4)_2 + 6\,SiO_2 + 10\,C \longrightarrow P_4 + 6\,CaSiO_3 + 10\,CO$

(v) $\mathbf{1}\ (10\,e^- + 10\,H^+ + 3\,H_2SO_4 + 2\,KMnO_4 \longrightarrow K_2SO_4 + 2\,MnSO_4 + 8\,H_2O)$

$\mathbf{5}\ (H_2S \longrightarrow S + 2\,H^+ + 2\,e^-)$

$3\,H_2SO_4 + 2\,KMnO_4 + 5\,H_2S \longrightarrow K_2SO_4 + 2\,MnSO_4 + 5\,S + 8\,H_2O$

(w) $\mathbf{2}\ (3\,e^- + 3\,H^+ + 7\,NH_3 + 3\,CuF_2 \longrightarrow Cu_3N + 6\,NH_4F)$

$\mathbf{1}\ (2\,NH_3 \longrightarrow N_2 + 6\,H^+ + 6\,e^-)$

$16\,NH_3 + 6\,CuF_2 \longrightarrow 2\,Cu_3N + 12\,NH_4F + N_2$

25. (a) $\overset{+4}{\mathbf{Se}}O_3^{2-} + 4\,\mathbf{I}^- + 6\,H^+ \longrightarrow 2\,\overset{0}{\mathbf{I}_2} + \overset{0}{\mathbf{Se}} + 3\,H_2O$

$\Delta ON = +1 \times 2$

$\Delta ON = -4$

(b) $\overset{0}{\mathbf{I}_2} + 5\,HO\overset{+1}{\mathbf{Cl}} + H_2O \longrightarrow 5\,\mathbf{Cl}^- + 2\,\overset{+5}{\mathbf{I}}O_3^- + 7\,H^+$

$\Delta ON = -2$

$\Delta ON = +5 \times 2$

(c) $\overset{+5}{\mathbf{N}}O_3^- + 4\,\overset{0}{\mathbf{Zn}} + 7\,OH^- \longrightarrow 4\,\overset{+2}{\mathbf{Zn}}O_2^{2-} + \overset{-3}{\mathbf{N}}H_3 + 2\,H_2O$

$\Delta ON = +2$

$\Delta ON = -8$

(d) $3\,\overset{+4}{\mathbf{S}}O_3^{2-} + \overset{+6}{\mathbf{Cr}_2}O_7^{2-} + 8\,H^+ \longrightarrow 2\,\mathbf{Cr}^{3+} + 3\,\overset{+6}{\mathbf{S}}O_4^{2-} + 4\,H_2O$

$\Delta ON = -3 \times 2$

$\Delta ON = +2$

(e) $3\,\overset{+3}{\mathbf{C}_2}O_4^{2-} + 2\,\overset{+3}{\mathbf{Au}}Cl_4^- \longrightarrow 2\,\overset{0}{\mathbf{Au}} + 8\,Cl^- + 6\,\overset{+4}{\mathbf{C}}O_2$

$\Delta ON = -3$

$\Delta ON = +1 \times 2$

(f) Oxidation numbers: P in $H_2PO_2^-$ = +1; Te in TeO_4^{2-} = +6; Te = 0; P in PO_4^{3-} = +5

$$3\,H_2\mathbf{P}O_2^- + 2\,\mathbf{Te}O_4^{2-} \longrightarrow 2\,\mathbf{Te} + 3\,\mathbf{P}O_4^{3-} + 2\,H_2O + 2\,H^+$$

Te: ΔON = −6
P: ΔON = +4

(g) Oxidation numbers: S in CdS = −2; N in NO_3^- = +5; N in NO = +2; S = 0

$$3\,Cd\mathbf{S} + 2\,\mathbf{N}O_3^- + 8\,H^+ \longrightarrow 2\,\mathbf{N}O + 3\,Cd^{2+} + 3\,\mathbf{S} + 4\,H_2O$$

N: ΔON = −3
S: ΔON = +2

(h) Oxidation numbers: As in As_4 = 0; Cl in NaOCl = +1; Cl in NaCl = −1; As in AsO_4^{3-} = +5

$$\mathbf{As}_4 + 10\,NaO\mathbf{Cl} + 12\,OH^- \longrightarrow 10\,Na\mathbf{Cl} + 4\,\mathbf{As}O_4^{3-} + 6\,H_2O$$

Cl: ΔON = −2
As: ΔON = +5 x 4

(i) Oxidation numbers: S in PbS = −2; N in NO_3^- = +5; N in NO = +2; S = 0

$$3\,Pb\mathbf{S} + 8\,\mathbf{N}O_3^- + 8\,H^+ \longrightarrow 3\,Pb(NO_3)_2 + 2\,\mathbf{N}O + 3\,\mathbf{S} + 4\,H_2O$$

N: ΔON = −3
S: ΔON = +2

(j) Oxidation numbers: N in HNO_2 = +3; N in NH_4^+ = −3

$$H\mathbf{N}O_2 + 6\,\mathbf{Ti}^{3+} + 7\,H^+ \longrightarrow 6\,\mathbf{Ti}^{4+} + \mathbf{N}H_4^+ + 2\,H_2O$$

Ti: ΔON = +1
N: ΔON = −6

(k) Oxidation numbers: Cr in CrO_4^{2-} = +6; C in HCHO = 0; C in $HCOO^-$ = +2; Cr in $Cr(OH)_3$ = +3

$$2\,\mathbf{Cr}O_4^{2-} + 3\,H\mathbf{C}HO + 2\,H_2O \longrightarrow 3\,H\mathbf{C}OO^- + 2\,\mathbf{Cr}(OH)_3 + OH^-$$

C: ΔON = +2
Cr: ΔON = −3

(l) Oxidation numbers: Pt = 0; N in NO_3^- = +5; N in NO = +2; Pt in $PtCl_6^{2-}$ = +4

$$3\,\mathbf{Pt} + 18\,Cl^- + 4\,\mathbf{N}O_3^- + 16\,H^+ \longrightarrow 4\,\mathbf{N}O + 3\,\mathbf{Pt}Cl_6^{2-} + 8\,H_2O$$

N: ΔON = −3
Pt: ΔON = +4

(m) Oxidation numbers: Mn in MnO_4^- = +7; Sb in Sb_2O_3 = +3; Sb in Sb_2O_5 = +5; Mn in MnO_2 = +4

$$4\,\mathbf{Mn}O_4^- + 3\,\mathbf{Sb}_2O_3 + 2\,H_2O \longrightarrow 3\,\mathbf{Sb}_2O_5 + 4\,\mathbf{Mn}O_2 + 4\,OH^-$$

Sb: ΔON = +2 x 2
Mn: ΔON = −3

(n) Oxidation numbers: Mn in MnO_4^- = +7; N in HN_3 = −1/3; N in N_2 = 0; Mn in $MnSO_4$ = +2

$$2\,\mathbf{Mn}O_4^- + 2\,SO_4^{2-} + 10\,H\mathbf{N}_3 + 6\,H^+ \longrightarrow 8\,H_2O + 15\,\mathbf{N}_2 + 2\,\mathbf{Mn}SO_4$$

N: ΔON = 1/3 x 6
Mn: ΔON = −5

26. $\text{mmoles } KMnO_4 = 0.2500 \dfrac{\text{mmol}}{\text{mL}} \times 35.25 \text{ mL} = 8.8125 \text{ mmol}$

$\text{mmoles } H_2C_2O_4 = 8.8125 \text{ mmol } KMnO_4 \times \dfrac{5 \text{ mmol } H_2C_2O_4}{2 \text{ mmol } KMnO_4} = 22.031 \text{ mmol}$

$[H_2C_2O_4] = \dfrac{22.031 \text{ mmol}}{25.00 \text{ mL}} = \mathbf{0.8813\ M}$

27. $\text{mmol } S_2O_3^{2-} = 0.150 \dfrac{\text{mmol}}{\text{mL}} \times 14.6 \text{ mL} = 2.19 \text{ mmol}$

$\text{mmol } HNO_2 = 2.19 \text{ mmol } S_2O_3^{2-} \times \dfrac{1 \text{ mmol } I_2}{2 \text{ mmol } S_2O_3^{2-}} \times \dfrac{2 \text{ mmol } HNO_2}{1 \text{ mmol } I_2} = 2.19 \text{ mmol}$

$[HNO_2] = \dfrac{2.19 \text{ mmol}}{25.0 \text{ mL}} = \mathbf{0.0876\ M}$

28. $[Fe^{2+}] = \dfrac{3.00 \text{ g}}{0.500 \text{ L}} \times \dfrac{1 \text{ mol}}{55.8 \text{ g}} = 0.1075 \text{ M}$

$\text{mmol } Fe^{2+} = 0.1075 \dfrac{\text{mmol}}{\text{mL}} \times 25.0 \text{ mL} = 2.688 \text{ mmol}$

$\text{mmol } MnO_4^- = 2.688 \text{ mmol } Fe^{2+} \times \dfrac{1 \text{ mmol } MnO_4^-}{5 \text{ mmol } Fe^{2+}} = 0.5376 \text{ mmol}$

$\text{volume} = \dfrac{0.5376 \text{ mmol}}{0.0500 \text{ mmol/mL}} = \mathbf{10.8\ mL}$

29. (a)

$$\mathbf{5 \times (}\ Sn^{2+} \longrightarrow Sn^{4+} + 2e^- \mathbf{)}$$
$$\mathbf{2 \times (}\ MnO_4^- + 8H^+ + 5e^- \longrightarrow Mn^{2+} + 4H_2O \mathbf{)}$$

$$2MnO_4^- + 16H^+ + 5Sn^{2+} \longrightarrow 2Mn^{2+} + 5Sn^{4+} + 8H_2O$$

(b) $\text{mmol } MnO_4^- = 0.135 \dfrac{\text{mmol}}{\text{mL}} \times 41.7 \text{ mL} = 5.63 \text{ mmol}$

$\text{mmol } Sn^{2+} = 5.63 \text{ mmol } MnO_4^- \times \dfrac{5 \text{ mmol } Sn^{2+}}{2 \text{ mmol } MnO_4^-} = 14.1 \text{ mmol}$, $\quad [Sn^{2+}] = \dfrac{14.1 \text{ mmol}}{25.0 \text{ mL}} = \mathbf{0.563\ M}$

(c) moles Sn = 14.1 mmol = 0.0141 mol , $\quad \text{mass Sn} = 0.0141 \text{ mol} \times \dfrac{118.7 \text{ g}}{1 \text{ mol}} = \mathbf{1.67\ g}$

30. $\text{mmol } OCl^- = 0.500 \dfrac{\text{mmol}}{\text{mL}} \times 25.0 \text{ mL} = 12.5 \text{ mmol}$

$\text{mmol } S_2O_3^{2-} = 12.5 \text{ mmol } OCl^- \times \dfrac{1 \text{ mmol } I_2}{1 \text{ mmol } OCl^-} \times \dfrac{2 \text{ mmol } S_2O_3^{2-}}{1 \text{ mmol } I_2} = 25.0 \text{ mmol}$

$\text{volume } Na_2S_2O_3 = \dfrac{25.0 \text{ mmol}}{0.750 \text{ mmol/mL}} = \mathbf{33.3\ mL}$

31. (a)

$$2Cu^{2+} + 2I^- + 2e^- \longrightarrow 2CuI$$
$$2I^- \longrightarrow I_2 + 2e^-$$

$$2Cu^{2+} + 4I^- \longrightarrow 2CuI + I_2$$

(b) mmoles $Na_2S_2O_3 = 0.1650 \frac{mmol}{mL} \times 15.69\ mL = 2.5889\ mmol$

mmoles $Cu^{2+} = 2.5889\ mmol\ S_2O_3^{2-} \times \frac{1\ mmol\ I_2}{2\ mmol\ S_2O_3^{2-}} \times \frac{2\ mmol\ Cu^{2+}}{1\ mmol\ I_2} = 2.5889\ mmol$

$[Cu^{2+}] = \frac{2.5889\ mmol}{25.00\ mL} = \mathbf{0.1036\ M}$

32. (a) $2\ IO_3^- + 12\ H^+ + 10\ e^- \longrightarrow I_2 + 6\ H_2O$

$10\ I^- \longrightarrow 5\ I_2 + 10\ e^-$

$IO_3^- + 5\ I^- + 6\ H^+ \longrightarrow 3\ I_2 + 3\ H_2O$ (after dividing by 2)

(b) mmoles $S_2O_3^{2-} = 0.248 \frac{mmol}{mL} \times 13.1\ mL = 3.249\ mmol$

mmoles $IO_3^- = 3.249\ mmol\ S_2O_3^{2-} \times \frac{1\ mmol\ I_2}{2\ mmol\ S_2O_3^{2-}} \times \frac{1\ mmol\ IO_3^-}{3\ mmol\ I_2} = 0.5415\ mmol$

$[KIO_3] = [IO_3^-] = \frac{0.5415\ mmol}{25.0\ mL} = \mathbf{0.02166\ M}$

(c) mass KIO_3 present $= 1.00\ L \times 0.02166 \frac{mol}{L} \times \frac{214.0\ g}{1\ mol} = 4.635\ g$

and percentage purity $= \frac{\text{actual mass } KIO_3}{\text{mass of impure sample}} \times 100\% = \frac{4.635\ g}{5.00\ g} \times 100\% = \mathbf{92.7\ \%}$

33. Pipette a sample of the H_2O_2 into a flask and fill a burette with the acidic MnO_4^- solution. At first, the excess H_2O_2 will destroy the pink colour of the MnO_4^- according to the reaction:

$$2\ MnO_4^- + 6\ H^+ + 5\ H_2O_2 \longrightarrow 2\ Mn^{2+} + 5\ O_2 + 8\ H_2O.$$

At the stoichiometric point, a slight excess of MnO_4^- will exist and the solution will take on a permanent faint pink colour. You need to know the volume of H_2O_2 solution used, the concentration of MnO_4^- and the volume of MnO_4^- used to get to the stoichiometric point.

Calculations:

a) find the moles of MnO_4^- by multiplying the volume and concentration of MnO_4^- solution used,
b) use a moles conversion to convert moles of permanganate into moles of H_2O_2, and finally
c) find the $[H_2O_2]$ by dividing the moles of H_2O_2 by the volume of H_2O_2.

34. **Analysis:** The half–cells must be $Ni \longrightarrow Ni^{2+} + 2\ e^-$ (oxidation)
$Cu^{2+} + 2\ e^- \longrightarrow Cu$ (reduction)

(a) Since oxidation occurs at the anode, then Ni(s) is the anode.
(b) SO_4^{2-} is an anion and travels toward the anode (Ni).
(c) Electrons flow from anode to cathode, so that electrons travel from Ni to Cu.
(d) From the reaction stoichiometry, 1 mol Cu is produced by 2 mol e^-. Therefore, 0.025 mol Cu is produced by 0.050 mol e^- and 0.050 mol e^- must have travelled through the wire.
(e) Ni^{2+} is a cation and travels toward the cathode (Cu).

35. **Analysis:** Since the Sn(s) seems to have gone into solution, then the oxidation reaction must be $Sn \longrightarrow Sn^{2+} + 2\,e^-$. The reduction reaction must then be $Ag^+ + e^- \longrightarrow Ag$.

(a)

$$\begin{array}{lll} Sn \longrightarrow Sn^{2+} + 2\,e^- & \text{(oxidation)} \\ 2\,Ag^+ + 2\,e^- \longrightarrow 2\,Ag & \text{reduction)} \\ \hline 2\,Ag^+ + Sn \longrightarrow Sn^{2+} + 2\,Ag & \text{(net ionic)} \end{array}$$

(b) Reduction occurs at the cathode and so the Ag(s) is the cathode.
(c) Ag^+ is a cation and migrates toward the cathode, which is Ag(s).
(d) Electrons flow from anode to cathode; that is, from Sn(s) to Ag(s).
(e) The Ag(s) gains mass since more Ag(s) is being produced at the cathode.
(f) Since 1 mol Sn produces 2 mol e^- (which flow through the wire), then 0.010 mol Sn produces 0.020 mol e^-.
(g) From the net ionic equation, 1 mol Sn is associated with 2 mol Ag, so that 0.020 mol Sn reacts with 0.040 mol Ag.
(h) Trick question! No electrons flow through the salt bridge, only through the wire.

36. (a)

$$\begin{array}{lll} Cr \longrightarrow Cr^{3+} + 3\,e^- & ; \; E^o = 0.74\text{ V} & \\ 3\,Ag^+ + 3\,e^- \longrightarrow 3\,Ag & ; \; E^o = 0.80\text{ V} & \\ \hline Cr + 3\,Ag^+ \longrightarrow Cr^{3+} + 3\,Ag & ; \; E^o_{CELL} = 1.54\text{ V} & \text{(spontaneous)} \end{array}$$

(b)

$$\begin{array}{lll} Cu^+ \longrightarrow Cu^{2+} + e^- & ; \; E^o = -0.15\text{ V} & \\ Fe^{3+} + e^- \longrightarrow Fe^{2+} & ; \; E^o = 0.77\text{ V} & \\ \hline Cu^+ + Fe^{3+} \longrightarrow Cu^{2+} + Fe^{2+} & ; \; E^o_{CELL} = 0.62\text{ V} & \text{(spontaneous)} \end{array}$$

(c)

$$\begin{array}{lll} Mn^{2+} + 2\,H_2O \longrightarrow MnO_2 + 4\,H^+ + 2\,e^- & ; \; E^o = -1.22\text{ V} & \\ I_2 + 2\,e^- \longrightarrow 2\,I^- & ; \; E^o = 0.54\text{ V} & \\ \hline Mn^{2+} + 2\,H_2O + I_2 \longrightarrow MnO_2 + 4\,H^+ + 2\,I^- & ; \; E^o_{CELL} = -0.68\text{ V} & \text{(non–spontaneous)} \end{array}$$

(d)

$$\begin{array}{lll} 3\,Cu \longrightarrow 3\,Cu^{2+} + 6\,e^- & ; \; E^o = -0.34\text{ V} & \\ 2\,NO_3^- + 8\,H^+ + 6\,e^- \longrightarrow 4\,H_2O + 2\,NO & ; \; E^o = 0.96\text{ V} & \\ \hline 3\,Cu + 2\,NO_3^- + 8\,H^+ \longrightarrow 3\,Cu^{2+} + 4\,H_2O + 2\,NO & ; \; E^o_{CELL} = 0.62\text{ V} & \text{(spontaneous)} \end{array}$$

(e)

$$\begin{array}{lll} 2\,Cr^{3+} + 7\,H_2O \longrightarrow Cr_2O_7^{2-} + 14\,H^+ + 6\,e^- & ; \; E^o = -1.23\text{ V} & \\ 3\,Pb^{2+} + 6\,e^- \longrightarrow 3\,Pb & ; \; E^o = -0.13\text{ V} & \\ \hline 2\,Cr^{3+} + 7\,H_2O + 3\,Pb^{2+} \longrightarrow Cr_2O_7^{2-} + 14\,H^+ + 3\,Pb & ; \; E^o_{CELL} = -1.36\text{ V} & \text{(non–spontaneous)} \end{array}$$

(f)

$$\begin{array}{lll} H_2O_2 + 2\,H^+ + 2\,e^- \longrightarrow 2\,H_2O & ; \; E^o = 1.78\text{ V} & \\ H_2O_2 \longrightarrow O_2 + 2\,H^+ + 2\,e^- & ; \; E^o = -0.70\text{ V} & \\ \hline 2\,H_2O_2 \longrightarrow 2\,H_2O + O_2 & ; \; E^o_{CELL} = 1.08\text{ V} & \text{(spontaneous)} \end{array}$$

(g) $Fe^{2+} + 2e^- \longrightarrow Fe$; $E^o = -0.45$ V
$2Fe^{2+} \longrightarrow 2Fe^{3+} + 2e^-$; $E^o = -0.77$ V

$3Fe^{2+} \longrightarrow Fe + 2Fe^{3+}$; $E^o_{CELL} = -1.22$ V (non–spontaneous)

(h) $Hg^{2+} + 2e^- \longrightarrow Hg$; $E^o = 0.85$ V
$2Hg \longrightarrow Hg_2^{2+} + 2e^-$; $E^o = -0.80$ V

$Hg^{2+} + Hg \longrightarrow Hg_2^{2+}$; $E^o_{CELL} = 0.05$ V (spontaneous)

37. (a) highest voltage = Ag and Mg (b) lowest voltage = Cr and Zn

38. Since the first reaction is not spontaneous, the reduction reaction is below the oxidation reaction on the Table of Reduction Potentials.

$Ru^{4+} + e^- \longrightarrow Ru^{3+}$
$Te^{4+} + 4e^- \longrightarrow Te$
} difference in voltage = 0.23 V

Since the second reaction is spontaneous, the reduction reaction is above the oxidation reaction.

$Ru^{4+} + e^- \longrightarrow Ru^{3+}$
$Nb^{5+} + 2e^- \longrightarrow Nb^{3+}$
} difference in voltage = 0.52 V

Since the Ru^{4+} half–reaction is 0.23 V above the Te^{4+} and 0.52 V above the Nb^{5+}, the final order is:

$Ru^{4+} + e^- \longrightarrow Ru^{3+}$
$Te^{4+} + 4e^- \longrightarrow Te$
$Nb^{5+} + 2e^- \longrightarrow Nb^{3+}$.

Therefore the reduction of Nb^{5+} is below oxidation of Te and a spontaneous reaction will not occur.

39. The half–reactions needed to solve this question are, when put in proper order:

$A^{2+} + 2e^- \rightleftharpoons A$; $E^o = 0.31$ V
$2H^+ + 2e^- \rightleftharpoons H_2$; $E^o = 0.00$ V
$A^+ + e^- \rightleftharpoons A$; $E^o = -0.29$ V
$2H_2O + 2e^- \rightleftharpoons H_2 + 2OH^-(10^{-7}\text{ M})$; $E = -0.41$ V.

(a) Metal A will NOT dissolve (react) in pure neutral water (the reduction of water is too low to oxidize A).
(b) Metal A WILL dissolve (react) in 1 M H^+, producing A^+.

$2H^+ + 2A \longrightarrow H_2 + 2A^+$; $E^o_{CELL} = 0.29$ V

40. $C^{2+} > D^{2+} > A^{2+} > B^{2+}$

41. $A^{3+} > D^{3+} > B^{3+} > C^{3+} > E^{3+}$

42. The half–reactions are: $Cu^{2+} + 2e^- \rightleftharpoons Cu$; $E^o = 0.34$ V
$Zn^{2+} + 2e^- \rightleftharpoons Zn$; $E^o = -0.76$ V.

Under standard conditions, the value of E^o_{CELL} is 1.10 V.

If $[Cu^{2+}] > 1$ M, then the copper half–reaction has an increased tendency to go forward and reduce, relative to standard conditions of 1 M, and the reduction potential increases. If $[Zn^{2+}] < 1$ M, then the zinc half–reaction has a decreased tendency to go forward and reduce, relative to standard conditions of 1 M, and the reduction potential decreases. Overall, the voltage difference (voltage gap between the half–reactions) increases and the voltage is greater than 1.10 V.

43. The thickness (that is, surface area) of the electrodes has no effect on the half–cell voltages. The lower the ion concentration in either half–reaction: $Pb^{2+} + 2\,e^- \rightleftharpoons Pb(s)$
$Zn^{2+} + 2\,e^- \rightleftharpoons Zn(s)$,
the lower the half–cell potential. Therefore:

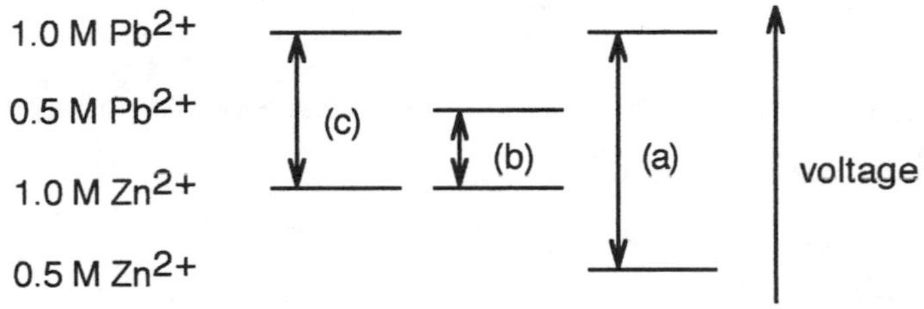

The differences between the half–cell voltages give the cell potentials. As a result, the cell potentials, in order from highest to lowest are: (a) > (c) > (b)

44. (a) 2 M Pb^{2+} (b) 2 M I^-

45. CASE 3

46. As the reaction proceeds, the reduction potential of the species being reduced is decreased and the reduction potential of the species being oxidized is increased. The voltage gap between the half–cell voltages decreases and the light dims.

47. (a) Species present: Br_2, Cl_2, Cu^{2+}, SO_4^{2-}, Cu. Preferred reduction and oxidation reactions are:

$$Cl_2 + 2\,e^- \longrightarrow 2\,Cl^-$$
$$Cu \longrightarrow Cu^{2+} + 2\,e^-$$
$$Cu + Cl_2 \longrightarrow Cu^{2+} + 2\,Cl^-.$$

(b) Species present: Al, Fe, Cr^{3+}. The preferred reduction and oxidation reactions are:

$$3\,Cr^{3+} + 3\,e^- \longrightarrow 3\,Cr^{2+}$$
$$Al \longrightarrow Al^{3+} + 3\,e^-$$
$$Al + 3\,Cr^{3+} \longrightarrow Al^{3+} + 3\,Cr^{2+}.$$

(c) Species present: Sn, H^+, NO_3^-. The preferred reduction and oxidation reactions are:

$$2\,NO_3^- + 8\,H^+ + 6\,e^- \longrightarrow 2\,NO + 4\,H_2O$$
$$3\,Sn \longrightarrow 3\,Sn^{2+} + 6\,e^-$$
$$3\,Sn + 2\,NO_3^- + 8\,H^+ \longrightarrow 3\,Sn^{2+} + 2\,NO + 4\,H_2O.$$

(d) Species present: Cu, H^+, NO_3^-. The preferred reduction and oxidation reactions are:

$$2\,NO_3^- + 8\,H^+ + 6\,e^- \longrightarrow 2\,NO + 4\,H_2O$$
$$3\,Cu \longrightarrow 3\,Cu^{2+} + 6\,e^-$$
$$3\,Cu + 2\,NO_3^- + 8\,H^+ \longrightarrow 3\,Cu^{2+} + 2\,NO + 4\,H_2O.$$

(e) Species present: Cu, H^+, Cl^- and O_2. The preferred reduction and oxidation reactions are:

$$\tfrac{1}{2}\,O_2 + 2\,H^+ + 2\,e^- \longrightarrow H_2O$$
$$Cu \longrightarrow Cu^{2+} + 2\,e^-$$
$$Cu + \tfrac{1}{2}\,O_2 + 2\,H^+ \longrightarrow Cu^{2+} + H_2O.$$

(f) Species present: Hg, H^+, SO_4^{2-}, K^+, MnO_4^-. The preferred reduction and oxidation reactions are:

$$MnO_4^- + 8\,H^+ + 5\,e^- \longrightarrow Mn^{2+} + 4\,H_2O$$
$$5\,Hg \longrightarrow 5/2\,Hg_2^{2+} + 5\,e^-$$
$$5\,Hg + MnO_4^- + 8\,H^+ \longrightarrow 5/2\,Hg_2^{2+} + Mn^{2+} + 4\,H_2O.$$

(g) Species present: H_2O_2, H^+, Cl^-. The preferred reduction and oxidation reactions are:

$$H_2O_2 + 2\,H^+ + 2\,e^- \longrightarrow 2\,H_2O$$
$$H_2O_2 \longrightarrow O_2 + 2\,H^+ + 2\,e^-$$
$$2\,H_2O_2 \longrightarrow 2\,H_2O + O_2.$$

48. Nitric acid reduces at +0.96 V and +0.80 V. Use the half cell at +0.96 V (greater tendency to reduce). Gold oxidizes at 1.50 V, but a gold/chloride ion mixture oxidizes at 1.00 V. So far:

$$AuCl_4^- + 3\,e^- \longleftarrow \boxed{Au + 4\,Cl^-} \quad \ldots\ldots\ 1.00\text{ V}$$
$$\boxed{NO_3^- + 4\,H^+} + 3\,e^- \longrightarrow NO + 2\,H_2O \quad \ldots\ldots\ 0.96\text{ V}.$$

These half–reaction voltages apply to 1 M concentrations of all dissolved species and 1 atm pressure of NO(g). The half cells only start with Au, Cl^-, H^+ and NO_3^-, using 15 M HNO_3 and 12 M HCl; no NO(g) or $AuCl_4^-$ exists at the start of the reaction. Therefore, there will be an increased tendency for the H^+ and NO_3^- half–reaction to be reduced and push the reduction potential higher on the Table. Similarly, there will be a greater tendency for the Au and Cl^- to oxidize, pushing that half–reaction lower on the Table. As a result, the reduction of H^+ and NO_3^- will be above the oxidation of the Au and Cl^-, giving rise to a spontaneous reaction.

49.

$$\mathbf{3}\ (C_2H_5OH + H_2O \longrightarrow CH_3COOH + 4\,H^+ + 4\,e^-)$$
$$\mathbf{2}\ (K_2Cr_2O_7 + 4\,H_2SO_4 + 6\,H^+ + 6\,e^- \longrightarrow Cr_2(SO_4)_3 + K_2SO_4 + 7\,H_2O)$$
$$3\,C_2H_5OH + 2\,K_2Cr_2O_7 + 8\,H_2SO_4 \longrightarrow 3\,CH_3COOH + 2\,Cr_2(SO_4)_3 + 2\,K_2SO_4 + 11\,H_2O$$

50. The air we breathe into our lungs, and therefore into the alveoli, is relatively high in $[O_2]$ and low in $[CO_2]$. There is free passage of O_2 and CO_2 back and forth between the alveoli and capillaries, but the concentration of CO_2 molecules inside the capillaries is higher and therefore there is a greater net probability that CO_2 will move from a capillary into an alveolus than vice versa. Similarly, since there is a higher $[O_2]$ inside the alveoli than in the capillaries, there is a greater net probability that O_2 will move from an alveolus into a capillary than vice versa. After this net transfer of O_2 into the capillaries and CO_2 into the alveoli, the air we breathe out is higher in $[CO_2]$ and lower in $[O_2]$.

51.
$$\begin{array}{rcl} \mathbf{3}\ \mathbf{(}CH_3OH & \longrightarrow & HCHO + 2\,H^+ + 2\,e^-\mathbf{)} \\ K_2Cr_2O_7 + 4\,H_2SO_4 + 6\,H^+ + 6\,e^- & \longrightarrow & Cr_2(SO_4)_3 + K_2SO_4 + 7\,H_2O \\ \hline K_2Cr_2O_7 + 4\,H_2SO_4 + 3\,CH_3OH & \longrightarrow & Cr_2(SO_4)_3 + K_2SO_4 + 3\,HCHO + 7\,H_2O \end{array}$$

52. The recharging reaction is the reverse of the discharging reaction. The recharging reaction is
$$Pb^{2+} + Pb^{2+} \longrightarrow Pb + Pb^{4+}$$
and since the Pb^{2+} is both reduced to Pb and oxidized to Pb^{4+}, a disproportionation occurs.

53. If one of the Pb anode plates touches one of the PbO_2 cathode plates, a "short–circuit" occurs and the electron flow is directly from Pb to PbO_2. The electron flow therefore does not occur through an external ciruit and the battery is "dead".

54. Because the $[Zn^{2+}]$ is decreased as a result of the formation of the species $Zn(NH_3)_4^{2+}$
$$Zn^{2+} + 4\,NH_3 \rightleftharpoons Zn(NH_3)_4^{2+},$$
there would be a greater tendency for the anode to oxidize and produce Zn^{2+} and therefore a greater oxidation potential (greater than +0.76 V).

55. (a) Adding together the anode and cathode reactions, the OH^- cancels and there is NO NET CHANGE in the amount of OH^-.
(b) As the anode reaction proceeds, the $[OH^-]$ decreases so that there is less tendency for the reaction to go forward and oxidize, lowering the oxidation potential.

56. No energy producing process is truly "pollution free" because heat must be disposed of in the environment and can sometimes be thought of as a pollutant. However, beside heat, this reaction produces only H_2O, which generally is not considered to be a pollutant.

57. Fe has a great tendency to oxidize while Au has an extremely small tendency to oxidize. Whereas water and oxygen are sufficient to oxidize iron, there are no naturally–occurring oxidizing agents for Au.

58. If oxygen were absent, native Fe would be more likely to exist. Any Fe^{3+} or Fe^{2+} exposed to the atmosphere would be reduced to Fe(s). For example:
$$\begin{array}{rcl} Fe^{2+} + 2\,e^- & \longrightarrow & Fe(s) \\ H_2 + 2\,OH^-\,(10^{-7}\,M) & \longrightarrow & 2\,H_2O + 2\,e^- \\ \hline H_2 + Fe^{2+} + 2\,OH^-\,(10^{-7}\,M) & \longrightarrow & Fe(s) + 2\,H_2O \end{array}$$

59. The pillar is in a desert region which receives very little rainfall, and the soil is very dry unless irrigated. (Incidentally, it has also been coated with a light film of fingerprint oil over the centuries since the pillar is a "good luck" object which local villagers frequently touch.)

60. method 1: paint the boat
method 2: plate another metal, such as zinc, over the aluminum.
method 3: supply electrons to the aluminum, in the form of an electric current.

61. Plate the iron with a layer of zinc before adding the chromium plating. Then, if the plating layers are scratched to expose the iron, the zinc will also be exposed and provide cathodic protection to the iron.

62. Since Fe(s) has a greater tendency to oxidize than does Sn(s), the Sn will not provide cathodic protection to the Fe. The iron underneath will rust away.

63. The Mg has a much greater tendency to oxidize than the Fe contained in the motor casing. Hence, the Mg provides cathodic protection to the motor casing. It is less expensive to replace a small bar of magnesium than the bearings in a motor.

64. (a) $2\,K^+ + 2\,e^- \longrightarrow 2\,K$; $E^o = -2.93$ V (cathode)
$2\,Br^- \longrightarrow Br_2 + 2\,e^-$; $E^o = -1.09$ V (anode)

$2\,K^+ + 2\,Br^- \longrightarrow 2\,K + Br_2$; $E^o_{CELL} = -4.02$ V (must apply at least +4.02 V)

(b) $Ca^{2+} + 2\,e^- \longrightarrow Ca$; $E^o = -2.87$ V (cathode)
$2\,I^- \longrightarrow I_2 + 2\,e^-$; $E^o = -0.54$ V (anode)

$Ca^{2+} + 2\,I^- \longrightarrow Ca + I_2$; $E^o_{CELL} = -3.41$ V (must apply at least +3.41 V)

(c) $Sn^{2+} + 2\,e^- \longrightarrow Sn$; $E^o = -0.14$ V (cathode)
$2\,Cl^- \longrightarrow Cl_2 + 2\,e^-$; $E^o = -1.36$ V (anode)

$Sn^{2+} + 2\,Cl^- \longrightarrow Sn + Cl_2$; $E^o_{CELL} = -1.50$ V (must apply at least +1.50 V)

65. (a) $Ni^{2+} + 2\,e^- \longrightarrow Ni(s)$; $E^o = -0.26$ V (cathode)
$2\,I^- \longrightarrow I_2 + 2\,e^-$; $E^o = -0.54$ V (anode) ; The minimum voltage required is +0.80 V.

(b) $2\,H_2O + 2\,e^- \longrightarrow H_2(g) + 2\,OH^-(10^{-7}\,M)$; $E^o = -0.41$ V (cathode)
$2\,I^- \longrightarrow I_2 + 2\,e^-$; $E^o = -0.54$ V (anode)
The minimum voltage required is +0.95 V.

(c) $2\,H_2O + 2\,e^- \longrightarrow H_2(g) + 2\,OH^-(10^{-7}\,M)$; $E^o = -0.41$ V (cathode)
$H_2O \longrightarrow \frac{1}{2}\,O_2(g) + 2\,H^+(10^{-7}\,M) + 2\,e^-$; $E^o = -0.82$ V (anode)
The minimum voltage required is +1.23 V.

(d) $2\,H^+ + 2\,e^- \longrightarrow H_2$; $E^o = 0.00$ V (cathode)
$2\,I^- \longrightarrow I_2 + 2\,e^-$; $E^o = -0.54$ V (anode) ; The minimum voltage required is +0.54 V

66. $Cu^{2+} + 2\,e^- \longrightarrow Cu(s)$; $E^o = 0.34$ V (cathode)
$2\,Cl^- \longrightarrow Cl_2(g) + 2\,e^-$; $E^o = -1.36$ V (anode)
Must apply AT LEAST +1.02 V before the cell will operate.

67. $Cu^{2+} + 2\,e^- \longrightarrow Cu(s)$; $E^o = +0.34$ V (cathode)
$H_2O \longrightarrow \frac{1}{2}\,O_2(g) + 2\,H^+(10^{-7}\,M) + 2\,e^-$; $E^o = -0.82$ V (anode)
Must apply AT LEAST +0.48 V before the cell will operate.

68. (a) $2\,H_2O + 2\,e^- \longrightarrow H_2 + 2\,OH^-(10^{-7}\,M)$ (cathode)
$2\,I^- \longrightarrow I_2 + 2\,e^-$ (anode)

$2\,I^- + 2\,H_2O \longrightarrow H_2 + I_2 + 2\,OH^-(10^{-7}\,M)$

(b) $Sn^{2+} + 2\,e^- \longrightarrow Sn$ (cathode)
$Sn^{2+} \longrightarrow Sn^{4+} + 2\,e^-$ (anode)

$2\,Sn^{2+} \longrightarrow Sn + Sn^{4+}$

(c) $Cu^{2+} + 2\,e^- \longrightarrow Cu$ (cathode)
$2\,Br^- \longrightarrow Br_2 + 2\,e^-$ (anode) * exception

$Cu^{2+} + 2\,Br^- \longrightarrow Cu + Br_2$

(d) $2\,H^+ + 2\,e^- \longrightarrow H_2$ (cathode)
$2\,Br^- \longrightarrow Br_2 + 2\,e^-$ (anode) * exception

$2\,H^+ + 2\,Br^- \longrightarrow H_2 + Br_2$

(e) $2\,H_2O + 2\,e^- \longrightarrow H_2 + 2\,OH^-\,(10^{-7}\,M)$ (cathode)
$H_2O \longrightarrow \frac{1}{2}\,O_2(g) + 2\,H^+\,(10^{-7}\,M) + 2\,e^-$ (anode)

$H_2O \longrightarrow H_2 + \frac{1}{2}\,O_2$ (note that: $2\,H^+\,(10^{-7}\,M) + 2\,OH^-\,(10^{-7}\,M) \longrightarrow 2\,H_2O$)

(f) $Co^{2+} + 2\,e^- \longrightarrow Co$ (cathode)
$2\,I^- \longrightarrow I_2 + 2\,e^-$ (anode)

$Co^{2+} + 2\,I^- \longrightarrow Co + I_2$

(g) $2\,Fe^{3+} + 2\,e^- \longrightarrow 2\,Fe^{2+}$ (cathode)
$2\,Cl^- \longrightarrow Cl_2 + 2\,e^-$ (anode) *exception

$2\,Fe^{3+} + 2\,Cl^- \longrightarrow 2\,Fe^{2+} + Cl_2$

(h) $SO_4^{2-} + 4\,H^+ + 2\,e^- \longrightarrow H_2SO_3 + H_2O$ (cathode)
$H_2O \longrightarrow \frac{1}{2}\,O_2(g) + 2\,H^+ + 2\,e^-$ (anode)

$SO_4^{2-} + 2\,H^+ \longrightarrow H_2SO_3 + \frac{1}{2}\,O_2(g)$

69. $2\,H_2O + 2\,e^- \longrightarrow H_2 + 2\,OH^-\,(10^{-7}\,M)$ (cathode)
$H_2O \longrightarrow \frac{1}{2}\,O_2(g) + 2\,H^+\,(10^{-7}\,M) + 2\,e^-$ (anode)

$H_2O \longrightarrow H_2 + \frac{1}{2}\,O_2$

At the anode, the solution starts at neutral conditions but slowly produces H^+ and becomes acidic. Litmus paper in this solution will turn pink.

At the cathode, the solution starts at neutral conditions but slowly produces OH^- and becomes basic. Litmus paper in this solution will turn blue.

The pH of the resulting mixed solution will remain at 7 (neutral) since the overall reaction shows that there is no net excess of H^+ or OH^- produced.

70. $AlCl_3 \longrightarrow Al^{3+} + 3\,Cl^-$. Since H_2O has a higher tendency to reduce than Al^{3+}, Al^{3+} will never be able to reduce as long as there is water present.

71. (a) 1.99 V

(b) The cell containing NaBr will become an electrolytic cell as a result of the electrical energy supplied by the silver–manganese cell. The reaction will be:

$$2\,H_2O + 2\,e^- \longrightarrow H_2 + 2\,OH^-(10^{-7}\ M) \quad ; \quad E^o = -0.41\ V \quad \text{(cathode)}$$
$$2\,Br^- \longrightarrow Br_2 + 2\,e^- \quad ; \quad E^o = -1.09\ V \quad \text{(anode)}$$

$$2\,H_2O + 2\,Br^- \longrightarrow H_2 + Br_2 + 2\,OH^-(10^{-7}\ M) \ ; \ E^o_{CELL} = -1.50\ V.$$

72. The half cells are: $Sn^{2+} + 2\,e^- \rightleftharpoons Sn$; $E^o = -0.14$ V
$Co^{2+} + 2\,e^- \rightleftharpoons Co$; $E^o = -0.28$ V.

Sulphate ions are anions, which migrate toward the anode, so that Sn is the anode and the Sn must be oxidizing. Since the tin half–reaction (oxidation) is above the cobalt half–reaction (reduction), the reaction is not spontaneous and an electrolytic cell is involved.

73. The iron should be the cathode, so as to allow the reaction $Cr^{3+} + 3\,e^- \longrightarrow Cr(s)$ to occur.

74. (a) The medallion can be made out of any conducting material which allows electrons to be transported to the species undergoing reduction. The cathode material doesn't get a chance to oxidize (react).
(b) The low $[Ni^{2+}]$, resulting from having precipitated most of the Ni^{2+} from solution, would prevent Ni(s) from plating out at the cathode.
(c) At first, the cathode reaction would be: $2\,H_2O + 2\,e^- \longrightarrow H_2 + 2\,OH^-(10^{-7}\ M)$.
However, the anode would be producing Ni^{2+}, as before, so that eventually sufficient Ni^{2+} would be present to allow Ni(s) to be formed at the cathode.

75.

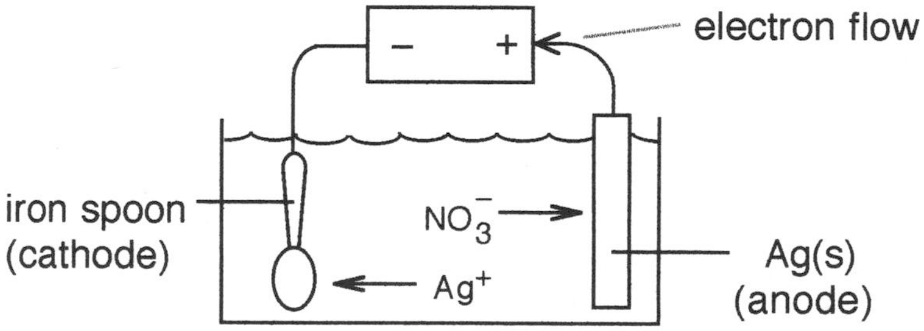

76.

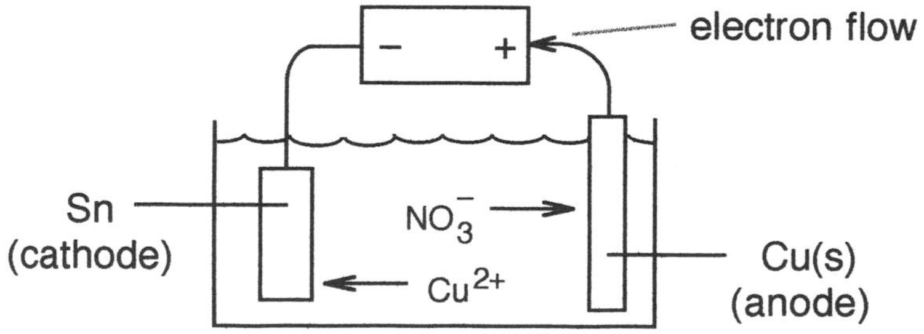

77. Substances oxidized = Sn(s), Zn(s) ; Substance reduced = Sn^{2+}

78. The water is reduced in preference to the Al^{3+}.

79. The AlF_3 and Na_3AlF_6 react to make Al(s), among other things. The Sn^{2+} and Fe^{3+} present in $SnCl_2$ and $FeBr_3$ would likewise reduce to form Sn(s) and Fe(s), which would contaminate the Al(s) produced.

80. Adding the anode and cathode reactions gives: $4\,Al^{3+} + 3\,C + 6\,O^{2-} \longrightarrow 4\,Al + 3\,CO_2$.

GLOSSARY

The number following each entry is the page number where the term is defined or first mentioned.

ACIDIC BUFFER – a solution which buffers the pH in the acidic region (180)

ACIDIC SOLUTION – a solution having $[H_3O^+] > [OH^-]$ (126)

ACID IONIZATION EQUATION (of a weak acid) – the equilibrium equation occurring when a weak acid dissociates in water, having the form: $HA + H_2O \rightleftharpoons H_3O^+ + A^-$ (128)

ACID IONIZATION CONSTANT – the value of K_a for the equilibrium expression: $K_a = \dfrac{[H_3O^+][A^-]}{[HA]}$ (128)

ACID RAIN –any precipitation with a pH less than 5.6 (186)

ACTIVATED COMPLEX – an intermediate molecule which occurs when reactants are in the process of rearranging to form products (21)

ACTIVATION ENERGY – the minimum potential energy required to change reactants into an activated complex (21)

AMPHIPROTIC SUBSTANCE – a substance which can act as either an acid or a base; apart from water, amphiprotic substances start with "H" and have a negative charge (117)

ANION – an ion having a negative charge (82)

ANODE –the electrode at which oxidation occurs; the electrode receiving the electrons from a substance being oxidized; the electrode toward which anions travel (215)

ARRHENIUS ACID – any substance which releases H^+ (aq) in water; any ionic species whose formula starts with an "H" (109)

ARRHENIUS BASE – any substance which releases OH^- (aq) in water; any ionic species whose formula ends with an "OH" (109)

BASE IONIZATION EQUATION (of a weak base) – the equilibrium equation occurring when a weak base dissociates in water, having the form: $B^- + H_2O \rightleftharpoons BH + OH^-$ (128)

BASE IONIZATION CONSTANT – the value of K_b for the equilibrium expression: $K_b = \dfrac{[HA][OH^-]}{[A^-]}$ (128)

BASIC BUFFER – a solution which buffers the pH in the basic region (180)

BASIC SOLUTION – a solution having $[H_3O^+] < [OH^-]$ (126)

BATTERY ACID – commercial term for sulphuric acid (112)

BINARY SALT – a salt made of only two different elements, such as NaCl, KBr, MgI_2, AlF_3, etc. (237)

BOND ENERGY – the amount of energy required to break a bond between two atoms (13)

BOTTLE-NECK STEP – see RATE–DETERMINING STEP

BRØNSTED–LOWRY ACID – a substance which donates a proton to another substance (116)

BRØNSTED–LOWRY BASE – a substance which accepts a proton from another substance (116)

BUFFER – a solution containing appreciable amounts of a weak acid and its conjugate weak base (177)

CATALYST – a chemical which can be added to a reaction to increase the rate of the reaction (9); a substance which provides an overall reaction with an alternative mechanism having a lower activation energy (30)

CATHODE – the electrode at which reduction occurs; the electrode supplying electrons to a substance being reduced; the electrode toward which cations travel (215)

CATHODIC PROTECTION – a term applied to the process of protecting a substance from unwanted oxidation by connecting it to a substance having a higher tendency to oxidize (235)

CATION – an ion having a positive charge (82)

CAUSTIC POTASH – commercial term for potassium hydroxide (114)

CAUSTIC SODA (or LYE) – commercial terms for sodium hydroxide (114)

CLOSED SYSTEM – a system which nothing can enter or leave (37)

COLLISION THEORY (or KINETIC MOLECULAR THEORY) – the theory stating that molecules act as small, hard spheres which bounce off each other and transfer energy among themselves during their collisions (12)

COMMON ION EFFECT – the lowering of the solubility of a salt by adding a second salt which has one ion "in common" with the first salt (106)

COMPLETE IONIC EQUATION – a balanced chemical equation in which all soluble ionic species are shown broken into their respective ions (85)

CONJUGATE ACID – the member of a conjugate pair which has the extra proton (119)

CONJUGATE ACID–BASE PAIR (or CONJUGATE PAIR) – a pair of chemical species which differ by only one proton (119)

CONJUGATE BASE – the member of a conjugate pair which lacks the extra proton (119)

CORROSION – a general term used to describe the undesired oxidation of metals (233)

CRYSTALLIZATION REACTION – the process in which a substance in solution forms crystals of a solid; the opposite of a dissolving reaction (75)

DESCRIPTIVE DEFINITIONS (of acids and bases) – a method of defining what acids and bases are by describing how they act (111)

DIPROTIC ACID – an acid which can supply up to two protons (117)

DISPROPORTIONATION REACTION – a redox reaction in which the same species is both reduced and oxidized (207)

DISSOLVING REACTION – the process of dissolving; the opposite of a crystallization reaction (75)

DYNAMIC EQUILIBRIUM – an equilibrium situation in which microscopic changes occur, but macroscopic changes do not (38)

ELECTROCHEMICAL CELL – a system of chemicals which produces electrical energy (189)

ELECTROCHEMISTRY – the branch of chemistry which is concerned with the conversion of chemical energy to electrical energy, and vice versa (189)

ELECTRODE – a conductor at which a half–reaction occurs (this is a general term) (215)

ELECTROLYSIS – the process of supplying electrical energy to a molten ionic compound or to a solution containing ions so as to produce a chemical change (237)

ELECTROLYSIS CELL – see **ELECTROLYTIC CELL**

ELECTROLYTE – a substance which dissolves to give an electrically conducting solution containing ions (73)

ELECTROLYTIC CELL (or ELECTROLYSIS CELL) – an apparatus in which electrolysis can occur (237)

ELECTROPLATING – an electrolytic process in which a metal is reduced or "plated out" at a cathode, and having the purpose of covering the underlying material (243)

ELECTROREFINING – the process of purifying a metal by electrolysis (245)

ELECTROWINNING – the process in which a metal to be purified is introduced in the form of a solution of the metal ion, and the desired pure form of the metal is produced by causing it to reduce at the cathode (246)

ELEMENTARY PROCESS – an individual step in a reaction mechanism (27)

ENDOTHERMIC REACTION – a reaction which absorbs heat, so that products have more energy than reactants (14)

END POINT (or TRANSITION POINT) – the point in a titration at which an indicator is half way through its colour change (160)

ENTHALPY – the total kinetic and potential energy which exists in a system when it is at constant pressure (14)

ENTROPY – the amount of randomness in a system (45)

EQUILIBRIUM – the situation which exists when the rate of the forward reaction is equal to the rate of the reverse reaction in a reversible reaction (37)

EQUILIBRIUM CONSTANT – the numerical value of K_{eq} in the equilibrium expression: $K_{eq} = \frac{[C] \times [D]}{[A] \times [B]}$ (57)

EQUILIBRIUM EQUATION – a reaction equation of the form $A + B \rightleftharpoons C + D$, showing the equilibrium which exists between reactants and products (57)

EQUILIBRIUM EXPRESSION – the ratio of the concentrations of the products divided by the concentrations of the reactants, having the form: $K_{eq} = \frac{[C] \times [D]}{[A] \times [B]}$ (57)

EQUIVALENCE POINT (or STOICHIOMETRIC POINT) – the point in a titration where the stoichiometry of the reaction is exactly satisfied (160)

EXOTHERMIC REACTION – a reaction which gives off heat, so that products have less energy than reactants (15)

FLUX – a substance added in order to reduce the melting temperature of another substance. The melting temperature of a mixture is always less than the individual melting temperatures of the substances in the mixture (246)

FORMULA EQUATION – a balanced chemical equation in which all the reactants and products are given by their chemical formulae (85)

FUEL CELL – an electrochemical device into which a fuel is continuously fed and from which electricity is continuously obtained (233)

HALF–CELL – a part of an electrochemical cell in which either a reduction or oxidation reaction occurs (190)

HALF–CELL REACTION (or HALF–REACTION) – an isolated reduction reaction or oxidation reaction (190)

HARD WATER – water containing significant amounts of Ca^{2+} and/or Mg^{2+} (103)

HETEROGENEOUS REACTION – a reaction in which the reactants are present in different phases (8)

HOMOGENEOUS REACTION – a reaction in which all the reactants are in the same phase (8)

HYDROLYSIS (of a salt) – a reaction between water and the cation or anion (or both) contained in the salt so as to produce an acidic or basic solution (144)

INDICATOR – a weak organic acid or base with different colours for its conjugate acid and base forms (159)

INHIBITOR – a chemical which reduces a reaction rate by combining with a catalyst or one of the reactants in such a way as to prevent the reaction from occurring (9)

IONIC SOLUTION – a solution containing ions (73)

KINETIC ENERGY – the energy which a system possesses because of movement within the system (13)

KINETIC ENERGY DISTRIBUTION – a graph showing how the number of particles having a given kinetic energy changes with increasing temperature (18)

KINETIC MOLECULAR THEORY – see COLLISION THEORY

LE CHATELIER'S PRINCIPLE– states that If a closed system at equilibrium is subjected to a change, processes will occur that tend to counteract that change (50)

LEVELLING EFFECT – the term describing the fact that all strong acids are 100% dissociated in aqueous solution and are equivalent to solutions of $H_3O^+(aq)$, while all strong bases are 100% dissociated in aqueous solution and are equivalent to solutions of $OH^-(aq)$ (125)

LOW SOLUBILITY – the solubility possessed by a substance which produces a saturated solution having a concentration of less than 0.1 M (81)

MACROSCOPIC CHANGES – visible, or large scale changes; as opposed to "microscopic" changes which occur on the atomic or molecular level (38)

MOLAR SOLUBILITY – the molar concentration of a saturated solution (75)

MOLECULAR SOLUTION – a solution containing only neutral molecules (73)

MONOPROTIC ACID – an acid which can supply only one proton (117)

MURIATIC ACID – commercial term for hydrochloric acid (112)

NATURE OF THE REACTANT – the term used to describe the chemical properties of a substance (6)

NET IONIC EQUATION – an equation showing only species which are actively involved in the reaction (86)

NEUTRAL SOLUTION – a solution having $[H_3O^+] = [OH^-]$ (126)

NON–ELECTROLYTE – a substance which dissolves to give a non–conducting solution containing only neutral molecules (73)

OPEN SYSTEM – a system in which substances can either enter or leave (14)

OVERALL REACTION – the sum of all the steps in a reaction mechanism (27)

OXIDATION NUMBER – the charge that an atom would possess if the species containing the atom were made up of ions (193)

OXIDATION REACTION – a half–reaction in which a species loses electrons (190)

OXIDIZING AGENT – a substance which is reduced during an electrochemical reaction (190)

PERCENTAGE DISSOCIATION – the amount of H_3O^+ produced in an acid dissociation reaction as a percentage of the original amount of acid present (149)

PERMANENTLY HARD WATER – water which contains Ca^{2+} and/or Mg^{2+} and does not contain HCO_3^- (104)

pH $-\log_{10}[H_3O^+]$ (134)

pOH $-\log_{10}[OH^-]$ (134)

POLYPROTIC ACID – a general term for an acid which can supply more than one proton (117)

POTENTIAL ENERGY – the energy existing as a result of an object's position in space, as well as the sum of all the attractive and repulsive forces existing among the particles which make up the object (13)

PRECIPITATE – a solid which forms in a reaction involving aqueous reactants (82)

PRIMARY STANDARD – a substance which can be obtained in a pure and stable form, which does not absorb water or carbon dioxide from the air, and which has a known molar mass such that it can be used to prepare a solution of known concentration (164)

QUALITATIVE ANALYSIS – the use of experimental procedures to determine which elements or ions are present in a substance (88)

RATE–DETERMINING STEP (or BOTTLE–NECK STEP) – the slowest step in a reaction mechanism (27)

REACTION INTERMEDIATE – molecules which are produced in one step of a reaction mechanism and subsequently used up in another step (27)

REACTION KINETICS – the study of the rates of reactions and the factors which affect the rates (1)

REACTION MECHANISM – the actual sequence of steps which make up an overall reaction (26)

REACTION QUOTIENT – a "trial value" for the equilibrium expression $\frac{[C] \times [D]}{[A] \times [B]}$, used for comparison with the value for K_{eq} to decide if a system is at equilibrium (67)

REACTION RATE – the amount of a reactant or product involved in a reaction in a specific time (1)

REDOX REACTION – see REDUCTION–OXIDATION REACTION

REDUCING AGENT – a substance which is oxidized during an electrochemical reaction (190)

REDUCTION–OXIDATION REACTION (or REDOX REACTION) – a reaction involving the loss and gain of electrons (190)

REDUCTION REACTION – a half–reaction in which a species gains electrons (190)

RUSTING – a specific term used to describe the undesired oxidation of iron (compare with corrosion) (233)

SALT – the neutralization product which results when an acid and a base react; any ionic compound which is neither an acid nor a base (109)

SALT BRIDGE – a tube containing a conducting solution which is used to connect the two halves of an electrochemical cell (189)

SATURATED SOLUTION – a solution in which a dissolved substance is in equilibrium with some of the undissolved substance (75)

SOLUBILITY – the maximum amount of a substance which can dissolve in a given amount of solvent at a given temperature (75); the equilibrium concentration of a substance in solution at a given temperature (75)

SOLUBILITY PRODUCT CONSTANT – the numerical value of K_{sp} in the solubility product expression $K_{sp} = [A^+][B^-]$ (91)

SOLUBILITY PRODUCT EXPRESSION – the equilibrium expression for a salt in equilibrium with its dissolved ions, having the form $K_{sp} = [A^+][B^-]$ (91)

SPECTATOR IONS – ions which do not take part in a reaction; if a solubility equilibrium, the ions do not form a precipitate (85) ; if an acid–base reaction, the ions do not undergo hydrolysis in water (144) ; if an electrochemical reaction, the ions do not undergo oxidation or reduction (228)

SPONTANEOUS REACTION – a reaction which occurs by itself, without outside assistance (43)

STANDARD REDUCTION POTENTIAL – the voltage of a reduction reaction occurring in an electrochemical cell where all reactants and products are at 1 M concentration or 1 atm pressure (218)

STANDARD SOLUTION (or **STANDARDIZED SOLUTION)** – a solution with an accurately known concentration (164)

STOICHIOMETRIC POINT – see EQUIVALENCE POINT

STRONG ACID – an acid which is 100% dissociated in solution (121)

STRONG BASE – a base which is 100% dissociated in solution (121)

TEMPORARILY HARD WATER – water which contains HCO_3^- and Ca^{2+}/Mg^{2+} (104)

TITRATION – a process in which a measured amount of a solution is reacted with a known volume of another solution (one of the solutions has an unknown concentration) until a desired equivalence point (or stoichiometric point) is reached (99)

TITRATION CURVE – a graph showing the change in pH which occurs when an acid is titrated with a base, or vice versa (166)

TRANSITION POINT – see END POINT

TRIAL ION PRODUCT, "TIP", (or **ION PRODUCT)** – the product of the ion concentrations which actually exist in solution, having the form $Q = [A^+][B^-]$, and used for comparison with the value of K_{sp} to decide if a solution is saturated (96)

TRIPROTIC ACID – an acid which can supply up to three protons (117)

UNIVERSAL INDICATOR – an indicator made from several different indicators and which changes colour several times over a range of pH values (161)

UNSATURATED SOLUTION – a solution which contains less than the maximum amount of a substance which can dissolve, so that no undissolved material is present and no equilibrium exists between dissolved and undissolved material (75)

VOLTAGE (or ELECTRICAL POTENTIAL to do work) – the tendency of electrons to flow in an electrochemical cell; the work done per electron transferred (218)

WASHING SODA – commercial term for sodium carbonate (104)

WEAK ACID – an acid which is less than 100% ionized in solution (121)

WEAK BASE – a base which is less than 100% ionized in solution (121)

NOTES